Art Parham
Rm 201a
       Homan Hall

BEEF CATTLE SCIENCE
(Animal Agriculture Series)

by

M. E. ENSMINGER, B.S., M.A., PH.D.

Former Manager, U.S.D.A., Dixon Springs Project, Robbs, Illinois

Former Assistant Professor in Animal Husbandry,
University of Massachusetts

Former Chairman, Department of Animal Science,
Washington State University

Consultant, General Electric Company,
Nucleonics Department (Atomic Energy Commission)

Consultant—Agriservices
Clovis, California

Distinguished Professor
Wisconsin State College

THE INTERSTATE
PRINTERS AND PUBLISHERS
Danville, Ill.

Copyright 1960

THE INTERSTATE
PRINTERS AND PUBLISHERS
Danville, Illinois

First Edition, 1951
Reprinted October, 1952
Reprinted July, 1953

Second Edition, March 1955
Reprinted November, 1957

Third Edition, 1960
Second Printing, 1961
Third Printing, 1962
Fourth Printing, 1964
Fifth Printing, 1965

Library of Congress
Catalog Card Number
60-7932

Printed in U. S. A.

TO CATTLEMEN—artists and scientists. Not artists whose tools are the clay and marble of the sculptor, but artists whose materials are the "green pastures and still waters" that have inspired musicians to capture their beauty in pastoral symphonies, and painters to reproduce their splendor in landscape designs; artists whose materials are the living flesh and blood of animals, molded to perfection through heredity and environment. Not scientists who look through a microscope or shake a test tube, but scientists who, from the remote day of domestication, have given attention to the breeding, feeding, care and management, and marketing of animals.

TO CATTLEMEN—who take pride in their brands, boots, hats, and canes. To them they are much more than a trade-mark of the profession; they are symbols of service, pledges of integrity of the men behind them, and marks of courage, character, and wisdom. They are indicative of the quality of the cattle raised, the class of bulls used, the condition of the pasture or range, and the kind of caretakers connected with the outfit.

PREFACE TO THE THIRD EDITION

From Adam to atom what tremendous changes have occurred! And never before in history has the future seemed so close to us as now! All of us occupy ringside seats in scientific and technological developments where, during the next few years, we shall witness more changes than our grandfathers saw in a lifetime. It is inevitable that these changes will affect people— and cattlemen are people—differently; those who worship at the shrine of "status quo" will seek to thwart adjustments; others, with limited vision, will neither help nor hinder; then, the more progressive will make, interpret and apply these new findings.

As men, machines, and ideals have progressed, so, too, have beef cattle. This progress is evidenced by the following changes, most of which have occurred in the last decade: Live weight production of cattle and calves per cow has increased by 48 per cent during the last 30 years. U.S. per capita consumption of beef has exceeded pork since 1953, and consumer preference has shifted to the higher grades and choicer cuts of beef. Cattle breeding has changed; the Santa Gertrudis, Brangus, Beefmaster and Charbray breeds have been created, production testing has expanded, bull testing programs to evaluate breeding soundness and detect infertility have been established, pregnancy testing has become common, partnership and syndicated sires are not infrequent, and artificial insemination has taken on a "new look" in beef cattle. Cattle feeding has changed; feed lots are getting bigger, most cattlemen have used one or more of the hormones or accessory ration ingredients, more commercial feeds are being used, and pelleted forages and all-pelleted rations are a reality. Buildings and equipment have been modernized and mechanized. Diseases have been combated; twenty years ago one cow out of each nine tested had brucellosis, now only one out of thirty-nine has it. Parasites are being controlled more effectively; systemics—materials that are absorbed in the body and circulate with the body fluids—are now being used in grub control. Marketing is changing; auctions and country selling are increasing in importance, and fewer two-year-old steers are being marketed. Integration is coming in; custom cattle feeding is increasing.

In order better to record these and other momentous changes in the beef cattle industry, this book has been rewritten, and, to reflects its contents, its name has been changed from *Beef Cattle Husbandry* to *Beef Cattle Science*.

M. E. Ensminger

January, 1960
Pullman, Washington

PREFACE TO THE SECOND EDITION

Admittedly, most cattlemen, and others, are not farming or ranching as well as they know how. By this I mean that more proved good practices, based on both successful operations and research, should be put into use. This is imperative if the beef cattle enterprise is to survive in a free market, especially during periods of declining prices and lower profits. To this end, the second edition of *Beef Cattle Husbandry* is dedicated. It is my earnest hope that this book will show, both the student and the stockman, how to achieve the following three objectives: (1) to lower the cost of beef cattle production, (2) to sell beef over the block at a price that the consumer is able and willing to pay, and (3) to make a fair profit.

M. E. ENSMINGER

March 1955
Pullman, Washington

PREFACE TO THE FIRST EDITION

Cattle are the most important of all the animals domesticated by man. Chief among the contributions of beef cattle are (1) their ability to convert coarse forage, grass, and grain crops into a highly palatable and nutritious food for human consumption; (2) the part they play in the maintenance of fertility through returning to the soil approximately 80 per cent of the plant-food value of the crops that are marketed through them; and (3) their influence upon the use of crop rotations.

Though the human population of this country has expanded much more rapidly than the beef cattle population, improved breeding together with improved feeding and management practices—including the marketing of cattle at earlier ages—have made it possible to retain about the same per capita beef consumption throughout the years. But this is not the end of beef cattle improvement! With our present knowledge of genetics, nutrition, physiology, and production and management, new achievements in beef cattle improvement are on the horizon.

Many beef cattle producers, including both amateurs and "old timers," have long felt a need for a practical, yet scientific, cattleman's reference book. It is hoped that *Beef Cattle Husbandry* will fulfill this need. *Beef Cattle Husbandry* is presented also as a high school and/or college textbook. It is hoped that this book will prove interesting and informative to cattlemen, teachers, and students alike, and that it will be accorded a place of honor and active use in the home library of cattlemen throughout America.

In the preparation of *Beef Cattle Husbandry*, the author has had the benefit of the authoritative review and suggestions of the following competent persons: Mr. Robert W. Lazear, Manager, Wyoming Hereford Ranch, Cheyenne, Wyoming; Mr. Alan Rogers, Walking T Ranch, Ellensburg, Washington, and Chairman of the Research Committee of the American National Cattlemen's Association; and Professor P. S. Shearer, former Head, Department of Animal Husbandry, Iowa State College, Ames, Iowa. The able assistance of other eminent authorities is gratefully acknowledged in the specific chapters that they reviewed. With the splendid help of all these fine folks from coast to coast, the author has tried earnestly and humbly to meet the objectives outlined above.

The author also wishes to make special acknowledgment of the assistance of Mr. Irvin H. Luiten, Head, Editorial Department, State College of Washington, who edited the entire manuscript; of the assistance of Professor Everett M. Webb, Head, Agricultural Education, State College of Washington, who reviewed the entire manuscript; of the assistance of three of my colleagues in the Department of Animal Husbandry, State College of Washington—Professor R. F. Johnson who prepared the illustrated drawings, Professor E. E. Goodwin, who did much of the library research, and Professor Charles Lindley, who made the final review of the manuscript; of the assistance of Mrs. Milton Mosher, who made many helpful suggestions and in some ingenious manner deciphered the original manuscript and put it through a typewriter; and of the assistance of my wife, Audrey Helen, without whose help and encouragement the task would not have been completed. The author also wishes to express his deep appreciation to all those who responded so liberally to the call for pictures.

M. E. ENSMINGER

September, 1951
Pullman, Washington

REFERENCES

The following books are by the same author and the same publisher as *Beef Cattle Science*:

Animal Science
Sheep and Wool Science
Swine Science
Horses and Horsemanship
The Stockman's Handbook

Animal Science presents a perspective or panorama of the far-flung livestock industry; whereas each of the specific class-of-livestock books presents specialized material pertaining to a class of farm animals.

The Stockman's Handbook is a modern know-how, show-how book which contains, under one cover, the pertinent things that a stockman needs to know in the daily operation of a farm or ranch. It covers the broad field of animal agriculture, concisely and completely, and, whenever possible, in tabular and outline form.

SELECTED GENERAL REFERENCES ON BEEF CATTLE

Title of Publication	Author(s)	Publisher
Beef Cattle	R. R. Snapp	John Wiley & Sons, New York, 1952.
Beef Cattle Production in the Range Area	Farmers' Bull. No. 1395	U. S. Department of Agriculture.
Beef Cattle Production in the South	D. W. Williams	Interstate Printers & Publishers, Danville, Illinois, 1941.
Beef Production	M. E. Ensminger	Extension Service Leaflet 183, Mass. State University, Amherst, Mass., 1939.
Beef Production	R. V. Diggins C. E. Bundy	Prentice-Hall, Inc., Englewood Cliffs., N. J., 1958.
California Beef Production	H. R. Guilbert G. H. Hart	Calif. Agri. Expt. Sta. and Extension Service, Manual 2.
Livestock Book, The	C. S. Hobbs et. al.	Vulcan Service Co., 403 Tuscaloosa Ave., S. W., Birmingham 11 Ala., 1952.
Practical Beef Production	Jack Widmer	Charles Scribner's Sons, New York, 1946.
Problems and Practices of American Cattlemen	M. E. Ensminger M. W. Galgan W. L. Slocum	Wash. Agri. Expt. Sta. Bul. 562, Washington State University, Pullman, Wash., 1955.

CONTENTS

CHAPTER I

HISTORY AND DEVELOPMENT OF THE BEEF CATTLE INDUSTRY[1]

Contents   Page

Cattle are the most important of all the animals domesticated by man, and, next to the dog, the most ancient. There are about 972 million cattle in the world.[2]

The word "cattle" seems to have the same origin as "chattle," which means possession. This is a very natural meaning, for, when Rome was in her glory, a man's wealth was often computed in terms of his cattle possessions, a practice which still persists among primitive people in Africa and Asia. That the ownership of cattle implied wealth is further attested by the fact that the earliest known coins bear an ox head; and the Roman word "pecunia" for money (preserved in our adjective "pecuniary") was derived from the Latin word "pecus," meaning cattle. It is also noteworthy that the oldest known treatise on agriculture, written by the Greek poet Hesiod, referred to cattle. Apparently having had some disturbing experience with young oxen, Hesiod

---

[1] In the preparation of Chapter I, the author was especially fortunate in having the valued counsel and suggestions of Mr. Karl P. Schmidt, formerly Chief Curator of the Department of Zoology, Chicago Natural History Museum, Chicago, Illinois, who so patiently and thoroughly reviewed this historical material.

[2] *Foreign Agriculture Circular*, USDA, May 5, 1958.

advised: "For draught and yoking together nine-year-old oxen are best because, being past the mischievous and frolicsome age, they are not likely to break the pole and leave the plowing in the middle."

ORIGIN AND DOMESTICATION OF CATTLE

It seems probable that cattle were first domesticated in Europe and Asia during the New Stone Age. In the opinion of most authorities, today's cattle bear the blood of either or both

Fig. 1. Ancient drawing of a bison on a rock, made by Paleolithic (Old Stone Age) man. Even prior to their domestication, man revered animals, according them a conspicuous place in the art of the day. (Courtesy, The Bettmann Archive)

of two ancient ancestors—namely, *Bos taurus* and *Bos indicus.* Other species or subspecies were frequently listed in early writings, but these are seldom referred to today. Perhaps most, if not all, of these supposedly ancestral species were also descendants of *Bos taurus* or *Bos indicus* or crosses between the two.

Bos taurus

Bos taurus includes those domestic cattle common to the more temperate zones, and it, in turn, appears to be derived from a mixture of the descendants of the Aurochs (*Bos primigenius*) and Celtic Shorthorn (*Bos longifrons*).

Fig. 2. Artist's conception of an Aurochs (*Bos primigenius*) based on historical information. This was the mighty wild ox that was hunted by our ancestors. Most cattle are believed to have descended mainly from the Aurochs. (Drawing by R. F. Johnson)

Most cattle, including the majority of the breeds found in the United States, are believed to have descended mainly from the massive Aurochs (also referred to as "Uri," "Ur," or "Urus"). This was the mighty wild ox that was hunted by our forefathers. It roamed the forests of central Europe down to historic times, finally becoming extinct about the year 1627. About the year 65 B. C., Caesar mentioned this ox in his writings, but it was domesticated long before (perhaps early in the Neolithic Age) and probably south of the Alps or in the Balkans or in Asia Minor. Caesar referred to these animals as "approaching the elephant in size but presenting the figure of a bull." Although this is somewhat of an exaggeration as to the size of the Aurochs, it was a tremendous beast, standing six or seven feet high at the withers, as is proved by complete skeletons found in bogs.

In addition to the Aurochs, another progenitor of some of our modern breeds and the earliest known domestic race of cattle was the Celtic Shorthorn or Celtic Ox. These animals, which have never been found except in a state of domestication, were the only oxen in the British Isles until 500 A. D., when the Anglo-

Saxons came bringing with them animals derived from the Aurochs of Europe. The Celtic Shorthorn was of smaller size than the Aurochs and possessed a dished face. It may have had a still different wild ancestor, or may have been an independent domestication from the Aurochs.

Bos indicus

Bos indicus includes those humped cattle common to the tropical countries that belong to the Zebu (or Brahman) group. They are wholly domestic creatures, no wild ancestors having been found since historic times. It has been variously estimated that cattle of this type were first domesticated anywhere from 2100 to 4000 B.C. The Zebu is characterized by a hump of fleshy tissue over the withers (which sometimes weighs as much as forty to fifty pounds), a very large dewlap, large drooping ears, and a voice that is more of a grunt than a low. These peculiar appearing animals seem to have more resistance to certain diseases and parasites and to heat than the descendants of *Bos taurus*. For this reason, they have been crossed with some of

Fig. 3. Zebu (*Bos indicus*). These wholly domestic animals were the ancestors of the humped cattle common to the tropical countries. (Drawing by R. F. Johnson)

the cattle of Brazil and in the southern states of this country, especially in the region bordering the Gulf of Mexico.

POSITION OF THE OXEN IN THE ZOOLOGICAL SCHEME

Domesticated cattle belong to the family *Bovidae,* which includes ruminants with hollow horns. Members of this family possess one or more enlargements for food storage along the esophagus, and they chew their cuds. In addition to what we commonly call oxen or cattle, the family *Bovidae* (and the subfamily *Bovinae*) includes the true buffalo, the bison, musk-ox, banteng, gaur, gayal, yak, and zebu.

The following outline shows the basic position of the domesticated cow in the zoological scheme:

Kingdom *Animalia*: Animals collectively; the animal kingdom.

Phylum *Chordata*: One of approximately twenty-one phyla of the animal kingdom in which there is either a backbone (in the vertebrates) or the rudiment of a backbone, the chorda.

Class *Mammalia*: Mammals or warm-blooded, hairy animals that produce their young alive and suckle them for a variable period on a secretion from the mammary glands.

Order *Artiodactyla*: Even-toed, hoofed mammals.

Family *Bovidae*: Ruminants having polycotyledonary placenta, hollow non-deciduous up-branched horns, and nearly universal presence of a gall bladder.

Genus *Bos*: Ruminant quadrupeds, including wild and domestic cattle, distinguished by a stout body and hollow, curved horns standing out laterally from the skull.

Species *Bos taurus* and *Bos indicus*: *Bos taurus* includes the ancestors of the European cattle and of the majority of the cattle found in the United States; *Bos indicus* is represented by the humped cattle (Zebu) of India and Africa and the Brahman breed of America.

USE OF CATTLE IN ANCIENT TIMES

Like other animals, cattle were first hunted and used as a source of food and other materials. As civilization advanced and man turned to tillage of the soil, it is probable that the domestication of cattle was first motivated because of their projected value for draft purposes. Large, well-muscled, powerful beasts were in demand; and any tendency to fatten excessively or to produce more milk than was needed for a calf was considered detrimental rather than desirable. Not all cattle were used for work purposes, however, in the era following their domestication. Instead of planting seeds, some races of people chose a pastoral existence—moving about with their herds as they required new pastures. These nomadic people lived mainly on the products of their herds and flocks.

As populations became more dense, feed became more abundant, and cattle became more plentiful, man became more interested in larger production of meat and milk. The pastoral people adopted a more settled life and began selecting out those animals that possessed the desired qualities—including rapid growth, fat storage, and milk production. Following this transformation, Biblical and other literature referred to milk cows, the stall-fed ox, and the fatted calf.

In contrast with the very great importance of cattle in western Asia and Europe in both ancient and modern times, it is noteworthy that cattle were never very highly valued in China, Japan, or Korea. The people of these countries have never used as much beef, milk, butter, and cheese, as we have. In India, on the other hand, cattle play as important a role as in our western civilization and still retain a great religious significance, which they have lost with us.

CATTLE IN MEDIEVAL FARMING

The best of medieval farms would excite the scorn or contempt of a modern farmer. Except for plowing and carting with oxen, all labor was done by hand. Although the fields were small, several oxen were often yoked to the plow. As few farmers owned many head, it frequently was necessary for an entire village to pool its oxen and plow the fields in common.

Cattle fared badly in these early days. Pastures were overgrazed and winter feed was scarce. In the fall of the year, it was the common practice to kill and salt the carcasses of all those animals not needed for draft or breeding purposes. Prior to slaughter, aged animals and worn-out oxen were grass fattened, after a fashion. Those that were wintered over were fed largely on straw and the forage they could glean from the fields. Often by spring they were so thin that they could hardly walk.

Very little cow's milk was available, most of it being produced during the grazing season. In fact, more goat's milk than cow's milk was consumed in liquid form. Even in the thirteenth century, when farming methods had improved, one writer indicated that three cows could be expected to produce only three and one-half pounds of butter per week. Most cow's milk was used in cheese making.

LATE MIDDLE-AGES AGRICULTURE OF ENGLAND

During the Middle Ages (500 to 1500) in England, as elsewhere, rotation and improvement of crops and improved breeding methods were not a necessity because virgin soil was abundant and worn-out lands could be deserted for new. Increasing population and the establishment of settlements were later to make improved husbandry a dire necessity.

Examples of the open-field system could still be found in England up to the eighteenth century. However, shortly before 1500, feudalism in England practically ceased to exist, and with its passing the system of enclosures and individual ownership became more prevalent.

IMPROVEMENTS IN ENGLISH CATTLE

English agrarian conditions began to improve during the reign of Elizabeth (1558-1603). No well directed efforts toward the improvement of cattle were made, however, even in England, until late in the eighteenth century. By 1700, from one-third to one-half of the arable land was still cultivated on the open-field system. No individual owner could attempt to improve his herd when all the cattle of the village grazed together on the same common.

Enclosing started about 1450, but progress in this direction was slow. Animals on the common were often "half-starved," and it was said that five acres of individually owned pasture was worth more than the pasture rights over two hundred and fifty acres of common.

During the eighteenth century, agricultural progress in England quickened. With the coming of field cultivation of clover and seeded grasses, sometime after 1600, and the introduction and cultivation of the turnip somewhat later, a great impetus was given to agriculture and livestock breeding. Winter feed could now be had, more livestock kept, more manure produced, and better crops grown. Indeed, the progress in stock raising in the eighteenth century cannot be understood apart from the progress made at the same time in general agriculture.

In cattle, size was the main criterion in selection, though power at the yoke and milking quality were not overlooked. Perhaps the ultimate in cattle size was represented by the Lincolnshire ox, standing nineteen hands high and measuring four yards from his face to his rump, a worthy descendent of the Aurochs.

BAKEWELL'S IMPROVEMENT OF ENGLISH CATTLE

Robert Bakewell of Dishley (1726 to 1795)—an English farmer of remarkable sagacity and hard, common sense—was the first great improver of cattle in England. His objective was to

Fig. 4. Robert Bakewell of Dishley (1726-1795), noted agriculturalist and the first great improver of cattle in England. Bakewell also contributed greatly to the improvement of the Leicester breed of sheep and the Shire horse. (Courtesy, Picture Post Library, London, England)

breed cattle that would yield the greatest quantity of good beef rather than to obtain great size. Bakewell had the imagination to picture the future needs of a growing population in terms of meat and set about creating a low-set, blocky, quick-maturing type of beef cattle. He paid little or no attention to fancy points. Rather, he was intensely practical, and no meat animal met with his favor unless it had the ability to put meat on the back.

Bakewell's efforts with cattle were directed toward the perfection of the English Longhorn, a class of cattle common to the Tees River area. He also contributed greatly to the improvement of the Leicester breed of sheep, and the Shire horse. Success crowned his patient skill and unwearied efforts. But success in breeding was no mere happenstance in Bakewell's program. Careful analysis of his methods reveals that three factors were paramount: (1) a definite goal as evidenced by the joints that he preserved in pickle and the skeletons of the more noted animals that adorned his halls, (2) a breeding system characterized by "breeding the best to the best" regardless of relationship rather than crossing breeds as was the common practice of the time, and (3) a system of proving sires by leasing them at fancy prices to his neighbors rather than selling them. Because of Bakewell's methods and success, he has often been referred to as the founder of animal breeding.

Bakewell's experiments were the top news of the day, and his successes the subject of much comment, both oral and written. The American poet, Emerson, for example, said of the British farmer, "He created sheep, cows, and horses to order . . . the cow is sacrificed to her bag, the ox, to his sirloin."

By the beginning of the Napoleonic Wars, Bakewell's methods were widely practiced in England, and sheep and cattle were raised more for their flesh than formerly. A new era in livestock improvement was born. As an indication of this change, it is interesting to observe the increase in weights of animals at the famous Smithfield market. In 1710, beeves had averaged 370 pounds, calves 50 pounds, sheep 28 pounds, and lambs 18 pounds; whereas in 1795 they had reached 800, 148, 80, and 50 pounds, respectively. Although the effect of improved agriculture is not to be minimized, the main influence in this transformation can be attributed to Robert Bakewell, whose imagination, initiative, and courage put a firm foundation under improved methods of livestock breeding.

THE GOLDEN PUREBRED ERA

The first emphasis on ancestry occurred in human genealogies, where it is older than recorded history itself. But human pedigrees were emphasized for social purposes, in order to determine the inheritance of property or of rank in a caste system of society, rather than because of any belief in the inheritance of physical and mental qualities. Human genealogies often recorded only the male or female line of descent, as in the early chapters of Genesis, in Icelandic sagas, or in Maori legend.

More than a thousand years ago, the Arabs memorized the genealogies of their horses, tracing the pedigrees in the female line. We have no detailed knowledge of how these pedigrees were used, or if they were used at all, as guides in a breeding program.

The use of pedigrees in the modern manner had its beginning in England late in the eighteenth century, and the general formation of breed registry societies began around the middle of the nineteenth century. Soon the improvement that Bakewell and his followers had made in their breeding stock came to be known in other lands. Agriculture was on the move, and the golden age of stockbreeding was at hand. Animals possessing common characteristics were no longer to be confined to a small area and restricted to a few breeders. The number of animal generations in the pedigree increased until no man could remember with certainty all the foundation animals back in the pedigree. To supply this knowledge and to prevent unscrupulous traders from exporting grades or common stock as purebreds, herdbooks were formed. The first herdbook, known as "An Introduction to the General Stud Book," for the Thoroughbred horse, appeared in 1791. A private Shorthorn herdbook came out in 1822, and others followed. Men with common interests in the same breed of livestock banded themselves together in breed associations in order to (1) protect the purity of the breed, and (2) promote the spread and value of the breed.

Both in England and on the continent, the breeding of superior cattle engaged the interest of many persons of wealth and high position, even of royalty itself. Albert, Prince Consort of Queen Victoria, had a magnificent herd of two hundred Shorthorns at the home farm near Windsor Castle, another herd of ninety Herefords at the Flemish Farm two miles distant, and one hundred Devons on the Norfolk Farm. King William of Württemberg, as early as 1824, began to import and breed Shorthorns, as did his contemporaries, Nicholas II of Russia, Francis Joseph of Austria, and Louis Philippe of France. Napoleon III was also a heavy buyer of English blooded stock; and if he could not buy the bulls that he desired, he often leased them—particularly was this true of sires from the Booth Herd at Warlaby. The King of Sardinia and the King of Spain became interested in stock breeding, crossing English Shorthorns on the long-horned white Tuscan cattle and black Spanish cows.

THE INTRODUCTION OF CATTLE TO AMERICA

Cattle are not native to the Western Hemisphere. They were first brought to the West Indies by Columbus on his second voyage in 1493. According to historians, these animals were intended as work oxen for the West Indies colonists. Cortez took cattle from Spain to Mexico in 1519. Then, beginning about 1600, other Spanish cattle were brought over for work and milk purposes in connection with the chain of Christian missions which the Spaniards established among the Indians in the New World. These missions extended from the east coast of Mexico up the Rio Grande, thence across the mountains to the Pacific Coast.

Fig. 5. Texas Longhorn steer. (Courtesy, N. H. Rose Collection, San Antonio, Texas)

Here, in a land of abundant feed and water, these Longhorns multiplied at a prodigious rate. By 1833, the Spanish priests estimated that their missions owned a total of 424,000 head of cattle,[1] many of which were running in a semi-wild state. The hardy Texas Longhorn, animals of Spanish extraction, were of little commercial value except for their hides. Today, only a few of these animals remain, more as a novelty and for show purposes than for use as meat producers.

The colonist first brought cattle from England in 1609. Other English importations followed, with Governor Edward Winslow bringing a notable importation to the Plymouth Colony in 1623. The latter shipment included three heifers and a bull. Three years later, at a public court, these animals and their progeny—and perhaps some subsequent importations—were appropriated among the Plymouth settlers on the basis of one cow to six persons. It is further reported that three ships carried cattle to the Massachusetts Bay Colony in 1625. Other colonists came to the shores of New England bringing with them their oxen from the mother country. As would be expected, the settlers brought along the kind of cattle to which they had been accustomed in the mother country. This made for considerable differences in color, size, and shape of horns, but all of these colonial-imported cattle possessed ruggedness and the ability to perform work under the yoke.

For a number of years, there were very few cattle in the United States. Moreover, those animals that the colonists did possess went without winter feed and shelter, and the young suffered the depredations of the wolves. It was difficult enough for the settlers to build houses for themselves, and they could barely raise enough corn in their fields to sustain human life.

Conditions presently changed for the better. The cattle of earlier importations multiplied, new shipments were received, and feed supplies became more abundant. Cambridge, Massachusetts, enjoyed the double distinction of being the seat of Harvard College, the first institution of higher learning in what later came to be the United States, and the most prosperous cattle center in early New England. In order to provide ample grass and browse for the increased cattle population, it was necessary that the animals range some distance from the com-

---

[1]Yearbook of Agriculture, 1921, USDA, p. 233.

mons (the town pasture). Thus the tale that the streets of Boston were laid out along former cowpaths is not legend but fact. Usually in their travels, the cattle were under the supervision of a paid "cowkeeper" whose chief duty consisted in safely escorting the cattle to and from pasture.

In the village economy, the bull was an animal of considerable importance. Usually the town fathers selected those animals that they considered most desirable to retain as sires, and those citizens who were so fortunate as to own animals of this caliber were paid an approved service fee on a per-head basis.

DRAFT OXEN MORE PRIZED BY COLONIST THAN BEEF

From the very beginning, the colonists valued cattle for their work, milk, butter and hides; but little importance was attached to their value for meat. In fact, beef was considered as much a by-product as hides are today. After all, wild game was plentiful, and the colonists had learned to preserve venison, fish and other meats by salting, smoking, and drying. So necessary were cattle for draft purposes that, in some of the early-day town meetings, ordinances were passed making it a criminal

Fig. 6. Oxen hauling logs to the saw mill. Draft oxen were more prized by the colonist than beef.

offense to slaughter a work oxen before he had passed the useful work age of seven or more years. The work requirement led to the breeding of large rugged cattle, with long legs, lean though muscular bodies, and heavy heads and necks. Patient oxen of this type were well adapted for clearing away the forest and turning the sod on the rugged New England hillsides, for hauling the harvested produce over the rough roads to the seaport markets, and for subsisting largely on forages.

AMERICAN INTEREST IN BREEDING

Interest in obtaining well-bred cattle on this side of the Atlantic was a slow one. All through the colonial period, the American farmer let his animals shift for themselves, never providing shelter and rarely feeding them during the winter months. Eventually the lot of the colonist improved, and with it came the desire to secure blooded stock. Fortunately for the United States, the stockman could draw on the improved animals already developed in Britain and on the Continent. Thus it is not surprising to find that the vast majority of the present established breeds of United States beef cattle originated across the Atlantic.

In 1783, three Baltimore gentlemen—Messrs. Patton, Goff, and Ringold—sent to England for the best cattle obtainable. They could not have had any particular breed in mind, for at that time no distinct breed can be said to have existed in England, unless it was Bakewell's Longhorns. Hubback, the celebrated foundation Shorthorn bull, was only six years old in 1783, and the fame of the Devon and Hereford was purely local. Other importations followed, and early in the nineteenth century progressive breeders, ever awake to their opportunity, proceeded to make large importations of cattle from England and Scotland. Gradually the native stock was improved.

By 1850, the "battle of the breeds," which for many years had divided English stockmen into rival camps, was transferred across the Atlantic, where it has raged ever since. Except for the occasional emphasis on fancy points to the detriment of utility values, perhaps this breed competition has been a good thing. Undoubtedly, the extensive importations of Shorthorns, Herefords, Ayrshires, and Jerseys in the decades before the Civil War materially improved the quality of American cattle, both for beef and milk production.

In due time, animals of this improved breeding were to make

their influence evident on the western range. The Texas Long-horns, which had multiplied at a prodigious rate since the time of their importation by the Spaniards in the sixteenth century, were decidedly lacking in early maturity and in development in the regions of the high priced cuts. Thus the infusion of blood of cattle of English ancestory resulted in a marked improvement in the beef qualities of the range cattle, but it must be admitted that no admixture of breeding could have improved the Texas Longhorns in hardiness and in ability to fight and to fend for themselves.

In order to supply the increased range demand for high-class bulls, a considerable number of purebred herds were established, especially in the Central States. In addition to selling range bulls, these breeders furnished foundation heifers and herd bulls for other purebred breeders.

EFFECT OF THE CIVIL WAR ON THE CATTLE INDUSTRY

In 1860, just prior to the Civil War, stock raising was on the threshold of becoming one of the nation's leading industries. At that time, the aggregate value of United States livestock was more than a billion dollars, representing an increase of more than 100 per cent since 1850. Texas, which had been admitted to the Union in 1845, was the leading cattle-producing state, and Chicago was the foremost packing center.

With the outbreak of the Civil War, the cattle of the South-west could no longer reach the normal markets to the north and east. Union gunboats patrolled the waterways and the Northern armies blocked land transportation. Not even the Confederate armies of the South could be used as an outlet. Prices slumped to where the best cattle in Texas could be purchased at $4.00 to $6.00 per head.

In sharp contrast to the conditions in the South and South-west, the Civil War made for a very prosperous cattle industry in the North. The war-made industrial prosperity of the densely populated East and the food needs of the Union Army produced an abnormal demand for beef. Inflated prices followed, with the result that choice steers were selling up to $100 per head at the close of hostilities. Many cattlemen amassed modest fortunes.

At the close of the Civil War, therefore, a wide difference existed between cattle values in the North and in the Southwest. With the return of normal commerce between the states, this

condition was soon rectified, only to receive another and more
serious jolt with the outbreak of cattle tick fever (Texas fever)
in 1868, which, a year later, was spread through cattle shipments northward to Illinois and eastward to the Atlantic coast.

THE ABILENE, KANSAS, SHIPPING POINT

Until 1867, the only convenient shipping point for Texas
cattle was at Sedalia, Missouri, on the Missouri Pacific Railroad.
But distance was not the only hazard to early-day trailing. At
that time, the Missouri Ozarks were the chief hide-away and
point of operation of numerous bands of cattle thieves and rob-
bers. Sometimes these outlaws operated under the guise of
sheriffs or other local officials who pretended to be enforcing laws
that prohibited the passage of Texas cattle. In any event, the end
result of their handiwork was always the same: (1) stampeding
the cattle and making away with a large number of them before
the drovers could get them under control, (2) beating or otherwise torturing the drovers until they were glad to abandon the
herd and to flee for their very lives, or (3) killing those drovers
who resisted. Because of these treacherous bands, it soon became
necessary for the Texas drovers to travel farther to the west
through eastern Kansas.

Fig. 7. Trail Herd — Flank Riders (from an etching by Edward
Borein.) The six flank riders held the herd in line. The five riders at the tail
of the herd were known as "drag" riders who kept watch on the crippled,
sick, and exhausted animals. The chuck wagon is in the center background
and the remuda (extra horses) in the left background. (Courtesy, Col.
E. N. Wentworth, Armour and Company)

Fig. 8. Early Abilene, Kansas, shipping point. This eastern Kansas cattle depot on the Kansas Pacific Railroad was established in 1867, for the purpose of providing safe transportation to the east, unmolested by the Ozark outlaws. (Courtesy, Swift and Co.)

Finally, in a desperate effort to circumvent the outlaw-hazards of the Missouri Ozarks, Mr. J. G. McCoy, a prominent Illinois stockman, in 1867, conceived the idea of establishing a rail shipping point further to the west. To this end, Mr. McCoy personally inspected the Kansas Pacific Railroad route through eastern Kansas in an effort to select a site where cattle could be grazed while awaiting shipment. Abilene (now famous as the home town of President Eisenhower) was decided upon because (1) It was located on a railroad (the Kansas Pacific Railroad, which was then being extended to Denver), (2) the surrounding country was sparsely populated, and (3) there was an abundance of grass and water upon which cattle could be held pending shipment. At the time, Abilene merely consisted of twelve small log huts, most of them with dirt floors. Very soon, a

TABLE 1

CATTLE SHIPMENTS TO ABILENE, KANSAS,
1867-1871

Year	Arrival of Cattle at Abilene
1867	35,000
1868	75,000
1869	150,000
1870	300,000
1871	600,000

thriving boom town was born, all of which, for the next few years, appeared to be fully justified as shown by Table 1.

In 1871, Abilene received 600,000 head of cattle. Both shipping and grazing facilities had been seriously overtaxed. With the arrival of winter, thousands of head of cattle remained unsold, and insufficient feed supplies were available. The severe winter that followed brought heavy losses. With the coming of spring, it was estimated that 250,000 head of cattle had starved to death within sight of Abilene. This disaster, coupled with the opening up of more plentiful and convenient shipping points, marked the rapid decline of Abilene as a shipping center.

THE OUTBREAK OF CATTLE TICK FEVER (Texas Fever)

Following the Civil War, the Texas cattle trade had received real encouragement with the establishment of the Abilene, Kansas, shipping point, in 1867, thus alleviating the hazards of the Missouri outlaws. In 1868, however, the Texas cattle trade received a serious set-back. That summer, a group of Chicago cattlemen shipped 40,000 head of cattle from Texas to Tolono, Illinois, in Champaign County, where they were sold to the local farmers (a part of this shipment was taken over into neighboring Indiana) for grazing and wintering. Soon after the arrival of the Texas shipment, the native cattle, with which they were turned to pasture, became mysteriously sick and died in great numbers; whereas the southern cattle—although apparently responsible for spreading the disease—remained in perfect health. According to reports, in some infested areas nearly every native cow died. In one township only one milk cow survived. The cause of the malady was unknown, and there was no cure. Farmers became panicky. In despair, many infected herds were shipped to eastern markets, thereby spreading the disease all the way to the Atlantic Coast.

Although the cause of the disease was unknown, the evidence pointed toward the Texas cattle as being the carriers. Strong prejudice against Texas cattle developed. Wild laws and regulations aimed at controlling the movement of Texas cattle and preventing the spread of the disease were enacted by several states. At this point, the price of Texas steers fell, and many cattle held at the Abilene, Kansas, shipping point could not be sold. The Texas cattlemen, however, were not to be outdone. Some of the more ingenious among them conceived a novel advertising campaign. This consisted (1) of shipping to St. Louis and Chicago a carload of buffaloes decorated with placards extolling the virtues of Texas cattle and beef, (2) of pointing out that Texas cattle were more hardy than northern cattle, for none of them contracted the disease when shipped north, and (3) of propagandizing the reputed superior carcasses and greater tenderness and palatability of beef from Texas cattle. Soon the pendulum swung back, with the result that Texas cattle became very popular, even commanding a premium over comparable animals native to the North or East.

THE FAR-WESTERN EXPANSION OF THE CATTLE INDUSTRY

From the very beginning, cattle raising on a large scale was primarily a frontier activity. As the population of eastern United States became more dense, the stock raising industry moved farther inland. The great westward push came in the nineteenth century. By 1800, the center of the cow country was west of the Alleghenies, in Ohio and Kentucky; in 1860, it was in Illinois and Missouri; and by the 1880's, it was in the Great Plains. The ranches and cowboys of the far West were the counterpart of the New England commons and cowdrivers of the seventeenth and eighteenth centuries.

The western range was recognized as one of the greatest cattle countries that the world had ever known. Plenty of water and unlimited grazing area were free to all comers, and the market appeared to be unlimited. Fantastic stories of the fabulous wealth to be made from cattle ranching caused a rush comparable to that of the gold diggers of 1849. All went well until the severe winter of 1886. It was the type of winter that is the bane of the cattleman's existence. Then, but all too late, it was realized that too many cattle had been kept and too little attention had been given to storing up winter feed supplies. The inevitable happened. With the melting of the snow in the spring of 1887, thousands of cattle skeletons lay weathering on the western range, a grim reminder of overstocking and inadequate feed supplies. Many ranchers went broke, and the cattle industry of the West suffered a crippling blow that plagued it for the next two decades. Out of this disaster, however, the rancher learned the never-to-be-forgotten lessons of (1) avoiding

over-expansion and too-close grazing, and (2) the necessity of an
adequate winter feed supply.

GROWTH OF THE UNITED STATES CATTLE INDUSTRY

Fig. 9 shows the growth of the United States cattle industry
since 1867, the period following the Civil War. The group designated as "milk cows" includes all cows and heifers two years old
and over kept for milk; whereas the curve showing "all cattle"
embraces milk cows and all other cattle combined. As can be observed, milk cows have shown a steady increase, with very little
in the way of either sharp increases or decreases. Although beef
cattle numbers have increased somewhat, the increases have not
been as great as those of milk cows nor have they kept pace with
increases in human population. It is interesting to note, however,
that the per capita beef consumption has not changed materially,
primarily because of the increased productive rate of the cattle—
the marketing of cattle as baby beeves or at slightly older ages

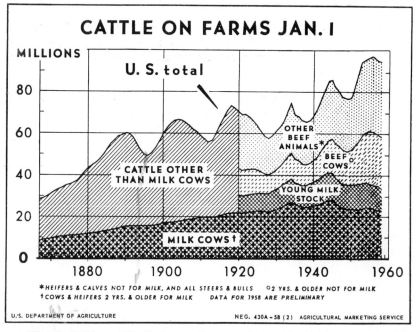

Fig. 9. Cattle on U. S. farms, Jan. 1, 1867-1958. Although beef cattle
numbers have increased somewhat, the increases have not been as great as
those of milk cows nor have they kept pace with increases in human population. (Courtesy USDA, Agricultural Marketing Service)

instead of as three- to five-year-old steers. Also, cattle are currently receiving better care. There is a marked improvement in feeding, more new born animals are saved, more attention is given to sanitation, disease prevention and parasite control, animals are more adequately housed, waste resulting from death, crippling and bruises in transit has decreased, and other improved management factors are receiving attention.

QUESTIONS FOR STUDY AND DISCUSSION

1. How do you account for the fact that most of the cattle in the U.S. are descendants of *Bos taurus* rather than *Bos indicus?*

2. Throughout the ages, and in many sections of the world, cattle have been used for work purposes more than horses and mules. Why has this been so?

3. Compare Robert Bakewell's breeding methods with those used in modern Production Testing programs. What three factors contributed most to his success as an animal breeder?

4. What accounts for the fact that per capita beef consumption has not changed materially through the years, although beef cattle numbers have not kept pace with the increases in human population?

5. Of what significance are each of the following in the history and development of the U.S. beef cattle industry?

      (1) The Civil War

      (2) Abilene, Kansas

      (3) J. G. McCoy

      (4) Cattle Tick Fever

SELECTED REFERENCES

Title of Publication	Author(s)	Publisher
American Cattle Trails 1540-1900	C.M. Brayer H. O. Brayer	Western Range Cattle Industry, Study and American Pioneer Trails Assn., Bayside, N. Y., 1952.
Cattle and Men	C. W. Towne E. N. Wentworth	University of Oklahoma Press, Norman, Oklahoma, 1955
Encyclopaedia Britannica		Encyclopaedia Britannica, Inc., Chicago, Illinois.
History of Livestock Raising in the United States 1607-1860	J. W. Thompson	U.S.D.A., Agric. History Series No. 5, Nov., 1942, Wash., D. C.
Meat on the Nation's Table		Am. Nat'l. Live Stock Assn., Denver, Colo., 1948-49.
Our Friendly Animals and Whence They Came	K. P. Schmidt	M. A. Donohue & Co., Chicago, Illinois, 1938.
Principles of Classification and a Classification of Mammals, The	G. G. Simpson	Bulletin of the Am. Museum of Natural History, Vol. 85, N. Y., 1945.
Stock Raising in the Northwest 1884	H. O. Brayer G. Weis	The Branding Iron Press, Evanston, Illinois, 1951.
Yearbook of Agriculture 1921	pp. 232 thru 264	U.S.D.A., Washington, D. C.

CHAPTER II

DISTRIBUTION, ADAPTATION, AND THE FUTURE OF THE BEEF CATTLE INDUSTRY

Contents   Page

It is important that producers be well informed concerning world-wide beef production in order to know which countries are potential competitors. Like the price of all commodities in a free commerce, the price of beef is determined chiefly by supply and demand—that is, by the demand existing in those countries that do not produce enough to meet their domestic needs and by the supply which can be spared by those nations producing a surplus.

WORLD DISTRIBUTION OF CATTLE

The production of beef cattle is world-wide. Table 2 gives the size and density of cattle population of the ten leading cattle-producing countries of the world, by rank. In 1958, world cattle numbers were estimated at 971.8 million head.

The United States is excelled in aggregate cattle numbers only by India. But India is of very negligible importance so far as world trade is concerned. This is due to a large number of Indian cattle either being sacred or used for draft or milk purposes and the fact that water buffaloes are included along with cattle numbers.

At the present time, certain of the South American nations and Mexico, Canada, Australia, and New Zealand are the chief countries which produce more than their domestic needs and thus have surpluses or potential surpluses of beef for export.

Beef Production in South America

Of the South American countries, Argentina is recognized as the outstanding beef producer. In fact, taken as a whole, Argentine cattle probably possess better breeding and show more all-round beef excellence than do the cattle of any other country in the world. The excellence of the Argentine cattle can be attributed to two factors: their superior breeding and the lush pastures of the country. Beginning in 1850 and continuing to the present time, large numbers of purebred animals have been imported from England and Scotland. No price has been considered too high for bulls of the right type; and, again and again, British and American breeders have been outbid by Argentine estancieros in the auction rings of Europe. These bulls and their progeny have been crossed on the native stock of Spanish extraction. Shorthorns are the most numerous cattle of the country, with Herefords ranking second and Aberdeen-Angus third.

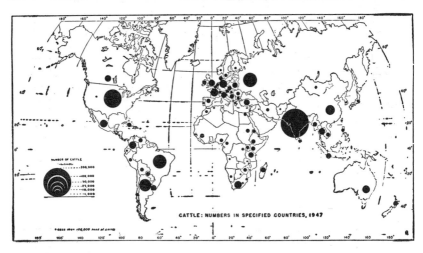

Fig. 10. World distribution of cattle. Cattlemen should be well informed concerning world-wide beef production in order to know which countries are potential competitors. (Courtesy, USDA—Office of Foreign Agricultural Relations)

TABLE 2
SIZE AND DENSITY OF CATTLE POPULATION OF TEN LEADING
CATTLE-PRODUCING COUNTRIES OF THE WORLD, BY RANK

Country	Cattle[1]		Human Population[2]		Area	Cattle per Capita	Cattle Per Square Mile
	Number	When Estimated	Number	When Estimated	(sq. mi.)		
India	203,800,000	1956	381,690,000	1955	1,221,880	.53	166.79
United States	93,967,000	1958	171,510,000	1957	3,022,387	.55	31.09
Brazil	68,120,000	1958	61,000,000	1957	3,288,050	1.12	20.72
China (mainland)	66,748,000	1956	601,912,371	1953	2,279,134	.11	29.29
U.S.S.R.	66,700,000	1958	200,200,000	1955	7,877,598	.33	8.47
Argentina	44,203,000	1957	19,470,000	1956	1,078,769	2.27	40.98
Pakistan	37,663,000	Av. 1951-55	83,603,000	1956	361,737	.45	103.26
France	17,928,000	1958	43,787,000	1957	212,659	.41	84.30
Mexico	16,900,000	1958	30,538,000	1956	760,373	.55	22.23
Australia	16,500,000	1958	9,533,334	1956	2,974,581	1.73	5.55
World Total	971,808,000	1958	2,734,000,000	1956	57,350,000	.36	16.95

[1]Foreign Agricultural Circular, USDA, FAS, FLM 2-58, May 5, 1958
[2]1958 World Almanac

Fig. 11. Scene in India showing water buffaloes (3 animals to left) and cattle. As these animals travel to pasture, they are usually herded by the young or old of the village. (Courtesy, Dr. Ralph W. Phillips)

The finest cattle pastures of the Argentine are found along the La Plata River, in the region known as the Pampas. Much of this fertile area is seeded to alfalfa upon which cattle are pastured the year round. Instead of fattening cattle largely on grains, as we do, the cattlemen in the Argentine fatten their stock on alfalfa pastures. The corn of the Pampas region, which represents an acreage one-half as great as that devoted to alfalfa, is largely exported. Usually two- and three-year-old steers are fattened by turning them into a lush alfalfa pasture for a period of 4 to 8 months prior to marketing. The surplus beef of Argentina is marketed as frozen or chilled beef to the European countries, especially to Great Britain. None of the frozen or chilled beef from the Argentine is admitted into the United States because of the hazard of foot-and-mouth disease.

Other South American countries of importance in beef production are Brazil, Colombia, Uruguay, and Paraguay.

Generally speaking, Brazil, which is slightly larger than the United States, produces hardy cattle of rather low quality, predominantly of Zebu breeding.

Colombia, which is as large as the four states of Texas, Oklahoma, Arkansas, and Louisiana combined, ranks eighth in

Fig. 12. Well-bred cattle on lush pastures in Argentina. (Courtesy, Counselor Office Cultural Relations, Republic of Argentina, Washington, D. C.)

world cattle numbers. Although beef production is one of the nation's principal industries, it is handicapped by lack of improved breeding, poor transportation facilities, and limited refrigeration.

Uruguay, which is but little larger than the state of Missouri, is noted (1) as an ideal cattle country (because of its rich pastures, abundant water supply, and temperate climate), (2) for Hereford and Shorthorn cattle of good breeding, although they are not equal in quality to the cattle in Argentina, (3) as one of the most highly specialized beef cattle countries in the world, and (4) as a beef exporting country, despite its small size (80 per cent of the nation's exports consisting of animal products).

Paraguay, which is about two and one-half times larger than Uruguay, produces cattle of similar breeding and quality to those in Brazil.

As in the Argentine, year-round grazing constitutes the basis of the beef cattle industry of the other South American countries. Virtually no grain is used in fattening animals, except for those being fitted for show. No attempt is made to fatten steers until they are fully mature.

In general, the foremost obstacles or unfavorable factors affecting South American beef production are the following:

1. The ever-present foot-and-mouth disease, which, though seldom fatal, results in enormous economic losses through retarded growth and emaciation and which limits the foreign sale of both beef and cattle on foot.

2. Droughts are rather frequent in many of the cattle sections, and they are likely to be of rather long duration.

3. Parasites and certain diseases other than foot-and-mouth disease are rather prevalent in the warmer sections.

4. Prices are very much dependent upon the export trade, thus making for an uncertain market.

5. Local markets are often unsatisfactory; modern packing plants are not too plentiful; and refrigeration facilities are limited. Many of the cattle slaughtered in the more isolated areas of South America, especially in Brazil and Paraguay, are still made into jerked or salted beef.

6. Transportation facilities are few and far between.

7. Except for the cattle of Argentina and Uruguay, much improvement in breeding is needed; but the introduction of improved blood is difficult because of the heavy infestation of diseases and parasites to which the native and Zebu cattle are more resistant.

Because of the glowing reports about the cattle industry of Argentina, many young men from the United States have, from time to time, been interested in establishing a cattle enterprise in South America. Without exception, experienced United States cattlemen who have visited in South America in person and who know whereof they speak point out the almost impossible odds of success in such a venture. In the first place, the land is in the hands of a comparatively few families who hold a monopoly on the cattle industry; and, secondly, the political unrest in these countries is usually not conducive to such private foreign investments in land or cattle.

Beef Production in Canada

Canada is still a frontier type of country with almost unlimited opportunities for expansion of the beef cattle industry. In general, Canadian cattle are noted for their size, scale, and ruggedness. This is due to the fact that in the great expanses of frontier agriculture cattle production is on a cost-per-head rather

Fig. 13. Cattle round-up in Canada. On their way to summer pasture, this herd fords the Milk River in southern Alberta. Canada had 10,293,000 head of cattle in 1958. (Courtesy, Canadian National Film Board)

than on a cost-per-pound basis; that is, it costs little more to produce a sizeable beast than to produce a small one. The main obstacles to increased beef production in Canada are: (1) the long severe winters in much of the cattle country centered primarily in the eastern and western provinces where up to seven months feeding is required; (2) the high duty and frequently closed borders for exports to the United States, the most natural potential market; and (3) the need for a permanent outlet for stocker and feeder cattle, as Canada has no fattening area comparable to the Corn Belt.

The cattlemen of Canada appear to be optimistic about the future of the industry. It is predicted that more and more cattle will be fattened on the small grains which are produced in great abundance. Also, the opening up of the St. Lawrence-Great Lakes waterway to shipping will provide cheaper transportation (1) to eastern Canada, and (2) for the export trade. Many authorities predict that sizeable meat packing plants will be established at Port Arthur.

Beef Production in Mexico

From December 1946 through 1954, except for a brief period of nearly nine months in 1952-53 when the country was declared disease free (from Sept. 1, 1952 to May 23, 1953, the border was open), no imports of Mexican cattle were permitted into the United States due to an outbreak of foot-and-mouth disease in that country. Since January 1, 1955, however, Mexico has been free of the disease and the border has been open, subject to the usual quotas and duties.

In addition to the foot-and-mouth disease hazard, other factors unfavorable to beef production in Mexico are: (1) the ravages of parasites, particularly the Texas tick; (2) lack of improved breeding, which is made difficult because of the susceptibility of newly imported cattle to diseases and parasites; and (3) frequent droughts, which, next to foot-and-mouth disease, constitute the greatest of all obstacles. Also, cattle are still a main source of power in Mexico.

Despite all the difficulties now existing in Mexico, the fact remains that cattle are afforded a long grazing season and that labor is cheap and abundant. Cattle can be produced very cheaply. It is reasonable to expect, therefore, that Mexico will annually provide several thousand head of steers for fattening on the ranges of the Southwest or for shipment to U.S. feed lots.

Beef Production in Australia

Australia slaughters for export about a half-million cattle annually. Most of the cattle are grazed the year round on unfenced ranges where they are herded by "musterers," who are the counterpart of the American cowboy. Slaughter animals usually consist of four-year-old steers which are grass fattened. Many of the cattle operations in Australia are very large; the ranches varying in size from 100,000 to 1,000,000 acres each, and the cattle numbers from 10 to 50 thousand head per unit.

The beef cattle industry of Australia is subjected to unfavorable factors much like those of South America, except that the country is free from foot-and-mouth disease. In comparison with South America, however, the greater distance from Europe makes shipping expensive with the result that it is almost impossible for Australian exporters to compete on any equitable basis.

BEEF PRODUCTION IN THE UNITED STATES

The present importance of beef cattle in the agriculture of the nation rests chiefly upon: (1) their ability to convert coarse

Fig. 14. An Australian "musterer" watching over a fine herd of Shorthorn breeding cows that are watering along a creek in the black soil alluvial
country. In 1958, Australia had 16,500,000 head of cattle, most of which are
of Shorthorn extraction. There is a big export of Australian chilled beef.
(Courtesy, Australian News and Information Bureau)

forage, grass, and grain crops into a palatable and nutritious
food for human consumption; (2) the part they play in the
maintenance of fertility through returning to the soil approximately 80 per cent of the plant-food value of the crops that are
marketed through them; and (3) their influence upon the use of
crop rotations.

The 1950 census indicated that cattle were kept upon 75.5
per cent of all farms and ranches. Table 3 shows the number and
value of cattle in the United States, in 1959. As noted, there were
96,851,000 cattle and calves on the nation's farms and ranches.
Because of the pastures released by declining horse and sheep
populations, plenty of forage appears to be available for some
expansion in cattle numbers.

The production of beef cattle differs from that of most other
classes of livestock in that the operation is frequently a "two-

TABLE 3

NUMBERS AND VALUE (TOTAL VALUE AND VALUE/HEAD) OF
CATTLE ON UNITED STATES FARMS, BY CLASSES,
JANUARY 1, 1959[1]

Class	Number	Farm Value	
		Value	Total Value
		(dollars/head)	(thousands dollars)
All cattle................................	96,851,000	153.00	14,809,134
Milk cows (cows and heifers 2 yrs. old or over kept for milk)..........	21,606,000	220.00	4,743,762

[1]Figures from *Livestock and Poultry on Farms and Ranches, January 1,*
pp. 1 and 2, USDA, Agricultural Marketing Service, Crop Reporting Board,
Release of February 13, 1959.

phase" proposition: (1) the production of stockers and feeders,
and (2) the fattening of cattle. In general, each of these phases
is distinctive to an area. The production of stockers and feeders,
or the cow-and-calf proposition, is characteristic of the western
range, whereas the fattening of cattle is characteristic of the
Corn Belt.

Areas of Beef Production

In addition to phases of production found in the two major
cattle-producing areas—the western range and the Corn Belt—
there are some rather characteristic production practices common to the other two less extensive areas; the Cotton Belt and
the Appalachian and Great Lakes region. Certainly, within each
area, variations from the most common practice are noted. For
example, a goodly number of cattle are fattened out in feed lots
located in or near irrigated districts in the western range area,
and many Corn Belt farmers have long successfully adhered to a
cow-and-calf type of enterprise.

THE WESTERN RANGE:

This area lies west of an irregular north and south line
cutting through the Dakotas, Nebraska, Kansas, Oklahoma, and
Texas. It is characterized by great diversity of topography, soil,
rainfall, and temperature. Accordingly, the amount of vegetation
and the resulting carrying capacity are variable factors. Except
in some small areas under irrigation, the units of operation are
large in size, and much of the range remains unfenced. In gen-

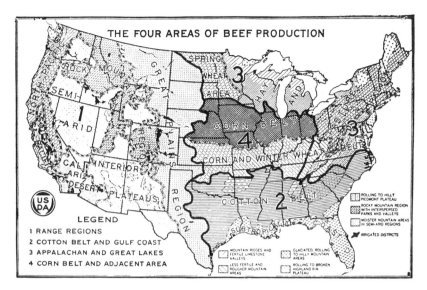

THE FOUR AREAS OF BEEF PRODUCTION

LEGEND
1 RANGE REGIONS
2 COTTON BELT AND GULF COAST
3 APPALACHAN AND GREAT LAKES
4 CORN BELT AND ADJACENT AREA

Fig. 15. The four important areas of beef production. In each area the methods followed are determined largely by the climate, feed supply, and economic conditions. (Courtesy, USDA)

eral, the western ranges supply an abundance of cheap grass but only a very limited amount of grain. Under these conditions, the cow-and-calf system is the dominant type of enterprise.

It has been estimated that about one-half of the cattle from the western ranges are sold for slaughter, whereas the remainder are purchased for further feeding or grazing. The more famous grass-fattening areas of the West—where the pastures normally are sufficiently good to produce animals suitable for slaughter without grain feeding—include the Sand Hills of Nebraska; the Flint Hills of Kansas (so-called because of the flinty rock which characterizes the hills of the area) ; and the Osage Pastures of Oklahoma. Sometimes the Flint Hills and Osage Pastures are collectively referred to as the Bluestem Pastures, because bluestem (big and little) is the dominant native grass of the area.

THE CORN BELT:

The Corn Belt is noted for its fertile soil, medium-sized farms, high-priced land, and its livestock-feeding operations. Most of the land is well suited to crop production, especially to corn. It is not surprising, therefore, that it is the cattle fattening center of the United States. Beef cattle, dairy cattle, and hogs compete for the available feeds.

Many of the farmers maintain small commercial breeding herds, the offspring of which are fattened out on home-grown feeds and sold at an early age. Luxuriant pastures furnish practically all the feed for the breeding herds from May to November, and cornstalks and other roughages are utilized as winter feeds.

In addition to keeping small breeding units, many Corn Belt farmers make a regular practice of buying in feeder cattle from the western ranges. These cattle are usually purchased in the fall of the year and are obtained through public stockyards, at auctions, through dealers, or direct from the range. Some of these are roughed through the first winter by utilizing stubble or stalk fields and then fattened on pastures the next season. Other cattle are carried on a program of winter feeding.

The Corn Belt occupies a unique location, with the range country to the west and the industrial meat-deficit area to the east. Thus, the natural movement of cattle is from west to east; and, in typical "two-phase" production, the feeder cattle are produced on the western ranges and are fattened and slaughtered in the Corn Belt. The carcasses are then shipped east for consumption. About 70 per cent of the cattle and calves of the United States is produced west of the Mississippi River, whereas 70 per cent of the beef and veal consumption is east of this location.

The Corn Belt is also noted for its excellent purebred herds. Because of their proximity to the western ranges and the demands of the ranch owners for bulls, there has always been a good market for superior breeding stock.

THE APPALACHIAN AND GREAT LAKES REGION:

The Appalachian and Great Lakes region is a densely populated area with great cities; it is noted for its manufacturing and commerce. The topography varies all the way from small, fertile valleys to mountainous territory. The valley areas are devoted to intensive methods of cultivation, whereas much of the upland area produces pasture and hay crops for the dairy enterprise. Much of this land is rough and stony, making it unsuited to cultivation. The agriculture is of a most intensive type, with small farm units and very limited diversification. Many of the more distant areas that cannot be used to advantage for the production of a perishable product like market milk are used for dual-purpose or beef production.

The production of beef cattle was formerly an important and highly developed industry through the northeast. However, the opening up of the western ranges; the rapid increase in population of the East, with the resulting industrialization; the division of the eastern farming lands into smaller units; and the adoption of more intensive systems of farming caused a decline of beef production in the eastern states. With these changes in economic conditions, beef production has to a large extent been supplanted by dairying. With the existence of these favorable conditions for milk production, beef cattle cannot compete with dairy cattle, particularly on small farms. On the other hand, where dairying is not feasible because of overproduction and consistent low prices for market milk, where the distance to market is too great, or where labor difficulties exist, beef cattle may come into increasing importance. But this industry, in the East, can never regain its former magnitude or hold the place it does in the West or Middle West.

In general, the less accessible areas of the Appalachian and Great Lakes region are devoted to dual-purpose production rather than either to straight dairy or beef enterprises. More dual-purpose herds are found in this area than in any other section of the country. Western Pennsylvania, Ohio, and upper New York enjoy a national reputation for Milking Shorthorns; whereas in the New England states, both the Milking Shorthorn and Devon breeds are very popular.

Included in this region are also the famous residual limestone lands of Kentucky (the best of which are used for horses) and the excellent pastures of Virginia, West Virginia, and North Carolina. Feeders of commercial cattle are located in Lancaster and Chester counties in Pennsylvania, where cattle are fattened primarily on corn.

THE COTTON BELT:

The Cotton Belt—which includes all or portions of each of the twelve southern states, stretching from eastern Texas to Virginia—has always been noted for its great acreage of cotton. However, with several years of low prices for this commodity prior to World War II and with ruinous soil erosion and farm abandonment caused by careless cultivation of rolling lands, there has been in recent years a decided interest in more diversification throughout the South. Mild winters and the fact that grazing throughout the year can usually be depended upon have encouraged many a southern farmer to turn to beef production.

Another factor which in the past has seriously retarded beef production throughout a part of the South has been the presence of the cattle fever tick, together with a heavy infestation of numerous internal and external parasities. With the eradication of the tick and the pushing of the "quarantine line" toward the Gulf, this difficulty has been almost completely removed. Furthermore, it has been found that Brahman cattle are more resistant to the cattle tick fever than other breeds, and the infusion of blood from this breed has been of great importance.

In addition to a reduction in the cotton acreage and the control of cattle tick fever, scientific findings also have assisted the livestock program of the South through providing suitable supplements for mineral deficiencies and methods of improving pastures and controlling parasites. The cattle of the area have also been improved through shipping in large numbers of purebred and high-grade cattle from the Corn Belt and the West. All of these improved conditions, together with year-round grazing of the area, would indicate that the South can and will expand its beef production on a sound basis.

Leading States in Beef Production

A ranking of the ten leading states in beef cattle production, together with total numbers for the United States, is given in Table 4. As may be noted, Texas is far in the lead, with Iowa and

TABLE 4

TEN LEADING STATES IN BEEF CATTLE NUMBERS, BY RANK, 1959[1]

State	No. Beef Cattle
Texas	7,402,000
Iowa	4,988,000
Nebraska	4,364,000
Kansas	3,800,000
Missouri	2,897,000
South Dakota	2,893,000
Illinois	2,790,000
Oklahoma	2,712,000
California	2,479,000
Montana	2,126,000
Total United States	64,025,000

[1]*Livestock and Poultry Inventory*, January 1, USDA, Agricultural Marketing Service, February 13, 1959, p. 23.

Nebraska in second and third positions, respectively. The large cattle numbers in the state of Texas may be attributed to the fact that it represents a truly great range-cattle country and to the immense size of the state. The cattle population of Iowa, Nebraska, and the other central states consists of native breeding herds and the sizeable cattle-fattening operations that go hand in hand with the great acreage of corn.

FACTORS FAVORABLE TO BEEF PRODUCTION

Some of the special advantages of cattle as compared to other kinds of livestock on the farm or ranch are:

1. Beef cattle efficiently utilize large quantities of coarse low-grade roughages produced on the farm or ranch, including straws and stover, coarse or low-grade hays, and coarser pastures or ranker growth.

2. Beef cattle are well adapted to the use of the millions of acres of land unsuited for the production of bread grains or for any other type of farming. Such areas include the arid and semiarid grazing lands of the West and Southwest (which beef cattle share with sheep) as well as the brush, forest, and cut-over lands and swamp areas found in various sections of the United States.

3. Cattle can use the total home-grown production of grains and roughages, with or without the purchase of other feeds, more efficiently than any other class of livestock.

4. Beef cattle require less labor for their care than do other farm animals. Under average commercial range conditions, one man is required for about two hundred cows.

5. Beef cattle greatly help to distribute the labor requirements throughout the year; they require but little attention except during the winter months.

6. Cattle afford a splendid means of maintaining soil fertility. In addition to returning to the soil approximately 80 per cent of the fertilizing constituents in their feeds, cattle offer a profitable way in which to utilize soil-building legumes that are usually a part of improved crop rotations.

7. Beef cattle require a comparatively small investment in buildings and equipment.

8. Cattle entail little death risk, as they are susceptible to comparatively few diseases and parasites. For example, it is

usually assumed that the death losses of steers in the fattening lot will not exceed 2 per cent.

9. Beef cattle production provides an elastic outlet for grain. When plentiful, more grain can go into beef. When scarce, less grain and more grass and roughage will still produce beef.

It is recognized that certain of the favorable factors listed above apply to both beef and dairy cattle.

FACTORS UNFAVORABLE TO BEEF PRODUCTION

Some factors which, under certain conditions, may be unfavorable to beef cattle production are:

1. A beef cattle herd cannot be built up quickly. Ordinarily, a heifer should not calve until at least twenty-four months of age, and usually only one young is produced at a time. Thus cattle are neither as prolific nor as early breeders as either sheep or hogs.

2. Should the federal controls on beef (tariffs, quotas, and embargoes) ever be completely lifted, the cattlemen of the United States would suffer ruinously low prices.

3. The presence of foot-and-mouth disease in certain other countries always constitutes a hazard.

4. During boom periods, high-quality purebred bulls are usually excessively high and difficult to obtain.

5. The operation of a cattle ranch requires a sizeable investment in cattle. Likewise, it is costly to establish a purebred herd.

6. The grazing regulations on the various federal- and state-controlled lands are often difficult to comply with.

7. Cattle fattening is often a risky venture; many a cattle feeder has literally "lost his shirt" in the enterprise.

8. Because of the high cost in conducting fundamental research with large animals, it is probably a true statement of fact that there is less real knowledge available about beef cattle than about any other class of livestock, with the possible exception of horses.

9. Under conditions in which it is desired that the maximum economy be obtained in converting concentrated feeds into meat, both the pig and the sheep are superior to beef cattle.

10. The spread in price in market cattle is usually greater than is obtained in any other class of livestock. Shelly old cows that have out-lived their life of usefulness in the breeding herd will bring comparatively less than an old brood sow. In other

words, a great spread usually exists between the price of Prime steers and Canner cows.

11. Unless cold-storage facilities are available, beef cannot be cured and stored on the farm as easily as pork.

THE FUTURE OF THE AMERICAN BEEF CATTLE INDUSTRY

The far-seeing cattleman is constantly projecting his thoughts into the future. This is but natural. Some of the factors of importance to the beef cattle industry of the future are:

1. **Foreign competition.**—Most of the South American countries—especially Argentina, Brazil, Uruguay, and Paraguay—and Canada, Mexico, New Zealand, and Australia are well adapted to beef cattle production. Many of these countries produce great surpluses; for example, in Argentina and Uruguay there are 2.3 and in New Zealand and Australia there are 2.7 and 1.7 cattle per capita, respectively. In the present scientific age, it is quite likely that rather rapid advances will be made in the control of parasites and diseases affecting cattle in each of these countries. Moreover, because of cheaper labor and feed supplies, ranchers in these countries can produce beef at a lower cost than the American cattlemen. Transportation distances and costs are not prohibitive in obtaining beef from any of these countries, except possibly from Australia; and, even in this case, the situation is not insurmountable. It would appear, therefore, that only protective walls—tariffs, quotas, and embargo legislation enacted by the United States government—can stand in the way of increased beef competition from foreign sources.

The same factors enumerated as affecting beef imports operate relative to possible beef exports from the United States. Because of our higher production costs—even if other factors were favorable for expansion—it is not likely that we could compete on a long-time basis with these foreign countries in exporting beef to the deficit areas of the world.

Thus exports of beef offer little possibility, but possible imports are likely to harass the cattle producers of this nation for some years to come.

Currently, the following protective duties and quotas apply:

(1) Breeding beef cattle, dairy cows weighing over 700 pounds, and all cattle between 200 and 700 pounds in weight are not subject to quotas. Cattle weighing over 700 pounds are subject

to a quota of 400,000 head per year (and, of course, these quotas include Canada, Mexico and other countries).

(2) Cattle numbers in excess of quotas can be imported, but at a high tariff rate; within the quotas the tariff is $1.50 per Cwt., in excess of quotas it is $2.50 per Cwt.

(3) Tariff on all beef is $3.00 per Cwt.; on canned and jerked beef it must be at least 20 per cent of the value.

2. Increased human population.—The population of the United States continues to expand. It is reasonable to surmise that—as has happened in the older and more densely populated areas of the world—gradually less meat per capita will become available; dairy and poultry production will increase; and more and more grains will be consumed directly as human foods. This does not mean that the people of the United States are on the verge of going on an Asiatic grain diet, but history often has an uncanny way of repeating itself—even though such changes come about ever so slowly. Certainly, these conditions would indicate the desirability of eliminating the less efficient animals.

3. Land use.—The two major beef-producing areas of the United States are the Corn Belt and western range. With the drastic reduction in the range sheep industry, beginning in 1941, a considerable acreage of grazing land was released for cattle production or for other purposes. Certain range areas of the West are not now stocked to capacity. It must be remembered, however, that maximum stocking cannot be based on the good pasture years which usually are determined by moisture conditions. The unfortunate experiences resulting from overstocking and inadequate forage supplies during the drought years is not pleasantly recalled by many cattlemen.

Each year, more areas are being brought under irrigation in the far West. Without doubt, these will provide for some expansion of the beef industry, particularly from the standpoint of supplying a greater abundance of cheap feed, some of which will be utilized in cattle-fattening operations and some for wintering the breeding herd. It is quite likely also that much of the more marginal land of the West, which was plowed and placed in grain production because of the remunerative grain prices received during and immediately following World War II, will be turned back to pastures.

No great expansion in the beef-cattle industry of the Corn Belt is anticipated. Some additional grazing facilities will probably become available as a result of increased grass-legume seedings for soil conservation purposes and continued reduction in horse numbers. But there will be competition from dairy cattle. Swine and sheep will also continue to compete for the available feeds in the Corn Belt.

One of the brightest hopes for expanding the United States beef cattle industry is in the South. With year-round pastures, the southern states are in a very strong position. Moreover, recent scientific developments offer new possibilities of controlling the parasites so common to the warmer climates. In the final analysis, however, the future development of the beef industry of the South is dependent upon (1) the comparative profits to be derived from cotton, peanut, and tobacco farming in relation to livestock farming, and (2) the steps which may be taken toward controlling the ravages of soil erosion, either through private initiative or government subsidy programs.

The industrial East is and will continue to support a predominantly intensive type of agriculture, with dairy and poultry dominating the livestock situation. There is room for increased beef cattle numbers, however, in some of the more isolated areas of the Northeast and East. Dual-purpose production also has a place in such areas.

On the basis of land use, therefore—and with all available factors considered—it does not appear that any marked increase in United States beef cattle numbers can be expected in the future.

4. **Quality of cattle.**—In 1930, the last year that this particular census item was taken, only 3 per cent of the total cattle population of the United States consisted of registered purebreds. Certainly, there is no "halo" around purebreds, and animals are not outstanding merely by virtue of being purebreds. But this is one criterion of the status of cattle improvement. Perhaps the most convincing evidence of the great need for further improvement in beef cattle numbers may be gained through casually inspecting the daily livestock receipts on any public terminal market.

Despite the acknowledged needs for continued improvements, it must be admitted to the everlasting credit of the American cattlemen that we have travelled a long way from the days of the Texas Longhorn to the prime bullock of today. Improved breeding together with improved feeding and management practices—

including the marketing of cattle at earlier ages—have made it possible to retain about the same per capita beef consumption throughout the years, even though the human population of this country has expanded much more rapidly than the cattle population since 1890. But this is not the end of beef cattle improvement! With our present knowledge of genetics, nutrition, physiology, and production and management, new achievements in beef cattle improvement are on the horizon. The Regional Beef Cattle Breeding Laboratory programs offer a modern and scientific approach to further advancement.

5. **Prices.**—Basically speaking, the value of both purebred and commercial cattle is determined by the price of meat over the block. Over a long period of time, it would be better for the cattle industry if the violent price fluctuations that have characterized the past could be reduced by dampening the enthusiasm of boom periods and stimulating interest during periods of depression.

QUESTIONS FOR STUDY AND DISCUSSION

1. What factors will continue to keep out or discourage more foreign imports of beef or veal, or of cattle on-foot?

2. What factors relative to beef production characterize the major potential beef competitors of the U.S.; namely, the South American nations, Mexico, Canada, Australia, and New Zealand?

3. Why is not the cattle per capita necessarily indicative of the type of agriculture predominating in an area?

4. Assuming that a young man had no "roots" in a particular location, in what area—(1) the Western range, (2) the Corn Belt, (3) the Appalachian and Great Lakes region, or (4) the Cotton Belt—would you recommend that he establish a beef cattle enterprise? Justify your answer.

5. On the whole, do you feel that the future of U.S. beef cattle production warrants optimism or pessimism? Justify your answer.

SELECTED REFERENCES

Title of Publication	Author(s)	Publisher
Beef Cattle	Roscoe R. Snapp	John Wiley & Sons, Inc., New York, N. Y., 1952.
Beef Production	Diggins and Bundy	Prentice-Hall, Inc., Englewood Cliffs N. J., 1958.

CHAPTER III

TYPES AND BREEDS OF BEEF AND DUAL-PURPOSE CATTLE

Contents

Early in the progress of cattle improvement, especially during the development of fenced holdings in England, man began to select out certain animals for specific purposes and to plan matings with such uses in mind. Fortunately, because of the diversity of genes carried by the parent stock, it was possible, through selection, to mold certain types, each of which proved superior to the common cattle or even to other types for specific purposes. Thus, there evolved beef-type, dairy-type, dual-purpose-type, and draft-type cattle.

THE FOUR TYPES OF CATTLE

Type may be defined as an ideal or standard of perfection combining all the characters that contribute to the animal's usefulness for a specific purpose. It should be noted that this definition of type does not embrace breed fancy points. These have certain value as breed trademarks and for promotional purposes, but in no sense can it be said that they contribute to an animal's utility value. There are four distinct types of cattle: beef type, dairy type, dual-purpose type, and draft type.

53

Beef-type animals are characterized by great width and depth of body and short legs. Their primary purpose is to convert efficiently feed into the maximum of high quality meat for human consumption.

Dairy-type animals are characterized by a lean, angular form and a well-developed mammary system. Their type is especially adapted to convert efficiently feed into the maximum of high quality milk.

Dual-purpose-type animals are intermediate between the beef type and dairy type in conformation and also in the production of both meat and milk.

Although many breeders have the dual-purpose type clearly in mind and although many fine specimens of the respective breeds have been produced, there is less uniformity in dual-purpose cattle. This is as one would expect when two important qualifications, beef and milk, are being combined.

Draft-type animals, when true to form, are characterized by great size and ruggedness with considerable length of leg. Although oxen are seldom seen in the United States, except in the New England states, it must be remembered that these patient, steady, plodding beasts are still the chief source of power in many parts of the world.

Several distinct breeds of cattle of each of the types have been developed in different parts of the world. Although each of these breeds possesses one or more characteristics peculiar to the group (breed characteristics), in general the type of cow that will produce a large flow of milk is the same the world over, despite acknowledged differences in size, color, shape of head and horns, or in any other distinctive breed characteristic. Likewise, there is a general similarity between all the beef-type breeds. Moreover, because of the great diversity of genes within any given breed, there is more difference within beef breeds than between them from the standpoint of beef type.

THE BREEDS OF BEEF AND DUAL-PURPOSE CATTLE IN THE UNITED STATES

A breed may be defined as a group of animals having a common origin and possessing certain well-fixed and distinctive characteristics not common to other members of the same species; these characteristics are uniformly transmitted. A breed

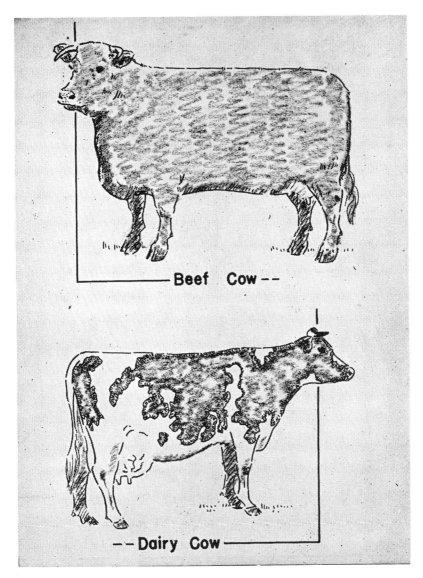

Fig. 16. Beef-type cow (above), characterized by great width and depth of body and short legs. Dairy-type cow (below), characterized by a lean, angular form and a well-developed mammary system. (Drawing by R. F. Johnson)

Fig. 17. Dual-purpose-type cow (above), intermediate between the beef type and dairy type in conformation. Draft-type-ox (below), characterized by great size and ruggedness with considerable length of leg. (Drawing by R. F. Johnson)

may come about as a result of planned matings; or, as has been more frequently the case, it may be purely a "happenstance." Once a breed has evolved, a breed association is usually organized.

The breeds of beef and dual-purpose cattle in the United States, classed according to type or purpose for which they are primarily produced, are:

Beef Breeds		Dual-Purpose Breeds
Aberdeen-Angus	Hereford	Devon
Beefmaster	Indu Brazil	Milking Shorthorn
Belted Galloway	Polled Hereford	Red Poll
Brahman[1]	Polled Shorthorn	
Brangus	Red Angus	
Charbray	Santa Gertrudis	
Charolais	Scotch Highland	
Galloway	Shorthorn	

RELATIVE POPULARITY OF BREEDS OF BEEF AND DUAL-PURPOSE CATTLE

Table 5 shows the 1958 and total registration to date of the common breeds of beef and dual-purpose cattle. In these changing times, the recent annual figures are probably more meaningful than the all-time registrations, although it is recognized that one year's data only fails to show trends.

THE BEEF BREEDS OF CATTLE

The ultimate objective in beef production is the sale of beef over the block. But this is not enough. In this day and age, it is also imperative that feeds be *efficiently* converted into the maximum of high quality meat. How well the different breeds measure up to these requisites will determine their popularity in the future.

Aberdeen-Angus

The Aberdeen-Angus is the most recent of the three major beef breeds to be brought to America. At the time Professor Brown first introduced a breeding herd of Aberdeen-Angus to America, Shorthorn cattle had been in this country nintey-five years and Herefords fifty-nine years.

---

[1]Actually, this embraces at least three breeds of *Bos indicus* cattle that have contributed or are contributing to beef production in the U. S.; namely, American Brahman, Indu-Brazil, and Africander.

TABLE 5

1958 AND TOTAL REGISTRATIONS OF BEEF AND DUAL-PURPOSE
CATTLE IN UNITED STATES BREED ASSOCIATIONS

Breed	1958 Registrations	Total Registrations
Hereford	453,874[1]	10,563,561[1]
Aberdeen-Angus	201,679	2,722,268
Polled Hereford	102,274	1,123,213
Shorthorn	21,686	2,997,927[2]
Polled Shorthorn	9,202	
Brahman	14,046	276,694
Milking Shorthorn	13,470	233,246[3]
Santa Gertrudis[4]	9,978	79,174[4]
Brangus	4,924	37,162
Red Poll	2,729	218,560
Charbray	1,979	15,000
Indu Brazil	1,275	23,288
Charolais	727	2,719
Galloway	664	56,630
Devon	547	38,140
Red Angus	510	1,710
Scotch Highland	370	3,109
Belted Galloway	21	124

[1]Including a considerable number of Polled Herefords most of which are registered in both the American Hereford Assn. and the American Polled Hereford Assn.

[2]Combined registration for Shorthorn and Polled Shorthorn.

[3]Registrations since 1948 when the American Milking Shorthorn Society separated from the American Shorthorn Breeders' Assn.

[4]Not registrations but animals classified and therefore accepted by the Santa Gertrudis Breeders International.

ORIGIN AND NATIVE HOME:

The native home of the Aberdeen-Angus breed is in northeastern Scotland, in the counties of Aberdeen, Kincardine, and Forfar. In its native home, the breed was often referred to as "Buchan Humlies" or "Angus Doddies," the words "homye" and "doddle" being Scotch terms for polled or hornless. The area in which they originated may be described as rolling to rough and not particularly fertile; and the climate is cold and damp much of the year. The origin is rather speculative. Some writers claim that the breed is a sport from an earlier black, horned breed of Scotland; whereas others are of the opinion that they sprang from the polled cattle of Britain.

EARLY AMERICAN IMPORTATIONS:

An Aberdeen-Angus cow named "Duchess" was brought to the United States from Porthetan, Scotland, in 1850. Then in

Fig. 18. George Grant Memorial, Victoria, Kansas. Mr. Grant—a native of Banffshire, Scotland, and a retired London silk merchant—imported the first Aberdeen-Angus bulls into the United States from Scotland in 1873. (Courtesy, American Aberdeen-Angus Breeders' Association)

1873, George Grant of Victoria, Kansas, imported three bulls to use on his native range cattle. However, the first breeding herd— including animals of both sexes—to be imported into the New World was brought to Canada in 1876 by Professor Brown of Ontario Agricultural College. It was not long, however, before the progeny of these early Aberdeen-Angus importations attracted attention, and other shipments from across the water followed.

ABERDEEN-ANGUS CHARACTERISTICS:

Aberdeen-Angus cattle are distinguished from other breeds by their black color, comparatively smooth coats of hair, and polled character. A moderate amount of white on the underline, back of the navel, is permitted.

As a rule, Aberdeen-Angus are not quite so heavy as Shorthorns or Herefords. Because of their compactness and closeness to the ground, however, they are likely to be underestimated in weight.

The body of the Aberdeen-Angus may be described as somewhat cylindrical, compact, broad, deep, smooth, and heavily muscled throughout. No other breed can boast of such an enviable reputation in the fat steer classes of the show-ring and in the carcass contests of the country. Aberdeen-Angus mature at an early age, are heavily muscled in the regions of the high-priced cuts, and yield a quality carcass with a high dressing percentage.

The following constitute disqualifications: horns, scurs or buttons; red color; a noticeable amount of white above the underline, or in front of the navel, or on one or more legs; or calves

Fig. 19. Dor-Mac Bardoliermere 60th; bred by J. C. McLean, Quincy, Illinois, and sold at 13 months of age for $35,000 to Mole Hill Farm, Sharon, Connecticut. He was Junior Champion bull at the 1956 International Livestock Exposition, and Grand Champion at the same show in 1957. (Courtesy, J. C. McLean)

from females less than 18 months of age when calf was dropped or from bulls less than 6 months of age at the time of service.

While still outnumbered in this country by both Shorthorns and Herefords, the breed is becoming more widely distributed; it is especially popular in the central, southern, and western states. The cattle are good rustlers, and seem to be able to endure both warm and cold climates. Because of their prepotency in stamping the solid color and polled characteristics, Aberdeen-Angus bulls are great favorites for cross-breeding work.

Brahman (Zebu)

Unfortunately, the average citizen in the northern part of the United States is likely to associate the Brahman breed of cattle with either the sacred cattle of India or the wild bulls or steers of the western rodeo.[1] Under such conditions, it is not surprising to find that many people—cattlemen included—may completely overlook the peculiar adaptation of the breed to areas characterized by hot climates, heavy insect infestations, and sparse vegetation. Because of these characteristics, Brahman blood is now being added to many herds of the deep South and Southwest, and new strains of beef cattle are in the making.

ORIGIN AND NATIVE HOME:

In the United States, the names Brahman, Brahma, or Zebu are applied interchangeably to any of the more than thirty breeds of cattle native to India. Although representatives of several of these breeds have been imported to this country, our chief interest is in three breeds; namely American Brahman, Indu-Brazil, and Africander. Of these three breeds, the American Brahman and the Indu-Brazil are more numerous. The Indu-Brazil type of Brahman as registered by the Pan American Zebu Association is patterned directly after the cattle imported into this country from India by way of Brazil and Mexico. The other U. S. registry association is known as the American Brahman Breeders' Association.

Without doubt, the *Bos indicus* cattle of India were domesticated and developed as provincial breeds or types long before the British breeds.

------

[1]It is reported that certain river tribes along the Nile in Egypt use Brahman cattle as a medium of exchange to buy wives and settle feuds.

EARLY AMERICAN IMPORTATIONS:

It is very difficult to import Brahman cattle to the United States because of the reluctance of the Hindus to part with these animals that they consider sacred and the prevalence of certain cattle diseases in India, especially rinderpest and surra.

The first importation of Brahman cattle to the United States was to South Carolina in 1849.[1] In 1904, a bull and a cow that Carl Hagenbeck, of Germany, exhibited at the Louisiana-Purchase Exposition at St. Louis were sold to a Texas breeder. In 1906, A. P. Borden of Mackaye, Texas imported thirty bulls and three cows directly from India. Other importations followed.

BRAHMAN CHARACTERISTICS:

Brahman cattle are characterized by a prominent hump over the shoulders, which serves as a storehouse of energy and metabolic water for times of feed shortage and drought, an abundance of loose, pendulous skin under the throat and along the dewlap; a somewhat narrow body, an upstanding appearance due to somewhat longer legs, a "tucked-up" middle; drooping ears and a long face; and a voice that resembles a grunt rather than a low. Many colors are accepted, including gray (light to dark), red (light to dark), gray or red with white spots, gray with an occasional red or brown spot, brown, black with white spots, white and gruella (a smutty or blackish red). Brindle colored animals are disqualified for registry.

Brahman cattle and their crosses appear to be particularly well adapted to the Gulf Coast region of Texas and to southeastern United States. They stand heat exceptionally well; and apparently they are little annoyed by ticks, flies, and mosquitoes. They are resistant to Texas fever. They are also great rustlers where the vegetation is scarce, and they can travel long distances to water.

In the southern part of this country, Brahman cattle have been used in producing several promising new crossbred strains. These new strains of cattle appear to be promising for those areas in which they are being developed, but additional research work should be conducted in order to determine their true merits for these areas and elsewhere in comparison with the

---

[1] Two head of Brahman cattle—a cow and a bull—were imported by Dr. James Bolton Davis, who was appointed by President Polk in 1846 to be agricultural adviser to the Sultan of Turkey.

Fig. 20. Thakore Imperator, Brahman bull bred and owned by W. H. Stuart, Bartow, Florida. During the 150-day post-weaning feeding period, this bull gained 2.5 pounds per day. He was Grand Champion at many shows in the 1958-59 show seasons. (Courtesy, W. H. Stuart)

existing beef breeds of English extraction. It is entirely possible that the crossbred strains may posses an adaptation especially suited to those areas having hot summers, heavy insect infestation, and frequently sparse vegetation. They may even be adapted to the northern part of the United States.

Galloway

For some obscure reason, the Galloway breed of cattle has steadily declined in importance in the United States. Some attribute this to the modesty of its friends in extolling the hardiness and thriftiness of the breed, whereas others feel that the slower development of the Galloway has prevented the breed from gaining wider popularity.

ORIGIN AND NATIVE HOME:

The Galloway breed originated in the province of Galloway, in southwestern Scotland. This country is rough and mountainous, and the climate is moist and often chilly. The pastures of the area have been described as luxuriant, even in the higher elevations.

Whether or not the cattle from which the Galloway descended were polled has been a debatable question. It seems fairly definite, however, that the breed descended from wild cattle native to the territory.

EARLY AMERICAN IMPORTATIONS:

The earliest recorded importation of Galloway cattle to America was made in 1853 by Graham Brothers, of Vaughan, Ontario, Canada. A few years later the breed was introduced into the United States. Because of their hardiness and ability to rustle in the colder regions, these cattle spread generally throughout the north central states.

GALLOWAY CHARACTERISTICS:

Black is the characteristic Galloway color; however, a brownish or reddish tint frequently occurs in the black. The hair is long and curly. White markings on the feet or legs, or above the underline, make animals ineligible for registry. The breed is polled.

The individuals are smaller than other beef breeds. The

Fig. 21. Emperor of Upper Barr, undefeated Champion Galloway bull of Scotland and England in 1956. This bull was bred and shown by Donald McQueen of Roughhills, Balgeattie, Scotland. He was imported to the U. S. and is owned by George S. Daniels, Forest Range Ranch, Laytonville, Calif. Galloway cattle are characterized by their long, curly, black hair; hardiness; and polled character. (Courtesy, American Galloway Breeders' Assn.)

Galloway has short legs and by way of comparison with the Aberdeen-Angus, is flatter of rib and longer bodied. The meat of the Galloway is of high quality. The cattle are good rustlers and extremely hardy.

Hereford

The Hereford is the dominant beef breed of the United States, both from the standpoint of purebred and commercial production. Herefords are easily recognized by the ever-present white face, the distinct trademark of the breed.

ORIGIN AND NATIVE HOME:

The Hereford breed originated in England in the County of Hereford. This area has a rolling topography and climatic conditions that are favorable to superior grazing—factors which account for the rustling habits of the present-day Hereford. The early development of the breed is clouded in obscurity. However, "white-faced" cattle had long been in England.

It is interesting to note that one of the great paintings of the world, "The Young Bull," by Paul Potter (1625-1654), has

Fig. 22. "The Young Bull," from one of the great paintings of the world, by Paul Potter. Painted in 1647. (Courtesy, The Netherlands Information Bureau)

among a group of animals a white-faced, red-bodied cow—an individual resembling many plain-looking Herefords of the past.

EARLY AMERICAN IMPORTATIONS:

The earliest importation of Hereford cattle into the United States, of which there is authentic record, was made by Henry Clay, of Kentucky, in 1817. He imported a bull and two females. Mr. Clay said, "My opinion is that the Herefords make better work cattle, are hardier, and will, upon being fattened, take themselves to market better than their rivals." In 1825, Admiral Coffin, of the British Royal Navy, presented a bull and a cow to the Massachusetts Society for Promoting Agriculture. These were soon followed by numerous other importations. The breed gained rapidly in favor and soon was widely scattered throughout the states.

HEREFORD CHARACTERISTICS:

The Hereford color is distinctive. The body color varies from a medium to a rich red, and the face color is white. The white color is also found on the underline, flank, crest, switch, breast, and below the knees and hock. White coloring back of the crops, high on the flank, or too high on the legs is objectionable. Likewise, dark or "smutty" noses are frowned upon by breeders. Herefords are often referred to as the "white-face" cattle. The weight of the Hereford is only slightly less than that of the Shorthorn.

Calves from females less than 24 months of age when the calf was dropped, or from bulls less than 12 months of age when the service producing the calf occurred, cannot be registered.

The Hereford is distinctly a beef breed. Individuals of the breed are rather rectangular in form, deep bodied, thick fleshed, and they possess excellent constitution and vigor. The breed is particularly noted for its foraging ability, which characteristic largely accounts for its popularity on the ranges of the West and Southwest where it outnumbers all other beef breeds combined. The thick coat of hair, robust constitution, and easy-keeping quality of the breed make it unusually well suited to range conditions. Although the cows are sometimes criticized for low milk production, in most cases they give ample milk to produce a good calf.

Fig. 23. BHR Silver Tone C 10, Champion Hereford bull at the National Western Stock Show, Denver, 1959; shown by Bianchi and Sanford, Macon, Mo. The Hereford color is distinctive—a red body with a white face. (Courtesy, American Hereford Association)

Polled Hereford

The Polled Hereford breed of cattle is rapidly gaining in favor and numbers. Certainly the polled characteristic is an asset, and, if enough really good Polled Hereford cattle can be produced, a bright future for the breed seems to be assured.

ORIGIN AND NATIVE HOME:

In 1902 Warren Gammon, of Iowa, circularized the membership of the American Hereford Breeders' Association in the interest of locating Polled Herefords. He succeeded in purchasing and bringing together a foundation herd of eleven animals. From this beginning, the present Polled Hereford breed has been developed.

POLLED HEREFORD CHARACTERISTICS:

As might be expected, Polled Herefords are similar to Herefords with the exception that they are without horns. The breed is increasing in popularity, particularly in those states where feeder cattle are produced and in regions where screw-worm infestation is troublesome.

Fig. 24. Warren Gammon (1846-1923), who, in 1902, assembled the eleven Hereford mutations from which the Polled Hereford breed developed. (Courtesy, B. O. Gammon)

Fig. 25. The Polled Hereford bull Giant 101740 AHR 1APHR, the sire that Warren Gammon used most extensively beginning in 1901. The occurrence of the polled characteristic within the horned Hereford breed is an example of a mutation or "sport" of economic importance. Out of this gene change arose the Polled Hereford breed of cattle. (Courtesy, B. O. Gammon)

Horned animals are disqualified. Likewise, no calf is eligible for registration unless its sire was at least 12 months of age at the time of conception and its dam at least 24 months of age at the time of calving.

Polled Hereford cattle that are recorded in both the American Hereford Breeders' Association and the American Polled Hereford Breeders' Association are called "Double Standard," whereas those that can be recorded only in the latter association are called "Single Standard."

Fig. 26. ALF Battle Mixer 30th, Grand Champion bull, National Polled Hereford Show, San Francisco, 1953; also champion at many other major shows. Owned by John M. Lewis and Sons, Polled Hereford Ranch, Larned, Kansas. The Polled Hereford breed is increasing in popularity. (Courtesy, American Polled Hereford Breeders' Association)

Polled Shorthorn

The best Polled Shorthorn cattle compare favorably with the best of their horned cousins. Certainly, the commercial producer prefers to dehorn cattle through genetic rather than mechanical means, but he will not sacrifice type and other productivity factors in order to obtain the polled characteristic. The main problem, therefore, is to produce more good Polled Short-horn cattle.

ORIGIN AND NATIVE HOME:

Polled Shorthorn cattle originated in the United States, in the north central states, chiefly in Ohio and Indiana.

Until 1919, Polled Shorthorns were known as Polled Dur-hams. This name was given because most of these early polled individuals came from the Shorthorn x "Muley" cross. Strains of Shorthorns developed from this cross are called "Single-Standard" animals because they are eligible for registry in the American Polled Shorthorn herd book, but not eligible for registry in the American Shorthorn herd book. Later, it was discovered that naturally polled animals could be found among registered Shorthorn herds. By 1919, approximately 95 per cent of the polled strains were "Double Standards"; that is, they were the polled

Fig. 27. TPS Max Coronet 5th, Grand Champion Polled Shorthorn bull at the 1953 Chicago International. He was bred and exhibited by Lewis W. Thieman, Concordia, Mo. In 1954, this bull sold at private treaty at the all-time record price for a Polled Shorthorn bull, $20,000. The buyer was Avenel Farms, Bethesda, Md. This bull possesses excellent breed character, thickness and balance. (Courtesy, American Shorthorn Breeders' Association)

offspring of parents both of which were registered in the American Shorthorn herd book.

POLLED SHORTHORN CHARACTERISTICS:

The Polled Shorthorn breed is very similar in type to Shorthorns, except that they are hornless. In general, however, there are more spotted animals in the Polled Shorthorn breed, and there is less uniformity in type. Yet great strides are being made in improving the breed, and the best specimens compare favorably with the best horned Shorthorns.

Santa Gertrudis

The Santa Gertrudis breed of cattle is strictly an American creation, developed by the King Ranch, of Kingsville, Texas—the largest ranch in the United States. At the present time, this breed is the most widely known of the new strains of cattle developed from the infusion of Brahman breeding.

ORIGIN AND NATIVE HOME:

In about 1910, the King Ranch was presented with a Brahman-Shorthorn bull which was subsequently turned to pasture with a purebred Shorthorn herd. Although none of these initial crossbreds were used as foundation animals for the Santa Gertrudis breed of cattle, their performance between the years 1910 to 1918 demonstrated conclusively to the management of King Ranch the value of infusing Brahman blood under the environmental and range conditions of the area.

The Santa Gertrudis breed of cattle is the result of a Shorthorn-Brahman cross—representing five-eighths Shorthorn and three-eighths Brahman. The initial cross consisted of mating 52 three-year-old seven-eighths Brahman bulls to 2,500 Shorthorn cows. The very best red heifers and bulls from this mating were retained and interbred. Finally, after two or three years of the initial cross, a very superior first-cross bull was singled out. This bull was known as Monkey, and he marked the real beginning of the breed of Santa Gertrudis cattle.

The breed derived its name from the Santa Gertrudis Land Grant, first granted by the Crown of Spain, on which the breed of cattle was evolved. The original land grant is now the headquarters division of King Ranch.

The Santa Gertrudis Breeders International, official breed

association, was organized in 1951 with a charter membership of 169.

SANTA GERTRUDIS CHARACTERISTICS:

Santa Gertrudis cattle are red or cherry-red in color. The hair should be short, straight, and slick; and the hide should be loose, with the surface area increased by neck folds and sheath. The hump over the shoulders has been eliminated, and representative animals are of very acceptable beef type. They are deep, thick and wide. Santa Gertrudis cattle are active but not nervous.

Animals possessing any of the following characteristics are disqualified: white or other spotting; fawn, cream or brindle color; black skin; long, wavy hair; absence of neck folds; and absence of sheath.

Fig. 28. Lola, Santa Gertrudis heifer owned by King Ranch, Kingsville, Tex. This two-year-old heifer weighed 1415 pounds. Carrying five-eighths Shorthorn and three-eighths Brahman blood, Santa Gertrudis cattle are red or cherry-red in color. (Courtesy, Santa Gertrudis Breeder's International)

Shorthorn

Shorthorn cattle have a long and illustrious history, being one of the oldest of the beef breeds and the first breed of cattle to have a breed registry association.

ORIGIN AND NATIVE HOME:

Shorthorn cattle originated in northeastern England in the counties of Northumberland, Durham, York, and Lincoln. Here, in the fertile Valley of the Tees, the Shorthorn received its early development and improvement and then spread out over Great Britain and the civilized world. The term "Shorthorn" is derived from the fact that the early improvers of the breed shortened, through selection and breeding, the horns of the original "Longhorned" cattle that were native to the district. It is not known what breeds or types of cattle were used in the early development of the Shorthorns, although it is probably safe to assume that the early invaders of England—the Romans, Normans, and others—brought over cattle which were crossed with native stock.

EARLY AMERICAN IMPORTATIONS:

Shorthorns were the first of the beef breeds to be brought to America. They were first introduced in 1783 by Miller and

Fig. 29. Grand Champion Steer—a Shorthorn—over all breeds at the Grand National Livestock Exposition (Cow Palace), San Francisco, 1958, shown by Washington State University, Pullman, Wash. The 1060-pound steer was bought by the Fairmont Hotel, San Francisco, at $5.25 per pound or a total of $5,565.00. (Courtesy, Washington State University)

Gough, of Virginia. These men made a second importation in 1792. Available information indicates that a Mr. Heaton brought Shorthorns into New York State in 1791. Other importations followed, and soon they were established in every part of the country.

SHORTHORN CHARACTERISTICS:

The breed has a wide range in color. Roans (blended red and white hairs) are perhaps most numerous, although Shorthorns may be red, white, or any combination of red and white. The skin on the nose should be "flesh color"; a "smutty nose" or dark nose is very objectionable. The horns are rather short, refined, and incurving.

In size, Shorthorns are the largest of the beef breeds. The rectangular shape is more or less characteristic of the breed. Of all the beef breeds, the Shorthorn excels in milk production, a factor which has been instrumental in making the breed a favorite on the small farm. Shorthorns are also noted for good temperament.

No Shorthorn calf is eligible for registration unless its sire

Fig. 30. Sittyton, where Amos Cruickshank—the beloved herdsman of Aberdeenshire—developed the "Scotch" strain of Shorthorns. (Courtesy, Mr. Arnold Nicholson, Managing Editor, *Better Farming*, Philadelphia, Pa.)

and dam were each at least 18 months of age at the birth date of the calf.

Two strains of Shorthorn blood are found in this country. The Bates strain, of England, led to the development of the "Milking Shorthorn." The "Scotch" strain, developed in Scotland —largely through the efforts of Amos Cruickshank—led to the development of the beef-type Shorthorns.

THE DUAL-PURPOSE BREEDS OF CATTLE

Dual-purpose cattle represent an attempt to obtain as much beef conformation as possible and at the same time considerable milk-producing capacity. In their truest form, dual-purpose cattle cannot be classed as either strictly beef or dairy breeds. Rather, their type is intermediate, combining in one animal, insofar as possible, valuable qualities of both meat and dairy types. Because of the stress on beef or dairy qualities and the resulting ideals among breeders and judges, the dual-purpose breeds have not experienced the uniformity of type that exists either in the strictly dairy or beef breeds.

For the most part, the dual-purpose breeds have been in the hands of the farmer who lives upon his land and who makes his living from the soil. This type of farmer often prefers a type of cow that will produce a fairly liberal supply of milk, that will fatten easily to meet the demands of the butcher, and that will also produce calves which will feed into satisfactory steers. Cows of this type are often referred to as the "farmer's cow."

One of the chief virtues of dual-purpose production is the flexibility which it affords. When dairy products are high and labor is available, the herd can be managed for market milk production. On the other hand, when dairy products are low in price or labor is not available, calves may be left running with their dams.

Three breeds of dual-purpose cattle will be discussed: Devons, Milking Shorthorns, and Red Poll.

Devon

Devon cattle are one of the oldest breeds in existence. In the early days, these strong, rugged cattle turned the first sod of many an equally rugged New England hillside, and down through the years the "ruby reds" have played an important part in New England's agricultural progress. Even today, the greatest number of Devons in the United States is found in the New England states.

ORIGIN AND NATIVE HOME:

The Devon originated in England in the County of Devon, which lies between the Bristol and English Channels. The climate of this section is damp and chilly much of the time; the topography is rolling to rough; and the soil is only fair in fertility. Two types of Devons were developed in England. They were known, according to location, as North Devons and South Devons. The North Devons were developed as dual-purpose cattle (for both beef and milk); whereas the South Devons were developed primarily for milk production. As practically all the importations into the United States have been of the northern type and all the developmental work has been with that type, only the North Devons are discussed here.

The origin of the Devon is prehistoric; most writers claim that they descended from the aboriginal cattle in Britain.

EARLY AMERICAN IMPORTATIONS:

The Devon in America goes back to Pilgrim days. Edward Winslow, one of the Pilgrim fathers and agent of the Plymouth Colony, brought over a consignment of a bull and three heifers in 1623. Beginning about 1800, many Devons were imported to New York, Massachusetts, and other Atlantic Coast states.

DEVON CHARACTERISTICS:

Devons are red in color—varying from a deep, rich red to a pale chestnut—with the bright, rich "ruby red" being the most popular. White other than in the switch or on small areas of the udder and belly constitutes a disqualification. The skin is yellow, and the head supports medium-sized horns that are creamy white with black tips. On the cows, the horns curve upward, but in the males the horns are shorter and come out fairly straight from the head. The breed is of medium size.

Devons are straight in their lines, strong in the back, level in the rump, compact in form, low set, and their bodies are well covered with flesh. They show considerable refinement, having neat, clean bone which is free from coarseness. The cows are considered good milkers.

Fig. 31. A fine herd of Devons on pasture at Batchelder Farm, Milford, New Hampshire. The "ruby reds" are one of the oldest breeds in existence. In addition to their rich red color, the Devon is characterized by creamy white horns with black tips. On cows, the horns curve upward. (Courtesy, New England Homestead)

Milking Shorthorn

As the name indicates, the Milking Shorthorn is a strain of Shorthorns bred especially for milk production. Although both the beef and milking strains are descended from the same native home and trace to some of the same early sires and dams, years of breeding and selection have caused them to differ rather markedly in type and characteristics. In the United States, the milking strain is known as the Milking Shorthorn; whereas in Canada, it is termed Dual-Purpose Shorthorn and in England and Australia, Dairy Shorthorn.

ORIGIN AND NATIVE HOME:

Milking Shorthorns trace back to a strain developed a century ago by Thomas Bates, of Kirklevington, Yorkshire, England. Bates bred for a reasonably good carcass animal with steady and profitable milk production. In England, the milking herds increased because of the rapid industrial development of the Victorian era and the consequent demand for more milk. Gradually the breed spread to other countries.

MILKING SHORTHORN CHARACTERISTICS:

As might be expected, there has been a tendency for Milking Shorthorn breeders to disagree somewhat in type—some placing greater emphasis on beef qualities, others on dairy temperament.

In general, however, the Milking Shorthorn differs from the beef-type Shorthorn chiefly in form, fleshing, and udder. The Milking Shorthorn is somewhat more upstanding, angular in appearance, and has a longer neck and body. Dry cows put on flesh rapidly but lose their flesh when in milk. The udders are usually large and shapely and have better teat placement than is found in beef-type Shorthorns.

Milking Shorthorn cattle are red, white, or any combination of red and white. The horns are fine and rather short. No calf is eligible for registration unless its sire and dam were each at least 18 months of age at the birth date of the calf.

Milking Shorthorns have long been favorites on many farms throughout the United States. This is especially true of the medium-sized herds in which the owner does not want to make a specialty of either dairy or beef production. Furthermore, Milking Shorthorns lend a certain flexibility that many owners desire —when milk prices are good, the production program can be shifted accordingly; and on the other hand, when economic con-

Fig. 32. Fairy Lou, National Milking Shorthorn Champion, 1958; owned by Bierhup Bros., Wellston, Ohio. As a four-year-old, she produced 11,212 lbs. milk and 400.85 lbs. butterfat. (Courtesy, American Milking Shorthorn Society)

ditions favor beef production, emphasis may be placed on meat production. When the animals are no longer valuable as milkers, they can be fattened out and sold to advantage.

Many notable production records have been made by Milking Shorthorns. On April 7, 1939, "Cherry," a non-pedigreed Dairy Shorthorn cow in England, completed a record of 41,644.5 pounds of milk. The Milking Shorthorn is the most popular milk-producing breed in England.

Red Poll

In America, the Red Poll breed has always been in the hands of the farmer. The greatest numbers are found in the Mississippi Valley.

ORIGIN AND NATIVE HOME:

The Red Poll breed of dual-purpose cattle had its origin in the counties of Norfolk and Suffolk, in the eastern middle-coastal section of England. The country is low and flat, and the soil is not too fertile.

The breed is a result of crossing horned Norfolk cattle with polled Suffolk cattle. The Norfolks were noted for their good fleshing qualities and beef type, whereas the Suffolks were bred for milk production. Little is known of the origin of Norfolk and Suffolk cattle.

EARLY AMERICAN IMPORTATIONS:

The first recorded American importation of Red Poll cattle for breeding purposes was made by G. F. Faber, of New York, in 1873. Faber made later importations, and soon other men joined him in quest of representatives of the breed.

RED POLL CHARACTERISTICS:

As the name indicates, cattle of this breed are red in color and polled. The color varies from light to dark red, the latter being preferred. The breed is considered as of medium size. The following disqualify animals for registry: white above underline, above switch of tail, or on legs; bulls with white on underline forward of the navel region or with only one testicle; solid black or blue nose; scurs or any horny growth; or total blindness.

Representative animals present the dual-purpose type in its truest form. The cows are capable of producing comparatively

Fig. 33. Red Poll Steer bred by Herman Warsaw, Saybrook, Ill.; exhibited by H. P. Olson & Sons, Altoona, Ill., in the 1956 International Livestock Exposition, Chicago, carcass contest where he won Reserve Champion "Other Breeds" carcass. This 1070-pound steer dressed 64.7% and graded Prime. (Courtesy, Red Poll Cattle Club)

large quantities of milk, and the calves which are evenly fleshed and smooth, fatten into desirable beef animals. As in other dual-purpose breeds, the Red Poll has not experienced the uniformity of type that exists in the strictly dairy or beef breeds. This has been due to the variation in ideals among breeders and judges.

NEW AND/OR LESS WIDELY DISTRIBUTED BREEDS

In addition to the more widely distributed breeds that have already been discussed, the new and/or less numerous breeds of cattle are listed in Table 6.

NEW AND/OR LESS WIDELY DISTRIBUTED BREEDS

Breed	Place of Origin	Color	Distinctive Head Characteristics	Other Distinguishing Characteristics	Comments: Disqualifications
BEEFMASTERS (Brahman X Shorthorn X Hereford)	United States; on the Lasater Ranch in Texas, beginning in 1908.	Red is the dominant color but color is variable and is disregarded in selection.		Milk production has been emphasized in developing the Beefmaster.	The Beefmaster is approximately ½ Brahman and ¼ each Shorthorn and Hereford. There is no Beefmaster registry association, but the name "Beefmaster" is copyrighted and permitted on a franchise basis only.
Belted Galloway	Scotland, the southwestern district of Galloway.	Black with a brownish tinge, or dun, with a white belt completely encircling the body between the shoulders and the hooks.	Polled	Heavy coat of hair.	Red color, incomplete belt, other white marks, or scurs.
Brangus (⅜ Brahman and ⅝ Aberdeen-Angus)	United States; on Clear Creek Ranch, Welch, Okla., owned by Frank Buttram, beginning in 19[illegible]2.	Black	Polled	Slight crest over the neck. Smooth, sleek coat.	Horns Off-color White on underline or legs.
CHARBRAY (¾ Charolaise and ¼ Brahman to ⅞ Charolais and ⅛ Brahman, solid color, golden to white are registered)	Unites States; in the Rio Grande Valley of Texas.	Light tan at birth but usually change to a cream white in a few weeks.	Horned	A slight hint of the Brahman dewlap remains.	To qualify for registration, must have at least ¼ Brahman. Charolais-Brahman of lesser percentages are recorded.
CHAROLAIS[1] (usually spelled Charollais in France)	France; in the province of Charolles in central France.	White to cream.	Horned	Pink skin.	The association disqualifies any animal (1) that has a black nose, (2) that is spotted, or (3) that has excessive dark skin pigmentation.
INDU BRAZIL[2] (Zebu)	India, by way of Brazil and Mexico.	Light grey to silver grey; dun to red.	Prominent forehead and long drooping ears. Symmetrical horns drawing upward and to the rear.	Prominent hump over the shoulders. An abundance of loose, pendulous skin under the throat and along the dewlap. A voice that resembles a grunt rather than a low.	Brindle color combinations. White markings on the nose or switch. Absence of loose, thick, mellow skin. Weak and improperly formed hump.
RED ANGUS	British Isles[3]	Red.	Polled	Similar to black Aberdeen-Angus, except for recessive red color.	Any color other than red; horns or scurs; noticeable white on legs, above underline, or in front of navel; dwarfism; or not of beef-type.
SCOTCH HIGHLAND	Scotland	Silver, golden, light red, brindle, black, or dun.	Long widespread horns and heavy foretop.	Long shaggy hair, short head, and short legs.	Mottled or spotted with white (white permissible on tip of tail or on udder), or polled.

[1]The American-International Charolais Assoc. accepts for registry only 31/32nd Charolais, or better; recordation is extended to cattle having less than 31/32nd Charolais blood.
[2]Actually, this is one of the three breeds of *Bos indicus* cattle that have contributed or are contributing to beef production in the U.S.; the other two being the American Brahman and the Africander.
[3]In England and Scotland, both reds and blacks are registered in same assoc., without distinction. In the U.S., however, red colored animals have been barred from registry in the American Angus Assoc. since 1917. Red Angus Assoc. of America was organized in 1954.

Fig. 34. Senorita Nieve, a yearling Beefmaster heifer. (Courtesy, *The Cattleman*, Ft. Worth, Texas)

Fig. 35. Clear Creek Perfection, age 3½ years, weight 1,863 lbs. Grand Champion Brangus cow, San Antonio Livestock Exposition, 1952. (Courtesy, American Brangus Breeders' Assn.)

Fig. 36. Belted Galloways, Aldermere Farm, Rockport, Maine. (Courtesy of The American Belted Galloway Cattle Breeder's Assn.)

Fig. 37. A Charbray bull. (Courtesy, Mrs. Quinta Arrigo, Sec., The American Charbray Breeders' Assn.)

Fig. 38. Charolais bull. Picture taken near Nevers, France. (Courtesy, American-International Charolais Cattle Raisers Assn.)

Fig. 39. Red Eagle, Red Angus sire in the herd of Mr. Eric L. C. Pentecost, of Cropwell-Butler, Nottinghamshire, England. This bull stood second to the Supreme Champion at the Royal Show, in England, where Red Angus and Aberdeen-Angus show together. (Farmer & Stock-Breeder photograph)

Fig. 40. Scotch Highland cow, on winter range, owned by Baxter Berry, XX Ranch, Belvidere, S. Dak. (Courtesy, American Scotch Highland Breeders Assn.)

QUESTIONS FOR STUDY AND DISCUSSION

1. In outline form, list the (1) distinguishing characteristics, and (2) disqualifications of each breed of beef and dual-purpose cattle; then discuss the importance of these listings.

2. With what breed (s) is each of the following associated?
    George Grant
    Hagenbeck
    Henry Clay
    Warren Gammon
    Monkey
    King Ranch
    Amos Cruickshank
    Miller and Gough
    Polled Durhams
    Single Standard and Double Standard
    Thomas Bates
    Lasater Ranch
    Clear Creek Ranch

3. Obtain breed registry association literature and a sample copy of a magazine of your favorite beef or dual-purpose breed of cattle. (See Tables VII and IX, Appendix, for addresses.)

Evaluate the soundness and value of the material that you receive.

4. Justify any preference that you may have for one particular breed of beef or dual-purpose cattle.

5. Must a new breed of cattle be approved by someone, or can anyone start a new breed?

SELECTED REFERENCES

Title of Publication	Author(s)	Publisher
Beef-Cattle Breeds for Beef and for Beef and Milk	Farmer's Bull. 1779	U. S. Department of Agriculture, Washington 25, D. C., 1954.
Breeds of Livestock, The	C. W. Gay	The MacMillan Co., New York, N.Y., 1918.
Breeds of Live Stock in America	H. W. Vaughan	R. G. Adams and Co., Columbus, Ohio, 1937.
Hereford in America, The	D. R. Ornduff	The author, Kansas City, Mo., 1957.
Hereford Heritage	B. R. Taylor	The author, Univ. of Arizona, Tucson, Arizona, 1953.
History of Linebred Anxiety 4th Herefords, A	J. M. Hazelton	Assoc. Breeders of Anxiety 4th Herefords, Graphic Arts Bldg., Kansas City, Mo., 1939.
Modern Breeds of Livestock	H. M. Briggs	The MacMillan Co., New York, N. Y., 1958.
Santa Gertrudis Breeders International Recorded Herds	R. J. Kleberg, Jr.	Santa Gertrudis International, Kingsville, Texas, 1953.
Santa Gertrudis Breed, The	A. O. Rhoad	Inter-American Institute of Agric Sciences, Turrialba, Costa Rica, 1949.
Shorthorn Cattle	A. H. Sanders	Sanders Publishing Co., Chicago, Illinois, 1918.
Stockman's Handbook, The	M. E. Ensminger	Interstate Printers & Pub., Danville, Ill., 1959.
Study of Breeds in America, The	Thomas Shaw	Orange Judd Co., New York, 1900.
Story of the Herefords, The	A. H. Sanders	Breeders Gazette, Chicago, 1914.
Types and Breeds of African Cattle	N. R. Joshi E. A. McLaughlin R. W. Phillips	Food and Agriculture Organization of the United Nations, Rome, Italy, 1957.

Title of Publication	Author(s)	Publisher
Types and Breeds of Farm Animals	C. S. Plumb	Ginn and Company, Boston, Mass. 1920.
World Dictionary of Breeds Types and Varieties of Livestock, A	I. L. Mason	Commonwealth Agricultural Bueraux, Slough, Bucks, England, 1951.
Zebu Cattle of India and Pakistan	N. R. Joshi R. W. Phillips	Food and Agric. Org. of the United Nations, Rome, Italy, 1953.

Also, breed literature pertaining to each breed may be secured by writing to the respective breed registry associations (see Sec. VII, Appendix, for the name and address of each Assoc.).

CHAPTER IV

ESTABLISHING THE HERD; SELECTING AND JUDGING BEEF CATTLE

Contents   Page

Whether establishing or maintaining a herd, cattlemen must constantly appraise or evaluate animals; they must buy, sell, retain and cull. Where the beef cattle herd is neither being increased nor decreased in size, on the average, about 20 per cent of the heifers are retained as replacements and about the same percentage of old cows is culled. In addition, bulls must be selected and culled, and steers and other surplus animals must be marketed. Thus, in normal operations, cattlemen are constantly called upon to cull out animals, to select replacements, and to market surpluses. Each of these decisions calls for an evaluation or appraisal, commonly called judging.

The great livestock shows throughout the land have exerted a powerful influence in molding animal types. At the same time, producers are ever aware of market demands as influenced by consumer preferences. It must be realized, however, that only a comparatively few animals on the farms and ranches are subjected annually to the scrutiny of experienced show-ring judges or market specialists. Rather, the vast majority of purebred animals and practically all commercial herds are evaluated by practical stockmen—men who select their own foundation or replacement stock and conduct their own culling operations. In general, these men are intensely practical; no animal meets with their favor unless it carries value in marketable products. Such stockmen have no interest in the so-called breed fancy points. These practical operators may not be able to express fluently their reasons for selecting certain animals while culling others, but usually they become quite deft in their evaluations. Whether young animals are being raised for market or for breeding stock, successful livestock operators are generally good judges of livestock.

FACTORS TO CONSIDER IN ESTABLISHING THE HERD

Except for the comparatively few persons who keep animals merely as a hobby, farmers and ranchers raise stock because, over a period of years, it has proved to be a profitable enterprise provided that the production and marketing phases are conducted in an enlightened and intelligent manner. Therefore, after it has been ascertained that the farm feeds and available labor are adapted to animal production, and that suitable potential markets exist, the next assignment is that of establishing a herd that is efficient from the standpoint of production and that meets market demands.

Purebreds or Grades

Many breeders will continue to produce purebred stock, but the vast majority of cattle producers will, for a long time to come, produce grade stock for market rather than purebreds. Such a system requires less outlay of cash, and less experience on the part of the producer. However, even with this type of production grading up of the herd through the use of purebred sires is always advocated. In a survey made by Washington State University, which included more than a half million cattle in a 24-state area, 94 per cent of the cattlemen reported using purebred bulls only.[1]

After some experience, the commercial breeder who has handled grade cattle may add a few purebred cows to the herd

---

[1] Ensminger, M. E., M. W. Galgan, and W. L. Slocum; Wash. Agri. Expt. Sta. Bul. 562.

and gradually build into purebreds, provided that his experience and his market for seed stock justifies the development of this type of production.

For the man with experience and adequate capital, the breeding of purebreds may offer unlimited opportunities. It has been well said that honor, fame, and fortune are all within the realm of possible realization in the purebred business, but it should also be added that only a few achieve this high calling.

During recent years, many successful industrialists have, as a hobby, established purebred herds of various classes of livestock. Ordinarily these men possess great ability, but they are inexperienced in the handling of animals. Such men are likely to derive more enjoyment from the venture and make a greater contribution to the livestock industry at less cost to themselves if they can be persuaded to (1) hire a competent manager in whom they have confidence and give him considerable freedom in the operation of the livestock enterprise and (2) start with the best animals obtainable and adhere to a sound breeding program.

Selection of the Breed

No one breed of cattle can be said to excel all others in all points of beef production for all conditions. The selection of a particular breed is most often a matter of personal preference, and usually the breed that the individual cattleman likes is the one with which he will have the greatest success. Where no definite preference exists, however, it is well to choose the breed that is most popular in the community—if any one breed predominates. If this procedure is followed, it is often possible to arrange for an exchange of animals, especially bulls. Moreover, if a given community is noted for producing good cattle of a particular breed, there are many advantages from the standpoint of advertisement and sales—this applies to both purebreds and grades. Above all, it should be remembered that *usually there is more difference among individuals within the same breed than between the different breeds.*

In selecting a purebred bull for a grade herd, the breed chosen should usually be one that the character of the cows most nearly approaches.

Size of the Herd

No minimum or maximum figures can be given as to the best size for the herd. Rather, each case is one for individual consideration. It is to be pointed out, however, that labor costs differ very little whether the herd numbers ten or eighty. The cost of purchasing and maintaining a herd bull also comes rather high when too few females are kept. The extent and carrying capacity of the pasture, the amount of hay and other roughage produced, and the facilities for wintering stock are factors that should be considered in determining the size of herd for a particular farm unit. The system of disposing of the young stock will also be an influencing factor. For example, if the calves are disposed of at weaning time or fattened as baby beef, practically no cattle other than the breeding herd are maintained. On the other hand, if the calves are carried over as stockers and feeders or are fattened at an older age, more feed, pasture, and shelter are required.

Then, too, whether the beef herd is to be a major or minor enterprise will have to be decided upon. Here again, each case is one for individual consideration. In most instances, replacements should be made from heifers raised on the farm.

Uniformity

In order to produce uniform calves, it is necessary that the cow herd be of similar type and breeding. This applies to both the purebred and grade herd. When this rule is followed, the herd bull can be selected with more intelligence. Secondly, uniform offspring sell at a premium at any age, whether they are sold as purebreds for foundation stock, as stocker and feeder calves, or as fat steers.

Health

All animals selected should be in a thrifty, vigorous condition and free from diseases and parasites. They should give every evidence of a life of usefulness ahead of them. The cows should appear capable of producing good calves, and the bull should be able to withstand a normal breeding season. Tests should be made to make certain of freedom from both tuberculosis and contagious abortion. In fact, all purchases should be made subject to the animals being free from these contagious diseases. With costly purebred animals, a health certificate should be furnished by a licensed veterinarian. Newly acquired animals should be isolated for several days before being turned with the rest of the herd.

Condition

Although an extremely thin and emaciated condition, which may mar reproduction, is to be avoided, it must be remembered that an overfat condition may be equally harmful from the standpoint of reproduction.

It takes a unique ability to project the effect of feeding a few hundred pounds of grain or hay to a thin animal, and fortunate indeed is the stockman who possesses this quality. This applies alike to both the purebred and the commercial producer. In fact, it is probably of greater importance with the commercial cattleman, for replacement females and stocker and feeder steers are usually in very average condition.

Age and Longevity

In establishing the herd, it is usually advisable to purchase a large proportion of mature cows (cows four to eight years of age) that have a record of producing uniformly high-quality calves. Perhaps it can be said that not over one half of the newly founded herd should consist of untried heifers. Aside from the fact that some of the heifers may prove to be non-breeders, they require more assistance during calving time than is necessary with older cows. Perhaps the best buy of all, when they are available, consists of buying cows with promising calves at their side and which are rebred to a good bull; a three-in-one proposition.

Once the herd has been established, the replacements should be made from the top heifers raised on the farm. Old cows, irregular breeders, and poor milkers sell to best advantage before they become thin and "shelly."

A sound practice in buying a bull is to seek one of serviceable age that is known to have sired desirable calves—a "proved" sire. However, with limited capital, it may be necessary to consider the purchase of a younger bull. Usually a wider selection is afforded with the latter procedure, and, also, such an individual has a longer life of usefulness ahead. Naturally, the time and number of services demanded of the bull will have considerable bearing on the age of the animal selected.

Since most beef females do not reproduce until they are approximately three years of age, their regular and prolonged reproduction thereafter has an important bearing upon the overhead cost of developing breeding stock in relation to the number of calves produced. The longer the good, proved, producing cows can be kept without sacrifice of the calf crop or too much decrease in salvage value, the less the percentage replacement required. Moreover, the proportion of younger animals that can be marketed is correspondingly increased. Selection and improvement in longevity are possible in all breeds and should receive more attention.

In a survey made by Washington State University, it was found that old cows were culled or removed from the breeding herd at an average age of 9.6 years, and bulls at 6.3 years.[1] It is recognized that the severity of culling will vary somewhat from year to year, primarily on the basis of whether cattle numbers are expanding or declining; and that purebred cattle are usually retained longer than commercial cattle.

Reproductive Ability

It is estimated that, for the United States as a whole, out of each one hundred cows bred only 80 per cent drop calves annually. The other 20 per cent are nonproducers, either temporarily or permanently. Many of the southern states have even lower calf crop percentages, some state averages running as low as 50 per cent. With a 50-per-cent calf crop, it simply means that two cows are being maintained an entire year for the production of one calf. As reproductive ability is fundamental to economical beef production, it can be readily understood that sterility constitutes a major annual loss in the cattle business. In fact, cattlemen acknowledge that the calf crop percentage is the biggest single factor affecting profit in beef cattle production.[2] Improper feeding and disease are the two most common causes of low percentage calf crops in cattle.

Overfeeding accompanied by extremely high condition, or underfeeding accompanied by an emaciated and run-down condition, usually result in temporary sterility that may persist until the condition is corrected. Lack of exercise, inflammation and infection of the reproductive tract resulting from retained afterbirth or other difficulties encountered at calving, and infec-

[1]Ensminger, M. E., M. W. Galgan, and W. L. Slocum; Wash. Agri. Expt. Sta. Bul. 562.

[2]Methods of computing calf crop percentages vary, but the three most common methods are: (1) number of calves born in comparison to the number of cows of breeding age, (2) number of calves marketed or branded in relation to the cows of breeding age, and (3) the number of calves that reach weaning age as compared to the number of breeding cows. Perhaps the first method is the proper and most scientific one, but, for convenience reasons, most ranches use the second method.

tions of various other kinds may also result in temporary sterility. The most common causes of permanent sterility in cattle are: old age; diseased reproductive organs, such as cystic ovaries; diseased fallopian tubes; and heredity. The reproductive ability of an individual or an entire herd may also be greatly affected, either temporarily or permanently, by the presence of brucellosis.

Sterility may be present in either sex. Occasionally bulls are sterile even though sexually active. Differences in the fertility of bulls are especially revealed by the records kept and the semen studies made.

In addition to the above factors affecting reproduction, the percentage calf crop may be affected by the proportion of bulls to cows, their distribution on the range, and the season of breeding.

Milking Ability

Most commercial cattle producers have long recognized the importance of good milking cows in producing heavy, thrifty calves. Unfortunately, insufficient attention is given to this factor by altogether too many purebred breeders. Instead, they have come to rely upon nurse cows for supplemental milk.

Beef cows that do not produce sufficient milk to raise satisfactorily their own calves should be culled from the herd. One can soon improve the milking ability of the herd by giving proper attention to this factor when selecting the herd bull. The best method is to select a bull whose sire and dam have both produced good milking daughters. If there is no opportunity to observe or to secure information on the daughters of the parent animals, then the milking ability of the mother and of the sire's mother is the next best criterion. Even though good milking ability is desired, an excessive flow of milk in commercial cattle is equally undesirable, for it results in difficulty in milking them out and many spoiled udders.

Size

The question of size of beef cattle has been a point of considerable controversy among beef cattle producers. Fashions in beef cattle type have gradually changed during the past fifty or sixty years, moving from the big, rugged, beefy—but oftentimes rough "farmer or rancher type" that our grandfathers produced—to the smaller, earlier-maturing, blockier, smoother types in vogue from about 1935 to 1945 (these extremes were known as "comprests" in Herefords and "compacts" in Short-horns).

The reasons for this shift in cattle type were many and varied, but perhaps the smaller types evolved principally because of the demand on the part of the consumer for smaller cuts of meat. The show-ring was, likewise, an important factor, and show-ring fashions for both the finished product and breeding animals tended to follow consumer preferences.

Fig. 41. Cattle fashions have changed! "Firly," a prize ox of Britain in 1835; shown at 4 years and 8 months of age and weighing 3,000 pounds. The near animal is Royal Jupiter, the Shorthorn steer that was grand champion over all breeds at the 1946 Chicago International; shown by Oklahoma State University. (Courtesy, The Shorthorn World)

Unfortunately, the tremendously important utility factor or economy of production was largely overlooked in this shift, and little information was available in regard to whether the smaller types could be produced as economically as larger cattle. Many producers felt that bigger cattle could be produced the most economically, especially under conditions where operating costs are on a "per-head" rather than a "per-pound" basis and where profit in a cattle enterprise depends primarily upon the ability of the animals to utilize efficiently large amounts of roughage. The opinion was also prevalent that show-ring fashions toward the low-set, blocky, earlier-maturing pony-type cattle went further than consumer demand justified. As a result, in recent years the pendulum has swung toward larger cattle; currently, medium or medium to large type cattle are favored by most breeders.

Fortunately, some experimental work, designed to answer these and other questions has been conducted. In a study involving large-, intermediate-, and small-type Hereford cattle— Stonaker of the Colorado Station reported[1] that wide variations in mature size are not antagonistic with present market demands,

Fig. 42. Hereford bulls of the two types (top row) were mated to the cows below them to produce the steers on the bottom row. The steers were photographed shortly before they were slaughtered. This interesting experiment at Colorado State University has presented some enlightening and much needed factual information relative to the subject of size in beef cattle. Weight, age, and efficiency data has been collected of the different sizes—large, medium, and "comprest." (Courtesy, Dr. H. H. Stonaker, Colorado State University)

[1]Stonaker, H. H., Colorado State University Bul. 501-S, 1958.

efficiency of feed use, or carcass cutout values and grades. However, the larger cattle produced a higher percentage calf crop and required some less fixed cost expenditure per pound of beef produced.

In the Colorado experiments, all groups of steers were fed to about the same degree of finish. This is important because fat is high in energy; and the fatter an animal becomes the less efficiently it utilizes its feed. Thus it stands to reason that smaller-type animals, when fed to the same weight as large-type animals, will be fatter and, therefore, will require more feed per hundred pounds gain.

In a study[1]—conducted cooperatively by the Kansas, Oklahoma, and Ohio Agricultural Experiment Stations—involving steers sired by small-, medium-, and large-size bulls, medium-size steers were favored; it was found that medium-size cattle tend to combine the gaining ability of large cattle and the finishing ability of small cattle without sacrifice of efficiency of gain.

The New Mexico station compared the gains of, and carcasses produced from, compact, medium and rangy steers. They found that the rangy steers weighed more when put on feed, gained more, and yielded a higher dressing percentage than the compact steers; and that the medium type was intermediate in each case. There was no indication of any differences in economy of gain, however.[2]

Perhaps, in the final analysis, the most practical size of cattle will vary according to: (1) the type and plane of nutrition available, and (2) whether or not the market is a critical one. Thus, if large acreages of range are to be utilized and it is desired to market the cattle as heavy steers (about 1,200-pound weights)—as either grass-fat steers or with a minimum of grain feeding—perhaps the large-type animals would be preferable. It must also be remembered that the labor costs under range conditions are no greater for handling large animals with their greater pounds than they are for the small animals.

On the other hand, under conditions where the available area is smaller, where a greater quantity of grain and less roughage is produced, and the market is a discriminating one in which

[1]Weber, A. D., A. E. Darlow, and Paul Gerlaugh, Am. Her. Jour., 41 (22): 20, 1951.

[2]Knox, J. H. and Marvin Koger, Jour. of An. Sc., Vol. 5, No. 4, p. 331, 1946.

the consumers desire high quality but smaller cuts of meat, the situation may favor the production of smaller-type cattle.

Certainly animals can be too big. Huge size is usually accompanied by coarseness, poor fleshing qualities, loose rather than compact conformation, and slow maturity and fattening. Perhaps, under most conditions and in the final analysis, medium-type cattle are best from the standpoint of widest adaptability, general vigor, reproductive efficiency, milk production, longevity, and marketability. Yet it is reasonable to conjecture that there are environmental and market conditions under which one or the other extremes in beef type (the large type or the small type) may be more profitable.

Adaptation

As has already been indicated—except in those localities where a certain breed greatly predominates, thus making possible the exchange of breeding stock and joint benefits in selling surplus stock—one will usually do best to select that breed for which the producer may have a decided preference. On the other hand, there are certain areas and conditions wherein the adaptation of the breed or class of animals should be given consideration. For example, in the South, Brahman cattle and certain strains of Brahman crossbreds seem to thrive despite the extreme heat, heavy insect infestation, and less abundant vegetation common to the area. Because of this, Brahman blood is now being added to many herds of the South and Southwest, and new strains of beef cattle are in the making.

The Missouri Station conducted some classical studies designed to show breed differences between Shorthorn, Santa Gertrudis (5/8 Shorthorn and 3/8 Brahman), and Brahman cattle. The animals were housed in "climatic chambers," in which the temperature, humidity, and air movements were regulated as desired. The ability of representatives of the different breeds to withstand different temperatures was then determined by studying the respiration rate and body temperature, the feed consumption, and the productivity in growth, milk, beef, etc. Dr. Brody reported the following pertinent findings:[1]

1. The most comfortable temperature for the Shorthorns was in the range of 30° to 60° F., while for the Brahmans it was 50° to 80° F. (20° higher for the Brahmans), and for the Santa

---

[1]Brody, Samuel, Missouri Agri. Expt. Sta., Jour. Series No. 1607.

Gertrudis it was intermediate between the ideal temperatures for the Shorthorn and Brahman.

2. The Brahman cattle could tolerate more heat—they could withstand higher temperature better than Shorthorns, whereas the Santa Gertrudis approached the Brahman in heat tolerance.

3. The Shorthorn cattle could tolerate more cold—they could withstand a lower temperature better than the other two breeds, while the Santa Gertrudis were more cold-tolerant than Brahman cattle.

Dr. Brody attributed the higher heat tolerance of Brahman cattle to their lower heat production, greater surface area (their loose skin) per unit weight, shorter hair, and "other body-temperature regulating mechanisms not visually apparent."

Translated into practicality, the Missouri experiment proved what is generally suspected; namely, (1) that Brahman and Santa Gertrudis cattle are better equipped to withstand tropical and subtropical temperatures than the European breeds, (2) that acclimatized European cattle do not need expensive, warm barns, they merely need protection from wind, snow, and rain, and (3) that more attention needs to be given to providing summer shades and other devices to assure warm weather comfort for cattle.

The livestock producer must always breed for a strong constitution—the power to live and thrive under the adverse conditions to which most animals are subjected sometime during their lifetime. Under natural conditions, selection occurs for this characteristic by the elimination of the unfit. In domestic herds however, the constitution of foundation or replacement animals should receive primary consideration.

Price

With a grade herd, it is seldom necessary to pay much in excess of market prices for the cows. However, additional money paid for a superior bull, as compared to a mediocre sire, is always a good investment. In fact, a poor bull is high at any price. With the purebred breeder, the matter of price for foundation stock is one of considerable importance. Though higher prices can be justified in the purebred business, sound judgment should always prevail.

SELECTION AND ITS BASES

In simple terms, selection in livestock breeding is an attempt to secure or retain the best of those animals in the current generation as parents of the next generation. Obviously, the skill with which selections are made is all important in determining the future of the herd. It becomes perfectly clear, therefore, that the destiny of breed improvement is dependent upon the selection for breeding purposes of those animals which are genetically superior. The use of genetically inferior animals for breeding purposes has ruined many a herd.

The profitability of any individual animal or of a herd of animals is determined by the following two factors:

1. **Type or individuality** based upon the ability to produce high-quality products for a discriminating market.

2. **Performance or efficiency of production,** which in beef cattle means ability to utilize feed efficiently to produce meat and milk. This also includes the ability to reproduce regularly.

Four bases of selection are at the disposal of the livestock producer: (1) selection based on type or individuality, (2) selection based on pedigree, (3) selection based on show-ring winnings, and (4) selection based on Production Testing.[1] Perhaps at the outset it should be emphasized that each method of selection has its own particular place. Certainly the progressive cattleman will make judicious use of all of them.

Selection Based on Type or Individuality

The ultimate objective in beef production is that of selling meat over the block. Thus fads or fancies in beef cattle selection that stray too far from this objective will, sooner or later, bring discredit and a penalty.

Strictly from the standpoint of the packer and the consumer, a meat animal should produce the maximum of the high-priced cuts, and there should be a very minimum of the less valuable bones and internal organs. On the other hand, in order to obtain efficiency of production under practical farm or ranch conditions, the producer must have animals with fairly good bone and a good middle. When such points of conflict exist, there must be a compromise. The most profitable beef animals, therefore, will be those that strike a happy balance between type, as related to the maximum production of a high-quality product, and the efficiency of production of this product.

---

[1]Term defined in Chapter VI.

Although environmental factors have a tremendous influence on animals, the fact remains that the performance and type of the animal itself (its phenotype or how it looks) are the best single indicators of the germ plasm that it carries (its genotype or what it actually is). Performance and type, therefore, are the most useful single factors in making selections. Naturally, this applies only to those characteristics that the animal itself can express. From a practical standpoint, this means that only those animals which are themselves average or preferably better than average should be used for breeding purposes, irrespective of the merit of near relatives.

The selection of animals on the basis of type or appearance alone is commonly called mass selection. This is the usual procedure followed in commercial herds, and, in a large part, it is responsible for the transformation of the Texas Longhorn to the present-day prime bullock.

In making selections based on type or individuality, it must be remembered that the characteristics found in the breeding herd are very likely to be reflected in the offspring; for here, as in any breeding program, a fundamental principle is that "like tends to produce like." Then, too, one must not overlook the fact that the herd bull is far more than half of the herd. A cow's inheritance will only influence one calf a year; whereas the herd bull may influence twenty to fifty times as many individuals in a given season.

Selection Based on Pedigree

In pedigree selection, the individuality and performance of the ancestors are relied upon for an estimate of the probable transmitting ability. This method is used in most purebred herds.

Pedigree selection is of special importance when progeny performance data is not available or when the animals are either so thin or so young that their individual merit cannot be ascertained with any degree of certainty. When selection is being made between animals of comparable individual merit, the pedigree may be the determining factor.

In making use of pedigree selections, however, it must be remembered that the ancestors close up in the pedigree are much more important than those many generations removed. Likewise, one must not be misled nor must he over-estimate the value of family names or favorite animals many generations removed from the foundation animal. Pedigree fads as such should be avoided, especially if there has not also been rigid culling and selection based on utility value. In all instances, poor individuals should not be saved, regardless of the excellence of relatives.

Selection Based on Show-ring Winnings

The show-ring has long been a major force in shaping the type of all classes of livestock. The first American show was held at Pittsfield, Massachusetts, in 1810, but livestock exhibitions had been initiated in Europe many years earlier.

As now conducted, our livestock shows have both advantages and disadvantages from the standpoint of breed improvement.

Among the advantages are the following:

1. The show-ring is the best medium yet discovered for molding breed type. For this reason, it behooves the breed registry associations and the purebred breeders alike to accept their rightful responsibility in seeing that the animals which win top honors are those that most nearly meet the efficiency of production demands on the part of the producer and the meat quality demands of the consumer.

2. It serves as one of the very best advertising or promotional mediums for both the breed and the breeder.

3. It brings breeders together for exchange of ideas and experiences.

4. It provides an incentive to breed better cattle, for only by comparing animals in the show-ring can the breeder ascertain whether or not he is keeping up with his competitors.

Some of the disadvantages of the show-ring are as follows:

1. Heavy fittings, in order to win, often results in temporary or permanent sterility.

2. The desire to win often causes exhibitors to resort to "surgical means" and "filling" in order to correct defects. Admittedly, such man-made corrections are not hereditary, and their effects are often not too durable—as is belatedly discovered by some innocent purchaser.

3. Valuable animals are frequently kept out of productive work or from reproduction in order to enhance their likelihood of winning in the show-ring.

Thus, in making selections from among show animals, one

should do so with a full understanding of both the virtues and the limitations therein.

Selection Based on Production Testing

Production Testing is the most infallible basis of selection. Further details relative to the traits of importance in beef cattle and the method of measuring each are presented in Chapter VI.

Progressive cattle breeders are beginning to select bulls backed by either an Individual Merit Test or Progeny Test. This interest will increase. The progressive purebred breeder, therefore, will start now to get his herd on a tested basis. It should be emphasized, however, that even though Production Testing is one of the keenest tools available to the breeder, for best results it is advocated that one continue to use all four methods of selection: individuality, pedigree, show-ring, and Production Testing. But increasing emphasis should be placed upon the latter method. In other words, Production Testing should be used to supplement individual, pedigree, and show-ring selection rather than to replace them as is sometimes advocated.

HERD IMPROVEMENT THROUGH SELECTION

Once the herd has been established, the primary objective should be so to improve it as to obtain the maximum production of quality offspring. In order to accomplish this, there must be constant culling and careful selection of replacements. The breeders who have been most constructive in such a breeding program have usually used great breeding bulls and then have obtained their replacements by selecting some of the outstanding, early-maturing heifers from the more prolific families.

Improvements through selection are really twofold: (1) the immediate gain in increased calf production from the better animals that are retained, and (2) the genetic gain in the next generation. The first is important in all herds, whereas the second is of special importance in purebred herds and in all herds where replacement females are raised. Most of the immediate gain is attained in selecting the cows, which are more numerous than the bulls; whereas the majority of the genetic gain comes from the careful selection of bulls. The genetic gain is small, but it is permanent and can be considered a capital investment.

Many good cattle breeders consider it a sound practice to make about 20 per cent replacement each year. Under such a system of management one-fifth of the heifer calves are retained each year for each one hundred cows.

JUDGING BEEF CATTLE

The discussion that follows represents a further elucidation of the first point discussed under selection—individuality. In addition to individual merit, the word judging implies the comparative appraisal or placing of several animals.

Judging beef cattle, like all livestock judging, is an art, the rudiments of which must be obtained through patient study and long practice. The master breeders throughout the years have been competent livestock judges. Shrewd traders have also been masters of the art, even to the point of deception.

The essential qualifications that a good judge of beef cattle must possess, and the recommended procedure to follow in selecting or judging are as follows:

1. **Knowledge of the parts of an animal.**—This consists of mastering the language that describes and locates the different parts of an animal (see Fig. 43). In addition, it is necessary to know which of these parts are of major importance; that is, what comparative evaluation to give to the different parts.

2. **A clearly defined ideal or standard of perfection.**—The successful cattle judge must know for what he is looking; that is, he must have in mind an ideal or standard of perfection.

3. **Keen observation and sound judgment.**—The good judge possesses the ability to observe both good conformation and defects, and to weigh and evaluate the relative importance of the various good and bad features.

4. **Honesty and courage.**—The good judge of any class of livestock must possess honesty and courage, whether it be in making a show-ring placing or conducting a breeding and marketing program. For example, it often requires considerable courage to place a class of animals without regard to: (1) placings in previous shows, (2) ownership, and (3) public applause. It may take even greater courage and honesty with oneself to discard from the herd a costly animal whose progeny has failed to measure up.

5. **Logical procedure in examining.**—There is always great danger of the beginner making too close an inspection; he often-

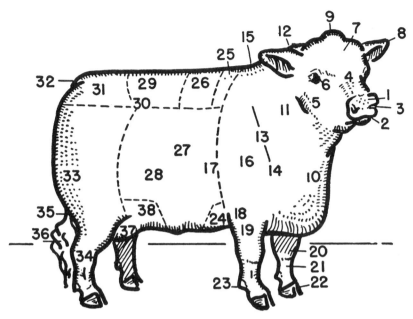

Fig. 43. Parts of a steer. The first step in preparation for judging beef cattle consists of mastering the language that describes and locates the different parts of the animal. (Drawing by R. F. Johnson)

1. Muzzle	11. Neck	20. Knee	30. Hip or hook
2. Mouth	12. Crest	21. Shank	31. Rump
3. Nostril	13. Shoulder vein	22. Foot	32. Tail-head
4. Face	14. Point of shoulder	23. Dew claw	33. Thigh
5. Jaw	15. Top of shoulder	24. Fore flank	34. Hock
6. Eye	16. Shoulder	25. Crops	35. Tail
7. Forehead	17. Fore ribs or	26. Back	36. Switch
8. Ear	heart girth	27. Ribs	37. Cod
9. Poll	18. Elbow	28. Belly	38. Rear flank
10. Dewlap	19. Arm	29. Loin	

times gets "so close to the trees that he fails to see the forest." Good judging procedure consists of the following three separate steps: (1) observing at a distance and securing a panoramic view where several animals are involved, (2) using close inspection (and handling cattle and sheep), and (3) moving the animal in order to observe action. Also, it is important that a logical method be used in viewing an animal from all directions, as for example (1) side view, (2) rear view, and (3) front view; thus avoiding overlooking anything and making it easier to retain the observations that are made. Actually, it makes little difference as to the order of the views in inspecting cattle, but it is im-

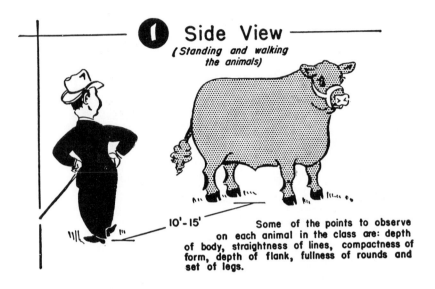

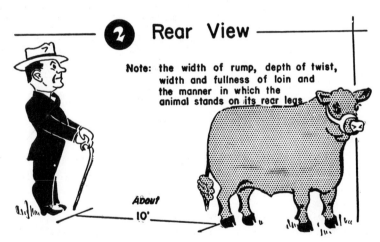

Fig. 44. Steps in examining: (1) side view, (2) rear view, (3) front view, and (4) handling. It is important that the judge follow a logical procedure in looking over animals. (Drawing by R. F. Johnson)

Fig. 44 (Continued)

③ Front View

About 10'

Study each animal's: head features and characteristics, spring of rib, width of chest and set and bone of forelegs.

④ Handling

This last step is to determine degree and quality of finish: with palm down, fingers held together feel the animals over upper and lower ribs, loin edge and top line from shoulder to rump. With thumb and fingers catch a roll of hide to test its pliability.

portant that the same procedure be followed each time. Though good judges differ, perhaps as logical a method of examining as any is illustrated in Fig. 44.

6. **Tact.**—In discussing either (1) a show-ring class, or (2) animals on a stockman's farm or ranch, it is important that the judge be tactful. The owner is likely to resent any remarks that imply that his animal is inferior.

Having acquired the above referred to knowledge, long hours must be spent in patient study and practice in comparing animals. Even this will not make expert and proficient judges in all instances, for there may be a grain of truth in the statement that "the best judges are born and not made." Nevertheless, training in judging and selecting animals is effective when directed by a competent instructor or experienced stockman.

Ideal Beef Type and Conformation

The next requisite in judging is to have clearly in mind a standard or ideal. Presumably, in beef cattle, this ideal should be based on a combination of: (1) the efficient performance of the animal from the standpoint of the producer and (2) the desirable carcass characteristics of market animals as determined by the consumer.

With beef animals, type is measured by the relative proportions between rounds, loins, ribs, shoulders, chucks, legs, and other cuts as well as by the estimated quality and the dressing percentage of the animal. The ideal beef animal should be low set and compact. The body should have great width and depth throughout, with good lines, and with all parts smoothly blended together. The animal should be thickly and evenly fleshed, with superior development in the regions of the high-priced cuts. The legs should be straight, true, and squarely set; the bone should be ample and show plenty of quality. With this splendid beef type, there should be style, balance, and symmetry and an abundance of quality. Beef cows should show femininity and breediness. The bull should show great masculinity. He should be burly, bold, and rugged and have an energetic yet manageable disposition. The great breeders of the past were men who visualized an ideal better than the current standards and who were not stampeded by passing fads. They possessed both a goal and a program.

It must be recognized, however, that the perfect specimen has never been produced. Each animal possesses one or several faults. In appraising an individual animal, therefore, its good points and its faults must be recognized, weighed, and evaluated in terms of an imaginary ideal. In comparative judging—that is, in judging a class of animals—the good points and the faults of each animal must be compared with the good points and the faults of every other animal in the class. In no other manner can they be ranked.

In addition to recognizing the strong and weak points in an animal, it is necessary that the successful judge recognize the degree to which the given points are good or bad. A sound evalua-

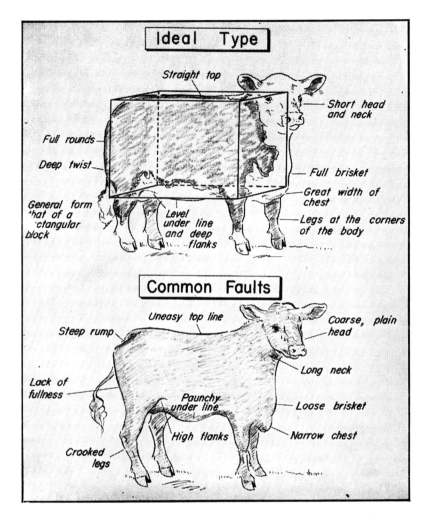

Fig. 45. Ideal beef type vs. common faults. After mastering the language that describes and locates the different parts of an animal, the next requisite in judging is to have clearly in mind a standard or ideal. In brief, the successful beef cattle judge must know what he is looking for, and be able to recognize and appraise the common faults. (Drawing by R. F. Johnson)

tion of this kind requires patient study and long experience. Fig. 45 shows the ideal beef type versus some of the common faults.

BULL GRADING

In recent years, bull grading programs have exerted a powerful influence in improving the commercial cattle on the western ranges of this country. Perhaps this movement received its greatest impetus in those areas where several owners run herds on unfenced public grazing lands. Formerly, those progressive ranchers who believed that only purebred beef bulls of high quality should be used could do nothing to prevent the presence of inferior bulls on these public ranges. The man who bought superior bulls got no more use from them than his neighbor who turned out scrubs because he could buy them cheaply. This problem was finally solved when groups of cattlemen using common ranges decided to have their bulls classified and to use only bulls of certain grades. Today, grazing permits are sometimes refused or delayed because of ranchers refusing to use graded bulls.

In some cases in the West, all animals consigned to range bull sales are graded and individual ranchers grade their young bulls before turning them with the cow herd. In some consignment sales, bulls must grade "2" or higher in order to be sold. Grading of sale bulls is especially popular with most buyers, but some sellers object to it.

In most of the bull grading programs of the West, the grades are designated as follows (with some states designating the grades alphabetically rather than numerically):

1. **"One-plus" grade** bulls (scoring 98 to 100) are well-nigh perfect specimens that are rarely produced.

2. **"One" grade** bulls (scoring 95 to 97) are very outstanding animals that are capable of making a good showing in the best of competition.

3. **"One-minus" grade** bulls (scoring 92 to 94) are top animals in most every respect; the kind that are good enough to head purebred herds.

4. **"Two-plus" grade** bulls (scoring 89 to 91) are outstanding bulls that have some minor faults. Some of them are used in purebred herds simply because there are not enough "one" grade bulls available. "Two-plus" bulls are top range bulls; the kind that have enough type and quality to improve any range herd.

5. **"Two" grade** bulls (scoring 86 to 88) are good useful kind of range bulls.

6. **"Two-minus" grade** bulls (scoring 83 to 85) are the lower end of range bulls; as far down in type and conformation

as one should go in any commercial herd. Because of their deficiencies, no self-respecting rancher wishes to display "two-minus" grade bulls.

7. **"Three" grade** bulls lack sufficient type and quality to give improvement in a commercial herd. They are the kind that should be castrated. In theory, "three" grade bulls are divided further into (1) "Three-Plus" grade bulls (scoring 80 to 82), (2) "Three" grade bulls (scoring 77 to 79), and (3) "Three-minus" grade bulls (scoring 74 to 76), but in actual practice generally all bulls grading below "Two minus" are eliminated from sales and from use on the range.

Recently, several college agricultural extension workers have expressed interest in establishing a uniform, nation-wide bull-grading system, using the following terms and values:

High Fancy—17, Fancy—16, Low Fancy—15
High Choice—14, Choice—13, Low Choice—12
High Good—11, Good—10, Low Good—9
High Medium—8, Medium—7, Low Medium—6
Common—5, Inferior—4, Very Inferior—3
Crippled—2, Deformed—1, Sick—0

In the West, bull grading is used rather extensively. Now, Production Testing is becoming an added and useful adjunct to bull grading.

HOW TO DETERMINE THE AGE OF CATTLE BY THE TEETH

The life-span of farm animals is relatively short, and their productiveness or usefulness declines with advancing years. The age of animals, therefore, is of practical importance to the breeder, the seller, and the buyer.

The approximate age of cattle can be determined by the teeth as described and illustrated herewith. There is nothing mysterious about this procedure. It is simply a matter of noting the time of appearance and the degree of wear of the temporary and of the permanent teeth. The temporary or milk teeth are readily distinguished from the permanent ones by their smaller size and whiter color.

It should be realized, however, that theoretical knowledge is not sufficient and that anyone who would become proficient must also have practical experience. The best way to learn how

TABLE 7

HANDY GUIDE TO DETERMINING THE AGE OF CATTLE BY THE TEETH

Drawing of Teeth[1]	Age of Animal	Description of Teeth
Fig. 46	At birth to 1 month	Two or more of the temporary incisor teeth present. Within first month, entire 8 temporary incisors appear.
Fig. 47	2 years	As a long-yearling, the central pair of temporary incisor teeth or pinchers is replaced by the permanent pinchers. At 2 years, the central permanent incisors attain full development.
Fig. 48	2½ years	Permanent first intermediates, one on each side of the pinchers, are cut. Usually these are fully developed at 3 years.
Fig. 49	3½ yaers	The second intermediates or laterals are cut. They are on a level with the first intermediates and begin to wear at 4 years.
Fig. 50	4½ y ars	The corner teeth are replaced. At 5 years the animal usually has the full complement of incisors with the corners fully developed.
Fig. 51	5 or 6 years	The permanent pinchers are leveled, both pairs of intermediates are partially leveled, and the corner incisors show wear.
Fig. 52	7 to 10 years	At 7 or 8 years the pinchers show noticeable wear; at 8 or 9 years the middle pairs show noticeable wear; and at 10 years, the corner teeth show noticeable wear.
Fig. 53	12 years	After the animal passes the 6th year, the arch gradually loses its rounded contour and becomes nearly straight by the 12th year. In the meantime, the teeth gradually become triangular in shape, distinctly separated, and show progressive wearing to stubs. These conditions become more marked with increasing age.

[1]The illustrations for this table were prepared by R. F. Johnson.

to recognize age in any class of farm animals is to examine the teeth of individuals of known ages.

At maturity cattle have 32 teeth, of which 8 are incisors in the lower jaw. The two central incisors are known as pinchers; the next two are called first intermediates; the third pair are called second intermediates or laterals; and the outer pair is known as the corners. There are no upper incisor teeth; only the thick, hard dental pad.

Table 7 illustrates and describes how one may determine the age of cattle by the teeth.

QUESTIONS FOR STUDY AND DISCUSSION

1. Select a certain farm or ranch (either your home farm or ranch, or one with which you are familiar). Assume that there are no beef cattle on this establishment at the present time. Then outline, step by step, (1) how you would go about establishing a herd, and (2) the factors that you would consider. Justify your decisions.

2. Cite examples as proof of the fact that show-ring standards have not always been practical.

3. What are the disadvantages to the score-card system of judging?

4. Discuss the practical importance of the Missouri Experiment Station study in which cattle were housed in "climatic chambers."

5. What bases of selection would you use, and why?

6. Under what conditions is bull grading particularly valuable? Why is bull grading generally more popular with buyers than sellers?

SELECTED REFERENCES

Title of Publication	Author(s)	Publisher
Beef Cattle; Selecting, Fitting, Showing	J. E. Nordby H. E. Lattig	Interstate Printers & Pub., Danville, Illinois, 1939.
Beef Production	R. V. Diggins C. E. Bundy	Prentice-Hall, Englewood Cliffs, N. J., 1956.
Breeding Better Livestock	V. A. Rice F. N. Andrews E. J. Warwick	McGraw-Hill Book Co., New York. 1953.
Determining the Age of Farm Animals by Their Teeth	Farmer's Bul. 1721	U. S. Department of Agriculture, Wash., 25, D. C.
Elements of Livestock Judging, The	W. W. Smith	J. B. Lippincott Co., Philadelphia, Pa., 1930.
Judging Livestock	E. T. Robbins	Cir. 579, Ext. Ser., Univ. of Illinois, Urbana, Illinois.
Livestock and Meat Manual, A	Ext. Misc. Pub. 40	Ext. Ser., Washington State University, Pullman, Wash.
Livestock Judging Handbook	J. E. Nordby W. M. Beeson David L. Fourt	Interstate Printers and Pub., Danville, Illinois, 1960.
Stockman's Handbook The	M. E. Ensminger	Interstate Printers and Pub., Danville, Illinois, 1959.

CHAPTER V

SYSTEMS OF BEEF PRODUCTION

Contents   Page

The general systems of beef production that are most extensively practiced include: (1) breeding purebreds; (2) cow-and-calf system; (3) growing of stockers; (4) baby beef production; (5) fattening cattle; and (6) dual-purpose production. In these systems, two area methods of management are involved: the farm herd method and the range cattle method.

BREEDING PUREBREDS

This is a specialized type of production. Generally speaking, only the experienced breeder should undertake the production of purebreds with the intention of furnishing foundation or replacement stock to other purebred breeders, or purebred bulls to the commercial producer. Unless prices are unusually favorable, the beginner had best start with grade cows and a purebred bull. Although there have been many constructive beef cattle breeders and great progress has been made, it must be remembered that only those "master breeders" like Bakewell, Cruickshank, and Gentry are among the immortals. Few breeders achieve the success which was theirs.

It is estimated that only 3 per cent of the cattle of the United States are purebreds at the present time and that more than 88 per cent of the farms on which beef cattle are kept do not possess a single purebred cow. Although limited in numbers, purebred herds are scattered throughout the United States and include both farm and ranch operations.

115

Fig. 54. Purebred Hereford herd on pasture. The breeding of purebreds
is a highly specialized type of production.

COW-AND-CALF SYSTEM

This system is sometimes referred to as the "production of
stockers and feeders." In this type of operation the calves run
with their dams until weaned, and the cows are not milked.
This particular type of production is followed more extensively
than any other throughout the United States. It is especially
adapted to regions where pasture is plentiful and land is cheap.
As might be expected, it represents the more or less standard
system of beef production in the western range country. The
breeding herd needs but little grain or other expensive feeds,
except when the ground is covered with snow.

GROWING OF STOCKERS

Stockers are thin animals, generally of beef breeding and
yearlings or under, upon which it is intended that gains shall be
produced on pasture or other cheap roughages. They may consist of steers or heifers that are intended for fattening purposes

Fig. 55. Cow-and-calf system of beef cattle production on the Black Ranch, Brewster, Nebraska. In this system, the calves are run with their dams until weaned and the cows are not milked. It is the most common system of beef production on the western range. (Courtesy, C.B.&Q. Railroad Co.)

at a later period, or heifers which will be used for breeding purposes. Usually such cattle are not held longer than a year, and, for the most part, they are fed chiefly on pasture and cheap roughage. This type of operation is conducted in both the farm and range states.

BABY BEEF PRODUCTION

"Baby beef" is the term applied to finished animals from twelve to eighteen months of age, that weigh 700 to 1,200 pounds, and which grade from "Good" to "Prime." Although animals classed as baby beef vary somewhat in weight, it is noteworthy that during the ten-year period 1948 through 1957, the champion steers at The Chicago International averaged 1,091 pounds. In its truest form, the production of baby beeves involves the breeding, rearing, and fattening of the calves on the same farm. The first requirement for baby beef production is superior breeding. Secondly, the calves intended for such use should never be allowed to lose their baby fat. Ordinarily the calves are "creep fed"; grain is placed before them as soon as they are old enough to eat, usually when they are from four to six weeks old. Cows producing calves intended for baby beef are generally fed a little more liberally than those producing calves for other purposes.

Well-finished baby beeves command top prices, and the demand is wide and insistent. An increasing number of beef men are, therefore, turning their efforts to this type of production. Boys and girls 4-H Club work has done much to focus attention on baby beef production.

THE FATTENING OF CATTLE

The cattle-fattening industry, in so far as grain feeding is concerned, is largely confined to the Corn Belt and the irrigated valleys of the West. Although some of the central states feeders maintain breeding herds from which they produce their own feeder calves, the majority of feeders continue to rely on the western ranges for their young stock.

Fig. 56. Hereford steers being fattened by Frank Friedrichsen, Andover, Iowa. The grain fattening of cattle is confined almost entirely to the Corn Belt and the irrigated valleys of the West. (Courtesy, The Corn Belt Farm Dailies)

For the inexperienced feeder or the "in-and-outer," this type of production is surrounded by many hazards. When feeders have the opinion that profits are due largely to clever buying and selling, the enterprise is often a "gamble." However, for the man who follows cattle feeding year after year as a method of marketing home-grown grain, who practices skillful feeding and management, and who conserves the manure as fertilizer, this system will give good returns over a period of years. The subject of fattening cattle is more fully discussed in Chapter IX.

DUAL-PURPOSE PRODUCTION

For the most part, dual-purpose production has been confined to the small farmer who lives upon the land and who makes his living therefrom. Cows of dual-purpose breeding are often referred to as the "farmer's cow." In this type of production, an attempt is made to obtain simultaneously as much beef and milk as possible. That is to say, in its truest form, this type of management can be classified as neither beef nor dairy production.

One of the chief virtues of dual-purpose production is the flexibility which it affords. When labor is available and dairy

Fig. 57. Red Poll steers on feed. Dual-purpose cattle provide considerable flexibility. Thus, when labor is scarce and dairy products are low in price, the emphasis may be placed on beef production. (Courtesy, Red Poll Cattle Club of America)

products are high in price, the herd may be managed for market milk production. On the other hand, when labor is scarce and dairy products are low in price, calves may be left running with their dams, and emphasis may be placed on beef production.

THE FARM HERD METHOD

In general, beef cattle production in the so-called farm states is merely part of a diversified type of farming. Grain and pasture crops are produced; and, on the same farm, beef cattle may compete with dairy cattle, hogs, and sheep for the available feeds. This applies to practically all the farms located to the east of the seventeen western range states. In general, farm beef cattle herds are much smaller than range herds of the West, and many of them lack the uniformity which now prevails in range cattle.

Fig. 58. A farm herd of beef cattle. In general, farm herds are much
smaller than range herds. Moreover, beef production in the farm states is
usually part of a diversified type of farming. (Courtesy, Purdue University)

THE RANGE CATTLE METHOD

Fifty-eight per cent of all U. S. beef cattle are produced on
the western range. Because a considerable portion of the range
area is not suited to the production of grains and because sheep
offer the only other major use of the grasses, it seems evident
that range beef cattle production will continue to hold a place of
prominence in American agriculture. Because of the magnitude
of the range beef cattle industry and the fact that it is a highly
specialized type of operation, considerable space will be given to
the range area and the care and management of cattle in the
range method (see Chapter XI).

QUESTIONS FOR STUDY AND DISCUSSION

1. Select a certain farm or ranch (your home farm or ranch,
   or one with which you are familiar). Assume that there are
   no beef or dual-purpose cattle on this establishment at the
   present time. Which of the six systems of beef production
   would you elect to follow? Justify your decision.

2. If you were purchasing a cattle establishment, would you
   select a farm-type or a ranch-type operation? Justify your
   decision.

Fig. 59 Hereford cattle on a range in Oregon. South Sister Peak in the background. (Courtesy, U. S. Forest Service)

SELECTED REFERENCES

Title of Publication	Author (s)	Publisher
Beef Cattle	R. R. Snapp	John Wiley & Sons, New York, 1952.
Beef Cattle Production in the South	D. W. Williams	Interstate Printers and Publishers, Danville, Illinois, 1955.
Beef Production	R. V. Diggins C. E. Bundy	Prentice-Hall, Inc., Englewood Cliffs, N. J., 1956.
Livestock Book, The	C. S. Hobbs et. al.	Vulcan Service Co., 403 Tuscaloosa Ave., S. W. Birmingham 11, Ala., 1952.

CHAPTER VI

SOME PRINCIPLES OF CATTLE GENETICS[1]

Contents

---

[1] The author gratefully acknowledges the authoritative review and helpful suggestions of the following reviewers in the preparation of this chapter: Drs. C. C. O'Mary and E. S. E. Hafez, State College of Washington; and Dr. S. H. Fowler, Animal Breeding Specialist, Louisiana State University.

During the past century, remarkable progress has been made in breeding better beef cattle—animals that are more efficient, and that produce cuts of meat more nearly meeting the exacting requirements of the consuming public. The Texas Longhorn steer—built for stamina, ability to fight and to furnish its own transportation, but producing tough, stringy meat—has been replaced by the earlier-maturing, prime bullock.

Despite the remarkable progress of the past, much remains to be done. A casual glance at the daily receipts of any public stockyards is convincing evidence of the need for further improvements. Also, cattle sterility, reproductive failures, and young calf losses are very costly. Moreover, the production of abnormal animals—even if they occur only to a limited extent—represents a considerable economic loss to the cattleman. In this age, there must be greater efficiency of production; this means more rapid growth, heavier weights, less feed to produce 100 pounds of beef, lifting the percentage calf crop well above the present U.S. average, and the production of tender, well-marbled beef with less exterior fat. The ultimate goal should be that of furnishing better animals for market and lowering the cost of production.

The laws of heredity apply to cattle breeding exactly as they do to all other classes of farm animals; but the breeding of cattle is less flexible in the hands of man because (1) cows seldom give birth to more than one offspring at a time, whereas sows are litter-bearing animals and ewes frequently produce twins or triplets, and (2) hogs and sheep breed at an earlier age, thus making for a shorter interval between generations. These and other breeding phenomena peculiar to beef cattle will be treated in this chapter.

With present, although incomplete, knowledge of genetics, progress should now be much more certain and rapid. In the past, cattle breeding has been an art; in the future, it should be both an art and a science.

MENDEL'S CONTRIBUTION TO GENETICS

Modern genetics was really founded by Gregor Johann Mendel, an Austrian monk, who smoked long, black cigars and gardened because of his obesity. He conducted breeding experiments with garden peas from 1857 to 1865, during the time of the Civil War in the United States. In his monastery at Brünn (now Brno, in Czechoslovakia), Mendel applied a powerful curiosity and a clear mind to reveal some of the basic principles of hereditary transmission. In 1866, he published in the proceedings of a local scientific society a report covering eight years of his studies, but for thirty-four years his findings went unheralded

Fig. 60. Gregor Johann Mendel (1822-1884), a cigar-smoking Austrian monk, whose breeding experiments with garden peas founded modern genetics. (Courtesy, Bettman Archives)

and ignored. Finally, in 1900, sixteen years after Mendel's death, three European biologists independently duplicated his findings, and this led to the dusting off of the original paper published by the monk thirty-four years earlier.

The essence of Mendelism is that inheritance is by particles or units (called genes), that these genes are present in pairs— one member of each pair having come from each parent—and that each gene maintains its identity generation after generation. Thus, Mendel's work with peas laid the basis for two of the general laws of inheritance: (1) the law of segregation, and (2) the independent assortment of genes. Later genetic principles have been added; yet all the phenomena of inheritance, based upon the reactions of genes, are generally known under the collective term, Mendelism. Thus modern genetics is really unique in that it was founded by an amateur who was not trained as a geneticist and who did his work merely as a hobby. During the years since the rediscovery of Mendel's principles (in 1900), many additional genetic principles have been added, but the fundamentals as set forth by Mendel have been proved correct in every detail. It can be said, therefore, that inheritance in both plants and animals follows the biological laws discovered by Mendel.

SOME FUNDAMENTALS OF HEREDITY IN CATTLE

In the sections which follow, no attempt will be made to cover all of the diverse field of genetics. Rather, the author will present a condensation of a few of the known facts in regard to the field and briefly summarize their application to beef cattle.

The Gene as the Unit of Heredity

Genes determine all the hereditary characteristics of animals, from the body type to the color of the hair. They are truly the fundamental units of genetics.

The bodies of all animals are made up of millions or even billions of tiny cells, microscopic in size. Each cell contains a nucleus in which there are a number of pairs of bundles, called chromosomes. In turn, the chromosomes carry pairs of minute particles, called genes, which are the basic hereditary material. The nucleus of each body cell of cattle contains thirty pairs of chromosomes, or a total of sixty,[1] whereas there are perhaps thousands of pairs of genes. These genes determine all the hereditary characteristics of living animals. Thus inheritance goes by units, rather than by the blending of two fluids as our grandfathers thought.

The modern breeder knows that the job of transmitting qualities from one generation to the next is performed by germ cells—a sperm from the male and an ovum or egg from the female. All animals, therefore, are the result of the union of two such tiny cells, one from each of its parents. These two germ cells contain all the anatomical, physiological, and psychological characters that the offspring will inherit. They determine whether a

---

[1]Horses also have 60 chromosomes; swine have 40; sheep have 54; and man has 48.

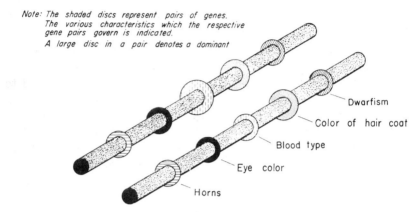

Fig. 61. A pair of bundles, called chromosomes, carrying minute particles, called genes. The genes determine all the hereditary characteristics of living animals, from length of leg to body size. (Drawing by R. F. Johnson)

calf shall be polled instead of horned, black instead of white, a bull instead of a heifer, etc.

In the body cells of an animal, each of the chromosomes is duplicated; whereas in the formation of the sex cells, the egg and the sperm, a reduction division occurs and only one chromosome and one gene of each pair goes into a sex cell. This means that only half the number of chromosomes and genes present in the body cells of the animal go into each egg and sperm (thus each reproductive cell of cattle has 30 chromosomes), but each sperm or egg cell has genes for every characteristic of its species. As will be explained later, the particular half that any one germ cell gets is determined by chance. When mating and fertilization occur, the single chromosomes from the germ cell of each parent unite to form new pairs, and the genes are again present in duplicate in the body cells of the embryo.

With all possible combinations in thirty pairs of chromosomes (the species number in cattle) and the genes that they bear, any bull or cow can transmit over one billion different samples of its inheritance; and the combination from both parents makes possible one billion times one billion genetically different offspring. It is not strange, therefore, that no two animals within a given breed (except identical twins from a single egg split after fertilization) are exactly alike. Rather, we can marvel that the members of a given breed bear as much resemblance to each other as they do.

Even between such closely related individuals as full sisters, it is possible that there will be quite wide differences in size, growth rate, temperament, conformation, and in almost every conceivable character. Admitting that many of these differences may be due to undetected differences in environment, it is still true that in such animals much of the variation is due to hereditary differences. A bull, for example, will sometimes transmit to one offspring much better inheritance than he does to most of his get, simply as the result of chance differences in the genes that go to different sperm at the time of the reduction division. Such differences in inheritance in offspring have been called both the hope and the despair of the livestock breeder.

If an animal gets similar determiners or genes from each parent, it will produce uniform germ cells; because any half of its inheritance is just like any other half. For example, regardless of what combination of chromosomes goes into a particular germ cell, it will be just like any other egg or sperm from the same individual. Such animals are referred to as being homozygous. Few, if any, of our animals are in this hereditary state at the present time. Instead of being homozygous, they are heterozygous. This explains why there may be such wide variation within the offspring of any given sire or dam. The wise and progressive breeder recognizes this fact, and he insists on the production records of all get rather than that of just a few meritorious individuals.

Variation between the offspring of animals that are not pure or homozygous, to use the technical term, is not to be marveled at, but is rather to be expected. No one would expect to draw exactly twenty sound apples and ten rotten ones every time he took a random sample of thirty from a barrel containing forty sound ones and twenty rotten ones, although, on the average—if enough samples were drawn—he would expect to get about that proportion of each. Individual drawings would, of course, vary rather widely. Exactly the same situation applies to the relative numbers of "good" and "bad" genes that may be present in different germ cells from the same animal. Because of this situation, the mating of a cow with a fine show record to a bull that on the average transmits relatively good offspring will not always produce calves of merit equal to that of their parents. The calves could be markedly poorer than the parents or, happily, they could in some cases be better than either parent.

Selection and close breeding are the tools through which the cattle producer can obtain bulls and cows whose chomosomes and genes contain similar hereditary determiners—animals that are genetically more homozygous.

Actually, a completely homozygous state would be undesirable and unfortunate. This is so because economic and environmental changes are apt to dictate animal changes from time to time. With complete homozygosity, such shifts would be impossible except through the slow and uncertain process of mutations; thus making it extremely difficult to affect a change in phenotype. Fortunately, enough heterozygosity exists in our improved breeds so that they are flexible in the hands of man; they can be molded in any desired direction (In fact, enough heterozygosity exists that it is nigh impossible to fix complete homozygosity). It may be said, therefore, that variation in the biological material permits the animal breeder to mold, change, and improve his stock.

Mutations

Gene changes are technically known as mutations. *A mutation may be defined as a sudden variation which is later passed on through inheritance and that results from changes in a gene or genes.* Mutations are not only rare, but they are prevailingly harmful, and most of them are recessive. Further, one cannot induce a particular kind of mutation. For all practical purposes, therefore, the genes can be thought of as unchanged from one generation to the next. The observed differences between animals are usually due to different combinations of genes being present rather than to mutations. Each gene probably changes only about once in each 100,000 to 1,000,000 animals produced.

Once in a great while a mutation occurs in a farm animal, and it produces a visible effect in the animal carrying it. These animals are commonly called "sports." Such sports are occasionally of practical value. The occurrence of the polled characteristic within the horned Hereford and Shorthorn breeds of cattle is an example of a mutation or sport of economic importance.[1] Out of this has arisen the Polled Hereford and Polled Shorthorn breeds.

Gene changes can be accelerated by exposure to X-rays, radium, mustard gas, and ultra-violet light rays. Such changes may eventually be observed in the offspring of both people and animals of Japan who were exposed to the atom bombs unleashed in World War II.

Although induced mutations have been used successfully in developing commercial varieties of plants, the technique does not appear very promising for the improvement of animals. This is so because (1) an enormous number of mutations would have to be induced in order to have much chance of getting one which had commercial value, and (2) its frequency would have to be increased by selection and as many of the concurrent undesirable mutations as possible eliminated from the stock.

Simple Gene Inheritance (Qualitative Traits)

In the simplest type of inheritance, only one pair of genes is involved. Thus, a pair of genes is responsible for the color of hair in Shorthorn cattle. This situation is illustrated by Fig. 62.

An animal having two genes for red (RR) is actually red in color, whereas an animal having two genes for white (rr) is white in color. On the other hand, a Shorthorn which has one gene for red (R) and one for white (r) is neither red nor white but roan (Rr), which is a mixture of red and white. Thus, red X white matings in Shorthorn cattle usually produce roan offspring. Likewise, white X white matings generally produce white offspring; but it must be remembered that white in Shorthorns is seldom pure, for the face bristles, eyelashes, and ears usually carry red hairs. Roans, having one gene for red and one for white on the paired chromosomes will never breed true and, if mated together, will produce calves in the proportion of one red, two roans, and one white. If one wishes to produce roans, the most certain way is to mate red cows with a white bull or vice versa, for then all the calves will be roan. If a roan animal is bred to a red one, one-half the offspring will be red, whereas the other half will be roan. Likewise when a roan animal is bred to a white one, approximately an equal number of roan and white calves will be produced.

---

[1]The horned gene mutates to the polled gene at a fairly high frequency; apparently at the rate of about 1 in 20 thousand.

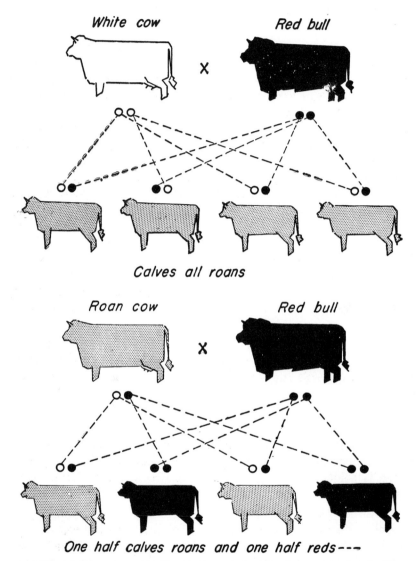

Fig. 62. Diagrammatic illustration of the inheritance of color in Short-horn cattle. Red X white matings in Shorthorn cattle usually produce roan offspring, whereas roan X red matings produce one-half red offspring and one-half roan offspring. (Drawing by R. F. Johnson)

This example illustrates the most important principles of inheritance; namely, (1) genes occur in animals in pairs because one member of each pair comes from each parent, and (2) each reproductive cell contains a sample half of the genes of that particular animal.

It should be borne in mind that there is no way to sort out the numerous genes so as to get the most desirable ones into the same reproductive cell except as it occurs by chance during the formation of eggs and sperm. Thus, it follows that the various gene combinations, such as referred to above, occur at random and that the various colors will appear in the offspring in the proportions indicated only when relatively large numbers are concerned. The possible gene combinations, therefore, are governed by the laws of chance, operating in much the same manner as the results obtained from flipping coins. For example, if a penny is flipped often enough, the number of heads and tails will come out about even. However, with the laws of chance in operation, it is possible that out of any four tosses one might get all heads, all tails, or even three to one. In exactly the same manner, a Shorthorn breeder may be highly elated in obtaining four red calves from roan X roan matings only to be greatly depressed when the next four calves, from the same matings, are white in color.

In addition to color of hair, other examples of simple gene inheritance in animals (sometimes referred to as qualitative traits) include color of eyes, presence or absence of horns, type of blood, and lethals.

DOMINANT AND RECESSIVE FACTORS:

In the example of Shorthorn colors, each gene of the pair (R and r) produced a visible effect, whether paired as identical genes (two red or two whites) or as two different genes (red and white).

This is not true of all genes; some of them have the ability to prevent or mask the expression of others, with the result that the genetic makeup of such animals cannot be recognized with perfect accuracy. This ability to cover up or mask the presence of one member of a set of genes is called dominance. The gene which masks the one is the dominant gene; the one which is masked is the recessive gene.

In cattle, the polled character is dominant to the horned character. Thus, if a *pure polled* bull is used on horned cows (or vice versa), the resulting progeny are not midway between two parents but are of polled character.[1] It must be remembered, however, that not all hornless animals are pure for the polled character; many of them carry a factor for horns in the hidden or "recessive" condition. In genetic terminology, animals that are pure for a certain character—for example the polled characteristic—are termed *homozygous,* whereas those that have one dominant and one recessive factor are termed *heterozygous.* A simple breeding test can be used in order to determine whether a polled bull is homozygous or heterozygous, but it is impossible to determine such purity or impurity through inspection. The breeding test consists of mating the polled sire with a number of horned females. If the bull is pure or homozygous for the polled character, all of the calves will be polled; whereas if he is impure or heterozygous, only half of the resulting offspring will, on the average, be polled and half will have horns like the horned parents. Many breeders of Polled Herefords or Polled Shorthorns test their herd sires in this manner, mating the prospective sire to several horned animals.

It is clear, therefore, that a dominant character will cover up a recessive. Hence an animal's breeding performance cannot be recognized by its phenotype (how it looks), a fact which is of great significance in practical breeding.

Another example of dominance is that of the white face of Hereford cattle—the white face being dominant over the type of coloration in which the head and body are of the same color. Undoubtedly, this condition of dominance, which constitutes a trademark of the breed, has been of importance from a promotional standpoint.

---

[1]It is noteworthy, however, that when a homozygous polled animal is crossed with a homozygous horned animal, some "scurs" or small loosely attached horns usually appear. There are conflicting reports and opinions concerning the inheritance of scurs, with the following theories prevailing:

1. That the gene for scurs is recessive and independent of the major genes for horns. According to this theory, scurs appear only in individuals homozygous for the scurred gene (sc sc).

2. That scurs are a sex-influenced character. According to this theory, scurs will occur in males either homozygous (Sc Sc) or heterozygous (Sc sc) for the character, but only in females homozygous (Sc Sc) for the character; in other words, it acts as a dominant in polled males and a recessive in polled females.

3. That the major gene (P) for polled condition is only partially dominant, with heterozygous individuals (Pp) tending to be scurred, especially in bulls.

Horns prevent the expression of any genes an animal may have for scurs, and thus complicate studies designed to determine the exact mode of inheritance of scurs.

As can be readily understood, dominance often makes the task of identifying and discarding all animals carrying an undesirable recessive factor a difficult one. Recessive genes can be

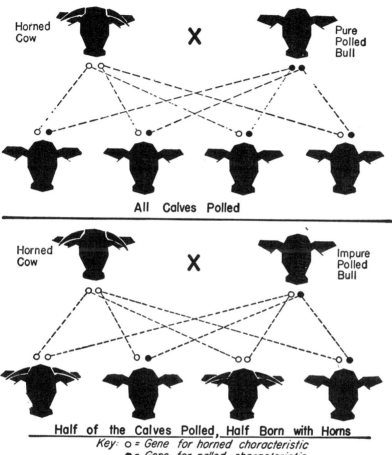

All Calves Polled

Half of the Calves Polled, Half Born with Horns

Key: o = Gene for horned characteristic
● = Gene for polled characteristic

Fig. 63. Diagrammatic illustration of the inheritance of horns in cattle of European extraction. Although there may be a very occasional exception, if a bull that is considered pure or homozygous for the polled character is mated with a number of horned females, all of the calves will be polled; whereas if a bull that is impure or heterozygous for the polled character is mated with a number of horned females, only half of the calves will, on the average, be polled. (Drawing by R. F. Johnson)

passed on from generation to generation, appearing only when two animals, both of which carry the recessive factor, happen to mate. Even then, only one out of four offspring produced will,

on the average, be homozygous for the recessive factor and
show it.

In cattle, the red color in the Aberdeen-Angus breed is an
example of such an undesirable recessive factor. Black polled
cattle have been known in Scotland since 1523; and since the
days of Hugh Watson, William McCombie, and George McPher-
son Grant, black has been the accepted color of the breed. Yet,
down through the years, a recessive factor for red coat color
has persisted in the breed. For this reason, a red calf occasionally and unexpectedly shows up in a purebred Aberdeen-Angus
herd (about one red calf appears in every 200 to 500 Aberdeen-
Angus calves dropped[1]). This occasional appearance of a red calf
in the Aberdeen-Angus breed does not signify any impurity of
breeding but merely the outcropping of a long hidden recessive
gene. When a red calf does appear, one can be very certain that
both the sire and dam contributed equally to the condition and
that each of them carried the recessive gene for red color. This
fact should be given consideration in the culling program.

As the factor for red is recessive, the red animals are pure
for color. The mating of two red animals, therefore, will always
produce red calves.[2]

Other examples of undesirable recessives are red color in
Holstein cattle, and dwarfism in cattle.

Assuming that a hereditary defect or abnormality has occurred in a herd and that it is recessive in nature, the breeding
program to be followed to prevent or minimize the possibility
of its future occurrence will depend somewhat on the type of
herd involved—especially on whether it is a commercial or
purebred herd. In a commercial herd, the breeder can usually
guard against further reappearance of the undesirable recessive
simply by using an outcross (unrelated) sire within the same
breed or by crossbreeding with a sire from another breed. With
this system, the breeder is fully aware of the recessive being
present, but he has taken action to keep it from showing up.

On the other hand, if such an undesirable recessive appears

---

[1]In order to obtain one red calf out of 200, one parent out of every 7
must be a carrier of the red gene. Actually, to get 1/196 red calves, there
must be 1/14 b (red gene) reproductive cells in both males and females because 1/14 x 1/14 = 1/196. Thus 1/7 of the parents must be Bb (black in
color, but carrying the red gene) while 6/7 are BB (pure for black).

[2]A separate U. S. breed registry association for these Red Angus cattle
was organized in 1954 (See Chapter III, Table 6). To these breed en-
thusiasts, the recessive gene for red is desirable.

in a purebred herd, the action should be more drastic. A reputable purebred breeder has an obligation not only to himself but to his customers among both the purebred and commercial herds. Purebred animals must be purged of undesirable genes and lethals. This can be done by:

1. Eliminating those sires and dams that are known to have transmitted the undesirable recessive character.

2. Eliminating both the abnormal and normal offspring produced by these sires and dams (approximately half of the normal animals will carry the undesirable character in the recessive condition).

3. Breeding a prospective herd sire to a number of females known to carry the factor for the undesirable recessive, thus making sure that the new sire is free from the recessive.

Such action in a purebred herd is expensive, and it calls for considerable courage. Yet it is the only way in which the purebred livestock of the country can be freed from such undesirable genes.

INCOMPLETE OR PARTIAL DOMINANCE:

The results of crossing polled with horned cattle are clear-cut because the polled character is completely dominant over its allele (horned). If, however, a cross is made between a red and a white Shorthorn, the result is a roan (mixture of red and white hairs) color pattern. In the latter cross, the action of a gene is such that it does not cover the allele, which is known as incomplete dominance; or, stated differently, the roan color is the result of the action of a pair of genes (joint action) neither of which is dominant. This explains the futility of efforts to develop Shorthorns pure for roan.

The above discussion also indicates that there are varying degrees of dominance—from complete dominance to an entire lack of dominance. In the vast majority of cases, however, dominance is neither complete nor absent, but incomplete or partial. Also, it is now known that dominance is not the result of single-factor pairs but that the degree of dominance depends upon the animal's whole genetic make-up together with the environment to which it is exposed, and the various interactions between the genetic complex (genotype) and the environment.

Multiple Gene Inheritance (Quantitative Traits)

Relatively few characters of economic importance in farm animals are inherited in as simple a manner as the coat color or polled conditions described. Important characters—such as meat production and milk and butterfat production—are due to many genes; thus they are called multiple-factor characters or multiple-gene characters. Because such characters show all manner of gradation—from high to low performance, for example—they are sometimes referred to as quantitative traits.

In quantitative inheritance, the extremes (either good or bad) tend to swing back to the average. Thus, the offspring of a grand champion bull and a grand champion cow are not apt to be as good as either parent. Likewise, and happily so, the progeny of two very mediocre parents will likely be superior to either parent.

Estimates of the number of pairs of genes affecting each economically important characteristic vary greatly, but the majority of geneticists agree that for most such characters ten or more pairs of genes are involved. Growth rate in cattle, therefore, is affected by the following: (1) the animal's appetite; (2) feed consumption; (3) feed utilization—that is, the proportion of the feed eaten that is absorbed into the blood stream; (4) feed assimilation—the use to which the nutrients are put after absorption; and (5) feed conversion—whether used for muscle, fat or bone formation. This should indicate clearly enough that such a characteristic as growth rate is controlled by many genes and that it is difficult to determine the mode of inheritance of such characters.

Inheritance of Some Characters in Cattle

Mendelian characters are inherited in alternative pairs (or series). These alternative forms of a gene, which are located at the same point on each one of a pair of chromosomes, are called *alleles*—for example, horns (recessive) and polled (dominant).

An individual that is heterozygous with respect to one pair of allelic genes is a *monohybrid*; one that is heterozygous with respect to two pairs of allelic genes is a *dihybrid*; and one that is heterozygous with respect to three pairs of allelic genes is a *trihybrid*. Practical examples of the inheritance of each of these and other characters in cattle will follow.

A MONOHYBRID CROSS:

When a homozygous polled animal (PP) is crossed with a homozygous horned animal (pp), the first cross (F_1) offspring is a monohybrid (Pp). This first cross animal is polled (see Fig. 63). If two of the monohybrids (Pp) are crossed, the second cross (F_2) offspring will be in the ratio of three polled to one horned. This phenomenon is explained and understood by assuming that one parent has the genes for the dominant polled characteristic and the other parent the genes for the recessive horned characteristic at similar loci in paired homologous chromosomes; that one pair of each of these genes is present in the monohybrid; but that these genes separate or segregate out when the monohybrid produces germ cells (sperms and eggs) with the half (haploid) number of chromosomes.

Also it is noteworthy that the classical explanation for inheritance of the polled or horned condition in cattle, where (PP) and (Pp) are polled animals and (pp) are horned animals, apparently applies only to cattle of the European breeds. Where Brahman blood is introduced into crosses, the situation is considerably complicated and the exact mode of inheritance is not known. Thus, where polled animals of the European breeds of either sex are crossed with Brahman animals, it has been observed (1) that polled animals cannot be depended upon uniformly to dehorn the calves, but that the offspring from such a cross may be either polled, horned, scurred, or buttoned; (2) that the inheritance of horns may differ according to the way in which the cross is made—that is, as to whether the Brahman parent is the sire or the dam; and (3) that there is a greater tendency for bull calves of such crosses to be horned than for heifer calves (the latter point applies to horns only; when horns, scurs, and buttons are considered collectively, there is apparently little or no difference between sexes).

A DIHYBRID CROSS:

Practical cattlemen are aware of the fact that the polled condition is dominant over the horned condition and that black color is dominant over red color. Aberdeen-Angus cattle are homozygous for both the polled characteristic and black body color,[1] whereas Devon cattle are homozygous for the horned

---

[1]As already mentioned, a few Aberdeen-Angus cattle carry a recessive for red color.

characteristic and red body color. Thus, if an Aberdeen-Angus bull is mated to Devon cows, the results of the first cross (F_1) will be as follows:

polled, black P P B B $\times$ p p b b horned, red
germ cells   P B   ⌐p b
F_1 dihybrid   P p B b   heterozygous polled, black

Apparently the genes for polled or horned and for black or red are located in different chromosomes, because, when we mate the dihybrids, Pp Bb, we get the following ratio in the second generation (F_2) crosses:

9 polled blacks
3 polled reds
3 horned blacks
1 horned red.

In tabular (checkerboard) form the results of crossing the F_1 dihybrids (Pp Bb $\times$ Pp Bb) are illustrated in Table 8.

TABLE 8

CHECKERBOARD OF THE F^2 (SECOND GENERATION) CROSS OF ABERDEEN-ANGUS X DEVON CATTLE

Sperms:	P B	P b	p B	p b
		Eggs:		
P B	P P B B	P P B b	P p B B	P p B b
P b	P P B b	P P b b	P p B b	P p b b
p B	P p B B	P p B b	p p B B	p p B b
p b	P p B b	P p b b	p p B b	p p b b

As can be noted through studying the above chart, the nine polled black animals appearing in the second cross are of the same phenotype (they look alike), but they are of different genotype (they are different genetically and will transmit differently). Only the animal with the genetic makeup of PPBB is pure for both dominant characters and will breed pure, but this animal cannot be detected by appearance. Only matings to horned red animals will with certainty single this animal out. On the other hand, the one ppbb (horned red) animal can be identified both as to genotype and phenotype purely on the basis of appearance.

A TRIHYBRID CROSS:

As already indicated, a trihybrid is one that is heterozygous for three pairs of allelic genes. A cross between Aberdeen-Angus and Hereford cattle represents such a cross. Thus, the situation is as follows:

Aberdeen-Angus (polled, black body, black face)＝PPBB ww
Hereford (horned, red body, white face)＝pp bb WW

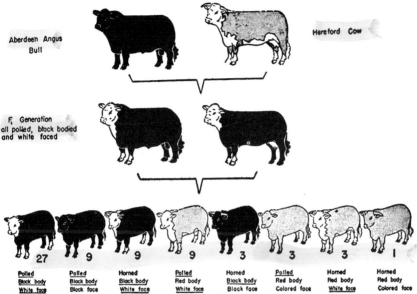

Fig. 64. Diagram showing a trihybrid cross; the inheritance of polled, white face, and black body characteristics in an Aberdeen-Angus X Hereford cross. Note that all first cross (F₁) animals are polled, black bodied, and white faced; whereas, on the average, the F₁ x F₁ cross results in the 27:9:9:9:3:3:3:1 ratio shown. (Drawing by R. F. Johnson)

All first-cross animals between the Aberdeen-Angus and Hereford breeds will be polled, with black body and a white face —all three dominant characteristics being in evidence. However, when these F_1 animals are interbred, on the average and out of each sixty-four animals produced, the following results will be obtained:

27 *polled,* with a *black body* and a *white face*
9 *polled,* with a *black body* and a black face
9 *polled,* with a red body and a *white face*
9 horned, with a *black body* and a *white face*
3 *polled,* with a red body and a colored face
3 horned, with a *black body* and a black face
3 horned, with a red body and a *white face*
1 horned, with a red body and a colored face.

TABLE 9

CHECKERBOARD OF F$_2$ (SECOND GENERATION) CROSS BETWEEN AN ABERDEEN-ANGUS (*polled*, black-faced and *black-bodied*) AND A HEREFORD (*horned*, red-bodied and *white-faced*)

Eggs:	Sperms:							
	PWB	PWb	PwB	Pwb	pWB	pWb	pwB	pwb
PWB	PP WW BB	PP WW Bb	PP Ww BB	PP Ww Bb	Pp WW BB	Pp WW Bb	Pp Ww BB	Pp Ww Bb
PWb	PP WW Bb	PP WW bb	PP Ww Bb	PP Ww bb	Pp WW Bb	Pp WW bb	Pp Ww Bb	Pp Ww bb
PwB	PP Ww BB	PP Ww Bb	PP ww BB	PP ww Bb	Pp Ww BB	Pp Ww Bb	Pp ww BB	Pp ww Bb
Pwb	PP Ww Bb	PP Ww bb	PP ww Bb	PP ww bb	Pp Ww Bb	Pp Ww bb	Pp ww Bb	Pp ww bb
pWB	Pp WW BB	Pp WW Bb	Pp Ww BB	Pp Ww Bb	pp WW BB	pp WW Bb	pp Ww BB	pp Ww Bb
pWb	Pp WW Bb	Pp WW bb	Pp Ww Bb	Pp Ww bb	pp WW Bb	pp WW bb	pp Ww Bb	pp Ww bb
pwB	Pp Ww BB	Pp Ww Bb	Pp ww BB	Pp ww Bb	pp Ww BB	pp Ww Bb	pp ww BB	pp ww Bb
pwb	Pp Ww Bb	Pp Ww bb	Pp ww Bb	Pp ww bb	pp Ww Bb	pp Ww bb	pp ww Bb	pp ww bb

Table 9 indicates what one may expect to secure, on the average, with sixty-four animals resulting from a second generation cross (F_2) of Aberdeen-Angus X Hereford. Careful analysis of this summary reveals that, of these sixty-four animals, twenty-seven different genetic combinations (genotypes) are listed. One and only one of these genotypes can be recognized on sight, namely, the last one involving all small letters or pure for the three recessive characters involved. Breeding tests would be necessary to reveal the genotypic differences between PP WW BB and Pp WW Bb individuals, etc. As is generally known, F_2 crosses of the above type are seldom produced in practical operations.

The ratios obtained in the cross with one, two, and three pairs of allelic genes are as follows:

the monohybrid cross $= 3:1$ ratio

the dihybrid cross $= 9:3:3:1$ ratio

the trihybrid cross $= 27:9:9:9:3:3:3:1$ ratio.

Crosses involving four or more pairs of contrasted characters are possible, but these are unwieldy. For that reason, very few of these more complicated crosses have been worked out.

Multiple Births

Multiple births among cattle, which are a rather frequent phenomenon, have been observed since their domestication. A review of the literature reveals that, on the average, such multiple births occur at the following frequencies:

Species	Twins		Triplets		Quadruplets	
all breeds)	(% of twin births)	(No. of twin births in each 1,000 births)	(% of triplet births)	(Ratio of triplet births)	(% of quad - ruplet births)	(Ratio of quadruplet births)
Beef cattle	0.5	5				
Dairy cattle	2.0	20	.03	4 in 14,111 (in Brown Swiss)	.01	1 in 14,111 (in Brown Swiss)

The tendency to produce twins is inherited to some extent; thus, more twins are produced in some breeds and in some families than in others. But factors other than heredity play a major part in determining whether any particular birth shall be a twin birth.

Most cattlemen prefer single births to twins due to (1)

the high incidence of freemartins (sterile heifers) in twins of opposite sexes, (2) the increased mortality rate of twins, and (3) the tendency of cows that have produced twins to have a lowered conception rate following twinning.

Twins may be either fraternal (dizygotic) or identical (monozygotic). Fraternal twins are produced from two separate ova that were fertilized by two different sperm. Identical twins result when a single fertilized egg divides very early in its embryology, into two separate individuals.

In humans, nearly half of the like-sexed twins are identical, whereas in cattle only 5 to 12 per cent of such births are identical. Such twins are always of the same sex, a pair of males or a pair of females, and alike genetically—their chromosomes and genes are alike; they are 100 per cent related. When identical twins are not entirely separate, they are known as Siamese twins.

Genetically, fraternal twins are no more alike than full brothers and sisters born at different times; they are only 50 per cent related. They usually resemble each other more, however, because they were subjected to the same intrauterine environment before birth and generally they are reared under much the same environment. Also, fraternal twins may be of different sexes.

Distinguishing between identical and fraternal twin calves is not easy, but the following characteristics of identical twins will be helpful:

1. Identical twins are usually born in rapid succession, and frequently there is only one placenta.

2. The calves are necessarily of the same sex.

3. The coat colors are identical; i.e., if there is a broken color, there must be a strong degree of resemblance in this respect.

4. There is little variation in birth weights, general conformation and, more particularly, the shape of the head, position of the horns and occurrence of skin pigmentation, rudimentary teats, etc.

5. Muzzle prints show a degree of resemblance.

6. The shape, twisting and position of the horns and behaviour of the twins can be observed at a later stage. Identical twins are inclined to keep together when grazing, walking, lying down or ruminating.

7. Identical twins have the same blood group.

Fig. 65. Quadruplet purebred Aberdeen-Angus heifers, at two weeks of age. Bred and owned by O. H. Delchamps, Point Clear, Alabama. (Courtesy, Mr. Delchamps)

How Sex Is Determined

The possibility of sex determination and control has fascinated mankind since time immemorial. For example, in a book published in 1662,[1] studmasters were admonished as follows: "For a male colt you must bind back with a cord, or pull back his left stone, and for the female, bind back the right stone, and thus you may do unto all other kinds of cattle." The same book revealed that "if the rams be put with the ewes when the wind is in the north, the ewes will bring males and if the wind be in the south when the ewes are covered, they will be females." These are but two of the hundreds of superstitions that have evolved concerning the control of sex.

On the average, and when considering a large population,

[1]Mascal, Leonard, *The Government of Cattel*, London, printed for John Stafford and William Gilbertson, "and are to be sold at the George-Yard near Fleet-bridge; and at the Bible without New Gate." 1662.

approximately equal numbers of males and females are born in all common species of animals. To be sure, many notable exceptions can be found in individual herds. The history of the Washington State University Aberdeen-Angus herd, for example, reads like a story book. The entire herd was built up from one foundation female purchased in 1910. She produced seven daughters.[1] In turn, her first daughter produced six females. Most remarkable yet and extremely fortunate from the standpoint of building up the cow herd, it was four years before any bull calves were dropped in the herd.

Such unusual examples often erroneously lead the stockman to think that something peculiar to the treatment or management of a particular herd resulted in a preponderance of males or females, as the case may be. In brief, through such examples, the breeder may get the impression that variation in sex ratio is not random but that it is under the control of some unknown and mysterious influence. Under such conditions, it can be readily understood why the field of sex control is a fertile one for fraudulent operators. Certainly, any "fool-proof" method of controlling sex would have tremendous commercial possibilities. For example, cattlemen wishing to build up a herd could then secure a high percentage of heifer calves. On the other hand, the commercial cattleman would then elect to produce only enough heifers for replacement purposes. From an economical standpoint, he would want a preponderance of bull calves for the reason that commercial steers sell for a higher price than do commercial heifers. Unfortunately, no such method of sex control is known.

The most widely accepted theory of sex determination at the present time is that sex is determined by the chromosomal makeup of the individual. One particular pair of the chromosomes is called the sex chromosomes. In farm animals, the female has a pair of similar chromosomes (usually called X chromosomes), whereas the male has a pair of unlike sex chromosomes (usually called X and Y chromosomes). In the bird, this condition is reversed, the females having the unlike pair and the male having the like pair.

The pairs of sex chromosomes separate out when the germ

---

[1]The probability of getting seven heifer calves in a row can be figured by multiplying ½ by itself seven times. This is one out of 128, meaning that all seven calves in a group of seven will be heifers in less than 1 per cent of the cases.

cells are formed. Thus, the ovum or egg produced by the cow contains the X chromosome; whereas the sperm of the bull are of two types, one half containing the X chromosome and the other one half the Y chromosome. Since, on the average, the egg and sperm unite at random, it can be understood that half

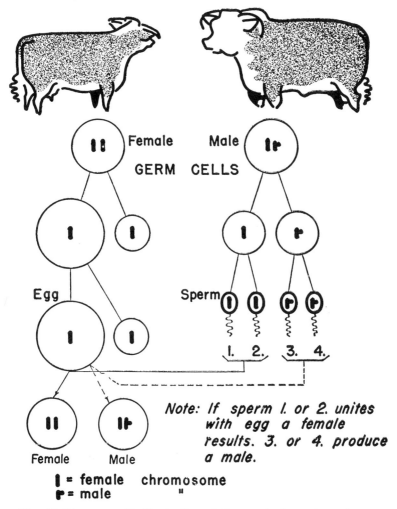

Fig. 66. Diagrammatic illustration of the mechanism of sex determination in cattle showing how sex is determined by the chromosomal makeup of the individual. The cow has a pair of like sex chromosomes, whereas the bull has a pair of unlike sex chromosomes. Thus, if an egg and sperm of like sex chromosomal makeup unite, the offspring will be a female; whereas if an egg and sperm of unlike sex chromosomal makeup unite, the offspring will be a male. (Drawing by R. F. Johnson)

of the progeny will contain the chromosomal makeup XX (females)[1] with the other one half XY (males).[1]

Research workers have employed many techniques designed to separate the X-bearing and Y-bearing sperm of males—including specific gravity, electrical potential, reaction to acid and alkaline media, and speed in movement through the reproductive tract. To date, none of these techniques has been successful. But the search continues. Perhaps, eventually, a successful method of separation will be found; thereby making sex determination possible.

Abnormal Development of Sex in Cattle

Sex abnormalities occasionally occur in cattle; freemartins, intersexes, and hermaphrodites are the most common ones. Each of these is discussed in Chapter VIII.

Lethals and Other Abnormalities in Cattle[2]

Many abnormal animals are born on the nation's farms and ranches each year. Unfortunately, the purebred breeder, whose chief business is that of selling breeding stock, is likely to "keep mum" about the appearance of any defective animals in his herd because of the justifiable fear that it might hurt his sales. With the commercial producer, however, the appearance of such abnormalities is simply so much economic loss, with the result that he generally, openly and without embarrassment, admits the presence of such defects and seeks correction.

The embryological development—the development of the young from the time that the egg and the sperm unite until the animal is born—is very complicated. Thus the oddity probably is that so many of the offspring develop normally rather than that a few develop abnormally.

Many such abnormalities (commonly known as monstrosities or freaks) are hereditary, being caused by certain "bad" genes. If a lethal is due to a dominant gene, it may be easily and quickly eliminated, since all of the animals carrying the gene exhibit the character. However, most lethals are recessive and may, therefore, remain hidden for many generations. The pre-

---

[1]The scientists' symbols for the male and female, respectively, are: ♂ (the sacred shield and spear of Mars, the Roman God of War), and ♀ (the looking glass of Venus, the Roman Goddess of Love and Beauty).
[2]The author's colleague, Dr. E.S.E. Hafez, was most helpful in the preparation of this section and Table 10.

vention of such genetic abnormalities requires that the germ plasm be purged of the "bad" genes. This means that, where recessive lethals are involved, the stockman must be aware of the fact that both parents carry the gene. For the total removal of the lethals, test matings[1] and rigid selection must be practiced.

In addition to hereditary abnormalities, there are certain abnormalities that may be due to nutritional deficiencies, or to "accidents of development"—the latter including those which seem to occur sporadically and for which there is no well-defined reason. When only a few defective individuals occur within a particular herd, it is often impossible to determine whether their occurrence is due to: (1) defective heredity, (2) defective

Fig. 67. Any observed defect may be hereditary, nutritional, or a freak of nature (as a result of faulty development in the embryological life). Six types of defects commonly observed in cattle are shown: 1. Bulldog, 2. Hairless streaks, 3. Muscle contraction, 4. Siamese twins, 5. Short spine, 6. Dwarfism. (Drawing by Dr. E. S. E. Hafez, Washington State University)

[1]To test a bull at the .05 level of significance for heterozygosity for a single autosomal recessive gene, the following numbers of progeny are required: (1) 5 from homozygous females, (2) 11 from known heterozygous females, or (3) 23 from matings on daughters. (From: Kidwell, J., *Journal of Heredity*, July-Aug. 1951)

nutrition, or (3) merely to accidents of development. If the same occurs in any appreciable number of animals, however, it is probably either hereditary or nutritional. In any event, the diagnosis of the condition is not always a simple matter.

The following conditions would tend to indicate an hereditary defect:

1. If the defect had previously been reported as hereditary in the same breed of livestock.

2. If it occurred more frequently within certain families or when there had been inbreeding.

3. If it occurred in more than one season and when different rations had been fed.

The following conditions might be accepted as indications that the abnormality was due to a nutritional deficiency:

1. If previously it had been reliably reported to be due to a nutritional deficiency.

2. If it appeared to be restricted to a certain area.

3. If it occurred when the ration of the mother was known to be deficient.

4. If it disappeared when an improved ration was fed.

If there is suspicion that the ration is defective, it should be improved, not only from the standpoint of preventing such deformities, but from the standpoint of good and efficient management.

If there is good and sufficient evidence that the abnormal condition is hereditary, the steps to be followed in purging the herd of the undesirable gene are identical to those for ridding the herd of any other undesirable recessive factor. An inbreeding program, of course, is the most effective way in which to expose hereditary lethals in order that purging may follow.

Table 10 includes most of the well-authenticated abnormal conditions that have been reported in cattle. As noted, to date many of these defects are limited to specific breeds and certain countries. For convenience, these abnormalities are classified into five categories as follows:

1. *Lethals are genetic factors which cause death of the calves carrying them.* (See Table 10, Part I.) Death may take

place in the embryonic life or shortly after birth. Most lethals are recessive in their mode of inheritance; achondroplasia I is incompletely dominant. Dominant lethal mutations are eliminated spontaneously. Being a dominant character, it would have to express itself; and this would mean that the calf dies.

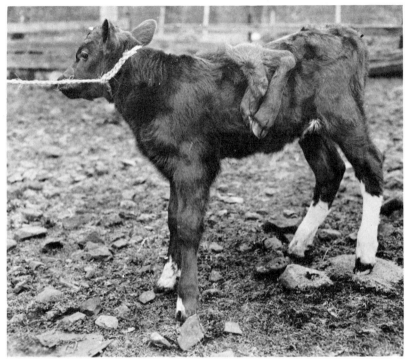

Fig. 68. Freak calf at two weeks of age. An accident of development, with three extra legs attached to the back. (Courtesy of the owner, C. M. Barker, White Salmon, Washington)

2. *Semi-lethals (or sub-lethals) are genetic factors which eventually cause death of the calf.* (See Table 10, Part II.) Semi-lethals are probably far more serious than lethals because they are more likely to go unnoticed; yet they may be causing considerable damage.

3. *Delayed lethals are gene changes which do not destroy the embryo or the newborn calf, but which so severely handicap the animal that it does not leave any offsring.* (See Table 10, Part III.) Delayed lethals interfere with normal reproduction of the cow or the bull.

TABLE 10
LETHALS AND OTHER ABNORMALITIES IN CATTLE.
PART I. HEREDITARY LETHALS
(Most lethals are recessive; the mode of inheritance of Achondroplasia I is incomplete dominance)

Lethal	Symptoms of Abnormality	Breed Reported In	Pertinent References
1. Achondroplasia I	Short legs and head; often have hernia and cleft palate. Most of them are absorbed from the fourth to eighth month of pregnancy. Delivery when close to term is usually difficult because of the extremely large head. About one-fourth of the Dexter X Dexter matings are "Bull-dogs."	Dexter	Crew, 1923, Proc. Royal Soc., (London), 95B, 228. Punnett, 1936, J. Genetics, 32, 65. Berger & Innes, 1948, Vet. Record, 60, 57.
2. Achondroplasia II	This type is similar to Achondroplasia I but less extreme. Calves are usually carried to term but die soon after.	Guernsey, Holstein, Jersey, Telmark	Mohr & Wriedt, 1925, Z. fur Zuchtüng, B. 3, 223. Mohr, 1930, Naturens Verden 14, 1. Brandt, 1941, J. Hered., 32, 183. Gregory et al, 1942, J. Hered., 33, 317.
3. Achondroplasia III	Less extreme than Bull-dog II. Calves may live several hours.	Jersey, Swedish Red-and-White	Gregory et al., 1942, J. Hered., 33, 317. Johansson 1953, Hereditas, 39, 75.
4. Acroteriasis congenita	Appendages short or absent. The calves are stillborn or die shortly after birth.	Swedish Holstein	Wriedt & Mohr, 1928, J. Genetics, 20, 187.
5. Agnathia	Very short lower jaw.	Jersey	Annett, 1939, J. Genetics, 37, 301. Ely et al, 1939, J. Hered., 30, 105. Grant, 1956, J. Hered., 47, 165.
6. Amputated (See Acroteriasis congenita)			

	Description	Breeds	References
7. Ankylosis	Ossification of joints. Legs rigid due to joints fusing; some cases of lower jaw fusions.	German, Norwegian Lyngdal	Mohr, 1930, Naturens Verden, *14*, 1. Eaton, 1937, J. Hered., *28*, 320. Stang, 1940, Z. fur Zuchtung, *36*. 280. Tuff, 1948, Skand. Vet. Tid., *38*, 379.
8. Bull-dog calves (See *Achondroplasia*)			
9. Congenital dropsy	Water in tissues and cavities. The calves are born one or two months previous to term or at term.	Ayrshire, Swedish Lowland black-and-white	Johansson, 1941, *Proc. 7th Int. Cong. Genet.* (Edinburgh), 169. Donald et al., 1952, Brit. Vet. J. *108*, 227. Herrick & Eldridge, 1955, J. Dairy Sci. *38*, 440.
10. Congenital ichthyosis	Scaly, cracked skin.	Norwegian Red Poll	Tuff & Gladitsch, 1949, Nordisk Vet. Med., *I*, 619.
11. Epithelial defects	Defective formation of skin below knees, one or more claws undeveloped, deformed integument of muzzle and the mucus membranes of nostrils, tongue, palate, and cheek.		Hadley & Cole, 1928, Wis. Agri. Exp. Sta. Bul. No. 86. Hutt & Frost, 1934, J. Herd., *25*, 41.
12. Epitheliogenesis or imperfecta	Imperfect skin, partly hairless; septicemia. The calves are usually born at term but die as a result of bacterial invasion.	Holstein, Jersey	Hadley & Cole, 1928, Wisc. Agri. Exp. Sta. Bul. No. 86. Regan et al., 1935, J. Hered., *26*, 357. Hutt & Frost, 1948, J. Herd., *39*, 131.
13. Fetal resorption	Various stages from decomposed masses to only bones or dried mummies have been reported.	Dairy and beef breeds	
14. Hairless (See *Hypotrichosis congenita*)			

TABLE 10. Part I (Continued)

Lethal	Symptoms of Abnormality	Breed Reported In	Pertinent References
15. *Hernia cerebri*............	Failure of frontal bones to fuse.		
16. *Hypotrichosis congenita*	A little hair is found on the muzzle, eyelids, ears, pasterns, and end of the tail. Most afflicted calves die shortly after birth; some live but grow slowly and never have normal hair.		Mohr & Wriedt, 1928, J. Genetics, *19*, 314. Regan *et al*., 1935, J. Hered., *26*, 357. Kidwell & Guilbert, 1950, J. Hered., *41*, 190. Surrarrer, 1943, J. Hered., *24*, 175. Hutt & Saunders, J. Hered., *44*, 97.
17. Hydrocephalus.............	Affected animals have excess fluid in portions of the brain.		Houck, 1930, Anat. Record, *45*, 83. Innes *et al*, 1940, J. Path. & Bact., *50*, 456. Cole & Moore, 1942, J. Agr. Res. *65*, 483. Godgluck, 1952, Monat. Fur Vet., *7*, 250. Giannotti, 1952, Mem. Soc. tosc. Sci. nat. B. *59*, 32. Gilman, 1956, Cornell Vet., *45*, 487.
18. Impacted molars..........	Short lower jaw, impacted teeth; die within week.	Dairy Shorthorn	Heizer & Hervey, 1937, J. Hered., *28*, 123.
19. Lameness in hind limbs....	Calves unable to stand.	Red Danish	Christensen & Christensen, 1952, Norsk. Vet. Tid., *4*, 861.

	Description	Breeds	References
20. Mummification	They have a short neck, stiff legs, and prominent joints. Fetuses die at about eight months gestation but carried to term.	Red Danish	Loje, 1930, Tidssk. for Landok., 10, 517.
21. Muscle contracture	Head and legs drawn; joints stiff. Calves born at full term.	Holstein, Norwegian breeds	Hutt, 1934, J. Hered., 25, 41. Nes, 1953, Nordisk Vet. Med., 5, 869.
22. Paralysis	Posterior paralysis—may have muscular tumors and blindness, die shortly after birth.		Tuff, 1948, Vet.-Tid. 38, 379. Cranek & Ralson, 1953, J. Anim. Sci. 12, 892.
23. Paralyzed hindquarters	Calves appear normal except that they cannot stand on hindquarters.	Norwegian Red Poll, Red Danish	Loje, 1930, Tidssk. for Landok., 10, 517.
24. Prolonged pregnancy I	The gestation period is from 311 to 403 days. Fetus grows in uterus almost as calves born normally, with the result that parturition is difficult or impossible.	Japanese breeds	Gregory et al., 1951, Portugualie Acta Biol. A, 861. Jasper, 1951, Cornell Vet., 40, 165.
25. Prolonged pregnancy II	Calves are carried up to 500 days. Calves show immature bone development, various degrees of hairlessness and lack of thyroid development; and they do not have a pituitary gland.		Hallgren, 1951, Nord. Vet. Med., 3, 1043.
26. Short limbs	Limbs short; hoofs undeveloped.	Russian breeds, Swiss breeds	
27. Short spine	Ribs and vertebrae fused; back bent down.	Norwegian, Mountain	Mohr & Wriedt, 1930, J. Genetics, 22, 279.
28. Skinless (See Epitheliogenesis)			

TABLE 10. Part I (Continued)

Lethal	Symptoms of Abnormality	Breed Reported In	Pertinent References
29. Spasms..............	Calves first appear normal, but soon develop spasmodic muscular contractions. Affected animals die within a few weeks after birth.	Jersey	Shrode & Lush, 1947, *Advances in Genetics*, Academic Press, Inc., N. Y. Gregory *et al.*, 1944, J. Hered., *35*, 195. Saunders, *et al.*, 1952, Cornell Vet., *42*, 559.
30. Streaked hairlessness.............	Gene carried only in females. Carrier females exhibit streaked hairlessness and produce a sex ratio of two females to one male.	Holstein	Eldridge & Atkeson, 1953, J. Hered., *44*, 265.
31. Tendon contracture.............	Tendons pulled rigidly; calves are either born dead or die shortly after birth.	Dairy Shorthorn	Dale & Moxley, 1952, Can. J. Comp. Med, *16*, 399.

TABLE 10 (Continued)

PART II. HEREDITARY SEMI-LETHALS

Semi-lethal	Symptoms of Abnormality	Probable Mode of Inheritance	Breed Reported In	Pertinent References
1. *Atresia ani*..............	Closed anus. Calves do not survive corrective surgery.			Kuppuswami, 1937, Ind. J. Vet. Sci. & Anim. Husb., 7, 305. Lerner, 1944, J. Hered., 35, 219
2. Albinism..............	Complete absence of pigmentation in the skin, muzzle, and hoofs, and in the walls of the rumen. However, the eyes are not pink, due to a slight greyish coloration of the cortex.	Probably Recessive	Hereford, Brown Swiss	Hafez et al., 1958, J. Hered., 49, 111.
3. Imperforate Anus (See *Atresia ani*..............				
4. Epilepsy..............	Cattle subject to epileptic type of attacks.	Dominant	Brown Swiss	Atkeson, et al., 1944, J. Hered., 35, 45.

TABLE 10. (Continued)

PART III. HEREDITARY DELAYED LETHALS

Delayed lethal	Symptoms of Abnormality	Probable Mode of Inheritance	Breed Reported In	Pertinent References
1. Atrophy of testis..........	a. Gross microscopic changes of testes, including atrophy, calcification, degeneration of the seminiferous tubules, and varying degrees of fibriosis.	?	Swedish Highland	Rollinson, 1955, Anim. Breed. Abstr., *23*, 215.
	b. Epithelium layers of seminal ducts are underdeveloped; in either one or in both testes.	?		
2. Cystic ovaries..........	Sterility; nymphomania.		Swedish Highland	Rollinson, 1955, Anim. Breed. Abstr., *23*, 215.
3. Female Sterility..........	Cows fail to settle.	Simple Sex-limited		Gregory, *et al.*, 1945, Genetics, *30*, 506. Gregory, *et al.*, 1951 J. Dairy Sci., *34*, 1047.
4. Gonad hypoplasia..........	Atrophy of one or two ovaries.	Autosomal		
5. Gonadless..........	Absence of ovaries.	?		
6. *Impotentia coeundia*..........	Bull does not possess ability to copulate due to failure of sigmoid curve of penis to straighten during coitus.	Autosomal, Recessive		Rollinson, 1955, Anim. Breed. Abstr., *23*, 215.

7. Knobbed spermatozoa......	Abnormal formation of sperm. Formation vaculoes in developing sperm heads may be related to some unknown changes in the nucleic acid metabolism of the sperm head. Absence of any chromosomal aberration, quantitative or structural.	Autosomal sex-limited gene		Rollinson, 1955, Anim. Breed. Abstr., 23, 215.
8. Turned sperm tails.........	Sperm tails turned back past the head.	?		
9. Hernia, Umbilical............	It appears to be limited to males.	Dominant (?)	Holstein	Warren & Atkeson, 1931, J. Hered., 22, 345.
10. White heifer disease	Persistent hymen or incomplete cervix; horns of uterus become distended with fluid. Most commonly found in white heifers of the Shorthorn breed, but it has been reported in roan and red Shorthorns and in colored animals of other breeds.	Probably Recessive	Shorthorn, Other breeds	Gilmore, 1949, J. Dairy Sci., 32, 71. Spriggs, et al., 1946, Vet. Record, 58, 405.

TABLE 10. (Continued)

PART IV. HARMFUL AND DEFECTIVE (NON-LETHALS) GENES

Type	Symptoms of Abnormality	Probable Mode of Inheritance	Breed Reported In	Pertinent References
1. Achondroplasia............	Short legs and head, curly coat and thin	Recessive	Shorthorn	Mead *et al.*, 1946, J. Hered., *37*, 183.
2. Cancer eye............	Herefords without pigmented eyelids more susceptible than other cattle. Usually occurs in older animals.	?	Hereford	Frank, 1943, J. A. V. M. A. *102*, 200. Guilbert *et al.*, 1948, J. Anim. Sci., *7*, 426. Woodward & Knapp, 1950, J. Anim. Sci., *9*, 580. Anderson *et al.*, 1957, J. Anim. Sci., *16*, 739.
3. Cataract............	Opaque condition of the lens of the eye.	Recessive	Jersey	Detlefson & Yapp, 1920, Am. Naturalist, *54*, 277.
4. Cerebellar hypoplasia......	Poor coordination. Cerebellum rudimentary, excessive fluid. Some walk like ballet dancers.	Probably Recessive	Holstein, Friesian, Jersey	Anderson & Davis, 1950, J. A. V. M. A. *117*, 460. Saunders *et al.*, 1952, Cornell Vet. *42*, 559.
5 . Comprest............	The animal is extremely bowlegged, often being unable to stand. The vertebrae do not have the spines which are pronounced in the "snorter dwarf."	Incomplete Dominancy	Hereford	Lucas, 1950, Thesis (M.S.) Colo. State Univ. (Fort Collins). Stonaker, 1958, Colo. Exp. Sta. Bul. 501-S Hafez, 1959. Unpublished data.

6. Crooked legs.............	Front legs crooked. Certain lines of breeding show this affliction whereas others do not, even in areas where it is prevalent. Those blood lines manifesting the condition in an area where it is prevalent are not afflicted in the areas where it is not found.	Nutritional-genetic interaction	Hereford	Stonaker, 1958, Colo. Exp. Sta. Bull. 501-S. Bogart, 1959, Personal Communication. Hafez, 1959, Unpublished data.
7. Cross eyes (See Strabismus).............				
8. Curly hair.............	Hair in tight curls, viable.	Dominant	Ayrshire	Eldbridge et al, 1949, J. Hered., 40, 205.
9. Double ear.............	A thin, flat piece of cartilage lies parallel to the long axis of the ear, extends beyond the ear tip.	Dominant	Brahman	Lush, 1924, J. Hered., 15, 93.
10. Double-muscled.............	Characterized by abnormally wide thighs, with this extreme width extending forward to include the loin. Deep grooves between the muscles are conspicuous externally. Little fat covering is present. (The "Doppelander" calf is a mutation of doubtful value; the valuable muscles in the back and loin are doubled but the animals are sterile [Hammond, 1935, Emp. J. Exp. Agric. 3, No. 9]).	Probably Autosomal Recessive	Aberdeen Angus, Hereford, Shorthorn	Weber & Ibsen, 1934, Proc. Am. Soc. Anim. Prod., p. 228. Kidwell et al, 1952, J. Hered., 43, 62.
11. Duck legged.............	Legs shorter than normal.	Dominant		Lush, 1927, J. Hered., 21, 85.

TABLE 10. Part IV. (Continued)

Type	Symptoms of Abnormality	Probable Mode of Inheritance	Breed Reported In	Pertinent References
12. Dwarfism..........	Animals small in size but well proportioned.	Recessive	Aberdeen-Angus, Hereford, Shorthorn	Mead, et al., 1942, J. Hered., 33, 411. Johnson, et al., 1950, J. Hered., 41, 177. Lindley, 1951, J. Hered., 42, 273. Gregory et al., 1953, Hilgardia, 22, 407. Pahinsh et al., 1955, J. Anim. Sci., 14, 200, 1025.
13. Extra toes (See Polydactylism)...........				
14. Flexed pasterns............	Toes turned under.	Recessive	Jersey	Habel, 1948, J. Vet. Res., 9, 131. Atkeson, et al., 1943, J. Hered., 34, 25. Mead, et al., 1943, J. Hered., 35, 367
15. Fused teats...............	The front and rear teats on the same side are fused.	Recessive	Hereford	Johnson, 1945, J. Hered., 36, 317. Hiezer, 1932, J. Hered., 23, 111.
16. Missing teat............	One teat on left side.	Recessive	Holstein-Friesian	Rollinson, 1955, Anim. Breed. Abstr., 23, 215.
17. Notched ears............	Ears imperfect in shape.	Dominant		
18. Pink teeth (See Porphyrinuria)...........				

Condition	Description	Inheritance	Breed	Reference
19. Polydactylism I	Affected animals have an extra toe on each front foot, with accompanying tenderness and lameness.	Probably Recessive	Hereford (males)	Roberts, 1921, J. Hered., 12, 484. Morrill, 1945, J. Hered., 36, 81. Shrode & Lush, 1947, Advances in Genetics, Academic Press, N. Y.
20. Polydactylism II	A three-toed condition.	Probably Recessive	Holstein	
21. Porphyrinuria	a. Cattle are photosensitive and develop lesions in unpigmented areas of skin. b. Excessive coproporphyrin and uroporphyrin.	?	Shorthorn, Holstein-Friesian	Fourie, 1939, Onderst. J. Vet. Sci. Anim. Indust., 13, 383. Jorenson & With, 1955, Nature (London), 176, 156. Clare, 1955, Advan. Vet. Sci., 2, 191.
22. Screw tail	Tail appears to be broken due to fusion of two or more vertebrae.	Recessive	Red Poll	Knapp, 1936, J. Hered., 27, 269.
23. Semi-hairlessness	Hair coat thin; calves wild.	Recessive	Hereford, Polled Hereford	Craft & Blizzard, 1934, J. Hered., 25, 385. Cole, 1919, J. Hered., 22, 345.
24. Spread hoofs	Hoofs spread greatly. Painful; animals often walk on knees.	Recessive	Jersey	
25. Strabismus	Cattle have a cross-eyed condition. Not evident at birth but identified by 12 months of age.	Recessive		Regan, et al., 1944, J. Hered., 35, 233.
26. Stumpy (See Achondroplasia)				
27. Syndactylism	One toe on each front foot instead of two.	Recessive	Holstein-Friesian	Elbridge et al., 1951, J. Hered., 42, 241.

4. *Harmful and defective genes include a host of minor abnormalities which may afflict cattle, some of which are probably of hereditary nature.* (See Table 10, Part IV.) These genetic factors are not lethals, but they interfere with the usefulness of the animals. Genetic factors reducing body size (dwarfism and comprest) are representative cases. Other developmental defects such as notched ears and screw tail are hereditary, but they do not have marked effects on production and fertility.

5. *Congenital defects refer to qualities that an animal shows evidence of having at birth—natal conditions.* The calf has lived for several months before it is born. When a calf is born with an abnormality, the abnormality may be due to heredity; or it may be due to some freak of nature during prenatal development that had nothing whatsoever to do with chromosomes and genes. Congenital abnormalities may occur in any external or internal organ.

Dwarfism in Cattle

In recent years, a disturbing condition known as dwarfism has appeared in increasing frequency among beef cattle, probably in all breeds. There are several different types of dwarfs, of which the short-headed, short-legged, pot-bellied dwarf—commonly referred to as the snorter dwarf—is the most frequent. The discussion that follows applies specifically to snorter dwarfism.

Though very small (usually weighing about half as much as normal calves), dwarf calves are exceedingly stocky and well-built. The heads are beautifully shaped and the eyes protrude, giving a characteristic "pop-eyed" appearance. Some dwarfs are weak and unsteady in gait at birth. Others appear to be strong enough, but soon develop a large stomach, heavy shoulders, crooked hind legs and somtimes labored breathing. Survival is somewhat lower than with normal calves, although most purebred breeders make no attempt to raise them.

On the basis of published and unpublished data, there is now almost complete agreement among scientists (1) that the dwarf condition is of genetic origin, and (2) that it is inherited as a simple autosomal recessive (the word "autosomal" merely means that it is not carried on the sex chromosomes) and conditioned by at least two pairs of modifying genes. Thus, the birth

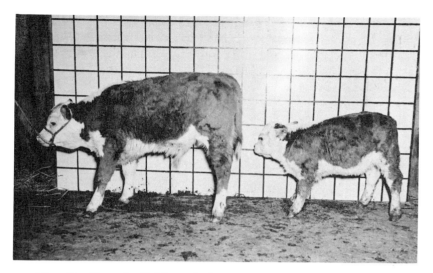

Fig. 69. Normal (left) and dwarf (right) Hereford calves. The normal calf is 2½ months of age while the dwarf is 3½ months of age. Note the smaller size of the dwarf and its stocky well built conformation. (Courtesy, Washington State University)

of a dwarf calf identifies both the sire and the dam as carriers of the dwarf gene.

CONDITIONS PREVAILING IN DWARF AFFLICTED HERDS:

Acceptance of the above theory leads to the conclusion that one or the other of the conditions (or perhaps both conditions) shown in figures 70 and 71 prevail in any herd of cattle in which dwarf-carrying animals are being used. Thus, one hundred offspring from matings of carrier bulls X non-carrier cows will, on the average, possess the following genetic picture from the standpoint of dwarfism:[1]

50 carriers, although not dwarfs
50 non-carriers and non-dwarfs
―――
100 total.

Likewise, one hundred offspring from matings of carrier bulls X carrier cows will, on the average, possess the following genetic picture from the standpoint of dwarfism:[1]

―――
[1]All ratios are averages based on large numbers; thus they may not apply to any given herd.

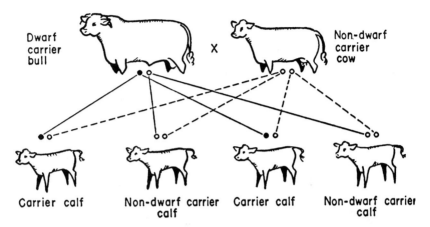

Fig. 70. Diagrammatic illustration of the probable inheritance of the most common type of dwarfism, showing what to expect when a carrier (heterozygous) bull(s) is mated to a non-carrier (homozygous normal) cow(s); or the sexes may be reversed. As shown, carrier X non-carrier matings will, *on the average*, produce calves of which (1) 50% are carriers, although not dwarfs, and (2) 50% are non-carriers and non-dwarfs. Unfortunately, the two groups look alike and cannot be detected by sight. (Drawing by R. F. Johnson)

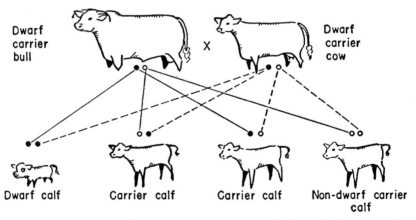

Fig. 71. Diagrammatic illustration of the probable inheritance of the most common type of dwarfism, showing what to expect when a carrier (heterozygous) bull(s) is mated to a carrier (heterozygous) cow(s); or the sexes may be reversed. As shown, carrier X carrier mating will, *on the average*, produce calves of which (1) 25% are dwarfs, (2) 50% are carriers, although not dwarfs, and (3) 25% are non-carriers and non-dwarfs. Unfortunately, only the dwarfs can be detected by sight; the two non-dwarf groups look alike and cannot be distinguished by sight. (Drawing by R. F. Johnson)

25 dwarfs
50 carriers, although not dwarfs
25 non-carriers and non-dwarfs
100 total.

On the basis of these facts, it may be concluded that the following dwarfism genetic picture applies to any given calf having (1) one carrier parent, or (2) both carrier parents:

1. A calf out of parents one of which is a known carrier and the other a non-carrier has a 50 per cent chance of being free of the dwarf factor.

2. A calf both of whose parents are carriers has only one chance in four of being free of the dwarf factor.

It is recognized that the percentage of carrier females in any given herd will vary. Obviously, where dwarf calves have appeared, there are both carrier bulls and carrier cows. Some breeders may remove carrier animals, especially cows, once they have dropped a dwarf calf, thus selecting away from the trait. Others may unwittingly select for, rather than against, animals of the carrier type, if such a carrier type exists and if it is associated with some much sought characteristic, such as a markedly dished face. The latter situation may explain, in part at least, the rapid increase of dwarfism in recent years.

From Figures 70 and 71 the following deductions of value to practical cattlemen may be made: (1) Where a carrier bull is mated to non-carrier cows, no dwarfs will be produced, but, on the average, one-half the calves will be carriers, and (2) the carrier heifers from this first cross can, and likely will, produce one-fourth dwarfs if they are mated back to a carrier bull. In other words, although the use of a carrier bull in a clean herd will not produce any dwarf calves, the seed for dwarfism is sown and it will crop out providing a second carrier bull is used in the herd.

Figures 70 and 71 also indicate the futility of continuing the use of carrier bulls or females. Such practice should be continued only (1) if the breeder wishes to accept the eventual economic loss from producing dwarf calves in about the proportion indicated, or (2) if the breeder feels that an animal is sufficiently valuable otherwise to warrant its use, despite propagating dwarf-factor-genes (and there are those who argue that they would rather get rid of one bad trait—such as dwarfism, than a lot of bad traits—such as may exist in some old fashioned animals that are free of dwarfism). Also, it should be recognized that any animal producing a dwarf is a carrier, regardless of the number of dwarfs produced (one or several).

PURGING THE HERD OF DWARFS:

The breeding program followed to remove or minimize the dwarf condition will depend somewhat on the type of herd involved—especially on whether it is a commercial or purebred herd.

In a commercial herd, the breeder may lessen the chances of obtaining dwarfs by simply using an outcross (unrelated) sire within the same breed or by crossbreeding with a sire from another breed. However, it is increasingly difficult to secure animals that are free of the dwarf factor. With this system, the dwarf carrying cows will remain, but—because of the recessive condition of the dwarf factor—it will be covered up.

In a purebred herd, the action taken in handling the dwarf situation should be more drastic. A reputable purebred breeder has an obligation, not only to himself, but to his customers among both the purebred and commercial herds. Purebred herds should be purged of the undesirable dwarf genes. This can be done through pursuing any one of the following three breeding systems:[1]

1. **Using sires of families free of the dwarf factor; pedigree-clean animals.** Without doubt, within each breed where dwarfs have appeared, certain families exist that are free of the dwarf factor. Securing and using bulls from such families will "cover up" the dwarf situation, but the practice has the following limitations: (1) Within some breeds, at least, it is increasingly difficult to locate families free of the factor; and (2) on the average, families free of the factor may be inferior to families known to carry the factor.

Pedigree information is especially useful for early screening of prospective breeding animals and for small breeders who cannot afford the expense of progeny testing.

---

[1]It is recognized that it is practically impossible to eliminate completely the dwarf factor from a herd or breed of cattle once it has appeared. With a proper breeding program, however, the incidence of dwarfism will become so small as to be unimportant—much as the occurrence of the red color (caused by another recessive factor) has been minimized in the Aberdeen Angus and Holstein breeds of cattle.

2. **Testing bulls of present breeding in the present herd.**
Continue to select bulls from within the herd or from herds from
which purchases have been made previously, but select bulls that
appear to be free from the dwarf factor as judged by pedigree
and family background. Next, test these bulls by mating each of
them to cows in the present herd that have produced dwarf
calves. If each bull tested is mated to 15 known carrier cows and
all the progeny are normal, there would be only 1.3 chances out
of a hundred (1.3%), or 1 chance in 75, that the bull is a dwarf-
carrier and yet passed the test undetected.[1] A test of about the
same validity can be secured by breeding a sire to 30 of his
daughters. Accordingly, such a tested bull could be used in any
herd with reasonable certainty that he is free of the dwarf-
producing factor.

If rigidly adhered to, this system will eventually produce
the desired results, but it has the following limitations: (1) It
necessitates retaining carrier cows in the existing herd for bull
testing purposes, thus giving doubting fellow breeders an opportunity to question the entire herd; and (2) there is always the
temptation to retain outstanding calves although they are likely
carriers.

3. **Using a commercial herd of test cows for the purpose of
proving bulls.** If carefully followed, this is the most desirable of
all the methods herein proposed, and over a period of years the
one which will pay the most handsome dividends. At first glance,
this method will appear drastic and expensive, but, in the end,
the approach is the soundest of the three proposals. Under this
system, it is suggested that the breeder assemble a herd of

---

[1] A lesser number than 15 might be used, but the breeder could not be
so sure of the results. For example, with 10 or 5 such matings, the chances
of failing to detect a carrier bull are increased from 1.3 per cent to 5.6
per cent and 23.7 per cent, respectively. Thus with 10 such matings and all
normal calves, there is only 1 chance in 18 that the bull is a dwarf-carrier
and yet passed the test undetected.

This is computed as follows: The chance of obtaining a dwarf calf from
a dwarf carrier bull bred to known carrier cows is one in four, or 1/4. The
chance of a dwarf not occurring from this type of mating is 1—1/4, or
3/4. Thus, if five such matings are made, $(3/4)^5 = 23.7$, or the chances of
failing to detect a carrier bull with 5 matings is 23.7%; with 10 matings it
is $(3/4)^{10}$, or 5.6%; and with 15 matings $(3/4)^{15}$, or 1.3%.

If only a limited number of carrier cows are available, it may be desirable to breed each prospective herd sire to 4 to 6 carrier cows initially,
followed by more thorough testing of those passing the initial screening.

If the factor becomes so rare that it is impossible to secure sufficient
carrier cows for bull testing, the incidence of dwarfism will be so small as
to be unimportant.

"tester cows" (from either purebreds or grades) each known to have dropped at least one dwarf calf, *with these animals operated strictly as a commercial herd.*

Prior to using any bull in the purebred herd, bulls that are otherwise desirable would be tested by mating each of them to approximately 15 of the dwarf-factor-carrying cows in this commercial herd. Then the top bulls from among those whose get are free of dwarfs could be used in the purebred herd with reasonable certainty.[1]

Carrier cows mated to bulls as indicated would, on the average, not produce in excess of 25 per cent dwarfs if all the bulls were dwarf-carriers (see section relative to "Conditions Prevailing in Dwarf Afflicted Herds"). Of course, fewer dwarfs would be produced if some of the bulls were dwarf-free, as expected. Thus, there would be considerable remuneration from the sale of calves in the operation of such a commercial herd. Further, and most important, the merits of young sires, from the standpoint of type and efficiency of production, could be determined in the commercial herd prior to using them in the purebred herd—thus making it possible to select sires by modern record of performance methods.

Under any of the three systems herein proposed, it would be wise to eliminate those bulls and cows that are known to have produced dwarf calves as soon as desirable replacement animals proved to be free of the factor are available.

Providing one does not select a larger than normal percentage of carrier heifers as replacements for the herd, each generation of calves sired by dwarf-free bulls would halve (lessen by 50 per cent) the number of carriers in the herd. True enough, there would always be some of the dwarf carriers present, for the incidence of carriers is halved with each generation of such matings, but not eliminated. Yet, after two generations of such matings, the incidence of dwarf carriers would be small. Also, it is noteworthy that the use of proved dwarf-factor-free bulls would give assurance that no more dwarf calves would be produced in the herd.

Scientists are now attempting to devise means of detecting dwarf-carrier animals. To this end, the following approaches have been, or are being, tried:

---

[1]The chances of avoiding a dwarf-factor-carrying bull through such testing on 15 carrier cows is covered in the section immediately preceding.

1. **The profilometer.**—This piece of equipment is designed to take a contour of the forehead. The fact that this technique is being used less and less speaks for itself.

2. **The X-ray.**—The lumbar vertebrae of carriers frequently show characteristic abnormalities which can be recognized by taking X-ray pictures of calves less than 10 days of age. Through this technique it appears (1) that about 80 per cent of dwarf-free animals can be detected, although this figure varies considerably in different blood lines, and (2) that about 90 per cent of the carrier animals can be identified.

The errors made in classifying X-ray pictures and the difficulties in getting clear pictures under practical conditions are great enough seriously to limit the technique for general use. Also, it is not considered sufficiently accurate for use as a basis for merchandizing cattle. It may, however, be a useful technique for screening purposes.

3. **The insulin test.**—This technique indicates that there is a physiological difference in response of carrier and dwarf-free animals to stress. At this time, the insulin test is still in the experimental stage, and its use is not recommended to the cattle industry.

These and other approaches are deserving of careful following. If any such method for detecting dwarf-carrier animals is perfected, it will be invaluable. It will then be possible to select and retain, without Production Testing, the non-dwarf-carriers which (as shown under the section relative to "Conditions Prevailing in Dwarf-Afflicted Herds") constitute 50 per cent and 25 per cent, respectively, of the offspring from the following types of mating: (1) carrier bulls X non-carrier cows, and (2) carrier bulls X carrier cows.

It is perfectly obvious that the elimination of the dwarf-producing factor is both slow and costly. Yet it is the only way in which cattle can be freed from dwarfs. Also it may require real courage to recognize openly the situation and discard outstanding animals that are known carriers. Those progressive breeders who do so, however, will make breed progress and, eventually, reap handsome financial rewards.

Because dwarfs represent an almost complete economic loss the problem deserves careful attention.

The Relative Importance of Sire and Dam

As a sire can have so many more offspring during a given season or a lifetime than a dam, he is from an hereditary standpoint a more important individual than any one female so far as the whole herd is concerned, although both the sire and the dam are of equal importance so far as concerns any one offspring. Because of their wider use, therefore, sires are usually culled more rigidly than females, and the breeder can well afford to pay more for an outstanding sire than for an equally outstanding female.

Experienced stockmen have long felt that sires often more closely resemble their daughters than their sons, whereas dams resemble their sons. Some sires and dams, therefore, enjoy a reputation based almost exclusively on the merit of their sons, whereas others owe their prestige to their daughters. Although this situation is likely to be exaggerated, any such phenomenon as may exist is due to sex-linked inheritance which may be explained as follows: The genes that determine sex are carried on one of the chromosomes. The other genes that are located on the same chromosome will be linked or associated with sex and will be transmitted to the next generation in combination with sex. Thus, because of sex linkage, there are more color-blind men than color-blind women. In poultry breeding, the sex-linked factor may be used in a practical way for the purpose of distinguishing the pullets from the cockerels early in life, through the process known as "sexing" the chicks. When a black cock is crossed with barred hens, all the cocks come barred and all the hens come black. It should be emphasized, however, that under most conditions it appears that the influence of the sire and dam on any one offspring is about equal. Most breeders, therefore, will do well to seek excellence in both sexes of breeding animals.

Prepotency

Prepotency refers to the ability of the animal, either male or female, to stamp its own characteristics on its offspring. The offspring of a prepotent bull, for example, resemble both their sire and each other more closely than usual. The only conclusive and final test of prepotency consists of the inspection of the get.

From a genetic standpoint, there are two requisites that an animal must possess in order to be prepotent: (1) dominance and (2) homozygosity. Every offspring that receives a dominant gene or genes will show the effect of that gene or genes in the particular character or characters which result therefrom. Moreover, a perfectly homozygous animal would transmit the same kind of genes to all of its offspring. Although entirely homozygous animals probably never exist, it is realized that a system of inbreeding is the only way to produce animals that are as nearly homozygous as possible.

Popular beliefs to the contrary, there is no evidence that prepotency can be predicted by the appearance of an animal. To be more specific, there is no reason why a vigorous, masculine-appearing sire will be any more prepotent than one less desirable in these respects.

It should also be emphasized that it is impossible to determine just how important prepotency may be in animal breeding, although many sires of the past have enjoyed a reputation of being extremely prepotent. Perhaps these animals were prepotent, but there is also the possibility that their reputation for producing outstanding animals may have rested upon the fact that they were mated to some of the best females of the breed.

In summary, it may be said that if a given sire or dam possesses a great number of genes that are completely dominant for desirable type and performance and if the animal is relatively homozygous, the offspring will closely resemble the parent and resemble each other, or be uniform. Fortunate, indeed, is the breeder who possesses such an animal.

Nicking

If the offspring of certain matings are especially outstanding and in general better than their parents, breeders are prone to say that the animals "nicked" well. For example, a cow may produce outstanding calves to the service of a certain bull, but when mated to another bull of apparent equal merit as a sire, the offspring may be disappointing. Or sometimes the mating of a rather average bull to an equally average cow will result in the production of a most outstanding individual both from the standpoint of type and performance.

So-called successful "nicking" is due, genetically speaking, to the fact that the right combination of genes for good characters are contributed by each parent, although each of the parents within itself may be lacking in certain genes necessary

Fig. 72. Anxiety 4th 9904, whose sons were alleged to "nick" exceedingly well on the daughters of North Pole in the Gudgell and Simpson herd of Hereford cattle. (Courtesy, Mr. D. R. Ornduff, Editor, The American Hereford Journal)

for excellence. In other words, the animals "nicked" well because their respective combinations of good genes were such as to complement each other.

The history of animal breeding includes records of several supposedly favorable "nicks," one of the most famous of which is the favorable result secured from crossing sons of Anxiety 4th with daughters of North Pole in the Gudgell and Simpson herd of Hereford cattle. At this late date, it is impossible to determine whether these Anxiety 4th×North Pole matings were successful because of "nicking" or whether the good results should be more rightfully attributed to the fact that the sons of Anxiety 4th were great breeding bulls and that they merely happened to be mated, for the most part, with daughters of North Pole because the available females in the Gudgell and Simpson herd were of this particular breeding.

Because of the very nature of successful "nicks," outstanding animals arising therefrom must be carefully scrutinized from a breeding standpoint, because, with their heterozygous origin, it is quite unlikely that they will breed true.

Family Names

In cattle, depending upon the breed, family names are traced through either the males or females. In Aberdeen-Angus and

Shorthorn cattle, the family names had their origin with certain great foundation females, whereas in Herefords the family names trace through the sires. Similar family names exist in horses, but in both hogs and sheep less importance is attached to them.

Unfortunately, the value of family names is generally grossly exaggerated. Obviously, if the foundation male or female, as the case may be, is very many generations removed, the genetic superiority of this head of a family is halved so many times by subsequent matings that there is little reason to think that one family is superior to another. For example, if a present-day Queen Mother (an old and well-known Aberdeen-Angus family) is 18 generations removed from the founder, she would carry the following relationship to the head of the family: ($\frac{1}{2}$) 18 or 1/262,144 or .0004%. Obviously, this Queen Mother may not have inherited a single gene from the foundation cow, and merely being a Queen Mother does not differentiate her much from other families which make up the breed.

The situation relative to family names is often further distorted by breeders placing a premium on family names of which there are few members, little realizing that, in at least some cases, there may be unfortunate reasons for the scarcity in numbers.

Such family names have about as much significance as human family names. Who would be so foolish as to think that the Joneses as a group are alike and different from the Smiths? Perhaps, if the truth were known, there have been many individuals with each of these family names who have been of no particular credit to the clan, and the same applies to all other family names.

Family names lend themselves readily to speculation. Because of this, the history of livestock breeding has often been blighted by instances of unwise pedigree selection on the basis of not too meaningful family names. The most classical example of a situation of this type occurred with the Duchess family of Shorthorn cattle, founded by the noted pioneer English Shorthorn breeder, Thomas Bates. Bates, and more especially those later breeders who emulated him, followed preferences in bloodlines within increasingly narrow limits, until ultimately they were breeding cattle solely according to fashionable pedigrees, using good, bad, and indifferent animals. Fad and fancy in pedi-

grees dominated the situation, and the fundamental importance
of good individuality as the basis of selecting animals for
breeding purposes was for the time largely ignored. The sole
desire of these breeders was to concentrate the Duchess blood.
The climax of the "Duchess boom" (or "Bates boom") came in
September, 1873, when the New York Mills herd was sold at auction with English and American breeders competing for the
offering. At this memorable event, 109 head of Duchess-bred
cattle averaged $3,504 per head, with the seven-year-old 8th
Duchess of Geneva selling at the world's record price of $40,600.

As with most booms, the New York Mills sale was followed
by a rather critical reaction, and eventually the bottom dropped
out of values. Even more tragic, the owners of Duchess Shorthorns suddenly came to a realization that indiscriminate inbreeding and a lack of selection had put the family name in
disrepute. As a result, the strain became virtually extinct a few
years later.

On the other hand, certain linebred families—linebred to a
foundation sire or dam so that the family is kept highly related
to it—do have genetic significance. Moreover, if the programs
involved have been accompanied by rigid culling, many good individuals may have evolved, and the family name may be in good
repute. The Anxiety 4th family of Hereford cattle is probably
the best-known family of this kind in meat animals. Even so,
there is real danger in assuming that an "airtight" or "straight-
bred" Anxiety 4th pedigree is within itself meritorious and that
this family is superior to that of any other family in Hereford
cattle.

Heredity and Environment

A massive purebred bull, standing belly deep in straw and
with a manger full of feed before him, is undeniably the result of
two forces—heredity and environment (with the latter including
training). If turned out on the range, an identical twin to the
placid bull would present an entirely different appearance. By
the same token, optimum environment could never make a
champion out of a bull with scrub ancestry, but it might well be
added that "fat and hair will cover up a multitude of sins."

Man-made treatments sometimes conceal undesirable traits
to the extent that improvements in heredity are impeded. For
example, the practice of cutting ties on cattle may be of imme-

diate benefit in improving the appearance of treated animals, but the trait continues to be transmitted. Likewise, the use of nurse cows for developing young show animals in beef herds tends to favor the perpetuation of the genes for poor milkers. Even though most breeders recognize that it is almost inevitable that the nurse cow system will cause the milking and mothering ability of our beef breeds to deteriorate, they use it to maintain a competitive position in the show-ring.

These are extreme examples, but they do emphasize the fact that any particular animal is the product of heredity and environment. Stated differently, heredity may be thought of as the foundation, and environment as the structure. Heredity has already made its contribution at the time of fertilization, but environment works ceaselessly away until death.

Experimental work has long shown conclusively enough that the vigor and size of animals at birth is dependent upon the environment of the embryo from the minute the ovum or egg is fertilized by the sperm, and now we have evidence to indicate that newborn animals are affected by the environment of the egg and sperm long before fertilization has been accomplished. In other words, perhaps due to storage of nutritive factors, the kind and quality of the ration fed to young, growing females may later affect the quality of their progeny. Generally speaking, then, environment may inhibit the full expression of potentialities from a time preceding fertilization until physiological maturity has been attained.

Admittedly, after looking over an animal or studying its production record, a breeder cannot with certainty know whether it is genetically a high or a low producer. There can be no denying the fact that environment—including feeding, management, and disease—plays a tremendous part in determining the extent to which hereditary differences that are present will be expressed in animals. In general, however, the results of a long-time experiment conducted at Washington State University support the contention that selection of breeding animals should be carried on under the same environmental conditions as those under which commercial animals are produced.[1]

Within the pure breeds of livestock—managed under average or better than average conditions—it has been found that,

---

[1]Unpublished data.

in general, only 30 to 45 per cent of the observed variation in a characteristic is actually brought about by hereditary variations. (See Table 11, pages 190-191.) To be sure, if we contrast animals that differ very greatly in heredity—for example, a champion bull and a scrub—90 per cent or more of the apparent differences in type may be due to heredity. The point is, however, that extreme cases such as the one just mentioned are not involved in the advancement within improved breeds of livestock. Here the comparisons are between animals of average or better than average quality, and the observed differences are often very minor.

The problem of the progressive breeder is that of selecting the very best animals available genetically—these to be parents of the next generation of offspring in his herd. The fact that only 30 to 45 per cent of the observed variation is due to differences in inheritance and that environmental differences can produce misleading variations makes mistakes in the selection of breeding animals inevitable. However, if the purebred breeder has clearly in mind a well-defined ideal and adheres rigidly to it in selecting his breeding stock, very definite progress can be made, especially if mild inbreeding is judiciously used as a tool through which to fix the hereditary material.

SYSTEMS OF BREEDING

The many diverse types and breeds among each class of farm animals in existence today originated from only a few wild types within each species. These early domesticated animals possessed the pool of genes, which, through controlled matings and selection, proved flexible in the hands of man. In cattle, for example, through various systems of breeding, there evolved animals especially adapted to draft purposes, beef production, milk production, and dual-purpose needs.

Successful breeders follow a breeding system, the purpose of which is to give greater control of heredity than if selection alone is used. Thus, breeders need to know about the different breeding systems; what they can do well, and what they can do poorly or not at all.

Perhaps at the outset it should be stated that there is no one best system of breeding or secret of success for any and all conditions. Each breeding program is an individual case, requiring careful study. The choice of the system of breeding should be determined primarily by size and quality of herd, finances and skill of the operator, and the ultimate goal ahead.

Purebreeding

A purebred animal may be defined as a member of a breed, the animals of which possess a common ancestry and distinctive characteristics; and he is either registered or eligible for registry in the herd book of that breed. The breed association consists of a group of breeders banded together for the purpose of: (1) recording the lineage of their animals, (2) protecting the purity of the breed, and (3) promoting the interest of the breed.

It must be emphasized that pure breeding and homozygosity may bear very different connotations. The term "purebred" refers to animals whose entire lineage, regardless of the number of generations removed, traces back to the foundation animals accepted by the breed or to any animals which have been subsequently approved for infusion. On the other hand, homozygosity refers to the likeness of the genes.

Yet there is some interrelationship between purebreds and homozygosity. Because most breeds had a relatively small number of foundation animals, the unavoidable inbreeding and linebreeding during the formative stage resulted in a certain amount of homozygosity. Moreover, through the normal sequence of events, it is estimated that purebreds become more homozygous by from $\frac{1}{4}$ to $\frac{1}{2}$ per cent per animal generation. It should be emphasized that the word purebred does not necessarily guarantee superior type or high productivity. That is to say, the word purebred is not, within itself, magic, nor is it sacred. Many a person has found to his sorrow that there are such things as "purebred scrubs." Yet, on the average, purebred animals are superior to nonpurebreds.

For the man with experience and adequate capital, the breeding of purebreds may offer unlimited opportunities. It has been well said that honor, fame, and fortune are all within the realm of possible realization of the purebred breeder; but it should also be added that only a few achieve this high calling.

Purebred breeding is a highly specialized type of production. Generally speaking, only the experienced breeder should undertake the production of purebreds with the intention of furnishing foundation or replacement stock to other purebred breeders or purebred bulls to the producer of grades. Although we have had many constructive cattle breeders and great progress has been made, it must be remembered that only a few achieve sufficient success to classify as master breeders.

Inbreeding

Most scientists divide inbreeding into various categories, according to the closeness of the relationship of the animals mated and the purpose of the matings. There is considerable disagreement, however, as to both the terms used and the meanings that it is intended they should convey. For purposes of this book and the discussion which follows, the following definitions will be used.

Inbreeding is the mating of animals more closely related than the average of the population from which they came.

Closebreeding is the mating of closely related animals; such as sire to daughter, son to dam, and brother to sister.

Linebreeding is the mating of animals more distantly related than in closebreeding, and in which the matings are usually directed toward keeping the offspring closely related to some highly admired ancestor; such as half-brother and half-sister, female to grandsire, and cousins.

CLOSEBREEDING:

Closebreeding is rarely practiced among present-day stockmen, though it was common in the foundation animals of most of the breeds. For example, it is interesting to note that Comet (155), an illustrious sire and noted as the first Shorthorn to sell for $5,000, came from the mating of Favorite and Young Phoenix, a heifer that had been produced from the union of Favorite with his own dam. Such was the program of the Collings Brothers and many another early-day beef cattle breeder, including those in all breeds.

Closebreeding is that system of breeding in which closely related animals are mated. In it there is a minimum number of different ancestors. In the repeated mating of a brother with his full sister, for example, there are only two grandparents instead of four, only two great-grandparents instead of eight, and only two different ancestors in each generation farther back—instead of the theoretically possible 16, 32, 64, 128, etc. The most intensive form of inbreeding is self fertilization. It occurs in some plants, such as wheat and garden peas, and in some of the lower animals; but domestic animals are not self-fertilized.

The reasons for practicing closebreeding are:

1. It increases the degree of homozygosity within animals, making the resulting offspring pure or homozygous in a larger proportion of their gene pairs than in the case of linebred or outcross animals. In so doing, the less desirable recessive genes are brought to light so that they can be more readily culled. Thus, closebreeding together with rigid culling, affords the surest and quickest method of fixing and perpetuating a desirable character or group of characters.

2. If carried on for a period of time, it tends to create lines or strains of animals that are uniform in type and other characteristics.

3. It keeps the relationship to a desirable ancestor highest.

4. Because of the greater homozygosity, it makes for greater prepotency. That is, selected closebred animals are more homozygous for desirable genes (genes which are often dominant), and they, therefore, transmit these genes with greater uniformity.

5. Through the production of inbred lines or families by closebreeding and the subsequent crossing of certain of these lines, it affords a modern approach to livestock improvement. Moreover, the best of the inbred animals are likely to give superior results in outcrosses.

6. Where a breeder is in the unique position of having his herd so far advanced that to go on the outside for seed stock would merely be a step backward, it offers the only sound alternative for maintaining existing quality or making further improvement.

The precautions in closebreeding may be summarized as follows:

1. As closebreeding greatly enhances the chances that recessives will appear during the early generations in obtaining homozygosity, it is almost certain to increase the proportion of worthless breeding stock produced. This may include such so-called "degenerates" as reduction in size, fertility, and general vigor. Also, lethals and other genetic abnormalities often appear with increased frequency in closebred animals.

2. Because of the rigid culling necessary to avoid the "fixing" of undesirable characters, especially in the first generations of a closebreeding program, it is almost imperative that this system of breeding be confined to a relatively large herd and to instances when the owner has sufficient finances to stand the rigid culling that must accompany such a program.

3. It requires skill in making planned matings and rigid selection, thus being most successful when applied by "master breeders."

4. It is not adapted for use by the man with average or below average stock because the very fact that his animals are average means that a goodly share of undesirable genes are present. Closebreeding would merely make the animals more homozygous for undesirable genes, and, therefore, worse.

Judging from outward manifestations alone, it might appear that closebreeding is predominantly harmful in its effects— often leading to the production of defective animals lacking in the vitality necessary for successful and profitable production. But this is by no means the whole story. Although closebreeding often leads to the production of animals of low value, the resulting superior animals can confidently be expected to be homozygous for a greater than average number of good genes and thus more valuable for breeding purposes. Figuratively speaking, therefore, closebreeding may be referred to as "trial by fire," and the breeder who practices it can expect to obtain many animals that fail to measure up and have to be culled. On the other hand, if closebreeding is properly handled, he can also expect to secure animals of exceptional value.

Although closebreeding has been practiced less during the past century than in the formative period of the different pure breeds of livestock, it has real merit when its principles and limitations are fully understood. Perhaps closebreeding had best be confined to use by the skilled master breeder who is in a sufficiently sound financial position to endure rigid and intelligent culling and delayed returns and whose herd is both large and above average in quality.

LINEBREEDING:

From a biological standpoint, closebreeding and linebreeding are the same thing, differing merely in intensity. In general, closebreeding has been frowned upon by stockmen, but line-

Fig. 73. Prince Domino 499611, calved September 13, 1914 and died
April 4, 1930. Many great Herefords have been produced from linebreeding
to this immortal sire. Prince Domino's final resting place at Wyoming
Hereford Ranch, Cheyenne, Wyoming, is marked with the following epitaph:
"He lived and died and won a lasting name." This is a rare tribute, indeed,
to any beast—or man. (Courtesy, The American Hereford Journal)

breeding (the less intensive form) has been looked upon with
favor in many quarters.

In a linebreeding program, the degree of relationship is not
closer than half-brother and half-sister or matings more distantly related; cousin matings, grandparent to grand offspring,
etc.

Linebreeding is usually practiced in order to conserve and
perpetuate the good traits of a certain outstanding sire or dam.
Because such descendants are of similar lineage, they have the
same general type of germ plasm and therefore exhibit a high
degree of uniformity in type and performance. During the past
four decades, for example, a great many Hereford herds have
been linebred to Prince Domino, that immortal Gudgell and
Simpson bred bull who, in the hands of Otto Fulscher and the
Wyoming Hereford Ranch, contributed so much to the improvement of the Hereford breed.

In a more limited way, a linebreeding program has the same
advantages and disadvantages of a closebreeding program. Stated

differently, linebreeding offers fewer possibilities both for good
and harm than closebreeding. It is a more conservative and safer
type of program, offering less probability to either "hit the jack-
pot" or "sink the ship." It is a "middle-of-the-road" program
that the vast majority of average and small breeders can safely
follow to their advantage. Through it, reasonable progress can be
made without taking any great risk. A degree of homozygosity
of certain desirable genes can be secured without running too
great a risk of intensifying undesirable ones.

Usually a linebreeding program is best accomplished through
breeding to an outstanding sire rather than to an outstanding
dam because of the greater number of offspring of the former.
If a breeder found himself in possession of a great bull—proved
great by the performance records of a large number of his get—a
linebreeding program might be initiated in the following way:
Select two of the best sons of the noted bull and mate them to
their half-sisters, balancing all possible defects in the subsequent
matings. The next generation matings might well consist of
breeding the daughters of one of the bulls to the son of the other,
etc. If, in such a program, it seems wise to secure some outside
blood (genes) to correct a common defect or defects in the herd,
this may be done through selecting one or more outstanding
proved cows from the outside—animals whose get are strong
where the herd may be deficient—and then mating this female
or females to one of the linebred bulls with the hope of producing
a son that may be used in the herd.

The owner of a small purebred herd or flock with limited
numbers can often follow a linebreeding program by buying
all of his sires from a large breeder who follows such a program—thus in effect following the linebreeding program of the
larger breeder.

Naturally, a linebreeding program may be achieved in other
ways. Regardless of the actual matings used, the main objective
in such a system of breeding is that of rendering the animals
homozygous—in desired type and performance—to some great
and highly regarded ancestor, while at the same time weeding
out homozygous undesirable characteristics. The success of the
program, therefore, is dependent upon having desirable genes
with which to start and an intelligent intensification of these
good genes.

It should be emphasized that there are some types of herds

in which one should almost never closebreed or linebreed. These include grade or commercial herds and purebred herds of only average quality.

The owner of a grade or commercial herd runs the risk of undesirable results, and, even if successful, as a commercial breeder, he cannot sell his stock at increased prices for breeding purposes.

With purebred herds of only average quality, more rapid progress can usually be made by introducing superior outcross sires. Moreover, if the animals are of only average quality they must have a preponderance of "bad" genes that would only be intensified through a closebreeding or linebreeding program.

Outcrossing

Outcrossing is the mating of animals that are members of the same breed but which show no relationship close up in the pedigree (for at least the first four or six generations).

Most of our purebred animals of all classes of livestock are the result of outcrossing. It is a relatively safe system of breeding, for it is unlikely that two such unrelated animals will carry the same "undesirable" genes and pass them on to their offspring.

Perhaps it might well be added that the majority of purebred breeders with average or below average herds had best follow an outcrossing program, because, in such herds, the problem is that of retaining a heterozygous type of germ plasm with the hope that genes for undesirable characters will be counteracted by genes for desirable characters. With such average or below average herds, an inbreeding program would merely make the animals homozygous for the less desirable characters, the presence of which already makes for their mediocrity. In general, continued outcrossing offers neither the hope for improvement nor the hazard of retrogression of linebreeding or closebreeding programs.

Judicious and occasional outcrossing may well be an integral part of linebreeding or closebreeding programs. As closely inbred animals become increasingly homozygous with germ plasm for good characters, they may likewise become homozygous for certain undesirable characters even though their general overall type and performance remains well above the breed average. Such defects may best be remedied by introducing an outcross through an animal or animals known to be especially strong in the character or characters needing strengthening. This having been accomplished, the wise breeder will return to the original closebreeding or linebreeding program, realizing full well the limitations of an outcrossing program.

Grading Up

Grading up is that system of breeding in which purebred sires of a given pure breed are mated to native or grade females. Its purpose is to develop uniformity and quality and to increase performance in the offspring.

Fig. 74. High-grade Shorthorn calves, the result of using registered Shorthorn bulls on grade Shorthorn cows since 1911. Grand Champion load of feeder calves at the National Western Stock Show, Denver; bred by Josef Winkler, Castle Rock, Colorado. (Courtesy, Josef Winkler)

Many breeders will continue to produce purebred stock. However, the vast majority of animals in the United States—probably more than 97 per cent—are not eligible for registry. In general, however, because of the obvious merit of using well-bred sires, farm animals are sired by purebreds. In comparison with the breeding of purebreds, such a system requires less outlay of cash, and less experience on the part of the producer. However, even with this type of production, grading up of the herd through the use of purebred sires is generally practiced. Thus one of the principal functions of the purebred breeder is that of serving as a source of seed stock—particularly of sires—for the commercial producer. In brief, it is hoped that concentrated doses of "good" genes may be secured through the use of purebred sires. As the common stock is improved, this means that still further improvement and homozygosity for good genes is necessary in the purebreds, if they are to bring about further advancement in any grading-up program.

Naturally, the greatest single step toward improved quality and performance occurs in the first cross. The first generation of such a program results in offspring carrying 50 per cent of the hereditary material of the purebred parent (or 50 per cent of the "blood" of the purebred parent, as many stockmen speak of it). The next generation gives offspring carrying 75 per cent of the "blood" of the purebred breed, and in subsequent generations the proportion of inheritance remaining from the original scrub females is halved with each cross. Later crosses usually increase quality and performance still more, though in less marked degree. After the third or fourth cross, the offspring compare very favorably with purebred stock in conformation, and only exceptionally good sires can bring about further improvement. This is especially so if the males used in grading up successive generations are derived from the same strain within a breed. High grade animals that are the offspring of several generations of outstanding purebred sires can be and often are superior to average or inferior purebreds.

Years of experience in grading up beef cattle through using registered Shorthorn bulls on good native red cows at Sni-A-Bar Farms, Grain Valley, Missouri, yielded the following results and conclusions:

1. The greatest single step toward improved quality, compared with common stock, occurred in the first cross. Subsequent crosses increased quality and market value still more, though in less marked degree.

2. After the third and fourth cross, the offspring compared very favorably with purebred stock in conformation and quality, and only exceptionally good sires could bring about further improvement.

3. The demonstration showed clearly that breeding is a dominant factor in the production of high-quality beeves and that good feeding and management will not return best results unless the element of good breeding is also present.

As evidence that cattle of high merit may be produced through grading up, it is interesting to note that many present-day champion steers are high grades. This fact should also inspire purebred breeders to still further improvement, if the use of purebred sires is to continue to bring about improvement in grading up the commercial herds.

After some experience, the commercial producer who has successfully handled grade animals may add a few purebreds to the herd and gradually build into the latter, provided that his experience and his market for seed stock justifies this type of production.

Crossbreeding

Crossbreeding is the mating of two animals both of which are purebreds but members of different breeds. In a broad sense, crossbreeding also includes the mating of purebred sires of one breed with high grade females of another breed. Crossbreeding is more common in swine and sheep than in cattle; estimates are that two-thirds to three-fourths of all market hogs are crossbreds, and a high percentage of western lambs are crossbreds.

No other system of breeding has been the object of more present-day controversy than crossbreeding. Perhaps, in the final analysis, however, all would agree that *any merits that crossbreeding may possess are and will continue to be based on improved "seed stock."* Certainly, from a genetic standpoint, it should be noted that crossbred animals generally possess greater heterozygosity than outcross animals—with the added virtue of hybrid vigor. It may also be added that, as in outcrossing, the recessive and undesirable genes remain hidden in the crossbred animal.

On purely theoretical grounds, it would appear that crossbreeding should result in some increase in vigor because the desirable genes from both breeds would be combined and the undesirable genes from each would tend to be overshadowed as recessives. That is to say, there has been an inevitable, though small, amount of inbreeding in all purebreds during the period of the last 100 to 150 years. This has been partly intentional and partly due to geographical limitations upon the free exchange of breeding stock from one part of the country to another. As a result of this slight degree of inbreeding, there has been a slow but rather constant increase in homozygosis within each of the pure breeds of livestock. Most of the factors fixed in the homozygous state are desirable; but inevitably some undesirable genes have probably been fixed, resulting in lowered vigor, slower growth rate, less ability to live, etc.

Theoretically, then, crossbreeding should be an aid in relegating these undesirable genes to a recessive position and in allowing more dominant genes to express themselves. Practical observation and limited experiments would indicate that this does occur in crossbreeding.

Crossbreeding programs usually consist of two types: (1) the maintenance of purebred females that are mated to a purebred sire of a different breed, and (2) the maintenance of crossbred females generation after generation, with matings to purebred sires of different breeds being on a rotation basis.

In the first system, the producer is sooner or later faced with the problem of breeding the females back to a purebred sire of the same breed in order to get the necessary replacement females to take the place of those lost through old age, injury, lower productivity, death, etc. As can be readily seen, this system allows for a very limited opportunity to build up the quality of the female herd. In the second system, the rotation of sires is often a difficult problem, and the producer will almost inevitably end up with a motley collection of females and progeny varying in type and color. Even though such motley animals may individually be superior, when sold they are very likely to be penalized because of their lack of uniformity in type and color. With many producers, this lack of uniformity also detracts much from the art and the challenge of animal breeding.

This discussion does not preclude the undeniable and proved value of crossbreeding in the creation of new breeds especially adapted to certain conditions. For example, the Santa Gertrudis breed of cattle, a breed derived from five-eights Shorthorn and three-eighths Brahman breeding, was developed to meet a need in the hot, dry and insect-infested area of the Southwest. Experienced cattlemen of the area will vouch for the fact that this is a practical example of a planned system of crossbreeding which has high utility value under the environmental conditions common to the country. Still other examples of crossbreeding in the creation of breeds may be cited.

Some cattlemen, especially those who calve out two-year-old heifers, use an Aberdeen-Angus bull, claiming that there is less trouble at calving time because of the smaller body size and smaller heads of such calves. However, in an extensive experiment, in which Hereford heifers were divided and mated to Angus and Hereford bulls, the Oklahoma Experiment Station did not find a breed difference.[1]

In summary, it can be said that crossbreeding has a place, particularly from the standpoint of increased vigor, growth rate, and efficiency of production; but pure breeding will continue to control the destiny of further improvement in any class of livestock and furnish the desired homozygosity and uniformity which many stockmen insist is a part of the art of breeding better livestock.

PRODUCTION TESTING BEEF CATTLE

Production Testing embraces both (1) Individual Merit Testing (sometimes called Performance Testing) and (2) Progeny Testing. The distinction between and the relationship of these terms is set forth in the following definitions:

1. **Individual Merit Testing**—*is the practice of evaluating and selecting animals on the basis of their individual merit.*

2. **Progeny Testing**—*is the practice of selecting animals on the basis of the merit of their progeny.*

3. **Production Testing**—*is a more inclusive term, including Individual Merit Testing and/or Progeny Testing.*

Production Testing involves the taking of accurate records rather than casual observation. Also, in order to be most effective, the accompanying selection must be based on characteristics of economic importance and high heritability (see Table 11, and an objective measure or "yardstick" (such as pounds, inches, etc.) should be placed upon each of the traits to be measured. Finally, those breeding animals that fail to meet the high standards set forth must be removed from the herd promptly and unflinchingly.

In comparison with that of chickens or even swine, Production Testing of beef cattle is slow, and, like most investigational work with large animals, it is likely to be expensive. Even so, in realization that such testing is absolutely necessary if maximum improvement is to be made, the progressive purebred beef cattle breeder will wish to make a start.

---

[1]Moore, Delbert Glenn, Thesis entitled, "Some Factors Affecting Difficulty at Parturition of Two-Year-Old Hereford Heifers," Oklahoma State University, May, 1956.

Table 11 lists the economically important characters in beef cattle. Certainly, from the ultimate experimental standpoint, the fifth point listed in Table 11 (Efficiency of feed utilization) would require that individual feed records be kept on each animal in the herd—a procedure which may be impractical under farm conditions. Instead, the practical cattleman may keep group feed records—through feeding together young animals of similar ages—or, if necessary, disregard this criterion and concentrate on the other points. In any event, individual feed records on prospective herd sires are extremely important.

But efficiency of feed utilization should not be the sole criterion. After all, certain Holsteins, for example, may produce beef more efficiently than many members of the established beef breeds, but the dairy-type animal does not add sufficient carcass weight in the regions of the high-priced cuts.

Body-type scores—based on the demands and prices of a *discriminating market as projected into the future*—had best be taken at a standard age, probably being evaluated in terms of either a numerical score or a letter. It is important that all animals be evaluated and their scores made a part of the permanent record. Consistently good production is to be desired. It should be realized that it is all too easy for a breeder to remember the good individuals produced by a given cow and to forget those which are mediocre or culls.

A prerequisite for any production data is that each animal be positively identified—by means of ear notches, ear tags, or tattoos. For purebred breeders, who must use a system of animal identification anyway, this does not constitute an additional detail. But the taking of weights and grades does require additional time and labor—an expenditure which is highly worthwhile, however.

In order not to be burdensome, the record forms should be relatively simple. Furthermore, they should be in a form that will permit easy summarization—for example, the record of one cow should be on one sheet if possible. Record forms now in use by Washington State University are shown in Figures 76 and 77.

Information on the productivity of *close relatives* (the sire and the dam and the brothers and sisters) can supplement that on the animal itself and thus be a distinct aid in selection. The

TABLE 11

ECONOMICALLY IMPORTANT CHARACTERS IN BEEF CATTLE, AND THEIR HERITABILITY[1]

Economically Important Characters	Approx. Heritability of Character (%)	Comments
1. Birth weight	45	The larger and more vigorous calves at birth usually retain these advantages to maturity.
2. Weaning weight	26	Heavy weaning weight is important because: (1) It is indicative of the milking ability of the cow. (2) Gains made before weaning are cheaper than those made after weaning. (3) Those who sell calves at weaning make more profit due to the heavier weight available to sell.
3. Weaning conformation score	32	Body type scores are difficult to make and are materially affected by condition. Yet they are important, for, after all, animals of dairy breeding may rank very high when judged by each of the other criteria. It is recommended that body type scores be taken at a standard age or ages, perhaps at weaning and at the close of the test feeding period.
4. Daily rate of gain from weaning to marketing	46	Daily rate of gain from weaning to marketing is important because: (1) It is highly correlated with efficiency of gain. (2) It makes for a shorter time in reaching market weight and condition, thereby effecting a saving in labor and making for a more rapid turnover in capital.

TABLE 11 (Continued)

Economically Important Characters	Approx. Heritability of Character	Comments
5. Efficiency of feed utilization.............	39	Where convenient, accurate feed records should be kept, for the most profitable animals are the ones which require the least pounds of feed to make 100 pounds of gain. Opinions differ as to the most desirable feed efficiency testing period or age and method. Most scientists recommend (1) testing from weaning (6 to 7 mo.) to 12 months, (2) either full- for self-feeding, and (3) group feeding where individual feeding is not practical.
6. On-foot grade at slaughter time.............	38	Where steer progenies are slaughtered, their carcass grades will constitute the best possible evaluation of type.
7. Carcass grade.............	39	High carcass grade is important because it determines eating and selling quality.
8. Area of rib eye.............	70	The rib eye (the large muscle which lies in the angle of the rib and vertebra) is indicative of the bred-in muscling of the entire carcass. Thus, a large area of rib eye is much sought.

¹The heritability figures used herein were provided to the author by Dr. E. J. Warwick, Head, Beef Cattle Research Section, USDA, Beltsville, Maryland.

Fig. 75. Progeny tests of these two shorthorn bulls showed that their appearance was not a reliable indicator of breeding ability. These animals are full brothers, but most cattlemen would agree that the top bull is the most attractive in appearance. However, the bull in the lower picture produced calves that were 42 pounds heavier at the end of a feeding period and that slaughtered out higher-grading carcasses. The average return per calf was nearly $5.00 greater than from those sired by the top bull. (Courtesy, USDA)

production records of more distant relatives are of little significance, because individually, due to the sampling nature of inheritance, they contribute only a few genes to an animal many generations removed.

Under practical conditions, Progeny Testing of cattle is usually confined to the bull, as a male produces during his lifetime many more offspring than a female. Because of the relatively small numbers of offspring, Progeny Testing with females (except with litter-bearing sows) is somewhat more difficult; and as a rule, a female cannot be thoroughly Progeny Tested until she has spent half or more of her lifetime in a herd. Certainly, the intelligent breeder should study his females and cull those which consistently fail to produce good offspring. If possible, the females should also be Progeny Tested—especially those that may become the dams of herd bulls.

A good plan in Progeny Testing bulls consists of retaining and mating one or more young bulls—the numbers depending upon the size of the herd—on a limited number of females during their first season of breeding. The progeny are then tested and evaluated, and only those bulls that prove to be best on the basis of their progeny are retained for further breeding purposes. If young bulls eighteen months of age are each mated to eight to twelve females, calves should be born nine months later, and the progeny can be tested between the ages of seven and twelve months. Thus, with good fortune, it is possible to have progeny data on a beef bull when he is approximately thirty-nine months of age. With dairy bulls, whose daughters must be in lactation in order to make the test, it is not possible to make an evaluation until the animal is six to seven years of age.

Animals too young to Progeny Test may be evaluated by Individual Merit Testing.

How to Use Herd Records in Selection

Herd records have little value unless they are intelligently used in culling operations and in deciding upon herd replacements. Also, most stockmen can and should use production records for purposes of estimating the rate of progress and for determining the relative emphasis to place on each character.

Fig. 76. Get of Sire Record. This form is now in use with cooperating beef cattle breeders in Washington, with the W.S.U. Agricultural Extension Service and Department of Animal Science supervising the studies.

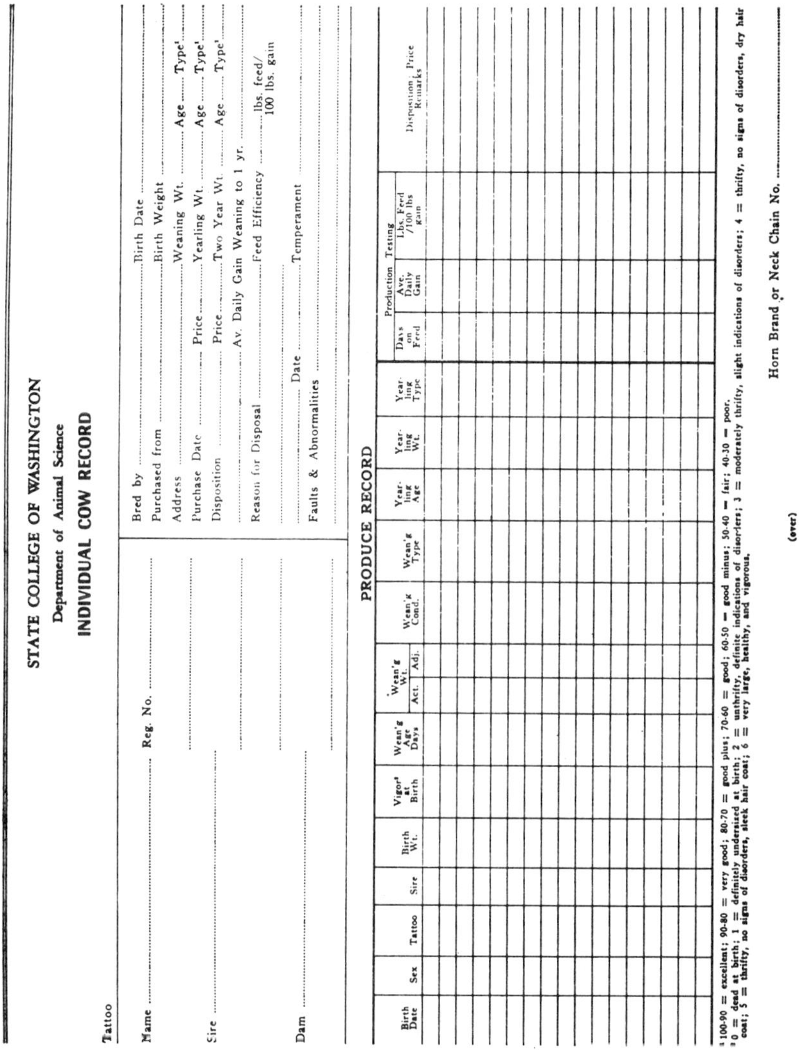

STATE COLLEGE OF WASHINGTON
Department of Animal Science
INDIVIDUAL COW RECORD

Tattoo

Name .... Reg. No. .... | Bred by .... Birth Date ....
Purchased from .... Birth Weight ....
Address .... Weaning Wt. .... Age .... Type[1] ....
Sire .... | Purchase Date .... Price .... Yearling Wt. .... Age .... Type[1] ....
Disposition .... Price .... Two Year Wt. .... Age .... Type[1] ....
.... Av. Daily Gain Weaning to 1 yr. ....
Reason for Disposal .... Feed Efficiency .... lbs. feed/100 lbs. gain
.... Date .... Temperament ....
Dam .... | Faults & Abnormalities ....

PRODUCE RECORD

Birth Date	Sex	Tattoo	Sire	Birth Wt.	Vigor[2] at Birth	Wean'g Age Days	Wean'g Wt. Act.	Wean'g Wt. Adj.	Wean'g Cond.	Wean'g Type	Year-ling Age	Year-ling Wt.	Year-ling Type	Production Testing: Days on Feed	Production Testing: Ave. Daily Gain	Production Testing: Lbs. Feed /100 lbs gain	Disposition; Price Remarks

[1] 100-90 = excellent; 90-80 = very good; 80-70 = good plus; 70-60 = good; 60-50 = good minus; 50-40 = fair; 40-30 = poor.
[2] 0 = dead at birth; 1 = definitely undersized at birth; 2 = unthrifty, definite indications of disorders; 3 = moderately thrifty, slight indications of disorders; 4 = thrifty, no signs of disorders, dry hair coat; 5 = thrifty, no signs of disorders, sleek hair coat; 6 = very large, healthy, and vigorous.

Horn Brand or Neck Chain No. ....

(over)

Fig. 77a. Individual Cow Record. This form is now being used by the Department of Animal Science, Washington State University (see next page for reverse side of record form).

APPRAISING PER CENT OF CHANGE IN CHARACTERS DUE TO (1) HEREDITY, AND (2) ENVIRONMENT:

Stockmen are well aware that there are differences in birth weight, in weaning weight, in daily rate of gain, in body type, etc. If those animals which excel in the desired traits would, in

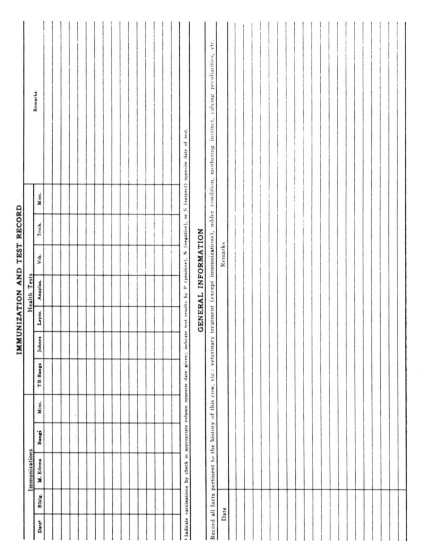

Fig. 77b. Individual Cow Record. This is the reverse side of the record form shown on the previous page.

turn, transmit without loss these same improved qualities to their offspring, progress would be simple and rapid. Unfortunately, this is not the case. Such economically important characters are greatly affected by environment [by feeding, care, management, type of birth (singles vs. twins), age, diseases, etc.]. Thus only part of the apparent improvement in certain animals is hereditary, and can be transmitted on to the next generation.

As would be expected, improvements due to environment are not inherited. This means that if most of the improvement in an economically important character is due to an improved environment, the heritability of that character will be low and little progress can be made through selection. On the other hand, if the character is highly heritable, marked progress can be made through selection. Thus body color in cattle—e.g. red, roan and white—is a highly heritable character, for environment appears to have little or no part in determining the difference between animals that are red and those that are roan or white. On the other hand, such a character as condition or degree of finish is of low heritability because, for the most part, it is affected by environment (feed, care, management, etc.).

There is need, therefore, to know the approximate amount or percentage of change in each economically important character which is due to heredity and the amount which is due to environment. Table 11 gives this information for beef cattle in terms of the approximate percentage heritability of each of the economically important characters. The heritability figures given therein are averages based on large numbers; thus some variations from these may be expected in individual herds. Even though the heritability of many of the economically important characters listed in Table 11 is disappointingly small, it is gratifying to know that much of it is cumulative and permanent.

ESTIMATING RATE OF PROGRESS:

For purposes of illustrating the way in which the heritability figures in Table 11 may be used in practical breeding operations, the following example is given:

In a certain beef cattle herd, the calf crop in a given year averages a daily gain of 1.5 pounds, with a range of 1 to 2 pounds. There are available sufficient of the heavier gaining (1.75 lb.) calves from which to select replacement breeding stock. What amount of this more rapid daily gain (0.25 lb. daily above the average) is likely to be transmitted to the offspring of these heavier gaining calves?

Step by step, the answer to this question is secured as follows:

TABLE 12

ESTIMATING RATE OF PROGRESS IN A BEEF CATTLE HERD

Economically Important Characters	Average of Herd	Selected Individuals for Replacements	Average Selection Advantage	Heritability Per cent	Expected Performance Next Generation
Average birth weight of calves, lbs.	60	70	10	45	64.5
Average weaning weight, lbs.	400	450	50	26	413
Average weaning conformation score, grade[1]	Grade 3	Grade 2	3 grades (see footnote)	32	About 3+
Average daily rate of gain, lbs.	1.5	1.75	0.25	46	1.615
Average efficiency of feed utilization, lbs.	750	650	-100	39	711

[1]The grade figures given to the right are based on the Bull Grading system used in the West (see section on Bull Grading), in which the grades from highest to lowest are: 1+, 1, 1—, 2+, 2, 2—, 3+, 3, 3—, 4+, 4, 4—. Most herds will not be able to select replacements averaging more than 1 to 2 grades above the average, which means that the expected increase in type in the next generation would be only 35 per cent of this. Naturally, the principle herewith illustrated may be applied to any measurable system of grading.

1. 1.75 − 1.5 = 0.25 lbs., the amount by which the selected calves exceed the average from which they arose.

2. By referring to Table 11, it is found that daily rate of gain is 46% heritable. This means that 46% of the 0.25 lb. can be expected to be due to the superior heredity of the stock saved as breeders, and that the other 54% is due to environment (feed, care, management, etc.).

3. 0.25 × 46% = 0.115 lbs.; which means that for rate of gain the stock saved for the breeding herd is 0.115 lbs. superior, genetically, to the stock from which it was selected.

4. 1.5 + 0.115 = 1.615 lbs. daily gain; which is the expected performance of the next generation.

It is to be emphasized that the 1.615 lbs. daily gain is merely the expected performance. The actual outcome may be altered by environment (feed, care, management, etc.) and by chance. Also, it should be recognized that where the heritability of a character is lower less progress can be made. The latter point explains why the degree to which a character is heritable has a very definite influence in the effectiveness of mass selection.

Using the heritability figures given in Table 11, and assuming certain herd records, the progress to be expected from one generation of selection in a given beef cattle herd might appear somewhat as summarized in Table 12.

APPRAISING FACTORS INFLUENCING RATE OF PROGRESS

Stockmen need to be informed relative to the factors which influence the rate of progress that can be made through selection. They are:

1. **The heritability of the character.**—When heritability is high, much of that which is selected for will appear in the next generation, and marked improvement will be evident.

2. **The number of characters selected for at the same time.** —The greater the number of characters selected for at the same time, the slower the progress in each. In other words, greater progress can be attained in one character if it alone is selected for. For example, if selection of equal intensity is practiced for 4 independent traits, the progress in any one will be only one-half of that which would occur if only one trait were considered; whereas selection for 9 traits will reduce the progress in any one

to one-third. This emphasizes the importance of limiting the traits in selection to those which have greatest importance as determined by economic value and heritability. At the same time, it is recognized that it is rarely possible to select for one trait only, and that income is usually dependent upon several traits.

3. **The genotypic and phenotypic correlation between traits.** —The effectiveness of selection is lessened by (1) negative correlation between two desirable traits, or (2) positive correlation of desirable with undesirable traits. For example, it is reported that the most important factor limiting improvement in the fleeces of Australian Merinos is the negative correlation which exists between fleece weight and crimps per inch. Because of this situation, the rate of improvement in fleece weight is reduced whenever selection pressure is increased for crimps per inch.

4. **The amount of heritable variation measured in such specific units as pounds, inches, numbers, etc.**—If the amount of heritable variation—measured in such specific units as pounds, inches, or numbers—is small, the animals selected cannot vary much above the average of the entire herd, and progress will be slow. For example, there is much less spread, in pounds, in the birth weights of calves than in weaning weights. Therefore, more marked progress in selection can be made in the older weights than in birth weights, when measurements at each stage are in pounds.

5. **The accuracy of records and adherence to an ideal.**—It is a well established fact that a breeder who maintains accurate records and consistently selects toward a certain ideal or goal can make more rapid progress than one whose records are inaccurate and whose ideals change with fads and fancies.

6. **The number of available animals.**—The greater the number of animals available from which to select, the greater the progress that can be made. In other words, for maximum progress, enough animals must be born and raised to permit rigid culling. For this reason, more rapid progress can be made with swine than with animals that have only one offspring, and more rapid progress can be made when a herd is either being maintained at the same numbers or reduced than when it is being increased in size.

7. **The age at which selection is made.**—Progress is more

rapid if selection is practiced at an early age. This is so because more of the productive life is ahead of the animal, and the opportunity for gain is then greatest.

8. **The generation interval.**—Generation interval refers to the period of time required for parents to be succeeded by their offspring, from the standpoint of reproduction. The minimum generation interval of farm animals is about as follows: horses, 4 years; cattle, 3 years; sheep, 2 years; and swine, 1 year. In actual practice, the generation intervals are somewhat longer. By way of comparison, it is noteworthy that the average length of a human generation is 33 years.

Shorter generation intervals will result in greater progress per year, provided the same proportion of animals are retained after selection.

Usually it is possible to reduce the generation interval of sires, but it is not considered practical to reduce materially the generation interval of females. Thus, if progress is being made, the best young males should be superior to their sires. Then the advantage of this superiority can be gained by changing to new generations as quickly as possible. To this end, it is recommended that the breeder change to younger sires whenever their records equal or excel those of the older sires. In considering this procedure, it should be recognized, however, that it is very difficult to compare records made in different years or at different ages.

9. **The calibre of the sires.**—Since a much smaller proportion of males than of females is normally saved for replacements, it follows that selection among the males can be more rigorous and that most of the genetic progress in a herd or flock will be made from selection of males. Thus if 2 per cent of the males and 50 per cent of the females in a given herd become parents, then about 75 per cent of the hereditary gain from selection will result from the selection of males and 25 per cent from the selection of females, provided their generation lengths are equal. If the generation lengths of males are shorter than the generation lengths of females, the proportion of hereditary gain due to the selection of males will be even greater.

DETERMINING RELATIVE EMPHASIS TO
PLACE ON EACH CHARACTER:

A replacement animal seldom excels in all of the econom-

ically important characters. The stockman must decide, therefore, how much importance shall be given to each factor. Thus,
the beef cattle producer will have to decide how much emphasis
shall be placed on birth weight, how much on weaning weight,
how much on daily rate of gain, how much on efficiency of feed
utilization, and how much on body type and carcass evaluation.

Perhaps the relative emphasis to place on each character
should vary according to the circumstances. Under certain conditions, some characters may even be ignored. Among the factors
determining the emphasis to place on each character are the
following:

1. **The economic importance of the character to the producer.**—Table 11 lists the economically important characters in
cattle, and summarizes (see comments column) their importance
to the producer.

By economic importance is meant their dollars and cents
value. Thus those characters which have the greatest effect on
profits should receive the most attention.

2. **The heritability of the character.**—It stands to reason
that the more highly heritable characters should receive higher
priority than those which are less heritable, for more progress
can be made thereby.

3. **The genetic correlation between traits.** One trait may be
so strongly correlated with another that selection for one automatically selects for the other. For example, rate of gain and
economy of gain in meat animals are correlated to the extent that
selection for rate of gain tends to select for the most economical
gains as well; thus, economy of gain may be largely disregarded
if rate of gain is given strong consideration. Conversely, one
trait may be negatively correlated with another so that selection
for one automatically selects against the other.

4. **The amount of variation in each character.**—Obviously,
if all animals were exactly alike in a given character, there
could be no selection for that character. Likewise, if the amount
of variation in a given character is small, the selected animals
cannot be very much above the average of the entire herd, and
progress will be slow.

5. **The level of performance already attained.**—If a herd
has reached a satisfactory level of performance for a certain

character, there is not much need for further selection for that character.

It should be recognized, however, that sufficient selection pressure should be exerted to maintain the desired excellence of a given trait; for once selection for many of the economic quantitative traits is relaxed, there is a tendency for the trait to regress rather rapidly toward the average of the breed. For simple quantitative traits (controlled by a single pair of genes), it may be possible to rid the herd of the undesired gene, following which selection against the trait could be dropped, except when adding outside animals to the herd.

SYSTEMS OF SELECTION:

Finally, the stockman needs to follow a system of selection which will result in maximum total progress over a period of several years or animal generations. The three common systems are:

1. **Tandem selection.**—*This refers to that system in which there is selection for only one trait at a time until the desired improvement in that particular trait is reached,* following which selection is made for another trait, etc. This system makes it possible to make rapid improvement in the trait for which selection is being practiced, but it has two major disadvantages: (1) Usually it is not possible to select for one trait only, and (2) generally income is dependent on several traits.

Tandem selection is recommended only in those rare herds where one character only is primarily in need of improvement.

2. **Establishing minimum standards for each character, and selecting simultaneously but independently for each character.**— This system, in which several of the most important characters are selected for simultaneously, is without doubt the most common system of selection. It involves establishing minimum standards for each character and culling animals which fall below these standards. For example, it might be decided to cull all calves weighing less than 55 pounds at birth, or weighing less than 375 pounds at weaning, or gaining less than $1\frac{1}{4}$ pounds daily, or requiring more than 900 pounds of feed per hundred pounds gain, or grading *Three* or less. Of course, the minimum standards may have to vary from year to year if environmental factors change markedly (for example, if calves average light at weaning time due to a severe drought and poor pasture).

The chief weakness of this system is that an individual may be culled because of being faulty in one character only, even though he is well nigh ideal otherwise.

3. **Selection index.**—*Selection indexes combine all important traits into one overall value or index.* Theoretically, a selection index provides a more desirable way in which to select for several traits than either (1) the tandem method or (2) the method of establishing minimum standards for each character and selecting simultaneously but independently for each character.

Selection indexes are designed to accomplish the following:

(1) To give emphasis to the different traits in keeping with their relative importance.

(2) To balance the strong points against the weak points of each animal.

(3) To obtain an over-all total score for each animal, following which all animals can be ranked from best to poorest.

(4) To assure a constant and objective degree of emphasis on each trait being considered, without any shifting of ideals from year to year.

(5) To provide a convenient way in which to correct for environmental effects, such as age of dam, etc.

Despite their acknowledged virtues, selection indexes are not perfect. Among their weaknesses are the following:

(1) Practical indexes are not available for all classes of animals.

(2) Their use may result in covering up or masking certain bad faults or defects.

(3) They do not allow for year to year differences.

(4) Their accuracy is dependent upon (1) the correct evaluation of the net worth of the economic traits considered, (2) the correctness of the estimate of heritability of the traits, and (3) the genetic correlation between the traits; and these estimates are often difficult to make.

In practice, the selection index is best used as a partial guide or tool in the selection program. For example, it may be used to select twice as many animals as are needed for herd or flock replacements, and this number may then be reduced through rigid culling on the basis of a thorough visual inspection for those traits that are not in the index, which may include such things as quality, freedom from defects, and market type.

QUESTIONS FOR STUDY AND DISCUSSION

1. Why is cattle breeding less flexible in the hands of man than swine or sheep breeding?

2. What unique circumstances surrounded the founding of genetics by Mendel?

3. Under what conditions might a theoretically completely homozygous state in cattle be undesirable and unfortunate?

4. How can you determine whether a polled bull is pure for the polled character?

5. Give examples of monohybrid, dihybrid, and trihybrid crosses in cattle; and describe each (1) the first cross animals, and (2) the second cross animals, and give the ratio of the second crosses.

6. Why do not fraternal (dizygotic) twins look more alike?

7. Explain how sex is determined.

8. When abnormal animals are born, what conditions tend to indicate each (1) an hereditary defect, or (2) a nutritional deficiency?

9. Give the expected genetic picture of dwarfism of 100 offspring from matings of (1) carrier bulls X non-carrier cows, and (2) carrier bulls X carrier cows. What steps can be taken to get rid of dwarfism?

10. The "sire is half the herd!" Is this an under- or overstatement?

11. In order to make intelligent selections and breed progress, is it necessary to fit, stall-feed, or place animals in show condition; or may they be selected in their "work clothes" off the farm or ranch?

12. What system of breeding do you consider to be best adapted to your herd, or to a herd with which you are familiar? Justify your choice.

13. How would you go about Production Testing a herd of beef cattle? List and discuss each step.

14. Why do not more cattlemen buy and use Production Tested bulls?

15. List the factors which should be considered in determining the relative emphasis to place on each character in a beef cattle selection program.

16. What system of selection—(1) tandem, (2) establishing minimum culling levels, or (3) selection index—would you recommend and why?

SELECTED REFERENCES

Title of Publication	Author(s)	Publisher
Animal Breeding	A. L. Hagedoorn	Crosby Lockwood & Son, Ltd., London, England, 1950.
Animal Breeding	L. M. Winters	John Wiley & Sons, Inc., New York, N. Y., 1948.
Animal Breeding Plans	J. L. Lush	Collegiate Press, Inc., Ames, Iowa, 1938.
Breeding and Improvement of Farm Animals	V. A. Rice F. N. Andrews E. J. Warwick J. E. Legates	McGraw-Hill Book Co., Inc., New York, N. Y., 1957.
Breeding Better Livestock	V. A. Rice F. N. Andrews E. J. Warwick	McGraw-Hill Book Co., Inc., New York, N. Y., 1953.
Breeding for Beef	H. H. Stonaker	Bull. 501 S. Colorado State University, Fort Collins, Colo.
Breeding Livestock Adapted to Unfavorable Environments	R. W. Phillips	Food and Agriculture Organization of the United Nations, Washington, D. C., 1949.
Elements of Genetics, The	C. D. Carlington K. Mather	The MacMillan Co., New York, N. Y., 1950.
Farm Animals	John Hammond	Edward Arnold & Co., London, England, 1952.
Gene .. .. ..The Universal Calf	L. N. Hazel L. E. Johnson	Fred Hahne Printing Co., Webster City, Iowa, 1956.
Genetic Resistance to Disease in Domestic Animals	F. B. Hutt	Comstock Publishing Assn., Cornell University Press, Ithaca, New York, 1958.
Genetics and Animal Breeding	E. J. Warwick	Agri. Expt. Sta. Popular Bull. 189, Washington State University, Pullman, Wash., 1948.
Highlight of Breeding Systems	V. A. Rice	Holstein-Friesian Assn. of America, Brattleboro, Vermont.
Improvement of Livestock	Ralph Bogart	The MacMillan Co., New York, N. Y., 1959
Inheritance in Cattle and Sheep	C. B. Roubicek	Wyo. Agri. Expt. Sta. Circ. 45, University of Wyoming, Laramie, Wyoming.
Problems and Practices of American Cattlemen	M. E. Ensminger M. W. Galgan W. L. Slocum	Wash. Agri. Expt. Sta. Bu. 1562 Washington State University Pullman, Wash., 1955.
Tables For Coefficients of Inbreeding in Animals	C. D. Mueller	Agri. Expt. Sta. Tech. Bull. 80, Kansas State College, Manhattan, Kansas.
Twenty Years at SNI-A-BAR Farms	William Rockhill Nelson Trust	1114 Bryant Bldg., Kansas City, 6, Missouri.

CHAPTER VII

PHYSIOLOGY OF REPRODUCTION IN CATTLE

Contents   Page

Cattle producers encounter many reproductive problems, a
reduction of which calls for a full understanding of reproductive
physiology and the application of scientific practices therein. In
fact, it may be said that reproduction is the first and most important requisite of cattle breeding, for if animals fail to reproduce the breeder is soon out of business.

Many outstanding individuals, and even whole families, are
disappointments because they are either sterile or reproduce
poorly. Twenty per cent of all cows fail to breed; and there is an

appalling calf loss of 21 per cent between birth and weaning.[1] The subject of physiology of reproduction is, therefore, of great importance.

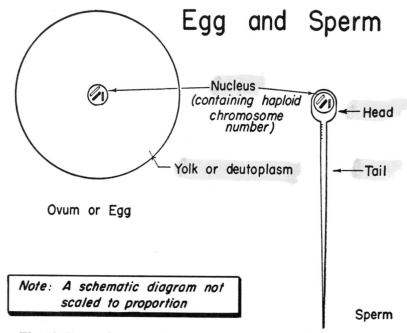

Fig. 78. Egg and sperm. The parent germ cells, the egg from the female and the sperm from the male, unite and transmit to the offspring all the characters that it will inherit. (Drawing by R. F. Johnson)

THE REPRODUCTIVE ORGANS OF THE BULL

The bull's functions in reproduction are: (1) to produce the male reproductive cells, the **sperm** or **spermatozoa**, and (2) to introduce sperm into the female reproductive tract at the proper time. In order that these functions may be fulfilled, cattlemen should have a clear understanding of the anatomy of the reproductive system of the bull and of the functions of each of its parts. Figure 79 shows the reproductive organs of the bull. A description of each part follows:

1. **Scrotum.**—This is a diverticulum of the abdomen, which encloses the testicles. Its chief function is themoregulatory; to maintain the testicles at temperatures several degrees lower than that of the body proper.

---

[1]Ensminger, M. E., M. W. Galgan, and W. L. Slocum; Wash. Agri. Expt. Sta. Bul. 562.

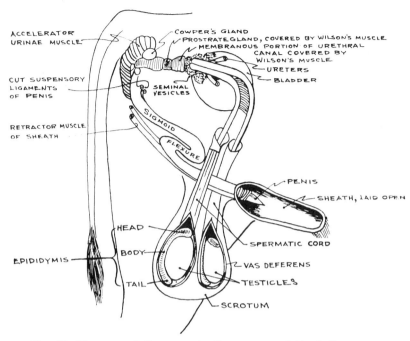

ACCELERATOR URINAE MUSCLE
CUT SUSPENSORY LIGAMENTS OF PENIS
RETRACTOR MUSCLE OF SHEATH
EPIDIDYMIS
HEAD
BODY
TAIL
SIGMOID FLEXURE
SEMINAL VESICLES
COWPER'S GLAND
PROSTRATE GLAND, COVERED BY WILSON'S MUSCLE
MEMBRANOUS PORTION OF URETHRAL CANAL COVERED BY WILSON'S MUSCLE
URETERS
BLADDER
PENIS
SHEATH, LAID OPEN
SPERMATIC CORD
VAS DEFERENS
TESTICLES
SCROTUM

Fig. 79. Diagram of the reproductive organs of the bull.

2. **Testicles.**—The testicles of the mature bull measure 4 to 5 inches in length and 2 to 3 inches in width. Their primary functions are the production of sperm and the male hormone, testosterone.

Once the animal reaches sexual maturity, sperm production in the seminiferous tubules—the glandular portion of the testicles, in which are situated the spermatogonia (sperm-producing cells)—is a continuous process. Around and between the seminiferous tubules are the interstitial cells which produce testosterone or androgen.

A sperm is a small (less than 1/500 inch in length), tadpole-shaped living entity, in which the head contains the unit of inheritance and the tail provides the means of locomotion.

Testosterone is essential for the development and function of male reproductive organs, male characteristics, and sexual drive.

Cryptorchids are males one or both of whose testicles have not descended to the scrotum. The undescended testicle(s) is usually sterile because of the high temperature in the abdomen.

The testicles communicate through the inguinal canal with the pelvic cavity, where accessory organs and glands are located. A weakness of the inguinal canal sometimes allows part of the vicera to pass out into the scrotum—a condition called *scrotal hernia.*

3. **Epididymis.**—The efferent ducts of each testis unite into one duct, thus forming the epididymis. This long and greatly coiled tube consists of three parts:

(1) **The head.**—Consisting of several tubules which are grouped into lobules.

(2) **The body.**—The part of the epididymis which passes down along the sides of the testis.

(3) **The tail.** The part located at the bottom of the testis.

The epididymis has four functions; namely, (1) as a passage way for sperm from the seminiferous tubules, (2) the storage of sperm, (3) the secretion of a fluid which probably nourishes the sperm, and (4) the maturation or ripening of the sperm.

4. **Vas deferens (Ductus deferens).**—This slender tube, which is lined with ciliated cells, leads from the tail of the epididymis to the pelvic part of the urethra in the penis. Its primary function is to move sperm into the urethra at the time of ejaculation.

The cutting or closing off of the vas deferens, known as *vasectomy,* is the most usual operation performed to produce sterility, where sterility without castration is desired.

5. **Spermatic cord.**—The vas deferens—together with the longitudinal strands of smooth muscle, blood vessels, and nerves; all encased in a fibrous sheath—make up the spermatic cord (2 of them) which pass up through an opening in the abdominal wall, the inguinal canal, into the pelvic cavity.

6. **Seminal vesicles (or vesicula seminalis).**—These compact glandular organs with a lobulated surface flank the vas deferens near its point of termination. They are the largest of the accessory glands of reproduction in the male (In the mature bull, they measure 4 to 5 inches in length and 2 inches in width at their largest part), and are located in the pelvic cavity.

The seminal vesicles secrete a fluid which provides a medium of transport of the spermatozoa.

7. **Prostate gland.**—This gland is located at the neck of the bladder, surrounding or nearly surrounding the urethra and ventral to the rectum. The secretion of the prostate gland is thick and rich in proteins and salts. It is alkaline, and it has a characteristic odor.

It cleanses the urethra prior to and during ejaculation, and provides bulk and a suitable medium for the transport of sperm.

8. **Cowper's gland (Bulbo-urethral gland).**—These two glands, which are deeply imbedded in muscular tissue in the bull, are located on either side of the urethra in the pelvic region. They communicate with the urethra by means of a small duct.

It is thought that these glands produce an alkaline secretion for the purpose of neutralizing or cleansing the urethra prior to the passage of semen.

9. **Urethra.**—This is a long tube which extends from the bladder to the glans penis. The vas deferens and seminal vesicle open to the urethra close to its point of origin.

The urethra serves for the passage of both urine and semen.

10. **Penis.**—This is the bull's organ of copulation. Also, it conveys urine to the exterior. It is composed essentially of erectile tissue, which, at the times of erection, becomes gorged with blood. Just behind the scrotum it forms an S-shaped curve, known as the sigmoid flexure, which allows for extension of the penis during erection. In the mature bull, the erected penis is about 3 feet long.

In total, the reproductive organs of the bull are designed to produce semen and to convey it to the female at the time of mating. The semen consists of two parts; namely (1) the sperm which are produced by the testes, and (2) the liquid portion, or semen plasma, which is secreted by the seminiferous tubules, the epididymis, the vas deferens, the seminal vesicles, the prostate, and the Cowper's glands. Actually, the sperm make up only a small portion of the ejaculate. On the average, at the time of each service, a bull ejaculates about 4 cubic centimeters of semen, containing about 20 billion sperm. The sperm concentration ranges from 25,000 to 1,000,000 per cubic millimeter.

THE REPRODUCTIVE ORGANS OF THE COW

The cow's function in reproduction are: (1) to produce the female reproductive cells, the *eggs* or *ova*, (2) to develop the new individual, the *embryo*, in the uterus, (3) to expel the fully developed young at time of *birth* or *parturition*, and (4) to produce milk for the nourishment of the young. Actually, the part played by the cow in the generative process is much more complicated than that of the bull. It is imperative, therefore, that the modern cattle producer have a full understanding of the anatomy of the reproductive organs of the cow and the functions of each part. Figure 80 shows the reproductive organs of the cow, and a description of each part follows:

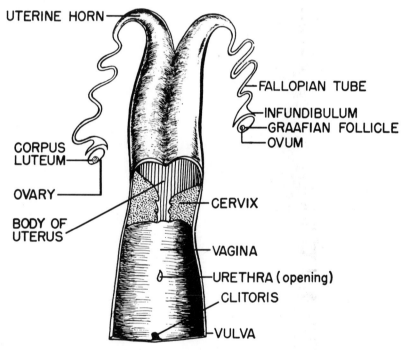

Fig. 80. The reproductive organs of the cow.

1. **Ovaries.**—The two irregular-shaped ovaries of the cow are supported by a structure called the broad ligament, but lie rather loosely in the abdominal cavity and 16 to 18 inches from the vulvar orifice. They average about one and one-half inches in length, an inch in width, and half an inch in thickness.

The ovaries have three functions: (1) to produce the female reproductive cells, the *eggs* or *ova*, (2) to secrete the female sex hormones, *estrogen* and *progesterone* (the latter is the hormone of the corpus luteum), and (3) to form the *corpora lutea*. The ovaries may alternate somewhat irregularly in the performance of these functions.

Ovary of Cow During Heat

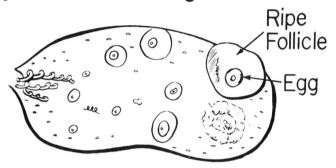

Ripe Follicle

Egg

Ovary of Cow Not in Heat

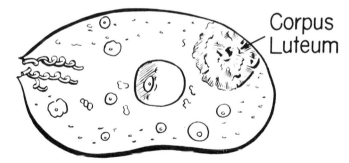

Corpus Luteum

Fig. 81. Diagrammatic illustration of the ovary of the cow. Top: Ovary of cow in heat. The ripe follicle secretes the estrogenic hormone responsible for the symptoms of heat. Bottom: Ovary of cow not in heat. The corpus luteum is a glandular structure and secretes the hormone progesterone which maintains pregnancy in the pregnant cow. (Drawing by Steve Allured)

The ovaries differ from the testes in that generally only one egg is produced at intervals, toward the end of the heat period or after heat symptoms have passed. Each miniature egg is contained in a sac, called *Graafian follicle,* a large number of which are scattered throughout the ovary (it has been estimated that there are more than 75,000 follicles in the ovaries of a heifer calf at birth). Generally, the follicles remain in an unchanged state until the advent of puberty, at which time some of them begin to enlarge through an increase in the follicular liquid within. Toward the end of heat, a follicle ruptures and discharges an egg, which process is known as *ovulation.* As soon as the egg is released, the corpus luteum makes its appearance. This corpus luteum secretes a hormone called progesterone, which (1) acts on the uterus so that it implants and nourishes the embryo, (2) prevents other eggs from maturing and keeps the animal from coming in heat during pregnancy, (3) maintains the animal in a pregnant condition, and (4) assists female hormone in the development of the mammary glands. If the egg is not fertilized, however, the corpus luteum atrophies and allows a new follicle to ripen and a new heat to appear. Occasionally the corpus luteum fails to atrophy at the normal time, thus inducing temporary sterility. This persistent corpus luteum can be squeezed out.

The egg-containing follicles also secrete into the blood the female sex hormone, estrogen. Estrogen is necessary for the development of the female reproductive system, for the mating behavior or heat of the female, for the development of the mammary glands, and for the development of the secondary sex characteristics, or femininity, in the cow.

From the standpoint of the practical cattle breeder, the ripening of the first Graafian follicle in a heifer generally coincides with puberty, and this marks the beginning of reproduction.

2. **Fallopian tubes (or oviducts).**—These small, cilia-lined tubes or ducts lead from the ovaries to the horns of the uterus. They are about 5 to 6 inches long in the cow and the end of each tube nearest the ovary, called *infundibulum,* flares out like a funnel. They are not attached to the ovaries but lie so close to them that they seldom fail to catch the released eggs.

At ovulation, the egg passes into the infundibulum where, within a few minutes, the ciliary movement within the tube, assisted by the muscular movements of the tube itself, carries it down into the oviduct. If mating has taken place, the union of the sperm and egg usually takes place in the upper third of the fallopian tube. Thence the fertilized egg moves into the uterine horn. All this movement from the ovary to the uterine horn takes place in 3 to 4 days.

3. **Uterus.**—The uterus is the muscular sac, connecting the Fallopian tubes and the vagina, in which the fertilized egg attaches itself and develops until expelled from the body of the cow at the time of parturition. The uterus consists of the two horns (cornua), the body, and the neck (or cervix) of the womb. In the cow, the horns are about 15 inches long, the body about 1½ inches long, and the cervix about 4 inches long. In the mature cow, the uterus lies almost entirely within the abdominal cavity.

In the cow, the fetal membranes that surround the developing embryo are in contact with the lining of the uterus through buttons or cotyledons.

The thick, muscular, fold-containing portion of the uterus, known as the cervix, forms an effective seal at the posterior end of the uterus. Cells within the cervix secrete copious amounts of mucus, forming the cervical plug. This gelatine-like material is discharged just prior to the occurrence of a normal heat period.

4. **Vagina.**—The vagina admits the penis of the bull at the time of service and receives the semen. At the time of birth, it expands and serves as the final passageway for the fetus. In the non-pregnant cow, the vagina is 10 to 12 inches in length, but it is somewhat longer in the pregnant animal.

5. **Clitoris.**—The clitoris is the erectile and sensory organ of the female, which is homologous to the penis in the male. It is situated just inside the portion of the vulva farthest removed from the anus.

6. **Urethra.**—The urine makes its exit through the opening of the urethra.

7. **Vulva (or urogenital sinus).**—The vulva is the external opening of both the urinary and genital tracts.

The reproductive system of the cow is regulated by a complex endocrine system. The functions of the reproductive organs and the occurrence of estrus, conception, pregnancy, parturition and lactation are all regulated and coordinated by the hormones of the pituitary, the ovarian follicle, the corpus luteum, and the placenta. The cyclic nature of these phenomena is shown in graphic form in Fig. 82.

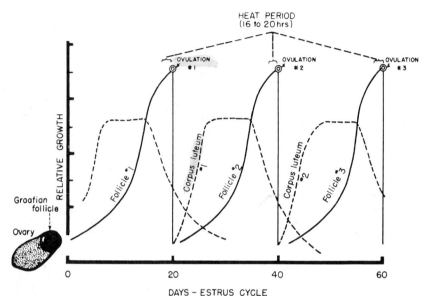

DAYS – ESTRUS CYCLE

Fig. 82. Diagrammatic illustration of recurrence of the estrus cycle and the chain of events which takes place in the ovary of the nonpregnant cow. Continuous line shows the relative growth of the Graafian follicle. When maximum growth of the follicle is attained, rupture takes place and the ova is released (see double circles on top of diagram). At rupture, the size of the follicle reaches zero and the follicle is replaced by the corpus luteum (dotted line) which increases in size, reaches a maximum, then declines before the subsequent follicle starts to develop. Note that the rupture of the follicles coincides with the end of heat symptoms. The interval between two ovulations is 19 to 20 days on an average. (Drawing by Steve Allured, from sketch prepared by Doctors E.S.E. Hafez and Clayton O'Mary, Department of Animal Science, Washington State University)

FERTILIZATION

Fertilization is the union of the male and female germ cells, sperm and ovum. The sperm are deposited in the vagina at the time of service and from there ascend the female reproductive tract. Under favorable conditions, they meet the egg and one of them fertilizes it in the upper part of the oviduct near the ovary.

In cows, fertilization is an all or none phenomenon, since only one ovum is ordinarily involved.[1] Thus, the breeder's problem is to synchronize ovulation and insemination; to ensure that large numbers of vigorous, fresh sperm will be present in the fallopian tubes at the time of ovulation. This is very difficult, because (1) there is no reliable way of predicting the length of

---

[1] In beef cattle, only about one birth in 200 produces twins.

heat or the time of ovulation (It is known that ovulation generally takes place toward the end of or following the heat period. However, it may occur during the heat period or as late as 36 hours after it), (2) like all biological phenomena, there is considerable individual variation, (3) the sperm cells of the

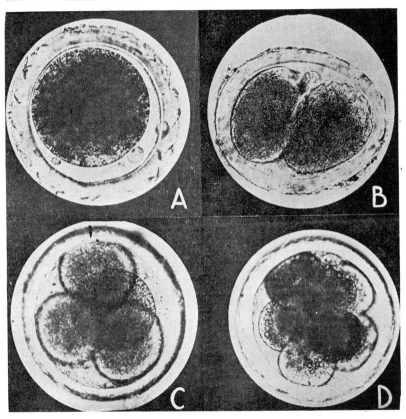

Fig. 83. Developmental changes in the egg at and after fertilization. (These four stages all occur in the fallopian tube.) See also Fig. 98.

A. A healthy egg in the one-cell stage. Several spermatozoa attempt to fertilize the egg, but only one sperm will be able to do so. A few may succeed but die in the zona pellucida (outer circle) where the tails of the dead sperms may be seen.

B. Fertilization is followed by the multiplication of cells. An egg in the two-cell stage; this stage in the cow takes place 24 to 30 hours after fertilization, i.e. some 46 hours after the last symptoms of estrus.

C. The egg cleaves further (an increase in number of cells) without any increase in cellular mass. An egg in the four-cell stage; this stage in the cow takes place 10 hours following stage "B."

D. An egg in the eight-cell stage; this stage in the cow takes place 16 hours after stage "C." After this stage the developing ovum migrates to the uterus where it will increase in cellular and protoplasmic mass.

(Courtesy, Dr. J. A. Laig, University of Bristol, Bristol, England)

bull live only 24 to 30 hours in the reproductive tract of the female, (4) an unfertilized egg will not live over about 12 hours, and (5) it may require less than 5 minutes for sperm cells to ascend the female reproductive tract of a cow.

From the above, it is perfectly clear that a series of delicate time relationships must be met; that breeding must take place at the right time. For the maximum rate of conception, therefore, it is recommended that breeding be done the latter part of the heat period; but, since the duration of heat in cattle is very short (seldom exceeding 20 hours), to delay too long may result in the cow being out of heat when mating is attempted. Thus, if cows are first observed in heat in the forenoon, and if only one service is permissible it is recommended that they be bred about midafternoon on the same day, shortly after the middle of estrus. Where two services are possible, it is recommended that the cow be bred soon after she is observed in heat and again in the late evening.

NORMAL BREEDING HABITS OF COWS

In general, cattle that are bred when out on pasture or range are mated under environmental conditions approaching those which existed in nature prior to domestication. Less breeding trouble is generally encountered among such animals than among beef or dairy animals that are kept in confined conditions and under forced production.

Age of Puberty

The normal age of puberty of cattle is eight to twelve months. It is recognized, however, that the age at which puberty is attained varies according to: (1) breeds, with the smaller breeds having an earlier onset of puberty than the larger, slower maturing ones; and (2) nutritional and environmental factors, with puberty occurring when animals have reached about one-third of their adult size.

Age to Breed Heifers

The age at which to breed heifers will vary with their growth and development. However, when heifers are reasonably well grown, a safe rule is to breed at the first breeding season after they are fifteen to twenty months old. The American Hereford Association will not register a calf dropped by a cow under twenty-four months of age at calving time. This means a minimum breeding age of fifteen months with Herefords when it is intended that the calf shall be registered.

There appears to be an increasing trend among commercial cattlemen to breed heifers to calve as two-year-olds. In a survey[1] made by Washington State University, which included more than a half million cattle in a 24-state area, 48.6 per cent of the cattlemen reported that they breed 80 per cent or more of their replacement heifers to calve as two-year-olds; another 27.3 per cent of the cattlemen breed up to 20 per cent of their replacement heifers. The more successful early-breeding advocates feed such heifers rather liberally, either (1) by grazing them on the choicest range, and/or (2) by feeding added concentrates during the winter months. Also, some cattlemen who calve out two-year-old heifers, use an Angus bull, claiming that there is less trouble at calving time because of the smaller body size and smaller heads of such calves. Certainly, if the dam and the calf are not adversely affected, breeding at an early age is advantageous from the standpoint of cutting production costs.

Under average conditions, it appears that the following disadvantages may accompany the practice of having heifers calve for the first time as two-year-olds:

1. It usually retards the growth of the heifers, for nature has ordained that the growth of the fetus and the lactation which follows shall take priority over the body requirements of the mother.

2. The percentage calf crop is smaller than that obtained with older cows handled in a comparable manner.

3. The calves have a lighter birth weight.

4. There is usually a higher death loss at calving time, unless the animals are under the close supervision of a good caretaker.

5. The conception rate of young heifers at puberty is lower than that in older ones. This results in spreading the calving season over a longer period, with accompanying greater inconvenience and expense.

The Oklahoma Agricultural Experiment Station conducted extensive crossbreeding studies in which Hereford heifers were divided into six groups and bred to (1) large-, (2) medium-, and

---

[1]Ensminger, M. E., M. W. Galgan, and W. L. Slocum; Wash. Agri. Expt. Sta. Bul. 562, p. 59.

(3) small-type bulls of each the Angus and Hereford breeds. They found[1] that the parturition difficulties of heifers calving as two-year-olds were affected by (1) size of heifer—the heavier heifers at breeding time dropped heavier calves, but they experienced less difficulty at calving; (2) sex of calf dropped—the heifers dropping bull calves experienced considerably more difficulty than those dropping heifer calves (the bull calves were 4 to 5 pounds heavier than the heifers); and (3) size of bull to which bred—within each breed, the heifers bred to large-type bulls dropped heavier calves and experienced more calving difficulty than those bred to medium-type bulls, and, in turn, those bred to medium-type bulls dropped heavier calves and had more calving difficulty than those bred to small-type bulls. However, breed was not a factor in this experiment.

From the above, it may be concluded that only exceptionally well-grown and liberally fed heifers should be bred to calve as two-year-olds. Even then, these heifers should have close supervision at calving time, and it is advisable that the calves be weaned at an early age in order to alleviate the strain of the lactation period.

For the below average breeder, it is best not to have the heifers calve until they are about thirty months of age. This practice can be followed if calves are being dropped in both spring and fall. When the management practice calls for either spring or fall calving and no departure therefrom, it is necessary to have the heifers calve when either two or three years of age rather than somewhere between these limits.

Heat Periods

The period of duration of heat—that is the time during which the cow will take the bull—is very short, usually not over sixteen to twenty hours, although it may vary from about six to thirty hours. Cows tend to have a characteristic pattern of estrus behavior; for example, they come in heat during the morning hours, go out of heat in the evening or early part of night, and then ovulate approximately fourteen hours after the end of heat.

Females of all species bred near the end of the heat period are much more likely to conceive than if bred at any other time.

---

[1]Moore, Delbert Glenn, Thesis entitled, "Some Factors Affecting Difficulty at Parturition of Two-Year-Old Hereford Heifers," Oklahoma State University, May, 1956.

The heat period recurs approximately at twenty-one day intervals, but it may vary from nineteen to twenty-three days. In most cases, cows do not show signs of estrus until some six to eight weeks after parturition, or in some instances even longer. Occasionally, an abnormal condition develops in cows that makes them remain in heat constantly. Such animals are known as nymphomaniacs.

SIGNS OF ESTRUS:

Experienced cattlemen can usually detect in-heat cows because they generally exhibit one or more of the following characteristic symptoms: (1) nervousness; (2) attempts to mount other members of the herd, which in turn often mount her; (3) a noticeable swelling of the labiae of the vulva; (4) an inflamed appearance about the lips of the vulva; (5) frequent urination; and (6) a mucous discharge. Dry cows and heifers usually show a noticeable swelling or enlargement of the udder during estrus, whereas in lactating cows a rather sharp decrease in milk production is often noted. A day or two following estrus, a bloody discharge is sometimes noted.

Gestation Period

The average gestation period of cows is 283 days, or roughly about 9½ months. Though there may be considerable breed and individual variation in the length of the gestation period, it is estimated that two thirds of all cows will calve between 278 and 288 days after breeding.

FERTILITY IN BEEF CATTLE

Fertility refers to the ability of the male or female to produce viable germ cells capable of uniting with the germ cells of the opposite sex and of producing vigorous, living offspring. Fertility is lacking in very young animals, manifests itself first at puberty, increases for a time, then levels out, and finally recedes with the onset of senility. In cattle, as with other classes of farm animals, fertility is determined by heredity and environment.

Of course, the final test for fertility is whether young are produced, but unfortunately this test is both slow and expensive. Through evaluation of the quality of semen, it is possible to make a fairly satisfactory appraisal of the male's fertility; but no comparable measure of the female's relative fertility has yet been devised, although a pregnancy test may be made.

METHODS OF MATING

Two methods of mating beef cattle are followed, (1) hand mating and (2) pasture mating. It has been found that 98 per cent of the commercial cattlemen and 68 per cent of the purebred breeders used pasture mating; the rest used hand mating.[1]

Hand Mating

In hand mating, the bull is kept separate from the cows at all times, except when an individual cow is to be bred and is turned in with him for this purpose. As a rule, in hand mating, only a single service is allowed, the cow being removed immediately after service. In the breeding of purebred cattle, when breeding records are so important, this method is usually followed. Hand mating allows for a more accurate check on whether the bull is settling the cows. It also permits a larger number of cows to be served by a bull, an especially important consideration with a proved sire.

Pasture Mating

In this system the bull is turned in with the herd, either throughout the entire year or during the breeding season. Even with pasture breeding, when it is desired to have the calves all come within a few weeks of each other thereby assuring more uniformity in size and offspring, the herd bull should be separated from the cows except during the breeding season. Uniformity in size is very important from the standpoint of marketing the calves advantageously. Furthermore, by having the calves come as nearly as possible at one time, closer observation may be given the herd at the time of parturition.

Pasture breeding is most often followed with a commercial herd. As a rule, this system requires less labor, and there is less danger of missing cows when they are in heat. However, the convenience of pasture mating should not result in neglect to check whether the cows are being settled during the breeding season.

---

[1]Ensminger, M. E., M. W. Galgan, and W. L. Slocum; Wash. Agri. Expt. Sta. Bul. 562.

SIGNS AND TESTS OF PREGNANCY

Pregnancy tests can cut the wintering bill and make for increased profits. It is expensive business to over-winter a cow that will not produce a calf; necessitating feed, interest, labor, and other costs.

Barren cows can usually be marketed satisfactorily following testing; most feeders and packers will actually pay a premium for cows known to be open. Where valuable purebred animals are involved, bred cows can be sold with a more certain guarantee of being safely in calf, and barren cows may be accorded special care or hormone treatment.

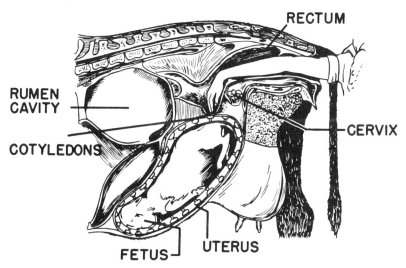

Fig. 84. Rectal method for determining pregnancy in the cow.

Absence of heat is not always a sign of pregnancy, but a positive diagnosis can be made. By about the second month in heifers and the third month in cows, the uterus becomes enlarged, especially in the pregnant horn, and drops into the abdominal cavity. An experienced technician can ascertain this sign of pregnancy by *feeling with the hand through the rectum wall.* Application of this method depends upon the recognition of changes in tone, size, and location of the uterine horns and changes in the uterine arteries. This is the most common test of pregnancy. It is popular because it affords early diagnosis, and there is little hazard when performed by experienced operators. It is recommended that cows be pregnancy tested, by this method, about two months after the bulls have been removed or at weaning time. On the average, a veterinarian will charge about $1.00 per head, depending on the size of the herd. With convenient facilities—corrals and squeeze—an experienced operator can pregnancy test 150 to 200 cows per day.

An internal examination for pregnancy may also be made via the vagina, but with this method there is danger of forcing an abortion, even when the test is performed by an experienced operator.

Other less-used tests for pregnancy in cows are:

1. **Abdominal ballottement** may be used from the fifth to the seventh months of pregnancy. This consists in feeling the fetus by the following techniques: (1) place the hand or fist against the abdomen in the lower right flank region, and (2) execute a short, vigorous, inward-upward thrust in this region and retain the hand in place. The hard fetus may be felt. Because of the amniotic fluid, the technique described above will make the fetus recede, but it will fall back in place almost immediately.

2. **The fetal heart beat** can sometimes be detected after the sixth month of pregnancy, though this method is not as certain in the cow as in other classes of farm animals. Use of a stethoscope is preferred, though good results are sometimes secured by merely placing the ear against the right lower abdominal region and listening. The fetal heart beat can be distinguished from that of the mother because of its greater frequency and lighter and higher pitch.

3. **Fetal movements** can sometimes be observed through the abdominal wall during the latter half of pregnancy. This method of detecting pregnancy requires much patience. The observer simply must wait until voluntary movement of the fetus on the right side of the cow is observed. The practice of trying to induce movement of the fetus by allowing a very thirsty cow to take on a fill of cold water is cruel and is to be condemned.

CARE OF THE PREGNANT COW

The nutritive requirements of the pregnant cow are less rigorous than those during lactation. In general, pregnant cows should be provided as nearly year-round pasture as possible.

During times of inclement weather or when deep snows or droughts make supplemental feeding necessary, dry roughages and silage are the common feeds. If produced on fertile soils, such forage will usually provide all the needed nutrients for reproduction. Further discussion of the nutritive needs of pregnant cows is contained in Chapter IX.

No shelter is necessary except during periods of inclement weather. Normally, the cows will prefer to run outdoors. This desire is to be encouraged—in order to provide exercise, fresh air, and sunshine. Where and when shelter is necessary, it should be neither elaborate nor expensive. An open shed facing away from the direction of prevailing winds is quite as satisfactory for the protection of dry cows as a warm bank barn with individual box stalls—and it is far less expensive. The chief requirements are that the shelter be tight overhead, that it be sufficiently deep to afford protection from inclement weather and remain dry (depths of thirty-four to thirty-six feet are preferred), that it is well drained, and that it is of sufficient size to allow the animals to move about and lie down in comfort.

CARE OF THE COW AT CALVING TIME

The careful and observant caretaker will be ever alert and make definite preparations for calving in ample time. It is especially important that first-calf heifers be watched at calving time, for frequently they will need some assistance. Older cows that habitually have trouble in parturition may well be culled from the herd.

Signs of Approaching Parturition

Perhaps the first sign of approaching parturition is a distended udder, which may be observed some weeks before calving time. Near the end of the gestation period, the content of the udder changes from a watery secretion to a thick, milky colostrum. As parturition approaches, there generally will be a marked shrinkage or falling away of the muscular parts in the region of the tail head and pin bones, together with a noticeable enlargement and swelling of the vulva.

The immediate indications that the cow is about to calve are extreme nervousness and uneasiness, separation from the rest of the herd, and muscular exertion and distress.

Fig. 85. A good start in life. When the weather is warm, the most natural and ideal place for calving is a clean, open pasture, away from other livestock. Under pasture conditions, there is less danger of either infection or mechanical injury to the cow and calf.

Preparation for Calving

At the time the signs of approaching parturition seem to indicate that the calf may be expected within a short time, arrangements for the place of calving should be completed.

During the seasons of the year when the weather is warm, the most natural and ideal place for calving is a clean open pasture away from other livestock. Hogs should not be allowed in the same place with the cow, for they are likely to injure or kill the young calf. They have even been known to injure the cow.

Under pasture conditions, there is decidedly less danger of either infection or mechanical injury to the cow and calf. In commercial range operations, it is common practice to ride the range more frequently at calving time. A better procedure consists of having a smaller pasture adjoining headquarters into which heavy springing cows are placed a few days before calving. With the added convenience of such an arrangement, the animals can be given more careful attention.

During inclement weather, the cow should be placed in a roomy (10 or 12 feet square) well-lighted, well-ventilated, comfortable box stall or maternity pen which should first be carefully cleaned, disinfected, and bedded for the occasion.

Normal Presentation[1]

Labor pains in a mild form usually start some hours be-

---

[1]Figures 86, 87, and 88 reviewed by Dr. Frank Bracken, D.V.M., Washington State University.

fore actual parturition. After a time, the water bag appears on the outside, usually increasing in size until it ruptures from the weight of its own contents. This is closely followed by the appearance of the amniotic bladder (the second water bag), with the fetus. With the rupture of the second water bag, the straining becomes more violent, and presentation soon follows. Most commonly in presentation, the front feet come first followed by the nose which is resting on them, then the shoulders, the middle, the hips, and then the hind legs and feet.

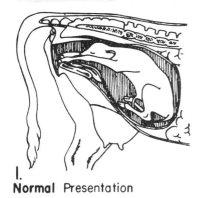 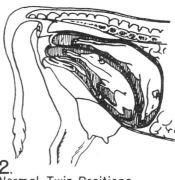

I.
Normal Presentation

2.
Normal Twin Positions

Fig. 86. 1. Normal single presentation; the back of the fetus is directly toward that of the mother, the forelegs are extended toward the vulva, and the head rests between the forelegs. If it is necessary to render assistance, apply ropes above the ankle joints and pull alternately downward on each leg as the cow strains.

2. Normal twin positions. If delivery does not proceed normally, this is a case for a veterinarian.

With posterior presentation (hind feet first), there is likely to be difficulty in calving. Moreover, there is considerably more danger of having the calf suffocate through rupture of the umbilical cord and strangulation.

Rendering Assistance

A good rule for the attendant is to be near but not in sight. If presentation is normal and within an hour or two after the onset of signs of calving, no assistance will be necessary. On the other hand, if the cow has labored for some time with little progress or is laboring rather infrequently, it is usually time to give assistance. Such aid will usually consist of fastening small ropes around the pasterns and pulling the young outward and downward as the cow strains. This should be done by an experienced caretaker or a competent veterinarian. It is always well

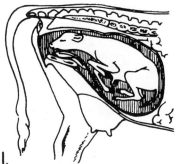

1.
Anterior Presentation; Both
Forelegs Bent at Knees

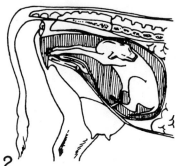

2.
Anterior Presentation; Head
Upward and Backward

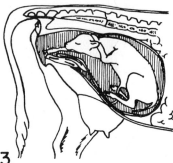

3.
Anterior Presentation; Foreleg
Crossed Over Neck

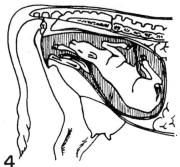

4.
Anterior Presentation; Head
First and Back Down

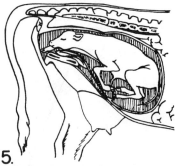

5.
Anterior Presentation; One Fore-
Leg Bent at Knee

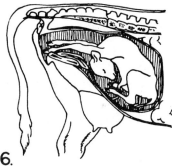

6.
Anterior Presentation; Head
Turned Back

Fig. 87. Some abnormal presentations with suggestions for correction:
1. Extend the legs so that delivery can be accomplished.
2. Push back the fetus, which will often bring the head into its normal position.
3. Grasp the crossed leg a little above the ankle, raise it, draw it to the proper side, and extend it in the genital canal.
4. Rotate the fetus, extend the forelegs and deliver by traction.
5. Lift the head and draw up and rope the leg so that it does not slip back again.
6. Rope the forelegs and then push them forward; place the head in normal position.

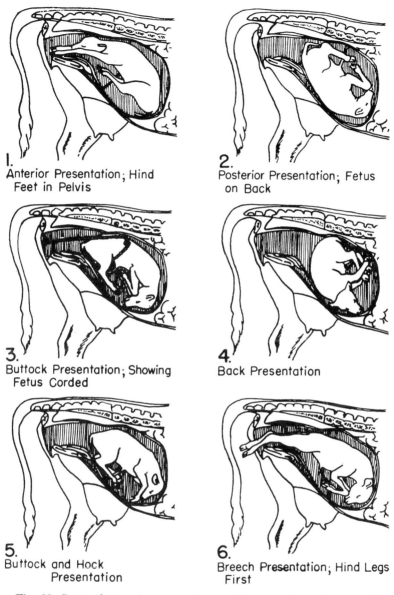

1.
Anterior Presentation; Hind
Feet in Pelvis

2.
Posterior Presentation; Fetus
on Back

3.
Buttock Presentation; Showing
Fetus Corded

4.
Back Presentation

5.
Buttock and Hock
Presentation

6.
Breech Presentation; Hind Legs
First

Fig. 88. Some abnormal presentations with suggestions for correction:
1. Force back the hind feet. This is a very serious malpresentation, in which it is generally impossible to save the fetus if delivery is far advanced.
2. Rotate the fetus, extend the rear legs, and deliver by traction.
3. Push the fetus forward and bring the legs properly into the genital passage.
4. Turn the fetus so that either the head and forelegs or the rear legs can be started through the pelvis.
5. Push the fetus forward and bring the legs properly into the genital passage.
6. Usually delivery is normal but traction may facilitate; beware of prolonged labor because calf may suffocate due to rupture of the navel cord.

to be reminded that rough, careless, or unsanitary methods at such a time may do more harm than good.

The Newborn Calf

If parturition has been normal, the cow can usually take care of the newborn calf, and it is best not to interfere. However, in unusual cases, it may be necessary to wipe the mucus from the nostrils to permit breathing; or more rarely yet, artificial respiration methods must be applied to some calves. This may be done by blowing into the mouth, working the ribs, rubbing the body rather vigorously, and permitting the calf to fall gently. The cow should be permitted to lick the calf dry.

With calves born in sanitary quarters or out on clean pastures, there is little likelihood of navel infection. To lessen the danger of such infection, the navel cord of the newborn calf should be treated at once with a 10-per-cent solution of tincture of iodine.

A vigorous calf will attempt to rise in about fifteen minutes and usually will be nursing in half an hour to an hour. The weaker the calf, the longer the time before it will be able to be up and nursing. Sometimes it may even become necessary to assist the calf by holding it up to the cow's udder.

The colostrum (the milk yielded by the mother for a short period following the birth of the young) is most important for the well being of the new-born calf. Experiments have shown that it is almost impossible to raise a calf that has not received any colostrum. Aside from the difference in chemical composition, compared with later milk, the colostrum seems to have the following functions:

1. It contains antibodies which temporarily protect the calf against certain infections, especially those of the digestive tract.

2. It serves as a natural purgative, removing fecal matter which has accumulated in the digestive tract.

3. It contains a very high content of vitamin A, from ten to a hundred times that of ordinary milk. This provides the young calf, which is born with little body storage of this vitamin, with as much vitamin A on the first day as it would secure in some weeks from normal milk.

Usually it is best to keep the cow and calf in a small pasture for a few days. After this, they may be turned back with the main herd. Nothing is better for the cow at calving time than plenty of grass, and both the cow and calf will be helped by an abundance of fresh air and sunshine. The cow may deliberately hide the calf for the first few days, and the job may be so thoroughly done as to require considerable cleverness on the part of the caretaker to find it.

The Afterbirth

Under normal conditions, the fetal membranes (placenta or afterbirth) are expelled from three to six hours after parturition. Should they remain as long as twenty-four hours after calving, competent assistance should be given by an experienced caretaker or a licensed veterinarian. The operation of removing a retained afterbirth requires skill and experience; and, if improperly done, the cow may be made a nonbreeder. Furthermore, before doing this, the fingernails should be trimmed closely; the hands and arms should be thoroughly washed with soap and warm water, disinfected, and then lubricated with vaseline or linseed oil. In no case should a weight be tied to the placenta in an attempt to force removal.

As soon as the afterbirth is ejected, it should be removed and burned or buried in lime, thus preventing the development of bacteria and foul odors. This step is less necessary on the open range, where animals traverse over a wide area.

CARE AND MANAGEMENT OF THE BULL

Outdoor exercise throughout the year is one of the first essentials in keeping the bull virile and in a thrifty, natural condition. The finest and easiest method of providing such exercise is to arrange for a well-fenced, grassy paddock (about two acres is a good size for one bull). Many valuable sires have been ruined through close confinement in a small stall—or more likely yet—through being kept knee deep in mud within a small filthy enclosure. In addition to the valuable exercise obtained in the grassy paddock, the animal gets succulent pasture, an ideal feed for the herd bull.

A satisfactory and inexpensive shelter should be provided for the bull. The most convenient arrangement is to have this within or adjacent to the paddock, so that the bull may run in and out at will. Sufficient storage space for feed and conveniences for caring for the bull should be provided in this building. Nor-

Fig. 89. This arrangement has proved most satisfactory at Washington State University. Note the size of the pasture paddock, the individual portable shelter, and the water tank, shade, and bull proof board fence. (Drawing by R. F. Johnson)

mally, purebred bulls are kept in separate stalls and enclosures, though some successful purebred breeders regularly run several valuable bulls in one enclosure. Bulls used in commercial herds are usually run together, both on the range and when separated out from the cows. Because of their scuffling and fighting, there is more injury hazard when bulls are handled in a group.

Under range conditions, it is rather difficult to give the bulls much attention during the breeding season. Usually the proper number of bulls is simply turned with the cow herd. During the balance of the year, however, the bulls are usually kept separate. Thus, if the producer desires calves that are dropped from February 1 to June 1, the bulls are turned with the cows about May 1 and are removed September 1.

The feeding of the herd bull is fully covered in Chapter IX. In brief, it may be said that the feeding program should be such as to keep the bull in a thrifty, vigorous condition at all times.

AGE AND SERVICE OF THE BULL

The number and quality of calves that a bull sires in a given season is more important than the total number of services. The number of services allowed will vary with the age, development, temperament, health, breeding condition, distribution of services, and system of mating (pasture or hand mating). With pasture mating, size of area, carrying capacity of the range, and the size of the herd are important factors. Therefore, no definite best number of services can be recommended for any and all conditions, and yet the practices followed by good cattlemen do not differ greatly. For best results, a bull should be at least fifteen months old and well grown for his age before being put into service. Even then, it is best to follow a system of hand mating until the bull is two years of age.

TABLE 13

HANDY BULL MATING GUIDE

Age	No. of Cows/yr.		Comments
	Hand-mating	Pasture-mating	
Yearling...............	10-12	8-10	Most western ranchers use 1 bull to about 25 cows.
Two-yr.-old.........	25-30	20-25	A bull should remain a vigorous and reliable breeder up to 10 yrs. or
Three-yr.-old or over.............	40-50	25-40	older; up to 6 to 7 yrs. under range conditions.

Table 13 gives pertinent information relative to the use of the bull, including consideration that should be given to age and method of mating.

In a survey conducted by Washington State University, it was found that one bull was used for every 21.5 cows and heifers bred.[1]

Should the bull prove to be an uncertain breeder, he should be given rest from service, forced to take plenty of exercise, and then placed in proper condition—neither fat nor thin. Sometimes a bull that is being "let-down" in condition following showing will be temporarily sterile during the reducing process. Even though this lack of fertility may last for a year, usually such animals "bounce back."

---

[1]Ensminger, M. E., M. W. Galgan, and W. L. Slocum; Wash. Agr. Expt. Sta. Bul. 562.

Fig 90. Breeding cows on pasture at Flat Top Ranch, Walnut Springs, Texas. Pregnant cows should be provided as much year-around pasture as possible. Also, shade is necessary in the southern states. (Courtesy, National Cottonseed Products Association, Inc.)

NORMAL BREEDING SEASON AND TIME OF CALVING

The season at which the cows are bred depends primarily on the facilities at hand, taking into consideration the feed supply, pasture, equipment, labor, and weather conditions; whether the cattle are being produced for ordinary commercial or for purebred purposes; and whether they are strictly beef or dual-purpose cattle.

The purebred breeder who exhibits cattle should plan the breeding program so that maximum advantage will be taken of various age groups. In most livestock shows throughout the country, the present classifications are based upon the dates of January 1, May 1, and September 1. For further information relative to show classifications, the reader may refer to Chapter XVI.

When it is intended to market milk from dual-purpose herds, the cows should be producing their largest flow of milk at a time when the product is likely to bring the highest price. Usually this means fall calves, in order that milk may be sold throughout the fall and winter months.

In the commercial herd of beef cattle, two systems of breeding are commonly practiced in regard to the season of the year. In one system, the bulls are allowed to run with the cows throughout the year so that calving is on a year-round basis. This

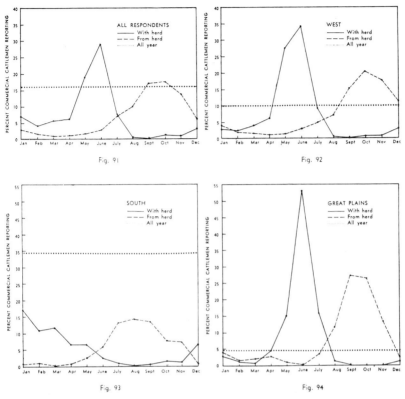

Fig. 91.

Fig. 92.

Fig. 93

Fig. 94

Fig. 91. The breeding season followed over most of the U. S. The solid line shows the period during which the bulls are put with the herd, whereas the broken line shows the dates for their removal. These curves show that most cattlemen breed within a restricted season of 3 to 4 months. The dotted line shows that about 16 per cent of the cattlemen leave the bulls with the herd the year-around. (Photo courtesy Washington State University)

Fig. 93. The breeding season followed in the southern states. As noted, a third of the cattlemen leave the bulls with the cows the year-around (see dotted line); the balance extend the breeding season over several months, reaching a peak in January. (Photo courtesy Washington State University)

Fig. 92. The breeding season followed in the 11 western states. Only about 10 per cent of the cattlemen of this area breed on the year-around basis (see dotted line); most of the rest breed from May to October. (Photo courtesy Washington State University)

Fig. 94. The breeding season followed in the Great Plains. As shown, less than 5 per cent of the bulls are left with the cows the year-around and the vast majority of the cattlemen breed during a relatively short season extending from June to October. (Photo courtesy Washington State University)

system results in greater use of the bull, and there is less delay in the first breeding of the heifers as soon as they are sufficiently mature. On the other hand, often the calves arrive at undesired and poorly adapted times; the breeding system is without order and regularity; and the calves usually lack uniformity. This system is frequently followed in the central and southern states.

The other system of breeding followed with the commercial herd, and the most widely used system on the western range, is that of having all of the breeding done within a restricted season (of about three months) so that the calves arrive within a short spread of time—usually in the spring. Sometimes in the central and southern states this system is used. Having the calves born about the same time, whether it be fall or spring, results in greater uniformity. Thus it is easier to care for (brand, dehorn, castrate, vaccinate, etc.) and market such animals. Each farm has its individual problems, and the decision must be made accordingly.

Figures 91, 92, 93, and 94, are based on a survey made by the Washington State University.[1] These figures show that there is a marked area difference in the breeding season followed by commercial cattlemen, due to weather conditions. Thus, in the South about a third of the cattlemen leave the bulls with the cow herd the year-around; where this is not done, the breeding season is much more prolonged and the peak of the breeding season is in January. In each of the other areas, however, the breeding season is later and more restricted; most cattlemen do all of the breeding within a season of 3 to 4 months.

Advantages of Spring Calves

The production of spring calves has the following advantages:

1. In producing spring calves, the cows are bred during the most natural breeding season—at a time when they are on pasture, gaining in flesh, and more likely to conceive. The calving percentage is usually higher, therefore, with a system of spring calving.

2. The calves will be in shape to sell directly from the cows in the fall, at which time there is a good demand for feeder calves.

---

[1]Ensminger, M. E., M. W. Galgan, and W. L. Slocum; Wash. Agri. Expt. Sta. Bul. 562.

3. If the calves are to be sold as yearlings, one wintering is saved; or if they are to be sold at weaning time, no wintering is required.

4. Because of greater utilization of cheap roughage, dry cows may be wintered more cheaply.

5. Less labor and attention is required in caring for the calves the first winter.

6. Spring calves require less grain and utilize the maximum amount of pasture and roughage.

Advantages of Fall Calves

The production of fall calves has the following advantages:

1. The cows are in better condition at calving time.

2. The cows give more milk for a longer period.

3. The calves make better use of the grass during their first summer.

4. The calves escape flies, screw worms, and heat while they are small (this is especially important in the South).

5. Upon being weaned the following spring, the calves can be placed directly on pasture instead of in a dry lot; or, if it is desired to sell, they usually find a ready market ahead of the influx of fall feeder calves from the range area.

6. When it is intended to sell market milk from dual-purpose cows, fall calves are usually best. The greater flow of milk is obtained during the period of highest prices.

ARTIFICIAL INSEMINATION

Artificial insemination is, by definition, the deposition of spermatozoa in the female genitalia by artificial rather than by natural means.

Legend has it that artificial insemination had its origin in 1322, at which time an Arab chieftain used artificial methods to impregnate a prized mare with semen stealthily collected by night from the sheath of a stallion belonging to an enemy tribe. There is no substantial evidence, however, to indicate that the Arabs practiced artificial insemination to any appreciable degree.

The first scientific research in artificial insemination of domestic animals was conducted with dogs by the Italian physiologist, Lazarro Spallanzani, in 1780. A century later, American veterinarians employed artificial means to get mares in foal that persistently had failed to settle to natural service. They noticed that because of obstructions the semen was often found in the vagina and not in the uterus following natural service. By collecting the semen into a syringe from the floor of the vagina and injecting it into the uterus, they were able to impregnate mares with these anatomical difficulties.

The Russian physiologist, Ivanoff, began a study of artificial insemination of farm animals, particularly horses, in 1899; and in 1922, he was called upon by the Russian government to apply his findings in an effort to reestablish the livestock industry following its depletion during World War I. Crude as his methods were, his work with horses must be considered the foundation upon which the success of the more recent work is based.

The shifting of the large-scale use of artificial insemination to cattle and sheep, two decades after it was first introduced for horses, was not caused by the fading importance of the horse and the increased demand for cattle and sheep. Rather, it was found that progress was quicker and more easily achieved with these animals, because the exact time of ovulation in relation to signs of heat is more easily detected in the cow and ewe than in the mare. It was also discovered that the sperm of bulls and rams survive better in storage than stallion sperm.

Following World War II, the British scientists were called upon to make wide use of artificial insemination in reestablishing the livestock industry of England. They looked upon it as: (1) a way in which to increase more rapidly the efficiency and utility value of their animals through making wider use of outstanding sires, (2) a means of controlling certain diseases, and (3) the best way in which to increase breeding efficiency.

Today, artificial insemination is more extensively practiced with dairy cattle than with any other class of farm animals. It is the fastest growing program in the American dairy cattle industry. In 1938, only about 7,000 cows were bred by this means in organized groups in the United States; whereas in 1957 about 6 million cows were artificially bred. Also, it is noteworthy that the average number of cows bred per bull increased from 228 in 1939—when the first artificial breeding association was organized in this country—to 2,284 in 1957; and that certain outstanding sires are now being used to breed 10,000 to 15,000 cows annually, and this is not the upper limit.

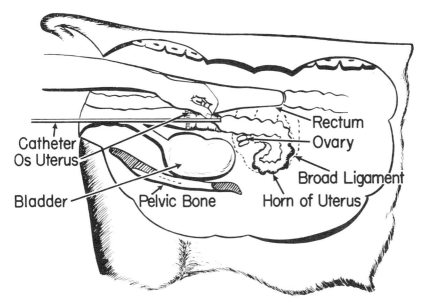

Fig. 95. Deep uterine insemination of the cow. The cervix is grasped per rectum, and the inseminating tube is carefully worked into and through the cervical canal. (Courtesy, Dr. H. A. Herman, Executive Secretary, National Association of Artificial Breeders)

It is recognized that—due primarily to their more frequent handling (in milking) and greater accessibility—artificial insemination is vastly easier to apply to dairy cattle than to beef cattle; and, therefore, more common in dairy cattle enterprises.

The current attitudes and rulings of the beef and dual-purpose cattle registry associations relative to artificial insemination are summarized in Table VIII in the Appendix of this book.

Frozen Semen[1]

The freezing of semen, particularly slow freezing such as might occur from exposure to ordinary sub-freezing weather conditions or from placing a vial of semen in the freezing compartment of a refrigerator, will kill all spermatozoa immediately. However, spermatozoa can be preserved for several years provided glycerine is first added and it is frozen at a certain rate by use of dry ice) to —79° C. or —110° F. Although the frozen

[1]In the preparation of this section, the author had the authoritative help of his colleague, Dr. E. S. E. Hafez, Department of Animal Science, Washington State University.

semen technique is now being used extensively in a practical way (in 1957, frozen semen was used on about 600,000 cattle matings in the U.S.), more research on the subject is needed; we still need to know more about the exact nature of freezing and thawing damages, the mechanism of action of glycerol, the optimum diluting media, freezing temperatures and techniques, storage conditions, and the probable length of survival of frozen semen. Because changes in recommendations are constantly being made in light of new findings, no attempt is made herein to detail frozen semen techniques. Instead, those wishing to use this method are admonished to contact their state agricultural college for the latest and most approved recommendations.

Frozen semen can be packed in shipping cartons, refrigerated with dry ice or liquid nitrogen, and shipped to all parts of the world. The thawing of the semen is accomplished by placing the vial in a container of water at 40° F. immediately prior to insemination.

Currently, several of the beef cattle registry associations have rules to the effect that the semen dies with the bull. Someday, these rules will likely be rescinded. In the meantime, the technique may prove valuable in commercial herds, and it is being used extensively in dairy herds.

Frozen semen is potentially the most valuable breeding technique yet known. Through it, the following may be achieved:

1. The usefulness of outstanding bulls can be extended far beyond their lifetime; also, it insures the proven sire should he die.

2. Outstanding bulls can be more widely used, provided breed registry association rules do not restrict such use to the farm of origin.

3. An adequate progeny test can be made at a much earlier age.

4. A stock of semen can be built up while waiting for a progeny record assessment.

5. Long-term storage of semen lessens semen wastage, and facilitates long-distance transport.

Advantages of Artificial Insemination

Some of the advantages of artificial insemination are:

1. **It increases the use of outstanding sires.**—Through arti-

ficial insemination, many breeders can avail themselves of the use of an outstanding sire, whereas the services of such an animal were formerly limited to one owner, or, at the most to a partnership.

2. **It alleviates the danger and bother of keeping a sire.**— Some hazard and bother is usually involved in keeping a sire, especially a bull or a stallion. Cooperative dairy cattle breeding programs are fast eliminating the necessity of owning a bull.

3. **It makes it possible to overcome certain physical handicaps to mating.**—Artificial insemination is of value (1) in mating animals of greatly different sizes; for example, in using heavy mature bulls on yearling heifers, and (2) in using stifled or otherwise crippled sires that are unable to perform natural service. It may also increase the use of monogamous species, such as the fox. Artificial insemination also promises to be a useful tool in hybridization experiments.

4. **It lessens sire costs.**—In smaller herds (for example, in dairy herds with less than 20 cows), artificial insemination is usually less expensive than the ownership of a worth-while sire together with the accompanying building, feed and labor costs.

5. **It reduces the likelihood of costly delays through using sterile sires.**—Because the breeding efficiency of sires used artificially is constantly checked, it reduces the likelihood of breeding females to a sterile sire for an extended period of time.

6. **It makes it feasible to prove more sires.**—Because of the small size of the herds in which they are used, many sires are never proved. Still others are destroyed before their true breeding worth is known. Through artificial insemination, it is possible to determine the genetic worth of a sire at an earlier age and with more certainty than in natural service.

7. **It creates large families of animals.**—The use of artificial insemination makes possible the development of large numbers of animals within a superior family, thus providing uniformity and giving a better basis for a constructive breeding program.

8. **It increases pride of ownership.**—The ownership of progeny of outstanding sires inevitably makes for pride of ownership, with accompanying improved feeding and management.

9. **It may lessen and control certain diseases.**—Artificial insemination may prove to be equally valuable as a means of preventing and controlling the spread of certain types of cattle

diseases, especially those associated with the organs of reproduction, such as vibriosis, trichomoniasis, and vaginitis. However, when improperly practiced, it may be an added means of spreading disease. Therefore, it is most essential (1) that all males be carefully examined for symptoms of transmissible diseases, (2) that bacterial contamination be avoided during the collection and storage of semen, and (3) that clean, sterile equipment be used in the insemination.

10. **It increases profits.**—The offspring of outstanding sires used artificially are usually higher and more efficient producers, and thus more profitable.

Limitations of Artificial Insemination

Like many other wonderful techniques, artificial insemination is not without its limitations. A full understanding of such limitations, however, will merely accentuate and extend its usefulness. Some of the limitations of artificial insemination are:

1. **It must conform to physiological principles.**—One would naturally expect that the practice of artificial insemination must conform to certain physiological principles. Unfortunately, much false information concerning the usefulness of artificial insemination has been encountered—for example, the belief that females will conceive if artificially inseminated at any time during the estrus cycle. Others have even accepted exaggerated claims that the quality of semen may be improved through such handling, only to be disappointed.

2. **It requires skilled technicians.**—In order to be successful, artificial insemination must be carried out by skilled technicians who have had considerable training and experience.

3. **It necessitates considerable capital to initiate and operate a cooperative breeding program.**—Considerable money is necessary to initiate a cooperative artificial insemination program, and still more is needed to expand and develop it properly. It is noteworthy, however, that 23 per cent of all cows bred artificially in 1956 were serviced with semen provided by privately-owned establishments; thus private enterprise is playing an increasingly important role in this rapidly growing industry.

4. **It is not always possible to obtain the services of a given sire.**—In cooperative insemination programs, a member cannot always obtain the service of the sire of his choice. Also, sires are generally collected from according to a definite schedule; for

example, bulls are usually collected from once every 6 to 7 days.

5. **It may accentuate the damage of a poor sire.**—It must be realized that when a male sires the wrong type of offspring his damage is merely accentuated because of the increased number of progeny possible.

6. **It may restrict the sire market.**—The fact that the market demand for poor or average sires will decrease if artificial insemination is widely adopted should probably be considered an attribute rather than a limitation. Also, it is noteworthy that over 40 per cent of the nation's cattle are still bred to scrub and nondescript bulls.

7. **It may increase the spread of disease.**—As previously indicated, the careful and intelligent use of artificial insemination will lessen the spread of disease. On the other hand, carelessness or ignorance may result in the rapid spread of disease.

8. **It may be subject to certain abuses.**—If semen is transported from farm to farm, the character of the operator must be above reproach. Trained workers can detect differences in the spermatozoa of the bull, ram, boar, stallion, or cock; but even the most skilled scientist is unable to differentiate between the semen of a Hereford and a Shorthorn, to say nothing of the difference between two bulls of the same breed.

Of course, with skilled workers performing the techniques required in artificial insemination, there usually is more check on the operations and perhaps less likelihood of dishonesty than when only the owner is involved, such as is usually the situation with natural service.

Some Practical Considerations

Artificial insemination finds useful application in large breeding establishments, especially with dairy cattle; but as yet, it has seldom found practical application with other classes of farm animals. Someday it may. The knowledge of the reproductive processes gained from artificial insemination, however, can contribute materially to the increased efficiency of animal production.

In the wild state, when a female was served several times during her heat period, an annual conception rate of 90 to 100 per cent was common rather than the exception. Aside from frequency of service, the outdoor exercise, vigor, good nutrition, and regular breeding habits and lack of contamination were conducive to conception. On the other hand, when handled under unnatural conditions in confinement, when the female is generally bred as soon as she starts to show signs of heat, it is not surprising that the conception rate rarely ranges higher than 50 to 80 per cent and is frequently much less. Perhaps, among its virtues, artificial insemination does offer some promise of assuring a higher conception rate.

Based on present knowledge, gained through research and practical observation, it may be concluded that stockmen can make artificial insemination more successful through the following:

1. Give the female a reasonable rest following parturition and before rebreeding; in cows this should be about sixty days.

2. Keep record of heat periods.

8. Watch carefully for heat signs, especially at the approximate time.

4. Where an association is involved, notify the insemination technician promptly when an animal comes in heat.

5. Avoid breeding diseased females or females showing cloudy mucus. The latter condition indicates an infection somewhere in the reproductive tract.

6. Have the veterinarian examine females that have been bred three times without conception or that show other reproductive abnormalities.

SUPEROVULATION[1]

The bull is capable of producing from several thousand to millions of sperm daily whereas the cow normally produces one ovum (occasionally two ova) every 17 to 21 days. Now it is possible, through the administration of gonadotropic hormones, to obtain 50 to 60 ova from a cow at one estrus cycle. It is also feasible to obtain a large number of eggs from very young calves, by injection of pituitary hormones.

Several methods of producing superovulation have given satisfactory results; among them the subcutaneous injection of pregnant mare serum (PMS) during the middle of the cycle and, at the same time, expression of the corpus luteum. The cow will

---

[1] In the preparation of this section, the author had the authoritative help of his colleague, Dr. E. S. E. Hafez, Department of Animal Science, Washington State University.

come in heat two to four days later (most frequently on the third day), at which time she can be bred naturally or artificially. Of course, the real economic value of superovulation lies in the successful transfer of excess eggs from more valuable donor

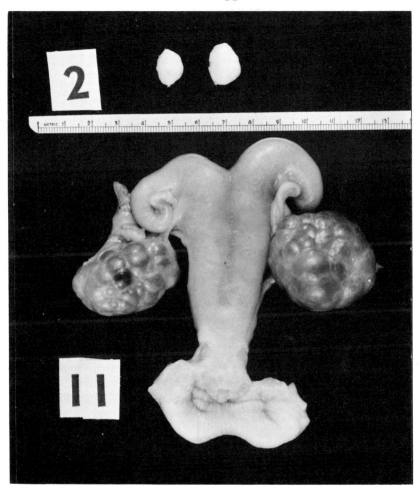

Fig. 96. Superovulation of the calf:
Calf No. 2—Ovaries of a control 4-month-old calf. The ovaries contain thousands of dormant Graafian follicles.
Calf No. 11—Ovaries and genital organs of a superovulated 4-month-old calf. The calf was not showing any signs of heat, since it had not reached sexual maturity. However, it was injected with 10 rat units of the gonadotropic hormone "Vetrophin" on each of three successive days and slaughtered 5 days after the last injection. The two ovaries contained 97 ripe follicles. Note the size of the superovulated ovaries in relation to the immature uterus. (Courtesy Dr. E. S. E. Hafez; photo, Washington State University)

cows to less valuable recipient cows. As a result of this technique, some day stockmen may refer to litter-bearing cows.

OVA TRANSPLANTATION[1]

Artificial insemination has given a means for the wide-spread distribution of desirable genes via the sperm. Similar genetic selection through high quality females has, however, been limited since, normally, one cow will produce one calf per year and the average number of offspring per female will seldom exceed five in a lifetime. Out of the latter arose the idea that a marked increase in the production of offspring from desirable cows might be effected by superovulation, followed by transfer of the fertilized ova to less desirable cows, with the latter serving as host-mothers or foster-mothers to the developing embryo. Ova transplantation has been achieved experimentally in four steps as follows:

1. **Obtain a large number of ova (superovulation).**—(See section entitled "Superovulation.")

2. **Collect ova.**—Either of the following two methods may be employed for collecting eggs:

(1) Slaughter the donor, dissect out the reproductive organs, and flush out the eggs. This is the easiest method, but it has the very obvious and serious disadvantage of destroying the donor cow in the process.

(2) Enter the abdominal cavity of the living female surgically and flush the eggs from the reproductive tract. A satisfactory instrument, consisting of a triple-lumen tube, has been developed for this purpose. One lumen permits entrance of a steel rod to hold the tube rigid during insertion through the cervix.

3. **Keep the ova in a satisfactory medium.**—In order to hold the ova outside the body, for a few minutes or for many hours, a satisfactory medium is essential—such as Kreb's solution, phosphate buffered Ringer-Dale solution, or blood serum.

4. **Transplant the ovum.**—The fertilized ovum should be inserted, through the abdominal wall, in the host cow at the appropriate period after heat.

Fertilized eggs may be transported long distances. For

[1]In the preparation of this section, the author had the authoritative help of Dr. E. S. E. Hafez, Department of Animal Science, Washington State University.

example, fertilized sheep eggs were obtained in England and injected into the uteri of living rabbits. Then the rabbits were shipped by air to South Africa, where they were slaughtered and the ova flushed from the uteri and transplanted into scrub ewes. By employing this technique, lambs of English mutton breeds have been born in Ondersteeport, South Africa.

The advantages to accrue from ova transplantation are:

1. The rate of progress in genetic improvement would be increased.

2. Valuable cows that produce normal ova but fail to conceive due to some hormonal or anatomic defects need not be culled because of sterility; such animals could be used as donors for supplying ova for transplantation.

3. Heifers could be effectively progeny-tested at an early age. If numbers of fertilized eggs could be procured from calves and transplanted to sexually mature recipients, the generation time of cattle could be reduced by one year or more.

4. It would be possible to produce calves of the beef breed of preference from dairy cows.

Although a few cases of ova transplantation in cows have been achieved, several problems must be overcome before the experimental feasibility of this technique can become a practical reality.

QUESTIONS FOR STUDY AND DISCUSSION

1. Twenty per cent of the nation's cows never calve, and there is an appalling calf loss of 21 per cent between birth and weaning. Discuss the causes and economics of this situation.

2. Diagram and label the reproductive organs of the bull.

3. Diagram and label the reproductive organs of the cow.

4. In order to synchronize ovulation and insemination, when should cows be bred with relation to the heat period?

5. Why are increasing numbers of cattlemen breeding two-year-old heifers? What precautions should be taken when following this practice? Would you recommend that crossbreeding be followed in first-calf heifers?

6. How do you account for (1) so much pasture mating among purebred breeders, and (2) so little use of artificial insemination in beef cattle?

7. Discuss the economic aspects of pregnancy testing cows.

8. For your home farm or ranch (or one with which you are familiar), what do you consider to be the most desirable breeding season and time of calving? Justify your answer.

9. What advantages could accrue from the practical and extensive use of (1) superovulation, and (2) ova transplantation in beef cattle?

SELECTED REFERENCES

Title of Publication	Author(s)	Publisher
Animal Breeding	A. L. Hagedoorn	Crosby Lockwood & Son, Ltd., London, England, 1950.
Animal Breeding	L. M. Winters	John Wiley & Sons, Inc., New York N. Y., 1948.
Animal Breeding Plans	J. L. Lush	Collegiate Press, Inc., Ames, Iowa, 1938.
Artificial Insemination in Livestock Breeding	A. H. Frank	U. S. Department of Agriculture, Circular No. 567, Washington, D. C., 1952.
Artificial Insemination of Dairy Cattle	H. A. Herman F. W. Madden	Lucas Brothers, Columbia, Mo., 1953.
Artificial Insemination of Farm Animals	W. W. Green L. M. Winters	Agri. Exp. Sta. Bull. 335, University of Minnesota, St. Paul, Minn., 1946.
Beef Cattle for Breeding Purposes	Farmers' Bull. 1916	U. S. Department of Agriculture, Washington, D. C.
Breeding Better Livestock	V. A. Rice F. N. Andrews E. J. Warwick	McGraw-Hill Book Co., Inc., New York, N. Y., 1953.
Breeding and Improvement of Farm Animals	V. A. Rice F. N. Andrews E. J. Warwick J. E. Legates	McGraw-Hill Book Co., Inc., New York, N. Y., 1957.
Developmental Anatomy	L. B. Arey	W. B. Saunders Co., Philadelphia, Pa.
Embryology of the Pig, The	B. M. Patten	P. Blakiston's Son & Co., Inc. Philadelphia, Pa., 1931.
Farm Animals	John Hammond	Edward Arnold & Co., London, England, 1952.
Inprovement of Livestock	Ralph Bogart	The Macmillan Co., New York, 1959.
Problems and Practices of American Cattlemen	M. E. Ensminger M. W. Galgan W. L. Slocum	Wash. Agri. Expt. Sta. Bull. 562, Washington State University, Pullman, Wash., 1955.
Reproductive Physiology	A. V. Nalbandov	W. H. Freeman & Co., San Francisco, Calif., 1958.

CHAPTER VIII

STERILITY AND DELAYED BREEDING IN BEEF CATTLE[1]

Contents   Page

[1]In the preparation of this chapter, the author had the authoritative help of Dr. E. S. E. Hafez, Associate Professor, Department of Animal Science, Washington State University. Also, this chapter was critically reviewed by the following: Prof. S. A. Asdell, Department of Animal Hus-

(continued bottom p. 250)

Sterility (*infertility or barrenness*) *may be defined as temporary or permanent reproductive failure; resulting from anestrus* (*lack of heat*), *failure to conceive, or abortion.* Animals are not simply fertile or sterile; rather, all degrees of fertility exist in both sexes.

In practical operations the breeding efficiency of most beef cattle is expressed in terms of the annual calf crop[1]—the most fertile herds being those in which the highest percentage of all cows conceive on a schedule which results in the spacing of calves each 12 months. In an extensive beef cattle survey[2] made by Washington State University, it was found that only 79.5 per cent of the cows and heifers bred dropped live calves; the other 20.5 per cent were nonproducers, either temporarily or permanently, or they dropped stillborn calves. Since reproductive ability is fundamental to economical beef production, it can be readily understood that sterility constitutes a major annual loss in the cattle business. In fact, most cattlemen acknowledge that the calf crop percentage is the biggest single factor affecting profit in beef cattle production.

It is recognized that the problem of sterility is difficult to study, especially under range conditions where the majority of beef cattle are found. For this reason, most of the experimental studies on this problem have been conducted with dairy cattle. It is believed, however, that most principles apply to all breeds of *Bos taurus* and *Bos indicus*, regardless of type.

The incidence of sterility varies greatly from herd to herd, and within the same herd from year to year. Despite this fact, cattlemen should establish arbitrary standards by which breeding performance may be gauged. To this end, the following reasonable averages are proposed: not more than 10 per cent breeding difficulty in the cows at any one time;[3] not more than an average of 1.85 service per conception;[3] and not lower

---

bandry, Cornell University, Ithaca, N.Y.; Dr. Durward Olds, D.V.M., Professor of Dairying, University of Kentucky, Lexington, Ky.; Dr. Clayton O'Mary, Department of Animal Science, Washington State University; Dr. S. H. Fowler, Department of Animal Husbandry, Louisiana State University, Baton Rouge, La.; and Dr. Charles E. Moon, practicing Veterinarian, Snohomish, Wash.

[1] Methods of computing calf crop percentages vary. See footnote on p. 93 for discussion of this subject.

[2] Ensminger, M. E., M. W. Galgan, and W. L. Slocum; Wash. Agri. Expt. Sta. Bul. 562, 1955.

[3] These were the average figures obtained in a survey of dairy cattle in New York, as reported in Northeastern States Regional Bulletin 32 (Cornell U. Agri. Expt. Sta. Bul. 924), 1957, p. 5.

than an 85 per cent calf crop. Of course, the better managed and the more fortunate herds will do better. If this standard is accepted, however, there should be reason for concern if performance falls below these averages—it should then be assumed that something is wrong and that investigation is needed.

Fortunately, comparatively few barren cows and sterile bulls are totally and permanently infertile. Those that are should be sold for slaughter without further delay or expense. Most of the others will regain their breeding abilities with good care and management and appropriate treatment. Mating at the proper stage of estrus and the correct training and use of bulls will do much to maintain a high conception rate. Care in the selection of disease-free breeding stock, isolation of newly purchased animals, and periodic health examinations are effective preventive measures. When breeding irregularities are noted or disease

TABLE 14

COMMON CAUSES OF INFERTILITY IN CATTLE AND THE
RELATIVE IMPORTANCE OF EACH[1]

Cause	Percentage of Infertile Cattle Affected by	Percentage of Affected Animals Having Lowered Fertility	Percentage of All Infertility Which it Accounts for
Vibriosis	25	60	15
Purulent metritis	10	100	10[2]
Glandular vaginitis	50	10	5
Leptospirosis	15	20	3
Brucellosis	3	50	1.5
Trichomoniasis	1	100	1.0
Silent heats	20	36	7.2
Nymphomania	5	100	5.0
Anestrus	10	30	3.0
Ovulation failure	3	30	0.9
Genetic defects			10
Nutritional deficiencies			10
Improper care at calving			10[2]
Lack of observation			2
Breeding too soon after calving			2
Total			75.6[2]

[1] Olds, Durward, D.V.M. and Ph. D., The Allied Veterinarian, March-April, 1958. The percentage figures in column one total more than 100 because of the fact that simultaneous infections occur in many cases.

[2] The 10 per cent due to purulent metritis is also listed as improper care at calving.

strikes, however, treatment should be prompt. In general, diagnosis and treatment should be left to a veterinarian who possesses training, experience, and skill in handling reproductive failures; and since infertility constitutes one of the major problems with which the veterinarian must deal, he will wish to be well informed.

Cattlemen should also be well informed relative to reproductive failures, because the enlightened producer will (1) encounter less trouble as a result of the application of preventive measures, (2) more readily recognize serious trouble when it is encountered, and (3) be more competent in carrying out the treatment prescribed by the veterinarian.

Table 14 lists the most common causes of infertility in cattle and shows the relative importance of each.

Table 14 accounts for 75.6 per cent of all infertility and reveals that infectious diseases and poor management are the most common causes of infertility in cattle. Additional causes are listed in the discussion that follows, and, of course, it is recognized that the calf crop may be affected by the proportion of bulls to cows, their distribution on the range, the season of breeding, and other factors.

STERILITY IN THE COW

Usually the failure of a female to have a heat period before 18 months of age, or to come in heat within 3 months after calving, or to conceive after 3 matings should constitute sufficient basis for assuming that an abnormal condition exists and that the services of a veterinarian should be obtained for diagnosis and possible treatment. Occasionally such conditions will correct themselves without treatment; in other cases, they subside for a time only to recur later—they become irregular breeders.

Repeat breeders—cows which exhibit regular or irregular heat periods, but fail to conceive—are most perplexing. The condition may be due to failure of fertilization or to early embryonic death.

When a cow fails to come in heat, she should first be checked for pregnancy (see section on Signs and Tests for Pregnancy, p. 223); approximately one cow in twenty thought to be sterile will be found safely in calf.

For convenience, the common causes of sterility and delayed breeding in beef cows are herein classified as (1) genital infections and diseases, (2) poor management and feeding, (3) physiological and endocrine disturbances, (4) inherited (genetic) abnormalities, (5) anatomical defects and injuries, and (6) miscellaneous and unknown causes. Of course, at the outset it is recognized that no definite demarkation exists between these classifications; that many of the causes of sterility may be, and are by some authorities, listed under other classifications than those given herein, and that there may be interaction between two or more forces. Also, whatever the cause of sterility, there are no "cure-alls"; rather, each individual case requires careful diagnosis and specific treatment for whatever is wrong.

Genital Infections and Diseases

Table 14 shows that specific genital diseases account for 35.5 per cent of all sterility in cattle. In addition, non-specific infections of the cervix and/or uterus are common causes of sterility.

NONSPECIFIC INFECTIONS OF THE GENITAL TRACT: Studies reveal that the invasion of the cervix and uterus by a variety of microorganisms normally follows parturition, but that such infections usually clear up, without treatment, within 40 to 50 days after calving. The return of estrual cycles of normal length and duration is, therefore, a reasonably good indication that the reproductive tract is again normal.

Because bacteria are likely to be present in the reproductive tract immediately following calving, and since breeding at this time may interfere with the normal breeding process and extend the period of infertility, it is recommended that cows not be rebred within 60 days after calving. But rebreeding should not be delayed longer than 90 days, because the latter will also result in a decrease in fertility due to impaired functioning of the accessory sex glands through disuse. If the placenta was retained or other calving difficulties were encountered, the cow should be allowed to go through at least one normal heat period before rebreeding.

The veterinarian-prescribed treatment for non-specific genital infections will depend upon their nature and the extent to which they have invaded the reproductive tract; antiseptics, antibiotics and other drugs may be indicated for local or systemic use, and/or sexual rest may be recommended.

SPECIFIC GENITAL DISEASES: Brucellosis, leptospirosis, metritis, trichomoniasis, vaginitis, and vibriosis are the most troublesome specific genital diseases of cows. Since each of these diseases is fully discussed in Chapter XIII of this book, only a few facts pertinent to them from the standpoint of sterility and delayed breeding will be discussed at this point.

Brucellosis in cattle is a serious genital disease caused primarily by the *Brucella abortus* bacteria, although the suis and melitensis types are also seen in cattle. It is characterized by (1) abortions at any stage of pregnancy, but most commonly between the 5th and 8th months, (2) above normal incidence of retained placenta, and (3) lowered conception rate. Brucellosis can be readily and accurately detected by both blood and milk tests.

Leptospirosis is caused by several species of cork-screw-shaped organisms of the spirochete group. Among other symptoms, it is apt to produce a large number of abortions anywhere from the 6th month of pregnancy to term. In newly infected herds, abortions may approach 30 per cent. The disease can be diagnosed by a blood test.

Metritis is caused by various types of bacteria. Lacerations at the time of calving, wounds inflicted by well-meaning but inexperienced operators, and/or retention of afterbirth are the principal predisposing factors. Metritis usually develops soon after parturition. It is characterized by a foul smelling discharge from the vulva that may be brownish or blood-stained and finally becomes thick and yellow.

Trichomoniasis is a genital-tract infection caused by the protozoan organism *Trichomonas foetus*. The disease is characterized by (1) irregular sexual cycles, (2) early abortions, usually between 60 and 120 days, (3) a whitish vaginal discharge, and (4) resorption of the fetus, while the uterus becomes filled with a thin grayish fluid. When these symptoms are observed in a herd known to be free of brucellosis, trichomonad infection should be suspected. The diagnosis can be confirmed microscopically by means of smears taken from the vagina of the cow just before an expected heat. The disease appears to be self-limiting in the cow; that is, cows appear to acquire an immunity after about three months of sexual rest.

Vaginitis is more or less a chronic infection of the vulva and vagina which causes an inflammation of varying intensity. The cause is unknown, and no treatment is entirely satisfactory. The veterinarian may prescribe one of a number of mild douches,

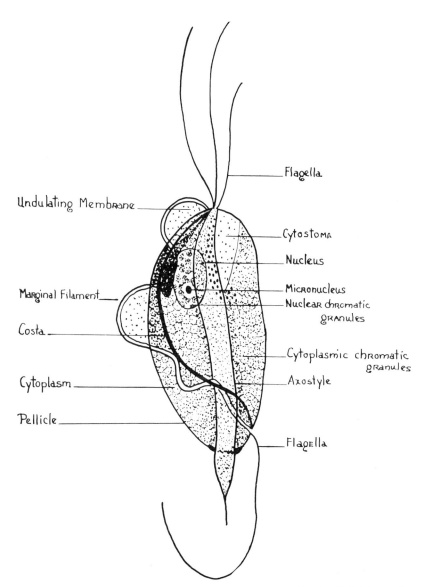

Fig. 97. Protozoan *Trichomonas foetus.* (From *The Artificial Insemination of Dairy Cattle*, p. 69, by Dr. H. A. Herman, published by Lucas Brothers, Columbia, Mo.; courtesy, the author)

such as (1) warm physiological salt solution (approximately 1 oz. salt to 1 gal. water; to which may be added 0.25% Lugol's Solution of Iodine, or 6.5% carbolic acid), (2) Gentian Violet (a saturated solution made by adding crystals of gentian violet to boiled water), (3) iodoform (made by dissolving 1 oz. of iodoform in 1 pint of warm mineral oil), (4) chlorine solution, or (5) a baking soda solution (made by dissolving 1 tablespoonful of baking soda in 1 qt. of boiled water).

Vibriosis is caused by the microorganism *Vibrio fetus*, which is transmitted at the time of breeding. The disease is characterized by (1) several (4 or more) services per conception, (2) cows exhibiting irregular heat periods, but finally settling without much difficulty and carrying calves to normal term, and (3) three to five per cent abortions, usually between the fifth and seventh month of pregnancy. For positive diagnosis, laboratory methods must be used. Infected cows may be treated by injecting drugs into the uterus and/or by allowing sexual rest; artificial insemination with antibiotic-treated semen is a rapid and practical method of stopping the transmission of infection from cow to cow. The disease tends to be self-limiting in the cow; a cow seems to be free of the disease once she has had a calf following an infection.

Poor Management and Feeding

The term "management" is somewhat elusive and all-inclusive. As used in the discussion that follows, reference is made only to those beef cattle management practices pertinent to breeding efficiency. It is noteworthy, however, that management is very important in determining breeding efficiency, and that the breeder largely determines his own destiny in this regard.

OVULATION AND BREEDING
NOT PROPERLY SYNCHRONIZED:

If the sperm are introduced in the female reproductive tract much in advance of the egg's release, the chances of fertilization are greatly reduced. It has been shown that the best conception rates are obtained when the cow is bred more than 6 hours, but less than 24 hours, before ovulation. To meet these timing relationships, cows that are detected in heat in the morning should be bred during the afternoon of the same day, and those detected in the afternoon should be bred late that evening or early the next morning.

When the beginning of heat is known with certainty, it is best to wait at least six to twelve hours before breeding. In general, good results will be obtained when cows are bred within 24 hours after the beginning of heat or within 6 hours after the end of heat.

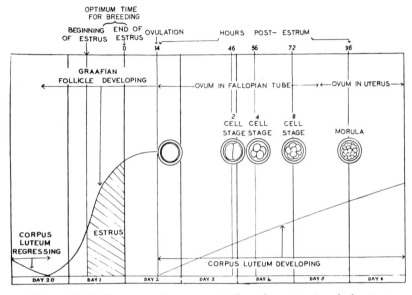

Figure 98. A diagrammatic representation of events at and about estrus in the cow. (From *Farm Animals*, p. 48, by Dr. John Hammond, published by Edward Arnold & Co., London, England; courtesy, the author)

Where hand mating is practiced, this means that failure to detect accurately when a cow is in heat may account for some breeding failures. Experience and careful observation are the answers to this problem. In addition to recognizing the signs of estrus (see p. 221), where hand mating is to be followed, the herdsman should keep a record of breeding dates and observed heat periods for each cow.

IMPROPER FEEDING:

Improper feeding may imply (1) uncommonly high or low feed intake, or (2) a deficiency of specific nutrients.

Restricted rations often occur during periods of drought, when pastures or ranges are overstocked, or when winter rations are skimpy. When such deprivations are extreme, there may be lowered reproductive efficiency on a temporary basis. It is noteworthy, however, that experimental results to date fail to show that the fertility of the germ cells is seriously impaired by uncommonly high or low feed and nutrient intakes.[1] In contrast to these findings, it is equally clear that the onset of heat and ovulation in young heifers is definitely and positively correlated with the level of nutrient intake; thus, if feed or nutrient intake is too low for normal rates of growth and development, the onset of reproductive function is delayed.[1]

Likewise, too liberal feeding and high condition may cause sterility. Sometimes the presence of an excessive amount of fat in the pelvic region leads to a partial protrusion of the vagina and eventual inflammation. Also, where a female remains in an excessively high condition for an extended period of time, degeneration of the ovarian follicles may occur, thereby producing a prolonged state of sterility.

Under natural conditions, a deficiency of vitamin A is the only vitamin likely to be lacking in cattle rations; and they obtain plenty of the precursor (carotene) when they are on green pasture or receive reasonable amounts of green hay not over one year old. A severe deficiency of vitamin A may result in a low conception rate, a small calf crop—with many calves weak or stillborn and with some calves born blind or without eyeballs, but estrus may remain normal.

Under practical conditions, it has been observed that when cows are on a phosphorus-deficient ration, there is a marked inhibition of estrus and a tendency to reproduce every other year. Also, it is believed that heat periods are suppressed when there is a copper deficiency. However, experimental results have failed to show that the fertility of cows is seriously impaired by low trace-mineral content rations.[1]

Although an adequate supply of minerals and vitamins is essential for normal growth and health, adding an excess of these nutrients to a well-balanced beef cattle ration fed according to recommended practices has no known value in curing breeding troubles.

---

[1]Northeastern States Regional Bulletin 32 (Cornell U. Agri. Expt. Sta. Bul. 924), Nov. 1957. p. 30.

EXERCISE:

Although heat periods are more easily detected when cows are out in the open, exercise is not essential for normal reproduction. It is recognized, however, that exercise is necessary for the normal well being of the individual.

SEXUAL REST:

For maximum reproductive efficiency, cows should not be rebred too soon after calving. Although the reproductive tract usually returns to normal within about six weeks, barring infection or other abnormalities, it is inadvisable to rebreed a cow earlier than 60 days following parturition. This will still allow time for a second service if needed without exceeding the 12 month calving interval. A New York study revealed that the highest conception rate was obtained when breeding was between 70 and 90 days after calving.[1] In case of retained placenta or other calving difficulties, the cow should be allowed to go through at least one normal heat period before rebreeding.

SEASON AND LIGHT:

Seasonal variations in conception rate have been observed in artificial insemination associations; poorest conception is obtained in the winter and maximum in the spring. From this it may be concluded that the amount of daylight (and perhaps the temperature) has an influence on fertility—as the amount of daylight increases, breeding efficiency increases proportionately until temperatures become too hot.

Physiological and Endocrine Disturbances

The development of the reproductive organs, the production of ova, sexual behavior, the attachment and development of the fetus, parturition, and lactation are primarily regulated by hormones. Many cases of reproductive failure, particularly of conception and early development, may be due to hormone imbalance.

If neither infection of the genital tract nor any unusual condition is observed, the administration of hormones may be indicated. A wide variety of both natural and synthetic hormones is available, but none should be used except under the direction of a well-informed practitioner. The temptation is always strong to administer a mixture of hormones in the hope that one of them will correct the trouble. A wiser plan is to prescribe the specific

[1]Northeastern States Regional Bulletin 32 (Cornell U. Agri. Expt. Sta. Bul. 924), Nov. 1957, p. 5.

hormone which it is believed will produce the desired results; however, this is often difficult or impossible, with the result that "trial and error" methods may be the only alternative.

ANESTRUS (FAILURE TO COME IN HEAT):

Anestrus is the prolonged period of sexual quiescence between the mating seasons of animals. The term is used to describe a cow which is not showing any external signs of heat, which may or may not be associated with ovarian inactivity. This condition is normal in cows immediately following calving. It may also occur in cows in the late winter and early spring when nutritional levels are low. Estrus can be readily induced in such animals by the administration of one of several natural or synthetic estrogens, such as estrone or diethylstilbestrol. Although it is unlikely that ovulation will accompany the induced heat, normal cycles are often re-established thereby and conception may occur at the next heat period.

In some cases of anestrus, it may be preferable to administer follicle stimulating hormones. Frequently, these will induce both estrus and ovulation, but there is a likelihood of undesirable multiple ovulations from such treatment.

DISTURBED ESTRUS CYCLES:

Numerous variations of the normal estrus cycle occur, all of which are explainable in terms of improper gonadotropin-estrogen-progesterone relationships. Among such conditions are the following:

1. Ovulation without estrus; silent heats; or estrus of such low intensity that recognition is difficult. It has been estimated that 20 per cent of ovulations in cows are not accompanied by external signs of heat.

2. Animals showing estrus cycles, but with a delay in ovulation.

3. Long or short heat periods.

4. Abnormal intervals between heat periods.

5. Estrus without ovulation, known as an anovulatory cycle.

If it is definitely determined that cows with disturbed estrus cycles are not pregnant, and if infections have been ruled out, the judicious and careful use of hormones may be appropriate. Such treatment may restore the endocrine balance, which, in turn, will condition the reproductive system for estrus, conception, and pregnancy.

SEXUAL INFANTILISM:

In this condition, the entire reproductive tract remains small. Ovulation may not occur; if it does, affected heifers may exhibit silent heat periods or be irregular in their sexual cycles. Sometimes sexual development is delayed but reproduction is normal after puberty. Heifers with this condition may become excessively fat and resemble spayed heifers or steers.

Sexual infantilism appears to be due to lack of gonadotropic hormone secretion by the anterior pituitary gland, but, unfortunately, treatment with gonadotropins is not often successful. If malnutrition does not appear to account for the condition, the possibility of a heritable factor should be suspected.

RETAINED CORPUS LUTEUM
(RETAINED YELLOW BODY):

After the ovarian follicle ruptures and the egg is released, the cells within the follicular cavity change in character and function, forming a corpus luteum or yellow body in the cavity of the ruptured follicle. If the corpus luteum persists, subsequent heat periods do not usually occur. The corpus luteum produces a hormone (progesterone) which suppresses the pituitary output of the follicle-stimulating hormone (FSH). Thus, future follicular development and ripening is inhibited and the estrogens which would induce heat periods are not produced.

A retained corpus luteum may be suspected if a cow is not seen in heat within 60 days after calving. The orthodox treatment for this condition consists in removing the corpus luteum by means of pressure applied through the rectal wall (rectal palpation). Experiments have shown that this procedure is neither beneficial nor harmful.[1] Instead of removing the corpus luteum, some advocate the use of estrogenic hormones.

CYSTIC OVARIES:

Cystic ovaries may result when the ovarian follicle fails to rupture. The follicle persists, increases in size, and forms a cyst. It is believed that this condition is due to a derangement of gonadotropic-hormone secretion. An excessive secretion of FSH without adequate luteinizing hormone (LH) to produce ovulation causes continued follicular development and estrogen production.

[1]Northeastern States Regional Bulletin 32 (Cornell U. Agri. Expt. Sta. Bul. 924), Nov. 1957, p. 24.

When the condition is allowed to persist in cows, they frequently become chronic "bullers" or nymphomaniacs. Such individuals may show pronounced anatomic and psychologic changes; the pelvic ligaments relax so that there is a sagging of the loin region and elevation of the tail head. Affected cows may

Fig. 99. A chronic "buller" or nymphomaniac cow, showing the characteristic sagging of the loin region and elevation of the tail head. (From *Physiology of Reproduction*, p. 667, by Marshall; courtesy, the Royal Society of Edinburgh)

acquire such male characteristics as thickened forequarters and may bellow and behave like a bull.

Recommended treatment for cystic ovaries consists in the administration of a gonadotropin preparation rich in the LH fraction, made either from anterior pituitary glands or from human pregnancy urine. Also, some advocate that the condition be corrected by rupturing the cyst through rectal palpation. A nymphomaniac cow should not be bred too soon after treatment; a waiting period of 40 to 60 days is suggested, or until the second apparently normal heat.

There is evidence that the tendency toward cystic ovaries is inherited in cattle. Also, there is a higher incidence in the dairy breeds than in the beef breeds.

RETAINED PLACENTA (RETAINED AFTERBIRTH):
Normally, the placenta is expelled within three to six hours after parturition. If it is retained as long as twenty-four hours after calving, competent assistance should be rendered.

Retained placenta is more common following abnormally short or abnormally long pregnancies, among older cows, and following twinning. Calves born when the placenta is retained are likely to be weak.

A retained placenta may cause pathological conditions resulting in uterine tissue destruction. This condition may or may not affect milk production, but it very likely will result in greater difficulty in getting affected cows settled.

When a retained placenta is encountered, appropriate treatment with antibiotics will often prevent serious damage and thus allow the animals to breed normally following a suitable rest period of 3 to 4 months.

INTERSEXES AND HERMAPHRODITES:
Stedman's Medical Dictionary gives the following definitions of intersexes and hermaphrodites:

Intersex.—An individual showing both maleness and femaleness, in which the sex differences are not confined to clearly demarcated parts of the body but blend more or less with one another.

Hermaphrodite.—An individual whose genital organs have the characters of both male and female in greater or less degree.

These conditions which occur only rarely in cattle, are a result of (1) imbalance in the maternal fetal endocrine system, or (2) genetic factors.

Inherited (Genetic) Abnormalities

The development of breeds or families within breeds which differ in prolificacy is good evidence that fertility may have a genetic basis. Thus, it is common knowledge that some once-popular families have become extinct because of the high incidence of infertility. A classical example of a situation of this type occurred in the Duchess family of Shorthorn cattle, founded by the noted pioneer English Shorthorn breeder, Thomas Bates. Bates, and more especially those later breeders who emulated him, followed preferences in bloodlines until, ultimately, they were selecting cattle solely on the basis of fashionable pedigrees, without regard to fertility. Ironically, during their heyday, the scarcity of this strain of cattle contributed to their value. Eventually, but all too late, the owners of Duchess Shorthorns suddenly came to a realization that indiscriminate inbreeding and lack of selection had increased sterility to the point that the family name was in disrepute; a high incidence of sterility had actually contributed to their scarcity. As a result, Duchess Shorthorns became virtually extinct a few years later.

Of course, reproductive disorders of a heritable nature should not knowingly be perpetuated.

LETHAL GENES:

Lethal genes, and other recessive genes causing sterility, belong in the group of highly heritable characters. Among such hereditary lethals are mummification, cystic ovaries, and gonad hypoplasia or gonadless (see Table 10, p. 150, of this book for a summary relative to lethal characters). Generally these abnormalities are easily recognized by their actions, and their mode of transmission can often be analyzed and determined. Although lethals are of interest to the geneticist, they are generally no great problem to the cattleman because their distribution remains under control. Usually recessive, their gene frequency is kept low by the self-destruction of the double recessive; thus, they are self-selective.

WHITE HEIFER DISEASE:

This name is a misnomer, for, although the condition is most commonly found in white heifers of the Shorthorn breed, it has been reported in roan and red Shorthorns and in colored animals of other breeds. It appears to be due to faulty development of the Mullerian ducts. Some of the more common characteristics are: closed hymen or hymen persisting in varying degrees, distention of one or both uterine horns, and uterine body present in rudimentary form, complete absence of cervix, and anterior vagina.

Anatomical Defects and Injuries

A long list of anatomical defects and injuries to the genital organs has been reported. Some of these are so severe as to cause sterility; others affect the degree of fertility. A Pennsylvania study of repeat breeders—cows which had failed to con-

ceive after 4 services—revealed that 13 per cent were anatom-
ically abnormal.[1] A brief account of some of the more general
anatomical defects follows.

FREEMARTIN HEIFERS:

*Sterile heifers that are born twin with a bull are known as
freemartins.* This condition prevails in about nine out of ten
twin births when a calf of each sex is involved. The fetal circu-
lations fuse, and the male hormones get into the circulation of
the unborn female where they interfere with the normal development of sex and modify the female embryo in the direction
of the male. In approximately 10 per cent of twin births of
unlike sexes, fusion of the circulation does not occur, and the
animal is normal and fertile.

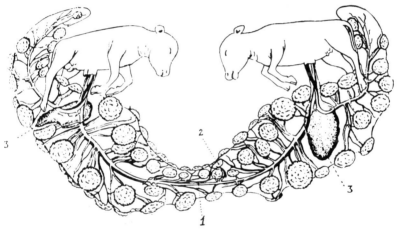

Fig. 100. Diagram showing fused fetal circulation of twin calves of
opposite sex. Note (1) the fetal circulation of the male fused with that of
the female, (2) fetal cotyledon free yolk sac, and (3) normal bull on the
left and freemartin heifer on the right. (From *Physiology of Reproduction*
by Marshall; courtesy, the publisher, Longmans, Green and Co., Ltd., London, England)

Since only about ten per cent of such heifers are fertile, it is
usually best to assume that they are sterile and market them,
unless (1) An experienced person determined at the time of birth
that their circulatory systems were not fused, (2) an examination of the vagina reveals that the animal is normal (in freemartin heifers, the vagina is usually about one-third normal

[1]Northeastern States Regional Bulletin 32 (Cornell U. Agri. Expt. Sta.
Bul. 924), Nov. 1957, p. 21.

!ength), or (3) skin-grafting[1] for blood-typing[2] techniques show that they are not freemartins and that they may, therefore, be regarded as reproductively normal.

MECHANICAL INJURIES TO THE GENITAL ORGANS:

Mechanical injuries may occur in the female at service and at parturition. A large vigorous male may inflict injury when breeding; and complicated parturition may result in the loss of the offspring, permanent damage to the reproductive organs, or even death of the cow herself. Perforation of the uterine or vaginal walls, laceration of the cervix, eversion of the vagina, cervix, and uterus or of the rectum may all be sequelae of complicated birth. In some cases, adhesions or secondary infections of the genitalia cause tissue damage which prevent further reproduction.

Miscellaneous and Unknown Causes

Unfortunately, many of the causes of sterility are unrecognized and unknown. A discussion of one of these follows.

EMBRYONIC MORTALITY (FETAL DEATH OR PRENATAL MORTALITY):

It is well known that early embryonic mortality occurs normally in the pig and the rabbit, where there is a surplus production of female gametes. Although it is not so common in the cow, it appears that 20 to 30 per cent of the ova fertilized may meet embryonic death in 2 to 6 weeks. In such cases, the embryo may be absorbed or be expelled unobserved from the female reproductive tract. The cow may assume normal sexual cycles with the conclusion the fertilization did not take place.

Fetal death, followed by resorption or abortion, may occur at any stage of pregnancy. Such fetuses may range from decomposed masses to bones or dried mummies.

The cause or causes of prenatal death are not known.

STERILITY IN THE BULL

Any bull of breeding age that is purchased should be a guaranteed breeder; in fact, this is usually understood among reputable cattlemen.

---

[1]Billingham, R. E. and G. H. Lampkin, J. Embryol. Exp. Morph., Dec. 1957, Vol. 5, part 4, pp. 351-367.
[2]Stormont, Clyde, *Journal of Animal Science*, Feb., 1954, Vol. 13, No. 1, pp. 94-98.

The most reliable and obvious indication of fertility in a bull is a large number of healthy calves from a season's service. However, a good evaluation of a bull's fertility may be obtained through a microscopic examination of the semen made by an experienced person. It is recommended that all bulls be semen tested prior to the breeding season; and, where valuable pure-bred bulls are involved, periodic tests during the breeding season are desirable. Such procedure may alleviate much loss in time, feed and labor, and avoid delayed and small calf crops.

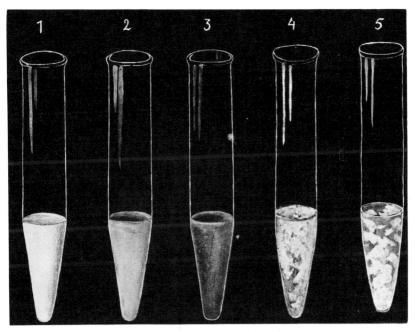

Fig. 101. Semen samples of different kinds. 1. Semen with normal appearance, about 1,000,000 spermatozoa per cubic m.m. 2 & 3. Semen from a bull with hypoplastic testicles. Sample 2 contains about 200,000 spermatozoa per cubic m.m. Sample 3, which is almost transparent, contains about 25,000 spermatozoa per cubic m.m. 4 & 5. Semen from a bull with inflammation in the seminal vesicles. In the semen, which is almost transparent, there are big, purulent flocci. (Courtesy, Professor Nils Lagerlof, Department of Obstetrics and Gynecology, Royal Veterinary College, Stockholm, Sweden)

For purposes of convenience, the common causes of sterility and delayed breeding in bulls are herein classified as (1) poor semen, (2) physical defects and injuries, (3) psychological, (4) genital infections and disease, (5) poor management and feeding, (6) physiological and endocrine disturbances, and (7) inherited

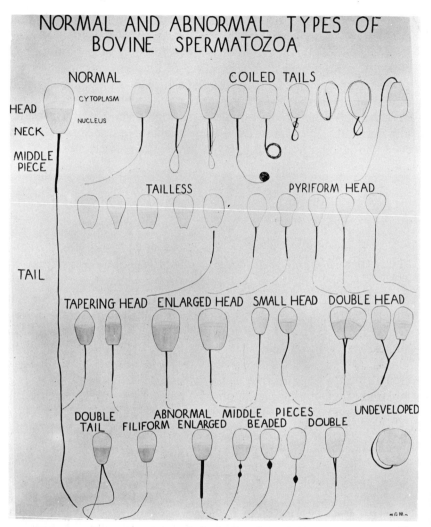

Fig. 102. Normal and morphologically abnormal spermatozoa of the bull. (From *The Artificial Insemination of Dairy Cattle*, p. 27, by Dr. H. A. Herman, published by Lucas Brothers, Columbia, Mo.; courtesy, the author)

(genetic) abnormalities. Also, a section on " 'Bull Testing' to Evaluate Breeding Soundness" follows.

Poor Semen

It is always well to obtain a sample of semen and to make a laboratory examination of the number and condition of the sperm. The four main criteria of semen quality are: (1) volume,

(2) sperm count, (3) progressive movement, and (4) morphology (shape). Although this technique is not infallible, an experienced person can predict with reasonable accuracy the relative fertility of bulls so examined.

Physical Defects and Injuries

Based on a study of 950 bulls, Colorado State University reported the following incidence of physical defects and injuries:[1]

Reproductive System.....................17%
Limbs and feet 7%
Eye 3%
Other 10%
                                        ———
                                        37%

It is noteworthy that this study revealed that one-third of the bulls exhibited some physical defect, ranging from harmless to serious.

The most common defects involving the reproductive system are: degenerating testes, abscessed testes, fibromas of the penis, broken penis, hematoma, adhesions within the sheath, and paralysis of the retractor muscle. Sometimes certain of these conditions can be corrected by skilled surgery. Although infrequent, temporary or permanent sterilty may result from bruising, inflammation, and lacerations of the scrotum and testes. Also, the penis may become bruised or lacerated during service.

Natural service is sometimes interfered with by unsound limbs and feet. This includes such conditions as broken limbs; bad sickle hocks; sore, over-grown or malformed feet; and arthritic or rheumatic joints. The latter condition is more prevalent in old bulls. Defects of the hind limbs are especially troublesome, because they make the bull unstable or cause severe pain when he shifts much of his weight onto them when mounting.

Keratitis (pink eye) and blindness, especially if in both eyes, will interfere with mating.

Frequently very short legged, compact bulls that are in show condition and are somewhat awkward and clumsy are unable to serve cows. Also, an extremely paunchy bull may be unable to mate, because the "pot-belly" acts as a mechanical

[1]*Cattle Guard*, official magazine of the Colorado Cattlemen's Assn., Jan. 1957, p. 30.

obstruction and causes the penis to be directed too low. Usually such inability is temporary and may be corrected by reducing the ration and increasing the exercise.

Improvements can be effected in some of these physical defects and injuries, while others are irreparable.

Psychological

Sterile bulls are frequently victims of psychological sterility. Usually, this condition expresses itself in either (1) absence of or lowered sex drive and (2) faulty reflex behavior during mating or ejaculation.

As is true in people, there is a wide individual difference in the reaction of bulls to their environment; and, likewise, these factors are, in part, hereditary. Thus, there are four major types of temperament in bulls; namely, the nervous, the sulky, the placid, and the treacherous. The treacherous types should always be culled at an early age. Then, in selecting from among the other three types, consideration should be given to the herd requirements—whether a commercial or purebred herd is involved, whether pasture- or hand-mating is to be used, etc. Also, it is generally recognized that bulls lacking in masculinity or secondary sexual characteristics (bulls that are very docile, very fine boned, and lacking development of the crest, etc.) are likely to possess poor psycho-physiological sexual activity.

Young inexperienced bulls mating for the first time are usually awkward to handle. They approach the cow hesitantly, spend a long time exploring the genitalia, mount hesitantly without erection, descend and try to mount again. Extreme patience and careful handling should be exercised during this critical first service; otherwise, difficult breeding habits may be established.

CAUSES OF PSYCHOLOGICAL STERILITY:

Some common causes of psychological sterility are:

1. **Excitement.**—Shouting, noises, distractions during mounting, and the presence of strangers may cause low sex drive. When restrained with a dog, a highly fertile bull may become sexually impotent. Bulls show evidence of such excitement when they urinate more frequently, as they do following the visit of strangers or the introduction of new animals.

Also, it is important to keep sires as quiet as possible in the nonbreeding season. Undue excitement causes sexual impulses and results in the flow of semen into the ampullae.

2. **Transportation.**—Psychological sterility is not uncommon in bulls that have been transported long distances by truck or rail.

3. **Animal management.**—Young bulls that are isolated from all cows for long periods of time manifest homosexual reflexes and may become impotent.

Also, inadequate sex drive may be due to an attempt to use a young bull on a cow that is too large for him to mount successfully. As a result of his failure to copulate, he develops a mild sense of frustration. Frequently, such a bull can be restored to a high state of breeding efficiency by giving him assistance and trying him on a heifer selected for her small size and willingness to stand quietly; or the same effect may be obtained by standing a large cow in a pit.

Where hand-mating is practiced, the bull should not be used immediately following feeding.

4. **Wrong technique during semen collection.**—Certain inhibitory reactions may develop from improper use of the artificial vagina, including wrong timing in applying it, too hot or too cold water, or holding it at a wrong angle.

Genital Infections and Diseases

The presence of bacteria in the semen of bulls will not only tend to decrease the viability of the sperm cells but may very easily infect the cows to which they are mated, thereby preventing their conception even when bred to other bulls. If this condition is due to inflammation of the seminal vesicles or prostate, the systematic use of the appropriate antibiotic or sulfa drug may be recommended by the veterinarian. Occasionally, rectal massage of an infected prostate or seminal vesicle will aid the passage of the purulent exudate into the urethra and thus hasten recovery.

Brucellosis, trichomoniasis, vaginitis, and vibriosis are the specific genital diseases of most concern in bulls. Each of these diseases is fully covered in Chapter 13; and, likewise, a pertinent discussion of each disease from the standpoint of the cow appears earlier in this chapter. Thus, the ensuing comments will be limited to effects on the bull.

The Brucella organism may localize in the testes, seminal vesicles, or vas deferens, and bulls may spread the disease by copulation. Sex drive is generally reduced if testicular involvement occurs.

In trichomoniasis, the bull is the source of infection. Positive diagnosis of infection in the bull may be made by means of (1) a microscopic examination of smears taken from the prepuce, or (2) mating him with a virgin heifer and checking her cervical and uterine smears for the organism as she approaches the next heat period.

It is believed that vaginitis is commonly transmitted by the bull at the time of service, but this is not the only means of transmission since virgin heifers may be infected. Artificial insemination may be helpful in a control program. Also, the veterinarian may direct that the genital organs of the bull be douched with a physiological salt solution (made by adding 1 ounce of common salt to 1 gal. of water to which may be added ¼ of 1% of Lugol's solution).

In vibriosis, no clinical lesions are observed in bulls. However, *V. fetus* appears to persist indefinitely in the genital tract of carrier bulls and the bull may transmit the infection. For diagnosis of vibriosis in individual bulls, one should (1) culture the semen and prepulial fluids, and, where possible, (2) breed to one or more virgin heifers and collect vaginal mucus for culture 10 to 20 days later. Effective control can be obtained by (1) adding antibiotics to diluted semen and breeding artificially, or (2) establishing a new herd of sexually immature animals.

Poor Management and Feeding

In all too many cases, little thought is given to the management and feeding of the bull, other than during the breeding season. Instead, the program throughout the entire year should be such as to keep the bull in a vigorous, thrifty condition at all times. Also, lack of fertility in the bull may often be traced back to his early care and feeding. He may have been small and weak at birth, he may have been improperly fed during the first year of his life, or he may have been prey to infection.

IMPROPER FEEDING:

Overfitted, heavy bulls should be regarded with suspicion, for they may be uncertain breeders. On the other hand, a poor, thin, run-down condition is also to be avoided.

Fitting bulls for show and sale results in a variable effect upon their semen producing ability; in some it has no detectable detrimental effect while others are severely affected by such practices. Many highly fitted bulls show a complete lack of sperm cells; others produce semen comparable in quality to a bull exhibiting testicular degeneration. Many, perhaps most, such fat bulls eventually reach normal breeding efficiency if they are properly let down—primarily by reducing the grain and by increasing the exercise.

Sterility in bulls has occasionally been traced to a lack of vitamin C. This can be determined by an analysis of a blood or semen sample. Should the analysis disclose a deficiency of vitamin C, the required amount can be supplied by injecting ascorbic acid under the skin of the bull. The usual treatment consists of injecting 1 gram of ascorbic acid dissolved in sodium-potassium phosphate buffer, physiologic saline, or sterile water, twice a week.

EXERCISE:

Exercise is necessary for the normal well being of the bull. Although it is difficult to show precisely to what extent lack of exercise induces low fertility, there seems to be ample reason for concluding that it constitutes a highly important factor.

Generally speaking, beef bulls should be exercised by allowing them the run of the pasture or large corral. However, it may be necessary to lead fat show bulls from 2 to 4 miles daily following the show season.

RETARDED SEXUAL MATURITY:

As stated earlier in this chapter, the normal age of puberty in cattle is twelve months. But there is wide variation in the age of sexual maturity of bulls as measured by semen quality. Some yearling bulls are fully equipped to produce a healthy percentage of calves; others are not. At the present time, it is not known whether such retarded sexual development is due to hereditary, nutritional, and/or management factors. There is need, therefore, for additional research on this subject.

THE OVERWORKED BULL:

Low fertility of the bull is frequently caused by over service. Table 13, p. 233, may be used as a bull mating guide for different age animals, under both hand-mating and pasture-mating practices.

In pasture breeding, the bull may copulate four or five times in succession, thereby correspondingly reducing his powers, and lessening the size of the herd on which he should be used. However, it is recognized that this situation is compensated for, in part, by the fact that bulls on pasture have sexual vigor not possessed by stall-fed bulls.

Physiological and Endocrine Disturbances

The development of the reproductive organs, the production of sperm and sexual behavior are primarily regulated by hormones; thus, the possibilities of endocrine disturbances are endless. Examples of some of the more common abnormalities follow.

SEXUAL INFANTILISM:

In this condition, the entire reproductive tract remains small and the testes are visibly reduced in size. Affected animals lack sex drive. If a low plane of nutrition does not appear to account for the condition, the possibility of a genetic factor should be suspected.

SEX DRIVE:

If sperm are being produced, but the bull is unwilling to perform service due to low sex drive, the administration of an androgen, such as testosterone, may restore mating.

Inherited (Genetic) Abnormalities

Lack of fertility in the bull may often be traced right back to his own sire and dam. He may have been sired by a bull of low vigor and fertility and out of a cow of equally low fertility.

Reproductive disorders of a heritable nature should not knowingly be perpetuated. In addition to those which follow, Table 10 contains a summary of some fertility-affecting hereditary abnormalities in bulls, including impotentia, atrophied testes, knobbed spermatozoa, and turned tails.

CRYPTORCHIDISM:

When one or both of the testicles of a bull have not descended to the scrotum, the animal is known as a cryptorchid. The undescended testicle(s) is usually sterile because of the high temperature in the abdomen. Since this condition may be heritable, it is recommended that animals so affected not be retained for breeding purposes.

SCROTAL HERNIA:

When a weakness of the inguinal canal allows part of the viscera to pass out into the scrotum, the condition is called scrotal hernia. This abnormality may interfere with the circulation in the testes and result in their atrophy.

UMBILICAL HERNIA:

This condition, which may interfere with breeding efficiency, has been reported as due to (1) a sex-limited dominant gene, or (2) one or more pairs of autosomal recessive factors.

"Bull Testing" to Evaluate Breeding Soundness

The term "bull testing" as used herein refers to a method for evaluating the breeding soundness of beef bulls; actually, it is a method for detecting infertility rather than determining fertility. An extensive program of this type was first initiated by Colorado State University, in 1949. Since then, it has spread to several states. Essentially, such testing embodies the following three evaluations, all of which have a bearing on a bull from the standpoint of the efficiency of his reproductive performance:

1. Checking for physical defects which might impair breeding capacity.

2. Collecting a representative semen sample by means of the electric ejaculator and examining it under the microscope. Semen quality is based on four criteria: degree of vigor, per cent living sperm as determined by the live-dead stain technique, concentration of sperm cells, and morphology.

3. Evaluating and determining the breeding history of a nonvirgin bull whose status, based on points 1 and 2, is questionable.

By use of these criteria,[1] Colorado State University classifies each bull examined to denote his relative breeding capacity. Their current grade classifications are:

1. **Satisfactory.**—This group includes bulls (1) that have no major physical defects which will impair their ability to travel and to serve females, and (2) that produce semen within the range of quality standards necessary for conception in natural mating. With normal females, conception rates with such bulls should be above 60 per cent with one service.

---

[1] Actually, the third criterion is not invoked unless the first two criteria show that the bull is questionable.

2. **Questionable.**—These bulls show some faults affecting ability to settle cows; many cows will not conceive to their services. Some bulls in this class may, in time, improve; but later calves and a low percentage calf crop will likely result. Such bulls should be rechecked before the breeding season. Conception rates would be expected to fall below 50 per cent on one service.

3. **Unsatisfactory.**—These bulls are, as the term indicates, unsatisfactory for breeding purposes and, unless very valuable, should be sold for slaughter without delay.

In $3\frac{1}{2}$ years testing, involving over 3,400 bulls, the Colorado workers found 6 per cent of the bulls questionable and 6 per cent unsatisfactory; or 12 per cent that gave reason for concern as breeders. This points up the need for a systematic and regular examination of breeding bulls.

A PROGRAM OF IMPROVED FERTILITY AND BREEDING EFFICIENCY

A program designed to give improved fertility and breeding efficiency in beef cattle follows, in summary form:[1]

1. **Keep complete breeding records.** Maintain complete fertility records on each animal, examine them periodically and cull low producers. Where hand-mating is followed, keep a record of dates bred and observed heat periods of each cow; calculate the expected estrus cycle by adding 21 days to the date of last estrus.

2. Before the breeding season, check the bull for physical defects and quality of semen.

3. Breed only healthy cows to healthy bulls.

4. Avoid either an overfat or a thin, emaciated condition in all breeding animals, and feed balanced rations.

5. Provide plenty of exercise for bulls and pregnant cows, preferably by allowing them to graze in well-fenced pastures in which plenty of shade and water are available.

6. Do not breed young animals until they are amply mature.

7. Provide an ample rest period between pregnancies; do not rebreed within 60 days after calving. Where the placenta was retained or other calving difficulties encountered, allow the

---

[1]In this section, special emphasis is placed on increased fertility and breeding efficiency; thus, there is some repetition and there are some additions to the section entitled, "A Program of Beef Cattle Health, Disease Prevention, and Parasite Control," as given in Chapter XIII of this book.

cow to go through at least one normal heat period before rebreeding.

8. Do not overwork the bull.

9. Observe breeding females carefully during the breeding season, otherwise heat periods of short duration may be missed. Also, keep a close watch for shy breeders; expose them to the bull often.

10. Diagnose cows for pregnancy.

11. Handle the new born so that its health shall be assured, and in order that it may have uninterrupted development.

12. Retain as future replacements only those animals which are the progeny of healthy parents, that were carried in utero for a normal gestation period of from 279 to 288 days, and that were born without difficult calving, retained afterbirth, or metritis.

13. Isolate newly acquired animals for a minimum of three weeks, during which time they should be tested for brucellosis, leptospirosis, trichomoniasis, and vibriosis. However, first make every reasonable effort to ascertain that they came from herds which are known to be free from these and other diseases.

14. When possible, purchase virgin heifers and bulls. Isolate non-virgin bulls for a period of three weeks, and then turn them with a limited number of virgin heifers; observe these heifers for 30 to 60 days after breeding as an aid in preventing the introduction of breeding diseases.

15. When sterility is encountered, promptly call upon the veterinarian for treatment; do not delay action until the condition is of long standing.

QUESTIONS FOR STUDY AND DISCUSSION

1. Compute the following for your beef cattle herd, or for a herd with which you are familiar:

(1) How much is being lost in annual gross sales of calves at weaning time, when considering the current calf crop percentage versus a 100 per cent calf crop?

(2) How much does it cost to maintain all of the barren cows for a year?

2. If a certain cattleman is experiencing (1) 15 per cent breeding difficulty in his cow herd at a given time, (2) 2.5 services per conception, and (3) a 75 per cent calf crop, outline,

step by step, your recommendations for determining the difficulties and improving the situation.

3. What precautions should a cattleman take to avoid the introduction into the herd of genital infections and diseases?

4. What symptoms characterize each of the following specific genital diseases in cows: brucellosis, leptospirosis, metritis, trichomoniasis, vaginitis, and vibriosis? What positive diagnosis, if any, can be made of each? What control program should be initiated when the presence of each disease is known?

5. For best results, (1) how many days should be allowed to elapse following parturition before rebreeding, and (2) how many hours should elapse following the known onset of heat before breeding?

6. May sterility be caused by (1) lack of feed as sometimes occurs during droughts, or (2) high conditions as when fitted for show?

7. Why should the cattleman call on the veterinarian if hormone injections are to be given to cattle?

8. On the basis of experimental evidence, should the corpus luteum be removed by an experienced technician by pressure applied through the rectal wall (rectal palpation) if the cow does not come in heat within 60 days after calving?

9. How should a cattleman handle a case of retained placenta?

10. Define the following: (1) nymphomania, (2) freemartin, (3) hermaphrodite, and (4) intersex.

11. How valuable would a heifer born twin with a bull have to be to warrant keeping her for breeding purposes?

12. What precautions should be taken when purchasing a bull to avoid sterility and delayed breeding?

13. When bringing in a new bull, what precautions should be taken to avoid psychological sterility?

14. What symptoms characterize each of the following specific genital diseases in the bull; brucellosis, trichomoniasis, vaginitis, and vibriosis; what positive diagnosis, if any, can be made of each? What control program should be initiated when the presence of each disease is known?

15. Prepare a recommended breeding schedule for bulls of different ages showing the interval between services.

16. How would you go about testing a bull for breeding soundness?

17. Write out a "program of improved fertility and breeding efficiency" for your herd or for a herd with which you are familiar.

SELECTED REFERENCES

Title of Publication	Author(s)	Publisher
Animal Breeding	A. L. Hagedoorn	Crosby Lockwood & Son, Ltd., Lon don, England, 1950.
Animal Breeding	L. M. Winters	John Wiley & Sons, Inc., New York, N. Y., 1948.
Animal Breeding Plans	J. L. Lush	Collegiate Press, Inc., Ames, Iowa, 1938.
Breeding and Improvement of Farm Animals	V. A. Rice F. N. Andrews E. J. Warwick J. E. Legates	McGraw-Hill Book Co. Inc., New York, N. Y., 1957.
Breeding Better Livestock	V. A. Rice F. N. Andrews E. J. Warwick	McGraw-Hill Book Co. Inc., New York, N. Y., 1953.
Breeding Difficulties in Dairy Cattle	S. A. Asdell	Cornell Univ. Agri. Expt. Sta. Bull 924 Cornell University, Ithaca N. Y., 1957.
Breeding Difficulties of Cattle	Charles Staff	General Mills, Larro Feeds, Chicago, Ill.
Cattle Fertility and Sterility	S. A. Asdell	Little, Brown and Co., Boston, Mass., 1955.
Factors Affecting Reproductive Efficiency in Dairy Cattle	Durward Olds D. M. Seath	Kentucky Agri. Expt. Sta. Bull 605, University of Kentucky, Lexington, Ky., 1954.
Farm Animals	John Hammond	Edward Arnold & Co., London, England, 1952.
Problems and Practices of American Cattlemen	M. E. Ensminger M. W. Galgan W. L. Slocum	Wash. Agri. Expt. Sta. Bull. 562, Washington State University, Pullman, Wash., 1955.
Reproductive Physiology	A. V. Nalbandov	W. H. Freeman & Co., San Francisco, Calif., 1958.
Reproduction and Infertility	Centennial Symposium	Agricultural Experiment Station, Michigan State University, Mich., 1955.
Reproduction in Dairy Cattle	C. H. Boynton	Extension Bull. 115, University of New Hampshire, Durham, N. H.

CHAPTER IX

FEEDING BEEF CATTLE[1]

Contents

[1]The author gratefully acknowledges the helpful suggestions of his colleagues, Drs. Wilton W. Heinemann and Irwin A. Dyer, Washington State University, who reviewed this chapter.

Although Webster defines the noun *ration* as "the amount of food supplied to an animal for a definite period, usually for a day," to most stockmen the word implies the feeds fed to an animal or animals, without limitation to the time in which they are consumed. In this and other chapters of *Beef Cattle Science*, the author accedes to the common usage of the word rather than to dictionary correctness.

Cattle inherit certain genetic potentialities, but how well they develop depends upon the environment to which they are subjected, and the most important factor in the environment is the feed. The feeding of cattle also constitutes the greatest single cost item of their production. It is important, therefore, that the feeding practices be as satisfactory and economical as possible.

Pastures and other roughages, preferably with a maximum of the former, are the very foundation of successful beef cattle production. In fact, it may be said that the principal function of beef cattle is to harvest vast acreages of forages, and, with or without supplementation, to convert these feeds into more nutritious and palatable products for human consumption. It is estimated (1) that 83.1 per cent of the total feed of beef cattle is derived from roughages (see Table 15), and (2) that 53.6 per cent of the land area of the United States is pastured all or part of the year, and much of this area is utilized by beef cattle. If produced on well-fertilized soils, green grass and well-cured, green, leafy hay can supply all of the nutrient requirements of beef cattle, except the need for common salt and whatever energy-rich feeds may be necessary for additional conditioning or dry-lot fattening.

Fig. 103. Hereford steers grazing on a western range, with hay stacked for winter feeding. Pastures and other roughages are the very foundation of successful beef cattle production. (Courtesy, U. S. Forest Service.)

TABLE 15

PERCENTAGE OF FEED FOR DIFFERENT CLASSES OF LIVESTOCK DERIVED FROM (1) CONCENTRATES, AND (2) ROUGHAGES, INCLUDING PASTURE, 1950-1955[1]

Class	Concentrates	Roughages
	(per cent)	(per cent)
Beef Cattle	16.9	83.1
Dairy Cattle	26.7	73.3
Sheep and Goats	7.3	92.7
Swine	95.3	4.7
Horses and Mules	25.9	74.1
Poultry	97.8	2.2
All Livestock	43.0	57.0

[1]Unpublished data provided by Mr. Earl F. Hodges, Agricultural Economist, Farm Economics Research Division, Agricultural Research Service, USDA.

High-percentage calf crops, heavy weaning weights, continuous and rapid growth of young stock, and optimum utilization of feed-lot rations in the fattening process are important; and all are based largely upon adequate nutrition. Improvements in each of these categories is well within the realm of realization on a practical basis.

SPECIFIC NUTRITIVE NEEDS OF BEEF CATTLE

The nutritive requirements of beef cattle have become more critical with the shift in beef production practices during the past two decades. Steers were formerly permitted to make their growth primarily on roughages—pastures in the summertime and hay and other forages in the winter. After making moderate and unforced growth for two to four years, usually the animals were either turned into the feed lot or placed on more lush pastures for a reasonable degree of finishing. With this system, the growth and fattening requirements of cattle came largely at two separate periods in the life of the animal.

Under the old system of moderate growth rate, reasonably good pastures and good quality hay fully met the protein requirements, as well as the mineral and vitamin needs. As the feeding period was not so long with these older cattle, in comparison with the period required in the fattening of calves or yearlings, there also was less tendency for vitamin deficiencies to show up in the feed lot; and the protein requirements were less important during the finishing period.

In recent years the preference of the consumer for smaller cuts of beef—meats that are more tender and have less fat—has made for a shift in management and marketing. Today, increasing numbers of cattle are fattened at early ages and marketed as baby beef. Such animals are in forced production. Their bodies are simultaneously laying on fat and growing rapidly in protein tissues and skeleton. Consequently, the nutritive requirements are more critical than those of older cattle, especially from the standpoint of proteins, minerals, and vitamins.

As feeds represent by far the greatest cost item in beef production, it is important that there be a basic understanding of the nutritive requirements. For convenience, these will be discussed under the following groups: (1) protein needs, (2) energy needs, (3) mineral needs, (4) vitamin needs, and (5) water needs.

The nutrient requirements of beef cattle for which there are reasonably reliable data have been summarized by a subcommittee of the National Research Council (Burroughs et al., 1958) and herewith reproduced in Tables 16 and 17. The figures in these tables differ from those contained in Tables 25 and 26 in that the latter are allowances (rather than requirements); thus Tables 25 and 26 provide for margins of safety to compensate for variations in feed composition, environment, and possible losses of nutrients during storage or processing.

Protein Needs

The protein allowance of beef cattle, regardless of age or sys-

TABLE 16

DAILY NUTRIENT REQUIREMENTS OF BEEF CATTLE
(BASED UPON AIR-DRY FEED CONTAINING 90 PER CENT DRY MATTER)[1]

Body Weight	Average[2] Daily Gain	Daily Feed per Animal	Total Protein	Digestible Protein	TDN	DE[3]	Ca	P	Carotene	Vitamin A[4]
(lb.)	(lb.)	(lb.)	(lb.)	(lb.)	(lb.)	(therm)	(gm.)	(gm.)	(mg.)	(IU X 1000)
Fattening calves finished as short yearlings										
400	2.3	12	1.3	1.0	8.0	16	20	15	7	2.8
600	2.4	16	1.8	1.3	10.9	22	20	17	10	4.0
800	2.2	20	2.0	1.5	13.6	27	20	18	14	5.6
1000	2.2	22	2.2	1.6	15.0	30	20	20	17	6.8
Fattening yearling cattle										
600	2.4	18	1.8	1.4	11.7	23	20	17	10	4.0
800	2.8	22	2.2	1.6	14.3	29	20	20	14	5.6
1000	2.5	26	2.6	2.0	16.9	34	20	24	17	6.8
1100	2.3	27	2.7	2.0	17.6	35	20	25	19	7.6
Fattening two-year cattle										
800	2.8	24	2.4	1.8	14.9	30	20	22	14	5.6
1000	3.0	27	2.7	2.0	16.7	33	20	25	17	6.8
1200	2.6	29	2.9	2.2	18.0	36	20	26	20	8.0
Wintering weanling calves										
400	1.0	11	1.1	0.7	6.0	12	13	10	7	2.8
500	1.0	13	1.3	0.8	7.0	14	13	10	9	3.6
600	1.0	15	1.4	0.8	8.0	16	13	10	10	4.0
Wintering yearling cattle										
600	1.0	16	1.3	0.8	8.0	16	13	11	10	4.0
800	0.7	18	1.4	0.8	9.0	18	13	12	14	5.6
900	0.5	18	1.4	0.8	9.0	18	13	12	15	6.0

Weight										
Wintering pregnant heifers										
700	1.5	20	1.5	0.9	10.0	20	15	14	28	11.2
900	0.8	18	1.4	0.8	9.0	18	13	12	36	14.4
1000	0.3	18	1.4	0.8	9.0	18	13	12	40	16.0
Wintering mature pregnant cows[5]										
800	1.5	22	1.6	1.0	11.0	22	16	15	32	12.8
1000	0.4	18	1.4	0.8	9.0	18	13	12	40	16.0
1200	0.0	18	1.4	0.8	9.0	18	13	12	48	19.2
Cows nursing calves, first 3–4 months postpartum										
900–1100	0.0	28	2.3	1.4	16.8	34	30	23	100	40.0
Normal growth heifers and steers										
400	1.6	12	1.4	0.8	7.0	14	16	11	7	2.8
600	1.4	16	1.5	0.9	8.5	17	15	12	10	4.0
800	1.2	19	1.5	0.9	9.5	19	15	13	14	5.6
1000	1.0	21	1.6	1.0	10.5	21	13	14	17	6.8
Bulls, growth and maintenance (moderate activity)										
600	2.3	16	2.0	1.2	10.1	20	21	15	36	14.4
1000	1.6	20	2.4	1.4	12.0	24	19	15	60	24.0
1400	1.0	24	2.4	1.4	14.2	28	17	16	84	33.6
1800	0.0	26	2.4	1.5	14.0	28	15	18	108	43.2

1 From *Nutrient Requirements of Beef Cattle*, revised 1958, NAS–NRC Publication No. 579, with the permission of the National Research Council. These are requirements and not allowances. Rations meeting these standards should promote optimum liveweight gains in fattening cattle, continuous and rapid growth of young stock, and high percentage calf crops in breeding herds with heavy weaning weights; but these standards do not provide for margins of safety to compensate for variations in feed composition, environment and possible losses during storage or processing (Tables 25 and 26 contain recommended allowances; they provide for margins of safety).

2 Average daily gain for fattening cattle is based upon cattle receiving stilbestrol. Fattening cattle not receiving stilbestrol gain from 10 to 20 per cent slower than the indicated values.

3 DE (digestible energy) was calculated on the assumption that one gram of TDN has 4.41 kcal. (large calorie) of digestible energy. New information suggested that the value of 4.41 is more accurate than the 4.45 value often used previously. DE may be converted to metabolic energy by multiplying by 82 per cent. 1,000 large calories equal one therm.

4 Multiply figures in column by 1,000. Vitamin A requirement computed on the basis of 1 mg. carotene equals 400 I.U. Vitamin A.

5 Under some range conditions it may not be economically justifiable to feed pregnant cows during winter months these levels of total feed and TDN. Short periods of moderate weight loss can be tolerated without serious effect.

TABLE 17
NUTRIENT REQUIREMENTS OF BEEF CATTLE EXPRESSED AS PERCENTAGE COMPOSITION OF AIR-DRY RATIONS[1]

Body Weight	Average[2] Daily Gain	Daily Feed per Animal	Percentage of Ration or Amount, per Pound of Feed							
			Total Protein	Digestible Protein	TDN	DE[3]	Ca	P	Carotene	Vitamin A[5]
(lb.)	(lb.)	(lb.)	(%)	(%)	(%)	(therms[4]/lb.)	(%)	(%)	(mg./lb.)	(I.U./lb.)
Fattening calves finished as short yearlings										
400	2.3	12	11.0	8.2	67	1.33	0.37	0.28	0.6	240
600	2.4	16	11.0	8.2	68	1.36	0.28	0.23	0.6	240
800	2.2	20	10.0	7.5	68	1.36	0.22	0.20	0.7	280
1000	2.2	22	10.0	7.5	68	1.36	0.20	0.20	0.8	320
Fattening yearling cattle										
600	2.4	18	10.0	7.5	65	1.30	0.25	0.21	0.6	240
800	2.8	22	10.0	7.5	65	1.30	0.20	0.20	0.6	240
1000	2.5	26	10.0	7.5	65	1.30	0.17	0.20	0.7	280
1100	2.3	27	10.0	7.5	65	1.30	0.16	0.20	0.7	280
Fattening two-year cattle										
800	2.8	24	10.0	7.5	62	1.24	0.18	0.20	0.6	240
1000	3.0	27	10.0	7.5	62	1.24	0.16	0.20	0.6	240
1200	2.6	29	10.0	7.5	62	1.24	0.15	0.20	0.7	280
Wintering weanling calves										
400	1.0	11	10.3	6.2	55	1.10	0.26	0.20	0.6	240
500	1.0	13	10.3	6.2	54	1.08	0.22	0.17	0.7	280
600	1.0	15	9.1	5.5	53	1.05	0.19	0.15	0.7	280
Wintering yearling cattle										
600	1.0	16	8.3	5.0	50	1.00	0.18	0.15	0.6	240
800	0.7	18	7.5	4.5	50	1.00	0.16	0.15	0.8	320
900	0.5	18	7.5	4.5	50	1.00	0.16	0.15	0.8	320

Wintering pregnant heifers

700	1.5	20	7.5	4.5	50	1.00	0.16	0.15	1.4	560
900	0.8	18	7.5	4.5	50	1.00	0.16	0.15	2.0	800
1000	0.5	18	7.5	4.5	50	1.00	0.16	0.15	2.2	880

Wintering mature pregnant cows[6]

800	1.5	22	7.5	4.5	50	1.00	0.16	0.15	1.5	600
1000	0.4	18	7.5	4.5	50	1.00	0.16	0.15	2.2	880
1200	0.0	18	7.5	4.5	50	1.00	0.16	0.15	2.6	1040

Cows nursing calves, first 3-4 months postpartum

900-1100	0.0	28	8.3	5.0	60	1.20	0.24	0.18	3.6	1440

Normal growth heifers and steers

400	1.6	12	11.7	7.0	58	1.16	0.29	0.21	0.6	240
600	1.4	16	9.3	5.6	53	1.06	0.20	0.16	0.6	240
800	1.2	19	7.8	4.7	50	1.00	0.17	0.15	0.7	280
1000	1.0	21	7.8	4.7	50	1.00	0.14	0.15	0.8	320

Bulls, growth and maintenance (moderate activity)

600	2.3	16	12.5	7.5	63	1.26	0.29	0.21	2.2	880
1000	1.6	20	12.0	7.2	60	1.20	0.21	0.17	3.0	1200
1400	1.0	24	10.0	6.0	59	1.18	0.16	0.15	3.5	1400
1800	0.0	26	9.3	5.6	54	1.08	0.13	0.15	4.2	1680

[1] From *Nutrient Requirements of Beef Cattle*, revised 1958, NAS–NRC Publication No. 579, with the permission of the National Research Council.

These are requirements and not allowances. Rations meeting these standards should promote optimum liveweight gains in fattening cattle, continuous and rapid growth of young stock, and high percentage calf crops in breeding herds with heavy weaning weights; but these standards do not provide for margins of safety to compensate for variations in feed composition, environment and possible losses during storage or processing (Tables 25 and 26 contain recommended allowances; they provide for margins of safety).

[2] Average daily gain for fattening cattle is based upon cattle receiving stilbestrol. Fattening cattle not receiving stilbestrol gain from 10 to 20 per cent slower than the indicated values.

[3] Digestible energy (DE) was calculated on the assumption that one gram of TDN contains 4.41 kilocalories (kcal.) of DE. DE may be converted to metabolizable energy by multiplying by 82 per cent.

[4] One therm equals 1,000 kilocalories or large Calories or 1,000,000 small calories (1,000,000 cal.).

[5] Vitamin A requirement computed on the basis of 1 mg. carotene equals 400 I.U. Vitamin A.

[6] Under some range conditions it may not be economically justifiable to feed pregnant cows during winter months these levels of total feed and TDN. Short periods of moderate weight loss can be tolerated without serious effects.

tem of production, should be ample to replace the daily break-down of the tissues of the body including the growth of hair, horns, and hoofs. In general, the protein needs are greatest for the growth of the young calf and for the gestating-lactating cow. The minimum protein requirements of different classes and weights of cattle are given in Tables 16 and 17. A deficiency of protein will result in poor growth, depressed appetite, reduced milk secretion, irregular estrus, and loss of weight.

As protein supplements ordinarily cost more per ton than grains, normally beef cattle should not be fed larger quantities of these supplements than actually needed to balance the ration. On the other hand, it may be economical in certain areas to pro-vide more protein supplements than are required. The latter sit-uation often prevails in the feeding of alfalfa hay in the West and cottonseed meal in the South. Under such circumstances, the protein requirements can be greatly exceeded without toxicity and without sacrificing performance of animals.

With yearlings or older cattle that are being fattened, or in the maintenance of the beef-breeding herd, it usually does not pay to add a protein supplement when a legume hay is fed. With younger cattle, or when the breeding herd is being wintered on a non-legume roughage, sufficient protein supplement—usually one to two pounds daily—should be added to the ration.

Because of rumen synthesis of essential amino acids by microorganisms, the quality of proteins is of less importance in the feeding of beef cattle than in feeding some other classes of stock. Proteins from plant sources, therefore, are quite satisfac-tory. Also, these microorganisms—which are a low form of plant life and are able to use inorganic compounds such as ammonia just as plants utilize chemical fertilizers—build body proteins of high quality in their cells from sources of inorganic nitrogen that non-ruminants cannot use. Since the life span of these bacteria is short, further on in the digestive tract, the ruminant digests the bacteria and obtains good protein therefrom. In ruminant nutri-tion, therefore, even such non-protein sources of combined nitro-gen as urea and ammonia have a protein replacement value. An exception is the very young ruminant in which the rumen and its synthetic ability are not yet well developed. For such an animal, high quality proteins in the diet are requisite to normal development.

Energy Needs

A relatively large portion of the feeds consumed by beef cattle is used in meeting the energy needs, regardless of whether the animals are merely being maintained (as in wintering) or fed for growth, fattening, or reproduction.

The first and most important function of feeds is that of meeting the maintenance needs. If there is not sufficient feed, as is frequently true during periods of droughts or when the winter rations are skimpy, the energy needs of the body are met by breaking down of tissue. This results in loss in condition and body weight.

After the energy needs for body maintenance have been met, any surplus energy may be used for growth or fattening. With the present practice of fattening cattle at early ages, growth and fattening are in most instances simultaneous, and, therefore, not easily separated.

In the fattening process, the percentage of protein, ash, and water steadily decreases as the animal matures and fattens, whereas the percentage of fat increases. Thus the body of a calf at birth may contain about 70 per cent water and 4 per cent fat; whereas the body of a fat two-year-old steer may contain only 45 to 50 per cent water but from 30 to 35 per cent fat. This storage of fat requires a liberal allowance of energy feeds.

Through bacterial action in the rumen, cattle are able to utilize a considerable portion of roughages as sources of energy. Yet it must be realized that with extremely bulky rations the animal may not be able to consume sufficient quantities to produce the maximum amount of fat. For this reason, fattening rations contain a considerable proportion of concentrated feeds, mostly cereal grains. On the other hand, when the energy requirements are primarily for maintenance, roughages are usually the most economical sources of energy for beef cattle.

At times, animal fats may be cheap enough to merit consideration as partial substitutes for standard energy feeds. Also, it is probable that very small amounts of fatty acids are essential for beef cattle, as is true in certain other species, but no requirements have thus far been established.

Mineral Needs

Table 18, Beef Cattle Mineral Chart, contains a complete summary of the mineral needs of and recommendations for beef

TABLE 18—BEEF CATTLE

Minerals Which May Be Deficient Under Normal Conditions	Conditions Usually Prevailing Where Deficiencies Are Reported	Function of Mineral	Some Deficiency Symptoms
Salt (Sodium and Chlorine)	Negligence; for salt is inexpensive.	Sodium and chlorine help maintain osmotic pressure in body cells, upon which depends the transfer of nutrients to the cells and the removal of waste materials. Also sodium is important in making bile, which aids in the digestion of fats and carbohydrates, and chlorine is required for the formation of hydrochloric acid in the gastric juice so vital to protein digestion.	Intensive craving of salt, depraved appetite (as evidenced by chewing wood, licking dirt, ev..), lack of appetite, unthrifty appearance, loss of weight, decreased efficiency of feed utilization, and marked decrease in milk production.
Calcium	When fattening cattle are fed heavily on concentrates and limited quantities of non-legume roughage; especially young cattle on a long feed. When the diet consists chiefly of dried mature grasses or cereal straws. When cows are in heavy lactation.	Essential for development and maintenance of normal bones and teeth. Important in blood coagulation and lactation. Enables heart, nerves, and muscles to function. Regulates permeability of tissue cells.	Calcium deficiency in beef cattle is rare and mild; the symptoms are inconspicuous. With severe privation, there may be fractured bones.
Phosphorus	When cattle subsist for long periods on mature, non-leguminous forages. When the fattening ration consists of a high proportion of beet by-products; especially for young cattle on long feed. When cattle subsist on pastures in phosphorus deficient areas.	Essential for sound bones and teeth, and for the assimilation of carbohydrates and fats. A vital ingredient of the chief protein in the nuclei of all body cells. Necessary for enzyme activation. Acts as a buffer in blood and tissue. Occupies a key position in biologic oxidation.	Loss of appetite, poor gains, low blood phosphorus, decreased milk production, decreased feed efficiency, depraved appetite with special craving for chewing bones, lameness and stiffness of joints, broken bones. Rickets in young animals and osteomalacia, osteoporosis, and osteitis fibrosa in mature animals.

¹As used herein, the distinction between "nutrient requirements" and "recommended allowances" is as follows: In nutrient requirements, no margins of safety are included intentionally; whereas in "recommended allowances" margins of safety are provided to compensate for variations in feed composition, environment, and possible losses during storage

MINERAL CHART

Nutrient Requirements[1]				
Daily Nutrients/ Animal	Percentage of Ration	Recommended Allowances[1]	Practical Sources of the Mineral	Comments
*For young, growing animals: 1.5 grams of sodium, and less than 5 grams of chlorine. *For lactating cows: 11 grams of sodium, and 15 grams of chlorine.	*Full fed cattle: 0.5% salt in the total ration.	Free choice feeding of salt. Cows on pasture or on high-roughage winter rations will consume from 1 to 3 lbs. salt per head per month; fattening steers on heavy grain rations in dry-lot will consume about ¾ lb. per head per month.	Free access to salt in the form of loose-, rock-, or block-salt. Cattle prefer loose salt to block salt, since it can be eaten more rapidly and with less effort. However, experiments with growing dairy heifers and lactating cows have shown fully as good results with block salt as with loose salt even though smaller quantities were consumed.	The salt requirements of cattle differ (1) between individuals, (2) according to whether or not milk is produced (being higher for lactating cows than for dry cows, because of the salt in tne milk), (3) from season to season, (4) according to the weathering losses to which the salt is subjected (being higher on pasture than in the dry-lot; exposed block salt loses about 15% per month), (5) between block and loose salt (animals often consuming twice as much easy-to-get loose salt as block salt), and (6) according to the salt content of the soil, feed, and water (being higher when vegetable proteins are fed, than when animal proteins are fed, higher on predominantly forage rations than on predominantly concentrate rations, and higher on lush early pasture than on more mature grasses). These are some of the reasons why free choice feeding of salt is advocated.
*13 to 30 grams calcium; according to class, age and weight of cattle (See Table 16).	*0.13 to 0.37% Ca.; according to class, age, and weight of cattle (See Table 17).	Free access to a calcium supplement, or 0.1 lb. of a calcium supplement added to the daily ration.	Ground limestone, steamed bone meal, oyster shell flour, di-calcium phosphate, or defluorinated phosphate; free choice, or 0.1 lb. per head daily added to the ration.	In addition to an adequate supply of calcium and phosphorus, proper utilization of these minerals is dependent upon (1) a suitable ratio between them (somewhere between 1 to 2 parts of calcium to 1 or 2 parts of phosphorus; this is one reason why bone meal is one of the better mineral supplements—its calcium-phosphorus ratio being satisfactory, with 29% calcium and 14% phosphorus), and (2) sufficient Vitamin D (as provided eitner by exposure to sunlight or through the ration). However, the calcium-phosphorus ratio is not as critical in the case of cattle as with some other species. Generally when cattle receive at least ⅓ of a legume forage, ample calcium will be provided. But even non-legume forages contain more calcium than cereal grains.
10 to 26 gms. P; according to class, age, and weight of cattle (See Table 16).	*0.20% P. in fattening rations, and 0.15% P. in other rations (See Table 17 for more specific recommendations for different classes, ages, and wts. of cattle).	Free access to a phosphorus supplement, or 0.1 lb. of a phosphorus supplement added to the daily ration.	Steamed bone meal, di-calcium phosphate, defluorinated phosphate, or spent bone char: free choice, or 0.1 lb./head daily added to the ration.	Phosphorus deficiency in cattle is world-wide, especially in semi-arid regions and where soils are deficient in the element. Cattle receiving 1 lb. or more per day of a protein supplement of plant origin (feeds high in phosphorus) will receive an ample supply of this mineral. Phosphorus requirements will be met when cattle receive (1) 1 lb. of grain, or (2) 2 lbs. of alfalfa hay/100 lbs. live wt. daily. (See statement under calcium pertaining to importance of calcium-phosphorus ratio and vitamin D.)

or processing. Where preceded by an asterisk, the nutrient requirements and recommended allowances listed herein were taken from *Nutrient Requirements of Beef Cattle*, revised 1958, NAS-NRC Publication No. 579.

TABLE 18

Minerals Which May Be Deficient Under Normal Conditions	Conditions Usually Prevailing Where Deficiencies Are Reported	Function of Mineral	Some Deficiency Symptoms
Iodine	In iodine-deficient areas (soils) where iodized salt is not fed (in northwestern U.S. and in the Great Lakes region).	Iodine is needed by the thyroid gland in making thyroxin (an iodine-containing compound which controls the rate of body metabolism or activity).	Production of big necked or goitrous calves; most of which do not live. Occasional borderline cases may survive; in these, the moderate thyroid enlargement disappears in a few weeks.
Cobalt	In cobalt-deficient areas (soils) where this element is not provided (in Florida and in parts of Mich., Wis., N. H., N. C., and N. Y.).	Essential (along with iron and copper) in the prevention of anemia. Also it is necessary for the synthesis of vitamin B_{12} and the growth of rumen bacteria.	Affected animals become weak, emaciated, and eventually die. Other symptoms include loss of appetite, craving for hair and wood, scaliness of skin, and sometimes diarrhea.
Copper	In copper-deficient areas (soils) as in Florida. Deficiencies have occurred in beef cattle kept on nurse cows for long periods beyond normal weaning age.	Copper, along with iron, is necessary for hemoglobin formation, although it forms no part of the hemoglobin molecule (or red blood cells).	Emaciation, depigmentation and loss of hair, stunted growth, anemia, and brittle bones. Also heat periods are suppressed, and there may be depraved appetite and diarrhea. Young calves may have straight pasterns and stand forward on their toes.
Magnesium	When milk feeding of calves is prolonged without grain or hay (milk is rather low in magnesium). Deficiencies under usual feeding practices are unlikely.	Essential for the bones and teeth, and required for various body processes.	Magnesium content of blood plasma is lowered, and there is irritability, lack of nerve control, poor appetite, and convulsions in calves.
Although thought to be essential under natural conditions, no evidence of deficiencies in cattle have been observed of the following mineral elements: manganese, zinc, sulfur, potassium, and iron.			

(Continued)

Nutrient Requirements[1]				
Daily Nutrients/ Animal	Percentage of Ration	Recommended Allowances[1]	Practical Sources of the Mineral	Comments
*400 to 800 micrograms iodine/day for a 1,000 lb. cow producing 40 lbs. of milk daily.		Free access to stabilized iodized salt containing 0.01% potassium iodide (0.0076% iodine). Or cuprous iodide (Cu2I2) may be used.	Stabilized iodized salt containing 0.01% potassium iodide. Or cuprous iodide (Cu2I2) may be used.	The enlargement of the thyroid gland (goiter) is nature's way of trying to make enough thyroxin, when there is insufficient iodine in the feed.
*0.07 to 0.10 mg. cobalt/100 lbs. body weight.		Free access to a cobaltized mineral mixture.	A cobaltized mineral mixture may be prepared by adding cobalt at the rate of 0.2 oz. per 100 lbs. of salt as cobalt chloride or cobalt sulfate.	Several good commercial cobalt-containing minerals are on the market. A vitamin B12 injection will relieve a cobalt deficiency.
	*4 to 8 ppm copper of total air-dry ration. When optimum ration conditions exist, such as low levels of molybdenum and sulfate, the copper requirement is probably 4 to 5 ppm.	*Copper deficiency can be prevented by adding 0.25 to 0.5% copper sulfate to salt fed free-choice.	Salt containing 0.25 to 0.5% mixture of copper sulfate.	Copper-deficient cattle can be returned to normal by feeding 3 grams of copper sulphate or blue vitriol every 10 days. An interesting interrelation exists between copper and molybdenum. An excess of molybdenum causes a condition which can be cured only by administering copper. Excess copper is toxic.
*0.6 gram magnesium per 100 lbs. body wt. for dairy calves.		Natural rations appear to contain adequate magnesium.	Commonly fed roughages and concentrates contain ample magnesium.	Although so-called grass tetany, which is characterized by lowered blood-serum magnesium, is sometimes attributed to magnesium deficiency, uncomplicated cases have been produced only on purified diets or by prolonged feeding of calves on milk.
	*6 to 10 ppm. manganese in the air-dry ration.	Natural rations appear to contain adequate manganese, since (1) many roughages contain 50 to 150 ppm. of manganese on a dry basis, and (2) grains other than corn contain 15 to 50 ppm.		
	*Probably less than 15 mg iron per lb. of feed.	Levels of iron in feed believed to be ample, since feeds contain 40 to 400 milligrams/lb. The likelihood of zinc deficiency in beef cattle appears remote since most forages contain from 10 to 100 ppm.		

See footnote on p. 290

cattle; thus needless repetition will be avoided in the ensuing discussion.

It is generally agreed that the mineral requirements of beef cattle are less critical than those of most other classes of livestock. On the other hand, cattle are subject to the usual inefficiencies and ailments when exposed to (1) prolonged and severe mineral deficiencies, or (2) excesses of fluorine, selenium or molybdenum. (See Table 27 for a summary of Nutritional Deficiency Diseases and Ailments of Cattle.)

A sound recommendation for all classes and ages of cattle is to provide free access to a mineral box containing two compartments, with (1) salt (iodized salt in iodine-deficient areas) in one side, and (2) a mixture of $\frac{1}{3}$ salt (salt added for purposes of palatability and $\frac{2}{3}$ bone meal (or other calcium-phosphorus supplement) in the other side. The salt will always be needed; and the bone meal will be cheap insurance, with the animal eating it if either calcium or phosphorus, or both, are lacking in the ration. In those areas where cobalt and/or copper deficiencies exist, these minerals should be added, either to the salt or to the salt-mineral mixture.

SALT:

Salt should be available at all times. It may be fed in the form of loose, rock, or block salt; but because of weathering

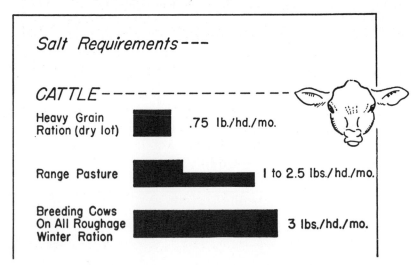

Salt Requirements---

CATTLE---------------

Heavy Grain Ration (dry lot)   .75 lb./hd./mo.

Range Pasture   I to 2.5 lbs./hd./mo.

Breeding Cows On All Roughage Winter Ration   3 lbs./hd./mo.

Fig. 104. The average salt requirements of cattle. (Drawing by Steve Allured)

losses, flake salt is not satisfactory for feeding in the open. If block salt is used, the softer types should be selected.

Most ranchers compute the yearly salt requirements on the basis of about twenty-five pounds for each cow.[1] Mature animals will consume two to three pounds of salt per month when pastures are lush and succulent and one to one and one-half pounds per month during the balance of the season.

Fig. 105. Steer licking block salt. Fattening cattle in the dry-lot consume about two-thirds of a pound of salt per head per month, whereas animals on pasture require about twice this amount. (Courtesy, Iowa State College)

Salt deficiency in cattle is manifested by intense craving for this mineral and the other deficiency symptoms shown in Table 18. High producing milk cows may even collapse and die when the salt deficiency has been of long duration.

Excessive salt intake can result in toxicity. However, as much as 3 pounds of salt can be consumed daily by cows without deleterious effects provided animals have free access to an abundant supply of drinking water.

The careful location of the salt supply is recognized as an

---

[1]Ensminger, M. E., M. W. Galgan, and W. L. Slocum, Wash. Agri. Expt. Sta. Bul. 562, p. 43.

important adjunct in proper range management. Through judicious scattering of the salt supply and the moving of it at proper intervals, the animals can be distributed more properly; and overgrazing of certain areas can be minimized.

See Table 18 for the sodium and chlorine requirements of beef cattle.

CALCIUM:

In contrast to phosphorus deficiency, calcium deficiency in beef cattle is relatively rare and mild and the symptoms much less conspicuous. In general, when the forage of cattle consists of at least one-third legume, (legume hay, pasture, or silage), ample calcium will be provided. But even non-legume forages contain more calcium than cereal grains. This indicates that a mineral source of calcium is less necessary when large quantities of roughage are being consumed. Also, plants grown on calcium-rich soils contain a higher content of this element.

As fattening steers consume a high proportion of grains to roughages—and the grains are low in calcium—they have a greater need for a calcium supplement than do beef cattle that are being fed largely on roughages. This is especially true of cattle of the younger ages and where a long feeding period is involved.

When the ration of beef cattle is suspected of being low in calcium, the animals should be given free access to a calcium supplement (plus ⅓ salt added for purposes of palatibility), with salt provided separately; or a calcium supplement may be added to the daily ration in keeping with nutrient requirements (see Table 18).

Table 19 gives the composition of some common calcium and phosphorus supplements.

PHOSPHORUS:

In some sections of this and other countries, the soils are so deficient in phosphorus that the feeds produced thereon do not provide enough of this mineral for cattle or other classes of stock. As a result, the cattle produced in these areas may have depraved appetites, may fail to breed regularly, and may produce markedly less milk. Growth and development are slow, and the animals become emaciated and fail to reach normal adult size. Death losses are abnormally high.

Fattening cattle that receive one pound or more per head daily of a protein supplement of plant origin (cottonseed meal, soybean meal, linseed meal, etc., or two pounds per head per day of cull peas—supplements high in phosphorus), will receive an ample supply of this mineral. Also, the phosphorus requirement will usually be met when cattle receive daily (1) one pound of

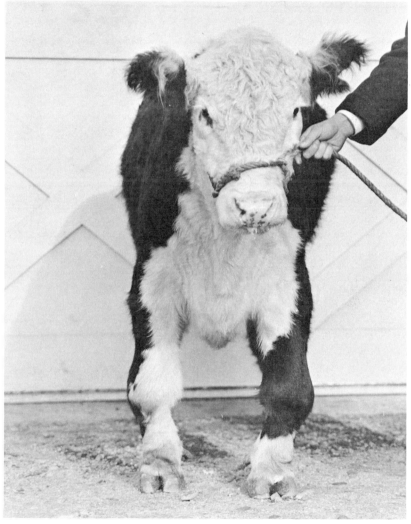

Fig. 106. This cow developed rickets early in life. Note the bowed front legs and enlarged joints. (Courtesy, USDA, Agricultural Research Service, Animal Husbandry Research Division)

TABLE 19

COMPOSITION OF CALCIUM AND PHOSPHORUS SUPPLEMENTS[1]

Mineral Supplement	Calcium		Phosphorus		Fluorine
	Percent	Grams per Pound	Percent	Grams per Pound	Percent
Bone meal, raw, feeding......	22.7	103	10.1	46	0.030
Bone meal, special steamed..	28.7	130	13.9	63	———
Bone meal, steamed............	30.0	136	13.9	63	0.037
Defluorinated phosphate rock a[2]............................	21.0	95	9.0	41	0.15 or less
Defluorinated phosphate rock b[2]............................	29.0	132	13.0	59	0.15
Defluorinated super- phosphate........................	28.3	128	12.3	56	0.15
Dicalcium phosphate...........	26.5	120	20.5	93	0.05
Disodium phosphate...........	——	——	8.6	39	———
Limestone (high calcium)....	38.3	174	——	——	———
Monocalcium phosphate......	16.0	72	24.0	109	0.05
Monosodium phosphate.......	———	——	22.4	102	———
Oyster shell flour.................	36.9	167	——	——	———
Spent bone black.................	22.0	100	13.1	59	———

[1]From *Nutrient Requirements of Beef Cattle*, revised 1958, NAS-NRC Publication No. 579, with the permission of the National Research Council.

[2]Because of the limited number of products on the market, figures given for two types of defluorinated rock which are being produced for livestock feeding.

grain, or (2) two pounds of alfalfa hay per hundred pounds body weight.

Fig. 107. Bone chewing by cattle is a common sign of phosphorus deficiency. (From Texas Station Bulletin 344, through the courtesy of The National Fertilizer Association)

In range areas where the soils are either known or suspected to be deficient in phosphorus, cattle should always be given free access to bone meal or other phosphorus supplement. The need for a phosphorus supplement in such areas is strikingly illustrated by the following observations made on the King Ranch in Texas:

"Analysis of records for two calving seasons showed that 85 per cent of the cows receiving phosphorus supplement produced calves, as compared with 64 per cent for the other cows. Calves from the phosphorus supplement-fed cows averaged 69 pounds more at weaning, and 126 pounds more at 18 months of age than the others. After deduction of the cost of the supplement, the value of the weaned calves averaged $5.78 more. In further tests, phosphorus was supplied (1) in the form of bone meal placed in self-feeders, (2) by dissolving disodium phosphate in the drinking water, and (3) by applying a super-phosphate fertilizer to the pasture. All methods were satisfactory, the last giving the best results."[1]

To be on the safe side, the general recommendation for beef cattle on both the range and in the fattening lot is to allow free choice of bone meal (or other phosphorus supplement) and salt in separate compartments of a mineral box, or to add a phosphorus supplement to the ration in keeping with nutrient requirements (see Table 18).

COBALT:

Cobalt deficiencies in cattle are costly, for the affected animals become weak and emaciated and eventually die. Florida is without doubt the most serious cobalt-deficient area in the United States, but similar deficiencies of a lesser order have been observed in Michigan, Wisconsin, New Hampshire, North Carolina, and New York. Cattle in these affected areas should have access to a cobaltized mineral mixture, made by mixing 0.2 ounce of cobalt chloride or cobalt sulfate per 100 pounds of either (1) salt, (2) bone meal, or (3) a mixture of ⅓ salt and ⅔ bone meal; or a good commercial cobalt-containing mineral should be provided.

In different sections of the world, a cobalt deficiency is known as Denmark disease, coastal disease, enzootic marasmus, bush sickness, salt sickness, nakuritis, and pining disease.

---

[1]*Research Achievement Sheet*, USDA. This work was done in cooperation with the Texas Agri. Exp. Sta. and the Bureau of Animal Industry.

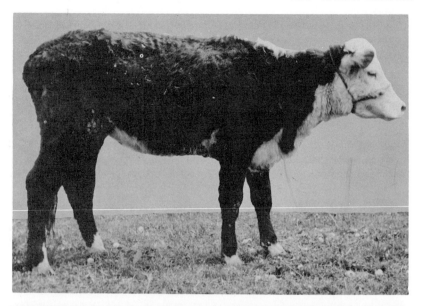

Fig. 108. Cobalt deficiency:
    The upper picture shows a heifer suffering from a cobalt deficiency. Anemia, loss of appetite and roughness of hair coat characterize the malady.
    The lower picture shows the remarkable recovery in the same animal brought about by the administration of cobalt.
(Courtesy, C. F. Huffman, Michigan State University)

OTHER MINERAL NEEDS:

Iodized salt should always be fed to cattle in iodine-deficient areas (such as northwestern U. S. and the Great Lakes region). This can be easily and cheaply accomplished by providing stabilized iodized salt containing 0.01 per cent potassium iodide (0.0076 per cent iodine).

Copper is sometimes deficient in the soils of certain areas, notably in the state of Florida. In such areas, 0.25 to 0.5 per cent of copper sulfate should be incorporated in the salt or mineral mixture. In addition to being an area disease, copper deficiencies have occurred in beef cattle kept on nurse cows for periods extending beyond normal weaning age.

Under usual feeding practices, magnesium deficiencies are unlikely. However, a deficiency of this mineral may occur when milk feeding of calves is prolonged without grain or hay, for milk is rather low in magnesium.

Recent research indicates that molybdenum is an essential mineral nutrient, being an integral part of an important enzyme system of the body. Although the requirement is unknown, it must be extremely small since 10 to 20 ppm in forage results in toxic symptoms. Thus, it is not recommended that molybdenum additions be made to beef cattle rations under most conditions pending more information on requirements.

Although thought to be essential, under natural conditions no evidence of deficiencies in cattle have been observed of the following mineral elements: manganese, zinc, sulfur, potassium, and iron.

COMPLEX MINERAL MIXTURES:

Most animal husbandmen favor the use of simple mineral mixtures. Either providing an excessive amount of minerals or a complex mineral mixture when it is not necessary is expensive and wasteful, and any imbalances may actually be injurious to animals. In general, the wise policy consists in knowing the mineral content of the available feeds and providing, in proper amounts, only those essential minerals which are deficient.

VALUE AND ECONOMY OF COMMERCIAL
MINERAL MIXTURES:

In a study made by Washington State University, it was found that 71 per cent of cattlemen contacted fed a mineral supplement other than salt.[1] Of those feeding a mineral supplement, 78.3 per cent reported feeding a commercial mineral mix, 17.3 per cent used a home-mixed mineral, and 4.4 per cent used both commercial- and home-mixed minerals.

Some commercial mineral mixtures are very good; others are equally bad. There is every reason why commercial mineral mixtures can and should be equal in quality to home-mixed products, but, unfortunately, this frequently is not the case. In altogether too many cases, commercial mineral mixtures have been compounded and sold by unscrupulous, misinformed and fraudulent operators.

Good commercial mineral mixtures, like good home-mixed mineral mixtures, supply only the specific minerals that are deficient, and in the quantities necessary. Excesses and mineral imbalances are avoided. Thus, the value of any commercial mineral mixture can be easily determined by how well it meets the needs.

It is noteworthy that many commercial mineral mixtures contain several unessential ingredients, including such things as silicates, charcoal, coal, Epsom salts, Glauber salts and sodium carbonate. Because of the presence of these and other ingredients, such mineral mixtures are variously extolled for their added properties as laxatives, worm expellers and tonics. In strict privacy, however, some mineral manufacturers refer to such added ingredients as "eye wash"; a phrase which implies their recognized lack of value except for sales purposes. It is no credit to stockmen who buy such products, for it takes little imagination to realize (1) that healthy animals do not need such treatment, and (2) that sick animals need more expert diagnosis and more specific treatment than could possibly be obtained through such cure-alls.

If a given commercial mineral mixture meets the specific needs as well as a home-mixed product, the choice between the two should be determined by their comparative economy; that is, which is the cheaper. This can be arrived at by comparing, per hundred pounds, (1) the cost of the commercial mineral mixture laid down on the farm, with (2) the cost of the ingredients which need to be purchased to home-mix, plus the cost of mixing.

---

[1]Ensminger, M. E., M. W. Galgan, and W. L. Slocum, Wash. Agri. Expt. Sta. Bul. 562, p. 43.

Vitamin Needs[1]

A rather complete summary of the vitamin needs of beef cattle is presented in Table 20, Beef Cattle Vitamin Chart; thus

Fig. 109. Effect of vitamin A deficiency on reproduction.

The heifer in the upper picture received a ration deficient in vitamin A but otherwise complete. She became night blind and aborted during the last month of pregnancy; also, note the retained placenta.

The heifer in the lower picture received the same ration, but during the latter part of the gestation period a supplement of 1 pound daily of dehydrated alfalfa meal containing 50 mg. of carotene was added. She produced a normal vigorous calf.

(Courtesy, California Agricultural Experiment Station)

[1]See Table 27 for a summary of Nutritional Deficiency Diseases and Ailments of Cattle.

TABLE 20—BEEF CATTL

Vitamins Which May Be Deficient Under Normal Conditions	Conditions Usually Prevailing Where Deficiencies Are Reported	Function of Vitamin	Some Deficiency Symptoms
A (Vitamin A is found only in animals; plants contain the precursor—carotene.)	Vitamin A deficiencies may occur when—(1) extended drought results in dry, bleached pastures, (2) winter feeding on bleached hays (especially over-ripe cereal hays or straws) with little or no green hay or silage, and (3) dry-lot fattening on rations with little or no green forage or yellow corn, especially for feeding periods longer than 2 to 3 months.	Vitamin A—(1) promotes growth and stimulates appetite, (2) assists in reproduction and lactation, (3) helps keep the mucous membranes of respiratory and other tracts in healthy condition, and (4) makes for normal vision.	Stunted growth or loss in appetite or weig Small calf crop, with many calves weak stillborn; some calves may be born bl' or without eyeballs. Night blindness (faulty vision in twilig or Xerophthalmia (an eye disease). Staggering gait. Diarrhea, especially in young calves. In fattening cattle, generalized edema anasarca may occur with clinical sympto of lameness in the hock and knee joi and swelling in the brisket area. Bulls of breeding age decline in sex activity; spermatozoa decrease in numb and motility, and there is a marked crease in abnormal forms. In breeding cows, estrus may be normal conception rate may be low. Tetany.
D	Young calves kept indoors, especially in the wintertime.	Aids in assimilation and utilization of calcium and phosphorus, and necessary in the normal bone development of animals–including the bone of the fetus.	Rickets in young calves Vitamin D deficiency in the pregnant a mal may result in dead, weak or deforn calves at birth.
E (Also see Table 27, page 409.)		Necessary for the development of the muscular system.	Muscular dystrophy (commonly called wl muscle disease) in calves 2 to 12 weeks age; characterized by heart failure paralysis varying in severity from sli lameness to inability to stand. Also dystrophic tongue often is seen in affec animals.
B Vitamins and K	Vitamin K deficiency may occur when the dicumarol content of hay is excessively high.		

[1]As used herein, the distinction between "nutrient requirements" and "recommended allowances" is as follows: In nutrient requirements, no margins of safety are included intentionally; whereas in nutrient allowances margins of safety are provided in order to compensate for variations in feed composition, environment, and possible losses during storage

VITAMIN CHART

Nutrient Requirements[1]			Amount per lb. of feed	Recommended Allowances[1]	Practical Sources of the Vitamin	Comments
Daily Nutrients/Animal						

Per 100 lbs. Body Wt.

	Mg. Carotene	Internat'l Units A[2]
Normal growth	1.4—1.7	500—680
Pregnancy	3.0—4.0	1200—1600
Lactation	10.0	4000

(See Table 16 for more specific recommendations.)

Amount per lb. of feed: (See Table 17)

Practical Sources of the Vitamin: Green pasture. Grass or legume silages. Yellow corn. Green hay not over 1 yr. old.
The average carotene content of some common feeds is as follows:

	Mg. Carotene/ lb.
Legume hays (including alfalfa), average quality	9–14
Non-legume hays, average quality	4–8
Dehydrated alfalfa meal, average quality	50–70
Yellow corn	2.2
Silages	5–20

Comments: Hay over 1 yr. old, regardless of green color, is usually not an adequate source of carotene or vitamin A activity.
The younger the animal, the quicker vitamin A deficiencies will show up. Mature animals may store sufficient vitamin A to last 6 months. When deficiency symptoms appear, it is recommended that there be added to the ration either (1) dehydrated alfalfa or grass, or (2) a stabilized vitamin A product.

Calves require 300 I.U. of Vitamin /100 lbs. live wt. daily.

Recommended Allowances: Normally beef cattle receive sufficient vitamin D from exposure to direct sunlight or from sun-cured hay.

Practical Sources of the Vitamin: Exposure to direct sunlight. Sun-cured hay. Irradiated yeast.

Comments: Sun-cured alfalfa hay contains 300 to 1,000 international Units/lb.

Calves require 40 milligrams of alpha-tocopherol/100 lbs. wt./day.

Recommended Allowances: Generally natural feeds supply adequate quantities of alpha-tocopherol for mature cattle, although muscular dystrophy in calves occurs in certain areas.

Practical Sources of the Vitamin: Alpha-Tocopherol.

Comments: There is no experimental evidence that the feeding of wheat germ oil will improve the fertility of either males or females.
The incidence of white muscle disease appears to be lower where the cows receive 2 to 3 lbs. of grain during last 60 days of pregnancy.

Comments: During the first 8 weeks of life of the calf, the dietary requirements for the B vitamins are usually adequately met by milk from the dam; after this, these vitamins are usually synthesized by the rumen bacteria.
Except when the dicumarol content of hay is excessively high (as in sweet clover hay) sufficient vitamin K is synthesized in the rumen of cattle.

---

or processing. Where preceded by an asterisk, the nutrient requirements listed herein were taken from *Nutrient Requirements of Beef Cattle,* Revised 1958, NAS-NRC Publication No. 579.

[2]Vitamin A requirements computed on the basis of 1 Mg. of carotene equals 400 I.U. Vitamin A.

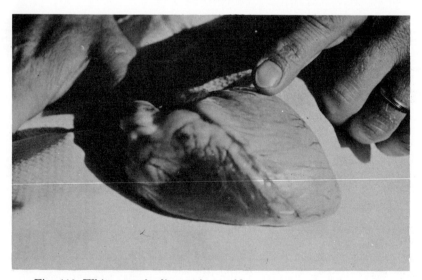

Fig. 110. White muscle disease in a calf.

Upper picture shows the generalized weakness of muscles, lameness, and difficulty in locomotion of an afflicted calf.

Lower picture shows abnormal white areas in the heart muscles of a six-week-old calf afflicted with white muscle disease.

(Courtesy, O. H. Muth, Oregon Agricultural Experiment Station)

needless repetition will be avoided in the ensuing discussion.

Under normal conditions, vitamin A is the only vitamin likely to be lacking in cattle rations; and they receive plenty of the precursor (carotene) when they are on green pasture, or when they are receiving ample amounts of grass silage or of green hay not over one year old. Yellow corn and green peas are also good sources of vitamin A for cattle that are being grain fed.

In meeting the vitamin A requirements of beef cattle, consideration should be given to (1) body storage of vitamin A as influenced by previous feeding, and (2) carotene destruction of feeds during storage. During periods of abundant intake from pasture and other feeds, cattle store vitamin A and carotene in the liver and in body fat. If sufficiently large, these storage reserves may be used for limited periods of time in reducing or completely covering the day-to-day needs of cattle for carotene or vitamin A. On the other hand, the day-to-day needs of cattle for carotene or vitamin A may appear to be increased due to oxidative destruction of these materials in feeds during storage.

Table 21 gives the estimated carotene content of feeds in relation to appearance and method of conservation.

Detection of vitamin A deficiency can be confirmed by carotene and vitamin A analysis of blood and liver tissues of cattle.

When vitamin A deficiency symptoms appear, it is recommended that there be added to the ration either (1) dehydrated alfalfa or grass, or (2) a stabilized vitamin A product.

In usual production methods, beef cattle are exposed to enough direct sunlight to acquire their vitamin D needs, for the ultra-violet light in the sunlight penetrates the skin and produces vitamin D from traces of cholesterol in the tissues; although there may be an exception with young calves kept indoors, especially in wintertime. Also, cattle generally consume sufficient sun-cured roughages to obtain their vitamin D needs.

Through rumen synthesis, it is most likely that all necessary quantities of the B vitamins and vitamin K are manufactured within the digestive tract; and adequate quantities of vitamin E are widely distributed in most all natural feeds, although there is some indication that a vitamin E supplement needs to be added to the ration of young animals under certain conditions. If vitamin C is required by cattle, it appears to be synthesized in ample quantities in the body.

TABLE 21

ESTIMATED CAROTENE CONTENT OF FEEDS IN RELATION
TO APPEARANCE AND METHODS OF CONSERVATION[1]

Feedstuff	Carotene
	(mg. per pound)
Fresh green legumes and grasses, immature	15 to 40
Dehydrated alfalfa meal, fresh, dehydrated without field curing, very bright green color[2]	110 to 135
Dehydrated alfalfa meal after considerable time in storage, bright green color	50 to 70
Alfalfa leaf meal, bright green color	60 to 80
Legume hays, including alfalfa, very quickly cured with minimum sun exposure, bright green color, leafy	35 to 40
Legume hays, including alfalfa, good green color, leafy	18 to 27
Legume hays, including alfalfa, partly bleached, moderate amount of green color	9 to 14
Legume hays, including alfalfa, badly bleached or discolored, traces of green color	4 to 8
Non-legume hays, including timothy, cereal, and prairie hays, well cured, good green color	9 to 14
Non-legume hays, average quality, bleached, some green color	4 to 8
Legume silage	5 to 20
Corn and sorghum silages, medium to good green color	2 to 10
Grains, mill feeds, protein concentrates, and by-product concentrates, except yellow corn and its by-products	.01 to 0.2

[1]From *Nutrient Requirements of Beef Cattle*, revised 1958, NAS-NRC Publication No. 579, with the permission of the National Research Council. This table was prepared by the late H. R. Guilbert, Davis, California.
[2]Green color is not uniformly indicative of high carotene content.

Water Needs

Water is the most vital of all nutrients. It is needed for all the essential processes of the body, such as the digestion and absorption of food nutrients, the removal of waste, and in regulating body temperature. Animals can survive for a longer period without feed than they can without water. Yet, under ordinary conditions, it can be readily provided in abundance and at little cost.

Beef cattle should have an abundant supply of water before them at all times. Mature cattle will consume an average of about twelve gallons of water per head daily, with younger animals requiring proportionally less. In the northern latitudes, heaters should be provided to make the water available, but they are not needed to warm the water further.

Fig. 111. Yearling steers near water on a New Mexico ranch. Water is cheap but essential. (Courtesy, C. B. & Q. Railroad Co.)

FEEDS FOR BEEF CATTLE

Beef cattle feeding practices vary according to the relative availability of grasses, dry roughages, and grains. Where roughages are abundant and grain is limited, as in the western range states, cattle are primarily grown out or fattened on roughages. On the other hand, where grain is relatively more abundant, as in the Corn Belt states, fattening with more concentrates is common.

Pastures for Beef Cattle

Good pasture is the cornerstone of successful beef cattle production. In fact, there has never been a great beef cattle country or area which did not produce good grass. It has also been said that a good farmer or rancher can be recognized by the character of his pastures and that good cattle graze good pastures. Thus the three go hand in hand—good farmers, good pastures, and good cattle. The relationship and importance of cattle and pastures has been further extolled in an old Flemish proverb which says, "No grass, no cattle; no cattle, no manure; no manure, no crops."

Approximately 53.6 per cent of the total land area of the United States is devoted to pasture and grazing lands. Much of this area, especially in the far West, can be utilized only by beef cattle or sheep. Although the term "pasture" usually suggests growing plants, it is correct to speak of pasturing stalk and

Fig. 112. Hereford cattle on pasture, owned by S. H. Pharr, Cecil, Alabama. In the deep South, year-long grazing is approached. (Courtesy, National Cottonseed Products Assoc., Inc.)

stubble fields. In fact, in the broad sense, pastures include all crops that are harvested directly by animals.

The type of pasture, as well as its carrying capacity and seasonable use, varies according to topography, soil, and climate. There is hardly any limit to the number of plants that are utilized as beef cattle pastures throughout the United States. In general, regardless of species or mixtures, pastures may be classified as follows:

1. **Permanent pastures.**—Those which, with proper care, last for many years. They are most commonly found on land that cannot be profitably used for cultivated crops, mainly because of topography, moisture, or fertility. The vast majority of the farms of the U. S. have one or more permanent pastures, and most range areas come under this classification.

2. **Rotation pastures.**—Those that are used as a part of the established crop rotation. They are generally used for 2 to 7 years before plowing.

3. **Temporary and supplemental pastures.**—Those that are used for a short period, usually annuals such as Sudan grass, millet, rye, wheat, oats, rape or soybeans. They are seeded for the purpose of providing supplemental grazing during the season when the regular permanent or rotation pastures are relatively unproductive.

Because of the hundreds of species of grasses and legumes that are used as beef cattle pastures, each with its own best adaptation, no attempt is made to discuss the respective virtues of each variety. Instead, it is recommended that the farmer or rancher seek the advice of his local county agricultural agent or vocational agriculture instructor, or write to his state agricultural college.

No method of harvesting has yet been devised that is as cheap as that which can be accomplished through grazing by animals. Accordingly, successful beef cattle management necessitates as nearly year-round grazing as possible. In the northern

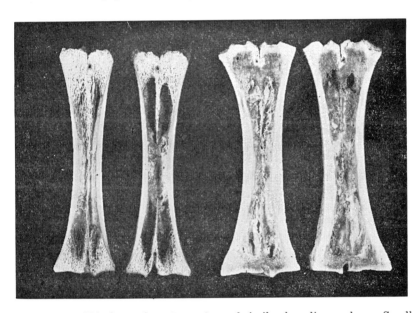

Fig. 113. Shin bones from two calves of similar breeding and age. Small bones (left pair) obtained from calf pastured on "belly deep" grasses grown on highly weathered but untreated soil. Heavy bones (right pair) obtained from calf pastured on grasses grown on moderately weathered but fertilized soil, including "trace" elements. (Courtesy, Dr. W. A. Albrecht, University of Missouri)

latitudes of the United States, the grazing season is usually of about six months' duration, whereas in the deep South year-long grazing is approached. In many range areas of the West, the breeding herds obtain practically all their forage the year round from the range, being given supplemental roughage only if the grass or browse is buried deep in snow.

During the winter months, and in periods of drought, the pasture utilized by beef cattle may consist of dried grass cured on the stalk. On a dry basis, the crude protein content of mature, weathered grasses may be 3 per cent or less. To supplement such feed, cattlemen commonly feed cake or cubes. The use of cake or cubes instead of meal reduces losses from wind blowing, an especially important factor on the range.

In some instances, cattle on pasture fail to make the proper growth or gain in condition because the soil is seriously deficient in fertility or the pasture has not been well managed. In such instances, striking improvement will result from proper fertilization and management.

Hays and Other Dry Roughages for Beef Cattle

Hay is the most important harvested roughage fed to beef cattle, although many other dry roughages can be and are utilized.

The dry roughages are all high in fiber and therefore low in total digestible nutrients. Hay averages about 28 per cent fiber and straw approximately 38 per cent, whereas such concentrates as corn and wheat contain only 2 to 3 per cent fiber. Fortunately, cattle are equipped to handle large quantities of roughages. In the first place, the paunch of a mature cow has a capacity of three to five bushels, thus providing ample storage for large quantities of less concentrated feeds. Secondly, the billions of microorganisms in the rumen attack the cellulose and pentosans of the fibrous roughages, such as hay, breaking them down into available and useful nutrients. In addition to providing nutrients at low cost, the roughages add needed bulk to cattle rations.

Roughages, like concentrates, may be classified as carbonaceous or nitrogenous, depending on their protein content. The principal dry carbonaceous roughages used by cattle include hay from the grasses, the straws and hays from cereal grains, corn cobs, and the stalks and leaves of corn and the grain sorghums. Cured nitrogenous roughages include the various legume hays such as alfalfa, the clover hays, peanut hay, soybean hay, cowpea hay, and velvet bean hay.

Although leguminous roughages are preferable, weather conditions and soils often make it more practical to produce the non-legumes. Also, in many areas, such feeds as dry grass cured on the stalk, cereal straws, and corn cobs are abundantly available and cheap. Under such circumstances, these feeds had best be used as part of the ration for animals that are not being fed for high production, such as for wintering beef cows or for wintering stockers that are more than one year of age.

In comparison with good quality legume hays, the carbonaceous roughages are lower in protein content and in quality of proteins, lower in calcium, and generally deficient in carotene (provitamin A). Thus, where non-legume roughages are used for extended periods, these nutritive deficiencies should be corrected; this is especially true with the gestating-lactating cow or the young, growing calf. To the end that the feeding value of some of the common non-legumes may be enhanced for beef cattle, the following facts are pertinent:

1. The feeding value of non-legume hays can be increased by cutting them at an early stage of maturity and curing so as to retain as much of the carotene content as possible.

2. Where dry and bleached pastures are grazed for an extended period of time or where there is an unusually long winter, it is important that at least part of the roughage be a legume, either silage or hay, and that suitable protein and mineral supplements be provided.

3. Potentially, corn cobs—which were formerly considered a waste product and of little worth—have a feeding value approaching that of hay. However, their energy cannot be utilized unless they are fortified with certain nutrients which help the bacteria and other organisms of the rumen break them down into a form which can be digested. Also, corn cobs are low in palatability.

4. Cereal straws may be incorporated in the wintering ration of pregnant cows or in the ration of fattening steers provided their fundamental characteristics and nutritional limitations are recognized and corrected (see sections on "Feeding the Dry and Pregnant Cows" and "Dry Lot Fattening").

Silages and Roots for Beef Cattle

Silage is an important adjunct to pastures in beef cattle production, it being possible to use a combination of the two forages in furnishing green, succulent feeds on a year-round basis. Extensive use of silage for beef cattle dates back only to about 1910. Prior to that time, it was generally thought of as a feed for dairy cows. Even today, only a relatively small percentage of the beef cattle of the United States are fed silage.

Where silage has been used, it has proved quite popular. Some of the more important reasons advanced in favor of silage are as follows:

1. On most beef cattle producing farms, silage is the cheapest form in which a good succulent winter feed can be provided.

2. It is the cheapest form in which the whole stalk of an acre of corn or sorghum can be processed and stored.

3. Good silage can be made during times of rainy weather when it would be impossible to cure properly hay or fodder.

4. It helps to control weeds, which are often spread through hay or fodder.

5. Silage is a better source of vitamins, especially carotene and perhaps some of the unknown factors, than dried forages.

6. There is no danger of fire loss to silage.

7. Silage is a very palatable feed and slightly laxative in nature.

8. Converting the crop into silage clears the land earlier than would otherwise be possible.

9. Silage makes for less waste, the entire plant being eaten with relish.

10. The removal of corn stalks, as is required in making silage, is one of the best methods of controlling the European corn borer.

11. Silage increases the number of animals that can be kept on a given area of land.

Corn was the first and still remains the principal crop used in the making of silage, but many other crops are ensiled in various sections of the country. The sorghums are the leading ensilage crop in the Southwest, and grasses and legumes are the leading ensilage crops in the Northeast. Also, in different sections of the country to which they are adapted, the following feeds are ensiled: cereal grains, field peas, cowpeas, soybeans, potatoes, and numerous fruit and vegetable refuse products. A rule of thumb is that crops that are palatable and nutritious to animals as pasture, as green feed, or as dry forage also make palatable and nutritious silage. Conversely, crops that are unpalatable and non-nutritious as pasture, as green feed, or as dry forage, also make unpalatable and non-nutritious silage.

With the increasing interest in grassland agriculture, more and more grass silage—silage made from green crops which might otherwise be pastured or dried and made into hay, such as

the grasses, legumes, grass-legume mixtures, and cereal grains
—is being fed to beef cattle. Also, grass silage can be produced
in those areas where the climate is too cool and the growing
season too short for corn or sorghum silage. Grass silage is generally higher in protein and carotene, but lower in total digestible
nutrients and vitamin D, than corn or sorghum silage. Generally
grass silage contains about 90 per cent as much Total Digestible
Nutrients (TDN) as corn silage, but it is equal in TDN when 150
pounds of grain per ton has been added as a preservative. Thus,
grass silage generally requires the addition to the ration of less
protein supplement but more total concentrates than corn or
sorghum silage. This would indicate that corn or sorghum silage
would be slightly preferable to grass silage in high roughage
fattening rations for beef cattle, whereas grass silage would be
preferable in high roughage rations for young, growing beef
cattle.

When silage is fed to cattle, it must be remembered that, because of its high moisture content, about three pounds of silage
are generally considered equivalent to one pound of dry roughage of comparable quality. Fifty-five to sixty pounds of corn sil-

Fig. 114. Iowa cattleman feeding corn silage. On most beef cattle establishments, silage is the cheapest form in which a good succulent winter feed
can be provided. (Courtesy, Wallace's Farmer & Iowa Homestead)

age plus one-half to three-fourths pound of a protein concentrate daily will carry a dry cow through the winter. The ration may be improved, however, by replacing one-third to one-half of the silage with an equivalent amount of a dry roughage, adding one pound of dry roughage for each three pounds of silage replaced.

Silage may be successfully used for fattening steers. Two-year-old steers will eat thirty to forty-five pounds a day at the beginning of the feeding period, the larger amounts being consumed when no hay is fed with it. Better results are obtained, however, if hay is included in the ration. The amount of silage is gradually decreased as the concentrates are increased. At the end of the feeding period, the cattle should be getting around fifteen to eighteen pounds of silage and two or three pounds of hay, or eighteen to twenty pounds of silage if no hay is fed. Because of the more limited digestive capacity, the allowance of silage fed to calves or yearlings should be correspondingly less.

Usually, silage provides a much cheaper succulent feed for beef cattle than roots. For this reason, the use of roots for beef cattle is very limited, being confined almost entirely to the northern districts.

Concentrates for Beef Cattle

The concentrates include those feeds which are low in fiber and high in nutritive value. For purposes of convenience, concentrates are often further classified as (1) carbonaceous feeds, and (2) nitrogenous feeds.

In general, the use of concentrates for beef cattle is limited to (1) the fattening of cattle, (2) the development of young stock, and (3) use as limited supplements in the winter ration. Over most of the United States, the cereal grains are the chief concentrates fed to beef cattle; these grains being combined, if necessary, with protein supplements to balance the ration.

CARBONACEOUS CONCENTRATES:

The chief carbonaceous concentrates used for beef cattle are the cereal grains and such processed feeds as hominy feed, beet pulp, and molasses. The choice of the particular feeds is usually determined primarily by price and availability.

For best results, the feeder should correct the nutritive deficiencies of the cereal grains. All of them are low in protein, low in calcium, and lacking in vitamin D. All except yellow corn are also deficient in vitamin A. Regardless of whether the cereal grains are fed to growing, breeding, or fattening animals, their nutritive deficiences can be corrected in a very effective and practical way either by adding (1) a good quality legume hay to the ration, or (2) a protein concentrate plus a suitable mineral source of calcium.

NITROGENOUS CONCENTRATES:

Figure 115 shows the leading nitrogenous or high protein feeds utilized by beef cattle in this country.[1] This indicates that cottonseed oil meal is used by more cattlemen than any other protein supplement and commercial feed supplements rank second, while 21.1 per cent of the cattlemen do not feed any supplement. Some area differences exist; for example, cottonseed oil meal is used more extensively in the South than elsewhere, due to its relatively greater abundance and lower price in that area. As is true in the selection of high energy feeds, the choice of a protein supplement should be determined primarily by price and availability.

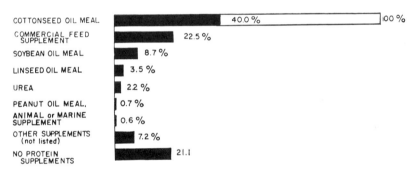

Fig. 115. Kind of protein supplements fed to beef cattle. (Photo courtesy Washington State University)

SOME NEW AND/OR LESS FAMILIAR CONCENTRATES:

It is not within the scope of this book to discuss each of the numerous concentrates fed to beef cattle; instead, only a few of the new and/or less familiar ones will be covered in the discussion which follows:

UREA

Approximately 75 thousand tons of urea are used annually

---

[1]Ensminger, M. E., M. W. Galgan, and W. L. Slocum, Wash. Agri. Expt. Sta. Bul. 562, p. 36.

in the U. S., as a source of protein for cattle, sheep, and goats.[1] In recent years, there has been increased interest in feeding urea to cattle, due primarily to the following circumstances:

1. **Shortage of oil meal proteins.**—The scarcity and high price of normal supplies of oil meal protein feeds is well known. The U. S. normally produces about 9 million tons of oil seed cake and meal from soybeans, cottonseed, flaxseed and peanuts; whereas an additional 4 to 5 million tons of these products could be used advantageously if all animals were supplied an adequate amount of protein.

2. **Progress in fundamental ruminant nutrition.**—Through basic studies, scientists have established many of the nutrient requirements of rumen microorganisms, thereby permitting the preparation of balanced supplements designed to enable animals to get the most out of the roughages that they consume. This knowledge has led to the extensive use of such low-grade roughages as corn cobs, straws, and poor-grade hays—many of which had been wasted previously.

These factors, plus meeting the needs of a rapidly expanding human population, are likely to continue to accentuate the interest of feed manufacturers and cattle producers in utilizing urea and other non-protein nitrogen sources.

When properly used, urea is a valuable cattle feed; when improperly used, it may be a needless expense, or, worse yet, a hazard. To the end that the first condition may more frequently prevail, the following summary is presented:

1. **Feed grade urea.**—Since pure urea cakes and becomes hard, the manufacturer adds conditioning agents to prevent such caking in preparing a feed grade product; thereby lowering the nitrogen content from 46.6 per cent (the content of pure urea) to 42 per cent. Thus, the protein equivalent value of feed grade urea is 42 (per cent nitrogen) times 6.25 (common protein factor), or 262 per cent protein.

One pound of urea contains as much nitrogen as 6.4 pounds of soybean oil meal of 41 per cent protein content. It is obvious, therefore, that comparatively small

---

[1]Urea should not be used in swine and poultry rations. It has little or no value as a protein substitute for swine and poultry, although it is not toxic to them when fed in amounts normally recommended for ruminants.

amounts of urea are required to satisfy the nitrogen requirements of ruminants under normal conditions.

2. **Feeding value of urea.**—One ton of feed grade urea combined with 6 tons of cereal grain provides the same amount of protein and nearly as much energy as 7 tons of soybean or cottonseed oil meals.

3. **Utilization of urea by ruminants.**—Nature has provided cattle and other ruminants with a remarkable digestive system centering around the first stomach or rumen. This rumen serves as a large fermentation vat where billions of bacteria and other microorganisms live and multiply, if properly nourished. Rumen bacteria are actually tiny plants, and, like the bacteria in field soils, they are able to break down tough, coarse, fibrous material into simpler carbohydrates and to use these carbohydrates along with the sugars and starches, protein, non-protein nitrogen (such as urea) and minerals in forming their own bodies.

Rumen bacteria have first access to all the feeds consumed by the ruminating animals. In carrying out their own living processes, they convert much of the feeds into simple substances which are absorbed by the animals and used for maintenance and for meat and milk production. As the bacteria grow and multiply they produce bacterial protein. They digest the proteins in the feeds and also make protein from simple sources such as urea. While scientists do not yet completely understand all aspects of protein utilization in the rumen, there is considerable evidence that the bacteria change a substantial amount of all proteins into bacterial protein, which is of good quality. This development enables ruminants to have good quality protein available and makes them comparatively independent of the quality of the protein in the feed. This is in marked contrast to the situation with man, dogs, swine and poultry where considerable care must be exercised to provide all the essential amino acids in proper proportions for efficient and economical production. Young calves are like other mammals and do need the high quality protein, such as that in their mother's milk, until the rumen has developed enough to function efficiently.

The rumen bacteria are very small, and they are constantly being carried down into the true stomach and small intestines of the animal where digestive juices produced by the animal break the bacterial protein down into the simple amino acids which are then absorbed and used by the host.

4. **Use of urea in balanced feeds.**—To obtain value from urea, it must be fed with some easily fermentable carbohydrates, such as the starches of grains or the sugar of molasses. The carbohydrates in grasses and hays appear to be so slowly available that the bacteria have difficulty in using the energy from roughages to make use of urea in preparing bacterial protein. It is generally held that some preformed protein should be present in the feed also. Part of this will be provided by the grains and frequently some oil meals are used in preparing the formula feeds. Evidence is accumulating that starch and protein provide one or more organic substances that are required for the bacteria to grow and multiply. This information has been discovered recently and the full implications are not yet understood.

Other components of a balanced feed include calcium, phosphorus, iron, copper, cobalt, manganese, and perhaps zinc and sulfur and magnesium. The need for these minerals as well as for vitamin A will depend upon local conditions with respect to the types of roughages produced and the influence of weather upon the quality of such roughages.

Other factors influencing the formulation include the purpose such as for the breeding herd, creep-feeding, or for use in the fattening lot.

5. **Quantity of urea that may be fed.**—Urea may constitute up to one-third[1] of the total protein of the ration of cattle, provided additional energy is added in the form of molasses or grain to compensate for the lack of energy in the urea,[2] to feed properly the rumen bacteria. By total protein is meant the protein intake of the entire ration—including forage, grain and protein supplements. This

---

[1]Some authorities place the upper limit at 50%. Cattle on fattening rations may consume up to 0.22 lb. of urea per day without deleterious effects. However, it appears that the most desirable level lies between 0.11 and 0.22 lb. per day—or near 0.15 lb. per steer daily.

[2]For every pound of urea added to the ration, 5 to 6 lbs. of a cereal grain or molasses should be added to replace the energy lost.

means that urea may safely constitute up to 1 per cent by weight, of the total feed—hay, dry grass, silage, grain, and supplement—consumed on a dry weight basis. Usually, amounts equivalent to this 1 per cent level, by weight, will be obtained provided the following rules of thumb are observed:

(1) Urea may constitute up to 2 to 3 per cent, by weight, of the concentrate (grain and supplement) alone.

(2) Urea may constitute up to 5 to 6 per cent by weight, of the protein supplement alone.

Less urea than indicated above is recommended in range cubes or pellets because (1) of the more limited grain and the poor quality roughage usually fed, and (2) of the uncertainty of feeds being consumed regularly under adverse weather conditions. Thus, it is recommended that urea be limited to 3 to 4 per cent, by weight, of range cubes or pellets[1] used primarily to supplement dried range grass cured on the stalk. Also, when feeding on the range, it is important that the supplement be spread out evenly and in such a manner that the gluttonous animals do not get more than their share and the weak ones, that need help the most, are denied the benefits of the supplementary feed.

6. **Palatability.**—Although various opinions exist relative to the palatability of urea and urea-containing feeds, most feeders feel that urea is not palatable and, therefore, that feed consumption may be lowered in comparison with rations in which oil meal protein supplements are used entirely. For this reason, care should be exercised in selecting an appetizing urea-supplemented mixture.

In contrast to the above opinion, it should be noted that, occasionally, cattle will consume straight fertilizer urea or ammonium nitrate in sufficient amount to poison themselves.

Sometimes cattle will consume a urea-containing feed for a few days or weeks and then refuse it. This has occurred in drought areas where farmers have tried to extend their roughage supplies by feeding straw and other mineral-poor low quality roughages. Appropriately in-

---

[1]The balance of the ingredients in range cubes or pellets usually consists of ground grain, molasses, oil meal proteins, and, under certain conditions, minerals (including trace minerals) and vitamin A supplements. Generally, the urea and molasses are first mixed, and then added to the rest of the concentrate.

creasing phosphorus and trace minerals has corrected the latter problem.

7. **Economy in feeding urea.**—Whether urea should be used in place of protein supplements should be decided on the basis of price relationships. If the cost of 1 ton of urea (42 per cent nitrogen) plus 6 tons of cereal grain is less than that of seven tons of common protein concentrate (41 per cent protein), then it is economical to use urea.

There is also a convenience angle in using urea. Because of its very high protein equivalent, it is possible to alter greatly the protein content of a feed by merely adding or withholding a small quantity of urea. Thus, the use of some urea simplifies the formulation of feeds of guaranteed analysis.

8. **Precautions and limitations in feeding urea.**—Like many good things in life, urea can be successfully and effectively used, or it can be abused. When an animal consumes too much urea, the consequences may range from mild indigestion to prostration and death. Of course, the better the management and feeding program, the safer it is to use urea.

Much more research needs to be done before some of the questions concerning the feeding of urea can be answered. In the meantime, the following precautions and limitations should be observed:

(1) **Urea does not provide any energy, minerals or vitamins.**—This is not a criticism; it is merely a factual recognition. Protein oil meal supplements do supply these nutrients in varying amounts.

This point is important because the utilization of urea is dependent on bacterial action, and bacteria require these nutrients for growth.

(2) **Since protein contains 1 part of sulfur to 16 parts of nitrogen, either methionine or inorganic sulfur supplements may prove beneficial when urea is fed to cattle.**—It is noteworthy, however, that studies have failed show any benefit from adding supplemental sulfur to practical rations containing as much as 40 per cent of the nitrogen in the form of urea, presumably due to adequate supplies of sulfur already present in the ration.

(3) **Mix thoroughly.**—Urea must be mixed **thoroughly** and **uniformly** in the ration, otherwise one animal may get enough to be poisoned.

(4) **Examine the feed tag.**—Always examine the feed tag to gain the benefits of the manufacturer's instructions.

(5) **Exercise caution in feeding very hungry animals.**— An animal that has not had anything to eat for several days is particularly susceptible to toxicity from urea-containing feeds. For this reason, it is recommended that starved animals be fed hay only for the first 1 to 2 days, and then very gradually given concentrates.

(6) **Feed daily.**—On the range, supplements should be fed daily; rather than once or twice per week, as is sometimes tried.

(7) **Gradually add urea to poor roughage rations.**— Animals on very poor roughages should be fed limited amounts of supplement for 1 to 2 days in order for the bacterial population in the rumen to be built up to a vigorous level, following which a regular level of supplementation may be employed.

(8) **Check feed ingredients for compatibility with urea.**— Raw soybeans, underheated soybean oil meal, jackbeans, lespedeza seed, alfalfa seed, and wild mustard seed contain the enzyme urease which will split urea into ammonia and carbon dioxide. The liberated ammonia may be strong enough to be objectionable to cattle. Eventually, the animals will eat the feed, but the protein level will be reduced.

(9) **Urea is likely poorly utilized under the following conditions:**
   a. When added to a hay ration and no grain or molasses is fed.
   b. When the balance of the ration consists of molasses and grass hay, with little or no grain or other source of starch.
   c. When a grass silage ration, which is fairly high in nitrogen, is fed.
   d. When the ration already contains sufficient nitrogen in the form of protein.

e. When there are interrupted feeding or starvation conditions for a few days followed by generous feeding or gorging.

9. **Other forms of non-protein nitrogen.**—Ammoniated molasses is now on the market, also ammoniated beet pulp and ammoniated citrus pulp have been prepared. The possibility exists that other ammoniated products will be forthcoming. In general, the availability and utilization of the ammonia in these products appears to involve about the same principles as in the use of urea. Yet, each such product should be evaluated by controlled feeding trials.

ANIMAL FATS

The feeding of animal fats was prompted in an effort to find a profitable outlet for fats, which were in great surplus.[1]

The energy content of fats is approximately 2.25 times that of carbonaceous feeds. This means that only small amounts are required substantially to increase the energy content of cattle rations. Not more than 4 to 6 per cent animal fat should be added to most cattle rations.

In compounding fat-containing cattle rations, consideration should be given to the following:

1. The fat should first be stabilized to prevent rancidity.[2]
2. Fats do not provide proteins, vitamins, or minerals.
3. High fat-containing rations are more difficult to mix and to pellet.

With favorable prices—that is, if price relationships are such that fats can be used to furnish energy more cheaply than carbohydrates—it is predicted that the feeding of animal fats will increase, because, in addition to feed efficiency and possible other animal benefits, there are several advantages to adding fats to rations from the standpoint of feed mixing. Among the latter are: (1) control of dustiness, (2) decreased wear on mixing machinery, and (3) improved appearance and "feel" of the ration.

---

[1] It is estimated that an annual surplus of 1.1 billion pounds of animal fats is produced. For the most part, these fats were formerly used for soap making; but they are not used extensively in detergents. Thus, with the rise in the use of detergents, they became a drug on the market.

[2] To prevent rancidity and to increase the utilization and stability of vitamin A and carotene, the use of the anti-oxidant butylated hydroxyanisole (BHA) or some formulation containing BHA is recommended.

MILK REPLACER (OR SYNTHETIC MILK)

Several reputable commercial companies now produce and sell milk replacers (or synthetic milks).

Although scientists have not yet learned how to compound a synthetic product that will alleviate the necessity of colostrum, in certain other respects they have been able to improve upon nature's product, milk. For example, it has long been known that milk is deficient in iron and copper, thus resulting in anemia in suckling young if proper precautions are not taken. In addition to correcting these deficiencies, synthetic milks are fortified with vitamins, minerals and antibiotics.

From the standpoint of the beef cattle producer, a milk replacer is of primary interest for two uses; namely, (1) for raising orphaned calves, and (2) for replacing nurse cows. Also, it is a valuable adjunct in certain disease control programs, especially those diseases that may·be transmitted from dam to offspring.

The raising of orphaned calves will be simplified if the calf has first received colostrum. For this purpose, the milk replacer should be mixed according to the directions of the manufacturer. For the first few days, the milk may be fed by using a bottle and a rubber nipple. Then the calf should be taught to drink from a pail. It is important that all receptacles be kept absolutely clean and sanitary (clean and sterilize each time) and that feeding be at regular intervals. Also, orphaned calves should be given a calf starter (grain) and hay at the earliest possible time.

A very high percentage of purebred cattle breeders who show young animals use nurse cows. This practice appears to be imperative if they win; for in no other manner can they obtain the necessary bloom and finish on animals in the younger age groups. Admittedly, the use of nurse cows has many disadvantages; namely, (1) the high cost in purchasing and maintaining them, (2) the added space requirements in keeping nurse cows, (3) the possibility of introducing a disease when bringing them into the herd, (4) the facts that they may not freshen when they are needed most, and that the amount of milk cannot be regulated, (5) the nursing of cows by large calves, with the accompanying "butting" and bruising, predisposes mastitis, (6) the cost of transportation for nurse cows when on the show circuit, and (7) the embarrassment in keeping a group of nurse cows about the premises.

Except for the cost factor—and the cost of milk replacer

will likely be less than the total cost in purchasing and keeping nurse cows—the use of milk replacer alleviates all of the disadvantages which accompany the use of nurse cows. Moreover, if properly used, the author is of the opinion that milk replacer will out-do a nurse cow. The following procedure is recommended for feeding show calves on milk replacer:

1. Let the calf nurse its dam until the regular weaning time, at 6 to 7 months of age.

2. At 3 to 4 weeks of age, feed dry milk replacer in a creep or in a separate feed box. At first, mix it with a little oat meal or other very palatable feed. Later, the dry milk may be mixed with calf starter or the regular show ration. Always keep the feed trough clean, and the feed fresh and sweet.

3. Feed as much milk replacer as desired. Thus, if it is the intent to give the calf an amount of dry milk replacer equivalent to what it would get from sucking a nurse cow giving 3 to 4 gallons of milk per day, about 3 to 4 pounds of dry milk replacer should be fed daily (Milk is about 13% solids; thus, 1 pound of dry milk replacer is equivalent to 1 gallon of milk).

4. Wean the calf at 6 to 7 months of age. At weaning time, the amount of milk replacer can be increased so as to replace whatever milk the calf was getting from its dam; thus alleviating any setback.

SELF-FEEDING SALT-FEED MIXTURES TO RANGE CATTLE[1]

In this country the practice of self-feeding a mixture of salt and protein supplement appears to have originated with range sheepmen in Texas, beginning about 1934. These ingenious operators devised the method to alleviate plant poisoning in sheep. Since then, the practice has become widespread among cattlemen, receiving its greatest impetus with the labor shortage during World War II.

---

[1]In the preparation of this section, the author had the benefit of the authoritative review and suggestions of the following persons: Professor E. B. Stanley, Department of Animal Husbandry, University of Arizona, Tucson, Ariz.; Professor J. K. Riggs, In Charge of Beef Cattle, Agricultural and Mechanical College of Texas, College Station, Texas; Professor A. B. Nelson, Department of Animal Husbandry, Oklahoma State University, Stillwater, Okla.; Professor J. H. Knox, Head, Department of Animal Husbandry, New Mexico State University, State College, N. M.; and Mr. J. A. Gray, Extension Specialist, Court House, San Angelo, Texas.

In a survey[1] made by Washington State University, 30 per cent of the responding cattlemen reported that they followed this practice.

Early reports of cattlemen and sheepmen self-feeding controlled amounts of protein supplement on the range by regulating

Fig. 116. The practice of self-feeding mixtures appears to be well adapted to inaccessible and rough areas, where daily feeding is difficult. In no case, however, should it be an excuse to accord neglect to animals, for herds and flocks need to be checked often. (Drawing by R. F. Johnson)

the amount of salt mixed with the meal were often dismissed as incredible, if not just a lazy man's way of supplemental feeding on the range. Some ranchers and scientists were skeptical, fearing salt poisoning and other hazards. Nevertheless, the practice grew in popularity, even after the war-time labor shortage was over. Today, more salt-feed mixtures are being self-fed than ever before.

Our present knowledge of self-feeding salt-feed mixtures to range cattle is very limited. More research work is needed. However, based on a combination of experience and available scientific research, the following deductions appear to be justified:

1. It is possible to control the self-fed consumption of feeds

[1]Ensminger, M. E., M. W. Galgan, and W. L. Slocum, Wash. Agri. Expt. Sta. Bul. 562, p. 39.

through regulating the proportion of salt in a salt-feed mixture, without any apparent harm to cattle.

2. It appears that the practice need not be limited to any specific protein supplement or feed. Some ranchers report successfully using (1) salt-cottonseed meal mixtures, (2) salt-soybean meal mixtures, or (3) mixtures of salt, alfalfa meal, molasses, grain, trace minerals, etc.

3. It is possible to feed salt-feed mixtures in either ground or pelleted form. Practical operators report that pelleting the salt-feed mixtures lessens wind losses, and makes for greater ease in storing and feeding. When the feed is pelleted, however, it is important that the pellets be small and not too hard; otherwise cattle are apt to swallow them without the salt being fully effective as an inhibitor, with the resulting hazard of overeating.

4. The Arizona Experiment Station found that cattle have a much higher tolerance for salt than was previously supposed. Subsequently, both the Texas and Washington Experiment Stations report that they have, without apparent harm, fed cows about 3 pounds of salt daily for several weeks. This amount is considerably in excess of the $\frac{1}{2}$ to 1 1/5 pounds per head consumed daily in self-feeding of salt-feed mixtures to range cattle under practical conditions.

5. It is reported that in practical operations the proportion of salt to feed supplement varies anywhere from 5 to 40 per cent (with 30 to $33\frac{1}{3}$ per cent salt content being most common), with the actual intake of feed supplement limited to 1 to $2\frac{1}{2}$ pounds daily. By varying the proportion of salt in the mixture, it is possible to hold the consumption of feed supplement to any level desired. In some range areas, a reduction of the salt level from $33\frac{1}{3}$ to 24 per cent will increase consumption by about 50 per cent. When a liberal feeding of grain on pasture is desired, 5 per cent salt may be sufficient.[1]

6. It is evident that the quantity of salt and the proportion of salt to supplement required to govern supplement consumption varies according to (1) the daily rate of feed consumption desired, (2) the age and weight of animals (higher quantities of salt are required in the case of older animals), (3) the fineness

---

[1]At the Irrigation Experiment Station, Prosser, Wash., it was found that 10 per cent salt limited grain consumption on pasture to 5 lbs. daily; 5 per cent salt limited grain c nsumption to 10-12 lbs.

of the salt grind (fine grinding lowers the salt requirement), (4) the salinity of the water, (5) the severity of the weather, (6) the quality and quantity of forage, and (7) the length of the feeding period (as animals become accustomed to the mixture, it may be necessary to increase the proportion of salt).

7. It is common practice to prepare the starting feed by mixing 1 pound of salt to 4 pounds of feed supplement, and to increase the proportion of salt in the mixture as the animals become accustomed to the feed.

8. It lessens the difficulty in starting cattle on a supplement, for sprinkling a little salt on the meal makes it more palatable.

9. It is recommended that animals be hand-fed a week or so before allowing free choice to a salt-feed mixture; thus getting them on feed gradually.

10. It is necessary to regulate or limit (by hand-feeding for a few days) the supply of salt-feed mixture when it is desired to shift animals from a straight feed supplement (such as cottonseed meal alone) to a salt-feed mixture. Otherwise, hungry animals may consume too much.

11. It is estimated that the practice increases the total salt consumption to 8 to 10 times that required in conventional salt feeding, and doubles or triples the water consumption.

12. If the salt-feed mixture is placed in close proximity to the water supply, it will likely make for restricted grazing distribution on the range, because of the greater intake of water on a high salt diet. On the other hand, if the salt-feed mixture is shifted about on the range, it will likely make for desirable distribution, because of the animals following the feed supply.

13. It reduces the labor required in feeding, promotes more uniform feed consumption (among the greedy and the timid), and permits animals to eat at their leisure with less disturbance during blizzards or cold weather.

14. It lessens the space required for feed equipment (bunks or feeders) to 20 per cent of that required in conventional hand-feeding, but makes it desirable that the feeder be constructed so as to protect the mixture from the weather (especially the wind and rain).

15. It is equally applicable to feeding during droughts, on dry summer range, and in the winter months.

16. It is commonly believed that under conditions of short

feed supply (sub-maintenance) and relatively inaccessible water supply, animals may consume sufficient salt in this manner to produce toxic effects, especially during the winter months when low temperatures tend to lessen the water intake.

17. It does not appear that high salt consumption will lower the breeding efficiency or otherwise prove harmful to breeding cows. This statement is based primarily on limited experimental work conducted by both the Arizona and the Washington Experiment Stations. There is need, however, for long-time experiments designed to answer this question more completely. It is not known, for example, whether a cow can, without harm, consume 1 pound of salt per day throughout the winter months and then continue on a high salt diet on dry summer range, with the same feeding regimen repeated year after year.

18. The practice of self-feeding salt-feed mixtures appears to be well adapted to inaccessible and rougher areas, where daily feeding is difficult. In no case, however, should it be an excuse to neglect animals, for herds need to be checked often.

19. It reduces the consumption of minerals other than salt to practically nil, with the result that mineral deficiencies must be considered.

20. It involves a different concept of feeding than stockmen have been accustomed to, in that animals are permitted to consume supplements when their appetites dictate the need rather than when man's judgment or energy causes him to hand-feed them.

Hormones, Antibiotics and Other Accessory Ration Ingredients[1]

Most cattlemen are familiar with, or have used, one or more of the hormones, antibiotics, or other accessory ration ingredients. In 1949, it was discovered that antibiotics were something new to be added to livestock feeds. Then, late in 1954, stilbestrol (diethylstilbestrol)—a synthetic female hormone, and not a nutrient—was released by the Food and Drug Administration for use in cattle fattening rations, thereby ushering in the hormone era in ruminant feeding. Two years later, in 1956, the Food and Drug Administration approved the use of stilbestrol

[1]This section and Table 22 were authoritatively reviewed by the following: Dr. Wise Burroughs, Dept. of Animal Husbandry, Iowa State University, Ames, Ia.; Dr. W. M. Beeson, Dept. of Animal Husbandry, Purdue University, Lafayette, Ind.; Dr. C. F. Chappel and Dr. T. M. Means, Eli Lilly & Co., Greenfield, Ind.; Dr. W. M. Reynolds, Chas. Pfizer & Co., Inc., Terre Haute, Ind.; and Dr. I. A. Dyer, Beef Cattle Nutritionist, Department of Animal Science, Washington State University, Pullman, Wash.

implants for steers. Soon, the race was on; other hormones and accessory ration ingredients were rushed in—and more will follow.

Today, many of these growth promotants are being tested and incorporated in practical rations in ruminant feeding for purposes of stimulating liveweight gains, improving feed utilization, and lessening diseases. Among such products are live rumen cultures, vermifuges, antibiotics, surface active agents, arsenical compounds, hormones, tranquilizers, and enzymes (singly and in combination). Many of them are being hailed as "wonder additives." Perhaps many of them have real merit and will be used in practical operations. At the present time, however, our knowledge of the role of most of these hormones and other additives is merely opened up; more research work is needed. For example, the mode of action of most of them is not known.

Despite some glowing reports to the contrary, there is no evidence to indicate that the use of these additives can or will alleviate the need for vigilant sanitation, improved nutrition, and superior management. Also, the benefits of each one must be weighed against its cost.

With the unfolding and applying of scientific information relative to these promotants, the producer will be able to achieve still greater efficiency of production. Although there are many gaps in our knowledge, and more experiments are needed, Table 22 summarizes the present status of the hormones, antibiotics, and other accessory ration ingredients.

In addition to the facts presented in Table 22, the following points are pertinent in the feeding of stilbestrol:

1. **Mixing.**—Stilbestrol must be added in the right amount. and with great care. Too little of the hormone will not produce maximum gains, whereas too much can prove toxic. About one gram per ton of concentrate seems to be about the right amount; this allows for feed consumption of stilbestrol at the rate of about 10 mg. per head daily. To assure proper mixing, the Food and Drug Administration requires that stilbestrol be added as a pre-mix.

2. **Steers vs. heifers; show steers; breeding cattle.**—Oral stilbestrol will give equally good results for either fattening steers or fattening heifers. It is not recommended for show steers, however, because it may result in lack of refinement.

TABLE 22—HORMONE AND OTHER

Animal and Ration	Type of Additive	Method of Administering	Dosage	Daily Rate of Gain
Cattle: 1. Yearling steers and heifers:	Stilbestrol (diethyl-stilbestrol)	Feeding (oral)		(% Incr.)
(1) Dry-lot fattening rations; 2 lbs. gain per day or more.			10 mg. per head daily	Range: 15–25 Av. :17
(2) Dry-lot growing rations: under 2 lbs. gain per day.	"	"	"	Range: 0–37 Av.: 11
(3) High roughage, wintering-type rations.	"	"	"	Av.: 13
(4) Pasture fattening (grain on pasture).	"	"	10 mg. per head daily	Range: 0–30 Av.: 15
2. Cattle under 600 lbs. wt.; in dry lot.	"	"	10 mg. per head daily	
3. Yearling steers:		Implantation		
(1) Dry-lot fattening rations.	"	"	24 to 36 mg.	Av.: 19.8
(2) Pasture only.	"	"	24 mg.	Av.: 20
(3) Pasture fattening (grain on pasture).	"	"	24 mg.	Av.: 13
4. Suckling calves, with or without creep-feeding.	"	"	12 to 24 mg.	

Keep stilbestrol away from breeding animals; it may make them sterile.

3. Adding stilbestrol will not cause cattle to go off feed.— Cattle that are on feed will not go off feed when stilbestrol is added to the ration.

ACCESSORY RATION INGREDIENTS CHART FOR RUMINANTS

	Effect On:		Comments
Feed Efficiency	Carcass Quality	Other	
(% Incr.)			Side effects are negligible when animals are not fed more than 10 mg. per head daily.
Range: 3–26 Av.: 12	No difference in grade or in dressing percentage.		Adequate protein in the ration is essential for satisfactory response to stilbestrol.
Av.: 10			Stilbestrol produces more lean meat and less fat; thus stilbestrol-fed cattle need to be fed to heavier weights.
Av.: 11.5			Stilbestrol can be fed continuously and still get beneficial results in excess of 250 days feeding.
Av.: 11			Response on pasture varies; probably due to the variable natural hormone content of the pasture.
Av.: 12.6	Carcasses from implanted cattle may grade slightly lower than oral stilbestrol-fed cattle.		Implanting of heifers not recommended, because of the side effects; excessive riding, high tailheads, vaginal prolapse and flattened loins. Implants produce slightly higher rate of gain and feed efficiency than oral feeding. Implants of 36 mgs. will be effective through 200 days of feeding. A second and subsequent implantation is recommended if animals go for 200 days or longer; with the second implantation made at around 150 days. Response from stilbestrol is greatest (1) when cattle are on high-energy diets, and (2) during the early phases of the fattening period.
Av.: 11			Implants are especially useful for animals on pasture

4. The fecal droppings of cattle fed estrogenic substances contain increased hormonal activity.—Thus, hogs following cattle fed female-hormone-like substances show mammary and genital stimulation.

5. Natural feed stuffs have been shown to have estrogenic

TABLE 22—

Animal and Ration	Type of Additive	Method of Administering	Dosage	Daily Rate of Gain
5. Fattening cattle.	Antibiotics (aureomycin or terramycin).	Feeding (oral)	10 mg./100 lbs. body wt. daily; or 75 to 80 mg./ head daily.	(% Incr.) Range: 0–21 Av.: 8
6. Creep-fed calves	Antibiotics (aureomycin or terramycin)	Feeding (oral)	15 to 20 mg./ 100 lbs. body wt. daily.	Range: 10–30
7. Fattening cattle	Stilbestrol + antibiotic	Feeding (oral)	10 mg./head daily + 80 mg./head daily.	Av.: 9.0 over stilbestrol alone.
8. Fattening cattle	Progesterone[1]- estradiol	Implantation only	20 mg. 1 gm.	Av.: 31
9. Fattening cattle	Dynafac	Feeding (oral)	1.5 to 2.0 g./ head daily	Variable; 0–16[3]
10. Fattening cattle	Tranquilizers[2]	Feeding (oral)	2.5 to 5 mg./ head daily	Range: 0–25 Av. 10.0 Variable; 0–14[3]

[1]Other modifying hormones that have been tested include testosterone and several of its derivatives. Progesterone and testosterone have each been tested with stilbestrol, hexestrol, and estradiol.

[2]Hydroxyzine and reserpine.

[3]More experimental work needed.

activity; particularly legume pastures, silage and hay.—This fact should be considered when administering hormones. Likewise, this may explain, in part, the variability in animal response.

6. **Removal of stilbestrol prior to slaughter.**—The Food and Drug Administration requires that stilbestrol be deleted from the ration 48 hours prior to slaughter; simply feed a comparable ration without the stilbestrol two days before marketing.

7. **Safety.**—The Food and Drug Administration has ruled that when used in keeping with its regulations, stilbestrol is,

(Continued)

Effect On:			Comments
Feed Efficiency	Carcass Quality	Other	
(% Incr.) Range: 0-17 Av.: 8	Improves carcass quality slightly; more fat deposition and marbling.	Antibiotics appear to reduce disease level; lessening shipping fever, foot rot, bloat, and liver abscess. For lessening shipping fever, feed a high level (50 mg./100 lbs. body wt.) for first 30 days after arrival at feed lot; or 100 mg./100 lbs. body wt. for 3 to 5 days followed by nutritional level.	Aureomycin and terramycin account for 99% of the antibiotics used commercially for feeding ruminants. Appear to be more effective on high roughage rations than on high concentrate rations. Antibiotics reduce calf scours and mortality.
Range: 18-26			
Av.: 6.0 over stilbestrol alone.	Carcass quality is slightly better when a stilbestrol-antibiotic combination is fed than when stilbestrol is fed alone.		Antibiotics have a complementary and additive effect with stilbestrol; improving gains and feed efficiency.
Av.: 21			None of the paste implants have been approved for use by Food and Drug Administration.
Av.: 15			Level to use needs further study.
Av.: 5			Not all tranquilizers have been released by Food and Drug Administration; more experimental work needed. Tranquilizers have an additive effect when used with stilbestrol and antibiotics.

safe for the feeder to handle, for the cattle, and for the consumer who eats the meat.

Preparation of Feeds for Beef Cattle

Perhaps no problem is so perplexing to the amateur feeder as the proper preparation of feeds. Table 23 is a summary of pertinent information relative to the preparation of feeds for beef cattle.

PELLETED FORAGES; ALL-PELLETED RATIONS:

There is increasing interest among cattlemen in (1) all-pelleted rations (grain and forage mixed) and (2) pelleted forages. But there are some problems. The biggest deterrent to pelleting forages is that of being able to process chopped forage

TABLE 23
PREPARATION OF FEEDS FOR BEEF CATTLE

Grinding or Rolling Grains	Pelleting	Soaking or Cooking (steaming)	Shredding and Cutting or Grinding Roughages
Grind cereal grains coarsely for cattle, other than those fitted for show. Professional herdsmen prefer rolled grains for show cattle; as ration is lighter and less digestive disturbances are encountered. It may not be profitable to grind grain for calves under 9 to 12 months of age, for young calves masticate grains well.	Many western stockmen prefer pellets or cubes for cattle, especially for range feeding.	Professional herdsmen often cook (or steam) feeds, thereby increasing palatability and feed consumption. But such preparation is not practical in commercial operations.	Cut or shred such coarse forages as corn fodder or stover; they are easier to handle and there is less waste. In the West, hay is frequently chopped because (1) it is easier to handle, (2) it can be stored in a smaller area at less cost, and (3) it is fed with less waste.

GENERAL COMMENTS RELATIVE TO PREPARATION OF FEEDS

I. *Grinding or Rolling Grains*
  1. Avoid grinding any feed too finely; fine, floury particles are unpalatable and it costs more to prepare them. Finely ground feeds are more palatable when pelleted.
  2. When whole grains are fed to fattening cattle, follow cattle with pigs.

II. *Pelleting*
  1. The practice of pelleting is increasing because:
     a. Pelleted feeds are less bulky and easier to store and to handle, thus lessening storage and labor costs.
     b. Pelleting prevents animals from selectively wasting ingredients likely to be high in certain dietary essentials; each bite is a balanced feed.
     c. Pelleting alleviates wastage of relatively unpalatable feeds, such as barley and ground alfalfa.
     d. Pelleting reduces losses from wind blowing—an especially important factor on the range.
  2. The increased value of pelleting should be appraised against the increased cost of pelleting.

III. *Soaking or Cooking (or Steaming)*
  1. Cooking may slightly increase the digestibility of the starches, but it is apt to decrease the digestibility of the proteins.
  2. Soaking does not improve feeding value.

IV. *Shredding and Cutting, or Grinding Roughages*
  1. The preparation of roughages does not increase the value of the initial product.
  2. For cattle, roughages should be coarsely chopped (not less than 2 in. in length)—if they are prepared.
  3. Chopping forages for cattle is more common in the West than elsewhere; primarily because in this area forages are relatively more abundant and cheaper than the grains, with the result that a higher proportion of them is fed. Also, it follows that there is apt to be greater waste of forage under liberal feeding, unless precautions are taken to alleviate it.
  4. In preparing forages, avoid (1) processing those with high moisture, which may heat and produce spontaneous combustion, and (2) processing those in which there are foreign objects (wire and other hardware) which the animals may not be able to select out, and which may ignite a fire when being processed.

which is coarse enough to allow for optimum cellulose digestion in the rumen, and which will not increase the incidence of bloat. As a rule of thumb, one would be on the safe side if the forage were not chopped more finely than silage. Also, there is the cost factor; processors charge about $6.00 to $7.00 per ton to prepare an all-pelleted ration, and $10.00 per ton for an all-roughage pellet.

Among the virtues ascribed to an all-pelleted ration are: (1) it prevents selective eating—if properly formulated, each mouthful is a balanced diet; (2) it alleviates waste; (3) it eliminates dust; (4) it lessens labor and equipment—just fill self-feeders; and (5) it lessens storage. In all-pelleted rations, the ratio of roughage to concentrate should be higher than where long hay is fed.

A practical pelleted forage will (1) simplify hay making, (2) lessen transportation costs and storage space—pelleted roughages require only 1/3 to 1/5 as much space as when the forage is in loose or chopped form, (3) reduce labor, (4) make automatic hay feeding feasible, (5) decrease nutrient losses, and (6) eliminate dust.

With pelleting, the spread between high and low quality roughage is narrowed; that is, the poorer the quality of the roughage, the greater the advantage from pelleting. This is so because such preparation assures complete consumption of the roughage.

Feed Substitution Tables for Beef Cattle[1]

The successful cattleman is a keen student of values. He recognizes that feeds of similar nutritive properties can and should be interchanged in the ration as price relationships warrant, thus making it possible at all times to obtain a balanced ration at the lowest cost.

Table 24, Handy Feed Substitution Table for Beef Cattle, is a summary of the comparative values of the most common U. S. feeds. In arriving at these values, two primary factors besides chemical composition and feeding value have been considered, namely palatability and carcass quality.

In using this feed substitution table, the following facts should be recognized:

---

[1](See Footnote 1, page 346.)

TABLE 24

HANDY FEED SUBSTITUTION TABLE FOR BEEF CATTLE

Feedstuff	Relative Feeding Value (lb. for lb.) in Comparison with the Designated (underlined) Base Feed Which=100	Maximum Percentage of Base Feed (or comparable feed or feeds) Which It Can Replace for Best Results	Remarks
GRAINS, BY-PRODUCT FEEDS, ROOTS AND TUBERS:[1] (Low and Medium Protein Feeds)			
Corn, No. 2	<u>100</u>	<u>100</u>	The most important concentrate for fattening cattle in the U. S. Grind coarsely unless pigs follow cattle.
Apple pomace, dehydrated............	82–86	33⅓	The heavier the barley and the smaller the proportion of hulls, the higher the feeding value.
Barley....................................	88	25–100	Pigs following barley-fed cattle produce less pork than where corn is fed. Grind coarsely for cattle. In Canada, where considerable barley is fed, it is often used as the only basal feed in the ration once animals are accustomed to it.
Beans, navy (cull)......................	65–75	15	Best when cooked, but can also be fed raw. When cooked, 3 to 4 lbs. per head daily; when raw, 1 to 2 lbs. Scouring may occur if constituting more than 15% of total ration. Use in fattening grain ration.

[1]Roots and tubers are of lower value than the grain and by-product feeds due to their higher moisture content.

Feed			Remarks
Beet pulp, dried	90–95	33⅓–50	50% the value of corn silage.
Beet pulp, molasses, dried	90–95	33⅓–50	Not very palatable. Fed chiefly to dairy cattle.
Beet pulp, wet	25	33⅓–50	Too bulky and usually too costly to be used in fattening rations.
Brewers' dried grains	55–80	33⅓	
Brewers' grains (wet)	13–15	33⅓	Grains usually come from barley.
Buckwheat	55–75	33⅓	Best to haul and feed directly. Can be stored in silo if salt is added at rate of 25 lbs. per ton of grains. Should be ground and mixed with other grains.
Carrots (cull)	10–15	20–25	Store 3 to 4 weeks before using; fresh carrots cause scouring. Feed whole or sliced.
Citrus pulp, dried	85–90	25–33⅓	
Corn and cob meal	85–90	100	
Corn gluten feed (gluten feed)	85–90	50	Rye distillers' dried grains are of lower value than similar products made from corn or wheat.
Distillers' dried grains	73–90	33⅓	Distillers' dried grains are used chiefly for dairy cattle.
Distillers' dried solubles	73–90	33⅓	The chief difference between distillers' dried grains and distillers' dried solubles is the higher B-vitamin content of the latter. Normally this is not important for cattle and sheep.
Hominy feed	100	50	Value is highest when used as an appetizer.
Molasses, beet	65–90	10–40	May be laxative if fed at levels above 6 lbs. daily. Value is highest when used as an appetizer.
Molasses, cane	65–90	10–40	
Molasses, citrus	65–90	10–40	
Molasses, wood	50–65	10–20	Not palatable.
Oats	70–90	10–100	Valuable for young stock, for breeding stock and for getting animals on feed. Oats have lowest value for fattening cattle and should be limited to ⅓ of such rations. Also, the feeding value of oats varies according to the test weight per bushel. Grind for cattle.

TABLE 24 (Continued)

Feedstuff	Relative Feeding Value (lb. for lb.) in Comparison with the Designated (underlined) Base Feed Which=100	Maximum Percentage of Base Feed (or comparable feed or feeds) Which It Can Replace for Best Results	Remarks
Peas, dried	100	40	Peas appear to be unpalatable to certain individuals. Also, there is bloat hazard if they exceed 40% of the ration.
Potato, (Irish)	20–25	85	When fed with alfalfa hay, they are worth about 80% as much per ton as corn silage. Do not feed frozen. Sunburned, decomposed, or sprouted potatoes should not make up more than 10% of potatoes fed. Keep steers' heads down while eating to prevent choking.
Potato, (Irish) dehydrated	90–95	50	
Potato, (Sweet)	25	85	
Potatoes, (Sweet) dehydrated	95–100	50	Dehydrated sweet potatoes are more palatable than dehydrated Irish potatoes.
Rice, (rough rice)	80	100	
Rice bran	66⅔–75	33⅓	Not palatable when fed in larger amounts.
Rice polishings	88	25	
Rye	100	33⅓	Should be finely ground to kill noxious weed seeds.
Screenings, refuse	30–90	25	Quality varies; good quality screenings are equal to oats, whereas poor quality screenings resemble straw.
Spelt and emmer	70–90	30–100	Similar to oats.

Sorghum, grain	90–95	100	All varieties have about the same feeding value. Grind for cattle.
Wheat	100–105	50	Grind coarsely.
Wheat bran	70–90	25–33⅓	Because of its bulk and fiber, bran is not desirable for fattening rations. Bran is valuable for young animals, for breeding animals, and for starting animals on feed.
Wheat-mixed feed (mill run)	95	33⅓	Sometimes fed to the breeding herd, to young calves, and to fattening cattle being started on feed.

PROTEIN SUPPLEMENTS:

Soybean oil meal (43%)	**100**	**100**	Slightly laxative effect.
Alfalfa or clover screenings	70–75	50	Grind finely to destroy weed seeds.
Brewers' dried grains	55–65	50	Not very palatable. Fed chiefly to dairy cattle.
Copra meal (coconut oil meal)	90–100	50	
Corn gluten feed (gluten feed)	65–75	50–100	Somewhat unpalatable.
Corn gluten meal (gluten meal)	90–100	50	
Cottonseed oil meal (43%)	100	100	Among practical cattlemen, the feeling persists that cottonseed meal has a constipating effect; some experimental work to the contrary. Although it may be fed as the only protein supplement, best results are obtained when it is fed with linseed meal for fattening cattle.
Distillers' dried grains	65–70	100	Rye distillers' dried grains are about 10% lower in protein than similar products made from corn or wheat. Low in palatability.
Distillers' dried solubles	70	100	
Linseed oil meal (33%)	100	100	Linseed meal has laxative effect. Some cattle will not tolerate more than 5 to 8% linseed meal in the ration.
For other than fattening cattle	100	100	
For fattening cattle	120–1	100	Higher value for fattening cattle due to both greater efficiency and higher selling price of the cattle because of the increased bloom.

TABLE 24 (Continued)

Feedstuff	Relative Feeding Value (lb. for lb.) in Comparison with the Designated (underlined) Base Feed Which=100	Maximum Percentage of Base Feed (or comparable feed or feeds) Which It Can Replace for Best Results	Remarks
Peanut oil meal (43%)	100	100	
Peas, dried	65–75	50	
Safflower meal, with hulls	40–45	100	Safflower meal with hulls is unpalatable. Thus, it should be mixed with more palatable feeds. Not satisfactory for fattening calves.
Soybeans	95–100	100	Soybean allowance should be limited to amount necessary to balance the ration. Larger amounts may be unduly laxative and throw cattle "off feed."
Sunflower seed meal	95–100	100	
DRY FORAGES AND SILAGES:[1]			
Alfalfa hay, all analyses	**100**	**100**	All the dry non-legume forages listed herein are satisfactory when needed minerals and either a limited amount of legume hay or a protein supplement is supplied to balance the ration. Does away with or lessens protein supplement requirements.
Alfalfa silage	33⅓–50	50–85	When alfalfa silage replaces corn silage, more energy feed must be provided but less protein. Usually fed as a substitute for corn or grass silage. 50% the value of corn silage.
Apple pomace silage	17–25	50–85	Sometimes fed out of a stack or trench silo.

[1]Silages are of lower value than dry forages due to their higher moisture content.

Feed			Remarks
Apples	17–25	50–85	Do not feed more than 25 lbs./cow. Not recommended for fattening cattle. Danger of choking when fed whole. Relatively high handling cost.
Barley hay	70	100	
Beet tops, fresh	16–25	33⅓–50	In the West, large acreages of fresh beet tops are pastured off by cattle and sheep. Bloat may be problem when tops are frozen. Tops are laxative. Add 2½ lbs. of ground limestone/ton of feed.
Beet top silage, sugar	17–25	33⅓–50	Feed 2 oz. of finely ground limestone or chalk with each 100 lbs. of tops, as calcium changes the oxalic acid to insoluble calcium oxalate.
Clover hay, crimson	90–100	100	Crimson clover hay has a considerably lower value if not cut at an early stage.
Clover hay, red	90–100	100	If the rest of the ration is adequate in protein, clover hay will be equal to alfalfa in feeding value; otherwise it will be lower.
Clover-timothy hay	80–90	100	Value of clover-timothy mixed hay depends on the proportion of clover present and the stage of maturity at which it is cut.
Corn fodder	75	100	
Corn silage	33⅓–50	50–85	
Corn silage, cannery waste	26–40	50–85	
Corn stover	35	50	Too low in nutrients to be of much value in fattening rations.
Cowpea hay	90–100	100	
Grass-legume mixed hay	80–90	100	Value depends on the proportion of legume present and the stage of maturity at which it is cut.
Grass silage	30–45	50–85	For fattening cattle, grass silage must be supplemented with additional energy feeds, such as cereal grain or molasses, to be of the same value as corn silage.

TABLE 24 (Continued)

Feedstuff	Relative Feeding Value (lb. for lb.) in Comparison with the Designated (underlined) Base Feed Which=100	Maximum Percentage of Base Feed (or comparable feed or feeds) Which It Can Replace for Best Results	Remarks
Grass-legume silage	32–47	50–85	Unless grain is added as a preservative, grass silage requires more energy feed, but less protein supplement than corn silage when fed to fattening cattle.
Hop vine silage	25–35	50–75	Should be chopped when placed in the silo.
Johnson grass hay	70	100	
Lespedeza hay	80–100	100	Feeding value of lespedeza hay varies considerably with stage of maturity at which it is cut.
Mint hay	80–95	75	Cattle tire of mint hay when it is fed as the only roughage for extended periods.
Oat hay	75	100	
Oat silage	32–47	50–85	Must be chopped finely to exclude air from silo.
Pea straw	45–75	75	
Pea-vine silage	33⅓–50	50–85	Unless grain is added as a preservative, pea-vine silage requires more energy feed, but less protein supplement than corn silage when fed to fattening cattle.
Pea-vine hay	100–110	75–75	Can constitute the only roughage for fattening cattle.
Potato silage	25–30	50–75	About 75% the value of corn silage.
Prairie hay	65–70	100	
Reed canary grass	70	100	
Sorghum fodder	70	100	

Sorghum silage (grain varieties)	32–47	50–85	For fattening cattle, sorghum silage is 85 to 90% as valuable as corn silage and must be supplemented in the same manner as corn silage.
Sorghum silage (sweet varieties)	25–30	50–85	Nearly equal to grain varieties in value per acre because of greater yield.
Sorghum stover	35	50	Too low in nutrients to be of much value in fattening rations.
Soybean hay	85–90	50–75	Lower value than alfalfa hay, largely due to greater wastage in feeding. It may cause scouring when fed alone.
Sudangrass hay	70	100	65 to 75% value of corn silage.
Sunflower silage	25–35	50–85	Somewhat unpalatable and may cause constipation. Harvest for silage when ½ to ⅔ of heads are in bloom.
Sweet clover hay	100	100	Value of sweet clover hay varies widely. Second year sweet clover hay is less desirable than first year sweet clover hay and is more apt to cause sweet clover disease.
Timothy hay	70	100	
Vetch-oat hay	80–90	100	The higher the proportion of vetch, the higher the value.
Wheat hay	70	100	

1. That, for best results, different ages and groups of animals within classes should be fed differently.

2. That individual feeds differ widely in feeding value. Barley and oats, for example, vary widely in feeding value according to the hull content and the test weight per bushel, and forages vary widely according to the stage of maturity at which they are cut and how well they are cured and stored.

3. That non-legume forages may have a higher relative value to legumes than herein indicated provided the chief need of the animal is for additional energy rather than for supplemented protein. Thus the non-legume forages of low value can be used to better advantage for wintering mature dry beef cows than for young calves.

On the other hand, legumes may actually have a higher value relative to non-legumes than herein indicated provided the chief need is for additional protein rather than for added energy. Thus no protein supplement is necessary for breeding beef cows provided a good quality legume forage is fed.

4. That, based primarily on available supply and price, certain feeds—especially those of medium protein content, such as brewers' dried grains, corn gluten feed (gluten feed), distillers' dried grains, distillers' dried solubles, peanuts, and peas (dried)—are used interchangeably as (1) grains and by-product feeds, and/or (2) protein supplements.

5. That the feeding value of certain feeds is materially affected by preparation. Thus, wheat must be coarsely ground for cattle. The values herein reported are based on proper feed preparation in each case.

¹The author gratefully acknowledges the helpful suggestions of the following authorities who reviewed this section and table: Dr. T. H. Blosser, Dairy Nutritionist, and Dr. W. W. Heinemann, Animal Nutritionist, both of Washington State University, Pullman, Wash.; Prof. John G. Archibald, Nutritionist, University of Massachusetts, Amherst, Mass.; Dr. Edward L. Stephenson, Animal Nutritionist, University of Arkansas, Fayetteville, Ark.; Dr. George L. Robertson, Head, Department of Animal Husbandry, Louisiana State University, Baton Rouge, La..; Dr. O. O. Thomas, Nutritionist, Montana State College, Bozeman, Mont.; Dr. L. E. Washburn, Prof. A. L. Esplin, Sheep Specialist, and Mr. M. H. Hazaleus, Swine Specialist, all of the Department of Animal Husbandry, Colorado State University, Fort Collins, Colo.; Prof. L. B. Embry, Animal Nutritionist, South Dakota State College, Brookings, S. D.; Dr. S. W. Terrill, Swine Nutritionist, University of Illinois, Urbana, Ill.; Professor J. Matsashima, Animal Nutritionist, The University of Nebraska, Lincoln, Neb.; Dr. T. J. Cunha, Head, Department of Animal Husbandry, University of Florida, Gainesville, Fla.; and Dr. E. W. Crampton, Prof. of Nutrition, MacDonald College, Quebec, Canada.

For the reasons noted above, the comparative values of feeds shown in the feed substitution table are not absolute. Rather, they are reasonably accurate approximations based on average quality feeds.

Home-Mixed versus Commercial Feeds

The value of farm-grown grains—plus the cost of ingredients which need to be purchased to balance the ration, and the cost of grinding and mixing—as compared to the cost of commercial ready-mixed feeds laid down on the farm, should determine whether it is best to mix feeds at home or depend on ready-mixed feeds.

Although there is nothing about the mixing of feeds which is beyond the capacity of the intelligent farmer or rancher, under many conditions a commercial mixed feed supplied by a reputable dealer may be the most economical and the least irksome. The commercial dealer has the distinct advantages of (1) purchase of feeds in quantity lots, making possible price advantages, (2) economical and controlled mixing, and (3) the hiring of scientifically trained personnel for use in determining the rations. Because of these advantages, commercial feeds are finding a place of increasing importance in American agriculture.

Also, it is to the everlasting credit of reputable feed dealers that they have been good teachers, often getting stockmen started in the feeding of balanced rations, a habit which is likely to remain with them whether or not they continue to buy commercial feeds.

HOW TO SELECT COMMERCIAL FEEDS:

There is a difference in commercial feeds! That is, there is a difference from the standpoint of what a stockman can purchase with his feed dollars. The smart operator will know how to determine what constitutes the best in commercial feeds for his specific needs. He will not rely solely on how the feed looks and smells or on the feed salesman. The most important factors to consider or look for in buying a commercial feed are:

1. **The reputation of the manufacturer.**—This should be determined by (1) conferring with other stockmen who have used the particular products, and (2) checking on whether or not the commercial feed under consideration has consistently met its guarantees. The latter can be determined by reading the bulletins

or reports published by the respective state departments in charge of enforcing feed laws.

2. **The specific needs.**—Feed needs vary according to (1) the class, age, and productivity of the animals, and (2) whether the animals are fed primarily for maintenance, growth, fattening (or show-ring fitting), reproduction, lactation, or work. The wise operator will buy different formula feeds for different needs.

3. **The feed tag.**—Most states require that mixed feeds carry a tag that guarantees the ingredients and the chemical make-up of the feed. Feeds with more protein and fat are better, and feeds with less fiber are better.

In general, if the fiber content is less than 8 per cent, the feed may be considered as top quality; if the fiber is more than 8 but less than 12 per cent the feed may be considered as medium quality; while feeds containing more than 12 per cent fiber should be considered carefully. Occasionally, a high fiber feed is good; the Iowa Economy Supplement is such an example. In this particular feed, corn cobs are used primarily as an agent to absorb the molasses and to act as a carrier for the urea, minerals, and stilbestrol. This formula is fed at the rate of about one pound per head daily and provides a convenient amount for even distribution in the daily feed. Likewise, many feeds are high in fiber simply because they contain generous quantities of alfalfa; yet they may be perfectly good feeds for the purpose intended. On the other hand, if oat hulls and similar types of high fiber ingredients are responsible for the high fiber content of the feed, the quality should be questioned. The latter type of fiber is poorly digested and does not provide the nutrients required to stimulate the digestion of the fiber in roughages.

4. **Flexible formulas.**—Feeds with flexible formulas are usually the best buy. This is because the price of feed ingredients in different source feeds varies considerably from time to time. Thus a good feed manufacturer will shift his formulas as prices change, so as to give the stockman the most for his money. This is as it should be, for (1) there is no one best ration, and (2) if substitutions are made wisely, the price of the feed can be kept down and the feeder will continue to get equally good results.

FEEDING THE HERD BULLS

The feeding program for the herd bull should be such as to keep him in a thrifty, vigorous condition at all times. He should neither be overfitted nor in a thin, run-down condition. In season, the nutritive requirements for the mature herd bull can usually be met through good pastures. With the young bull, during the breeding season or winter months, adequate grain and roughage should be provided. Mature bulls in high condition will consume feeds in amounts equal to about 1.5 per cent of their live weight; thin bulls and young bulls will consume up to twice this amount.

Usually, the bull is kept separate from the cow herd except during the breeding season.

FEEDING THE BEEF BREEDING COWS

Heavy grain feeding is uneconomical and unnecessary for the beef breeding herd. The nutrient requirements should merely be adequate to provide for maintenance, growth (if the animals are immature), and reproduction. Fortunately, these requirements can largely be met through the feeding of cheap roughages.

Feeding the Dry and Pregnant Cows

Breeding cows should neither be permitted to get overfat nor in a thin, run-down condition. The best calf crop is produced by cows that are kept in vigorous breeding condition. Usually, the pregnant cow should gain in weight sufficient to account for the growth of the fetus (sixty to ninety pounds). In addition, she should slightly increase her body weight to carry her through the suckling period. An exception may be made in the case of fat cows and heifers; animals which may lose some weight in winter without forfeiting any of their productiveness, provided the ration is otherwise adequate.

Most of the feed for dry and pregnant cows should consist of pasturage and other home-grown roughages such as silage or root crops and hay. Except during the winter months, there is no finer place for the breeding cows than the run of a pasture or range. Aside from supplying the necessary nutrients at low cost, this system provides much valuable exercise. Should the pasture become very short—because of droughts, deep snow, or over-grazing—a supplemental feed of silage, dry forage crops, or concentrates should be provided.

The winter feeding period is the most expensive, necessitating good management to hold down the cost. The cheaper home-grown roughages should constitute the bulk of the winter ration for dry or pregnant cows. Most of the grain and the higher class roughages then may be used by other classes of livestock. A practical ration may consist of silage or root crops and dry roughages (legume or grass hays) combined with a small quantity of protein-rich concentrates (such as linseed meal or cottonseed meal). With the use of a leguminous roughage, the protein-rich concentrates may be omitted.

Pregnant cows that are in medium to good condition in the fall can be wintered satisfactorily on 12 to 20 pounds of straw daily plus 1 pound oil seed cake or meal (or equivalent protein supplement), or on straw plus 4 to 5 pounds of alfalfa or other legume hay. Unless the cows have had good green pasture in the fall, and consequently have a store of vitamin A in their bodies, alfalfa meal or another vitamin A supplement should be fed. In addition, straw-fed cattle should always have access to a mineral supplement high in calcium.

Dusty or moldy feed and frozen silage should be avoided in feeding all cattle but especially in the case of the pregnant cow, for such feed may produce complications and possible abortion.

Feeding in the fall should not be delayed so long that the cows begin to lose weight. Furthermore, the herd should be fed in the spring until the grass has attained sufficient growth and substance.

Proper development of the fetus requires an abundance of calcium. When legume hays are fed, this need is usually met. However, when non-legumes are being utilized, it is wise to provide free access to a calcium mineral such as ground limestone or feeding steamed bone meal. Bone meal should be selected for most conditions for the reason that it will take care of both the calcium and phosphorus needs. In addition, plenty of salt should be available at all times.

Feeding at Calving Time

Proper feeding at calving time is very important. If the calves are dropped out on a pasture or range where both forage and water are reasonably accessible, cows will satisfactorily regulate their own needs. On the other hand, when inclement weather or other conditions make it necessary to confine the cow at calving time, the skill and good judgment of the caretaker becomes a matter of importance. Under such unnatural conditions of confinement, the cow may be watered at frequent intervals immediately before and after calving, but in no case should she be allowed to gorge. It is also a good plan to take some of the chill off the water in the winter time. It is considered good practice to feed lightly and with laxative feeds during this period. A satisfactory ration at calving time may consist of a mixture of bran and oats, together with a generous allowance of hay. The quantity of feed given should be governed by the milk flow, the condition of the udder, the demands of the calf, and the appetite and condition of the cow.

Feeding the Lactating Cows

Until weaning time, at approximately six months of age, the growth of the calf is chiefly determined by the amount of milk available from its dam. The principal part of the calf's ration, therefore, may be cheaply and safely provided by giving its mother the proper feed for the production of milk. In season, green, succulent pastures afford the most effective and practical way in which to stimulate lactation. When pastures are scanty or during the winter months, grain and protein supplement feeding of both the dam and the calf may be essential.

Dual-purpose cows that are producing market milk as well as calves should receive feeds nearly identical to those provided

Fig. 117. Hereford cows and calves on pasture at the University of Nebraska. In season, green, succulent pastures afford the most effective and practical way in which to stimulate milk production of cows suckling calves. (Courtesy, C. B. & Q. Railroad Co.)

for dairy cows in the same area. Generally speaking, they should be fed one pound of concentrates for every three to four pounds of milk produced, the exact amount depending upon the fat content of the milk.

FEEDING GRAIN TO SUCKLING CALVES

The vast majority of calves are raised on their mothers' milk plus whatever pasture or other feed they share with their dams. If calves are to be marketed at weaning time or soon thereafter, if they are to be fattened as baby beeves, or if they are to be sold as purebred stock, liberal grain feeding should be started at the earliest possible age. Calves handled in this manner will have a greater selling weight and more finish when they are marketed. Even when calves are not to be marketed at an early age—when fattened over a longer feeding period or when carried as stockers—they should be taught to eat grain and hay so that the transition during weaning will not result in loss of flesh. Likewise, calves from dual-purpose cows from which market milk is to be produced should be taught to eat supplemental feeds within a few weeks after birth. Calves may be fed grain in a creep in the pasture, or they may be kept and fed separately from their mothers and allowed to nurse twice daily. Since the latter practice involves more labor, "creep" feeding is usually resorted to for feeding calves on pasture.

Creep Feeding Calves

A "creep" is an enclosure for feeding purposes made accessible to the calves but through which the cows cannot pass. This allows for the feeding of the calves but not the dams. For best use, the creep should be built at a spot where the herd is inclined to loiter. The ideal location is on high ground, well drained, in the shade, and near the place of watering. Keeping the salt supply nearby will be helpful in holding the cow herd near the creep.

It is important that calves be started on feed very carefully. At first only a small amount of feed should be placed in the troughs each day, any surplus feed being removed and given to the cows. In this manner, the feed will be kept clean and fresh, and the calves will not be consuming any moldy or sour feed. When calves are on luxuriant pasture and their mothers are milking well, difficulty may be experienced in getting them to eat.

In experiments at Sni-A-Bar Farms comparing creep-fed calves with calves allowed to nurse the cows without grain, it was found that Shorthorn calves fed $8.97 worth of grain in a creep on pasture during the nursing period averaged one hundred pounds heavier at weaning time than similar calves allowed to nurse the cows without grain. In addition, these creep-fed calves were worth $2.00 per hundred or $17.88 per head more than the calves that received no grain.[1]

Fig. 118. A calf creep. Note available shade, and calves at feed. (Courtesy, Purdue University, Lafayette, Ind.)

In a survey made by Washington State University, 25 per cent of the responding cattlemen reported that they creep-fed calves.[2] Perhaps the main factors determining whether it will be profitable to creep-feed the calves in any given herd are (1) the future handling of the calves, and (2) the market. If calves are to be sold at weaning time, the cattlemen should not overlook the fact that creep-feeding usually will make for a two-way market; namely, (1) to the feeder, as feeder calves, or (2) to the packer, for slaughter. Without creep-feeding, calves seldom wean off fat enough for slaughter and can be sold the feeder route only.

FEEDING STOCKERS

Stockers are young heifer replacements or steers and heifers that are intended for market and which are being fed and cared

[1]Experiments conducted by the U. S. Dept. of Agri. and the Missouri Expt. Sta. in cooperation with Sni-A-Bar Farms of Grain Valley, Missouri.

[2]Ensminger, M. E., M. W. Galgan, and W. L. Slocum, Wash. Agri. Expt. Sta. Bul. 562, p. 39.

for in such manner that growth rather than fattening may be realized. Because of the very nature of the operation, the successful feeding of stockers requires the maximum of economy consistent with normal growth and development. This necessitates cheap feed—either pasture or range grazing or such cheap harvested roughages as hay, straw, fodder, and silage. In general, the winter feeds for stockers consist of the less desirable and less marketable roughages.

The feed consumption of stockers will vary somewhat with the quality of the roughage available, the age of the cattle, and the rate of gain desired. Usually, the daily gains should range from three-fourths to one and one-fourth pounds. If a young, rapidly-growing stocker calf is not gaining at least three-fourths of a pound daily, he may lose too much in condition.

FEEDING FATTENING CATTLE

The fattening of cattle is what the term implies, the laying on of fat. The ultimate aim of the fattening process is to produce meat that will best answer the requirements and desires of the consumer. This is accomplished through an improvement in the flavor, tenderness, and quality of the lean meat which results from "marbling." Fat also adds to the digestibility and nutritive value of the product.

In a general way, there are two methods of finishing cattle for market: (1) dry-lot fattening and (2) pasture fattening. Prior to 1900, the majority of fat cattle sent to the market were four- to six-year-old steers that had been fattened primarily on grass. Even today, the utilization of pastures continues to play an important part in all types of cattle-feeding operations.

Amount to Feed

Fattening cattle should receive a maximum ration over and above the maintenance requirements. In general, they will consume feeds daily in amounts (air-dry basis) equal to 2.5 to 3.0 per cent of their liveweight. Feed intake is limited by (1) the bulk-handling capacity of the intestinal tract, and (2) the daily TDN intake. However, feed consumption and gains vary according to the condition of the cattle, the palatability of the feeds, the weather conditions, and the management practices. For example, older and more fleshy cattle consume less feed per hundredweight than do younger animals carrying less condition; thus mature bulls in high condition will consume feeds in amounts equal to about 1.5 per cent of their liveweight, whereas thin steers under two years of age will consume fully twice as much feed per unit liveweight.

Over-feeding is also undesirable, being wasteful of feeds and creating a health hazard. When over-feeding exists, there is usually considerable left-over feed and wastage, and there is a high incidence of bloat, founder, scours, and even death. Animals that suffer from mild digestive disturbances are commonly referred to as "off feed."

Roughage; (1) Amount, and (2) Roughage-to-Concentrate Ratio

Experiments and practical observations indicate that fattening cattle should receive a minimum daily roughage allowance of 0.5 to 0.8 pound for each 100 pounds liveweight. Full fed cattle that receive less roughage than this are subject to bloat and other digestive disturbances. Also, it is desirable that this roughage be coarse, and not finely ground, to achieve normal physiological activity of the gastro-intestinal tract.

The proportion of grain to roughage for cattle should be varied according to their comparative price and the age and quality of the animals. Fortunately, a very wide range in concentrate-to-roughage ratios is satisfactory for fattening cattle; anywhere from 30:70 to 70:30.

Fattening rations containing 70 to 75 per cent concentrates will permit the maximum TDN intake and still provide the minimum roughage allowance given above. When the roughage is finely ground and incorporated in an all-pelleted ration, perhaps the concentrate should not exceed 50 per cent of the ration.

Dry-Lot Fattening

As implied, dry-lot fattening refers to finishing cattle in the dry-lot. Such operations vary all the way from small, mostly hand-labor, barnyard enterprises—usually conducted during the winter months for the purpose of marketing home-grown feeds and obtaining the manure—to large and highly mechanized year-around business enterprises that grow little or none of the feed that is utilized. Many of the latter operators custom feed.

As might be expected, dry-lot fattening has shown its greatest development in the Corn Belt states. This may be attributed to the proximity of the central states to the feeder cattle supply of the western ranges and the great amount of corn and other

Fig. 119. Hereford cattle being dry-lot fattened on the farm of John P. Kurt, Cascade, Iowa. About four million cattle are grain-fattened annually in the Corn Belt. (Courtesy, The Corn Belt Farm Dailies)

fattening feeds produced on the productive farms of this area. Even in the Corn Belt, however, cattle are usually carried on pasture for a part of the fattening period.

Approximately one-third of all the feeder cattle of the western range area are shipped into the Corn Belt for fattening. In addition, many of the farms in the central states produce feeder cattle which are finished out on the same farm or a farm in the general area. About four million cattle are grain-fattened annually in the Corn Belt. In addition, sizable and increasing numbers are dry-lot fattened in the irrigated valleys of the West.

In dry-lot fattening, the kind of roughage fed varies from area to area. This is so because, normally, it is not practical to move roughages great distances, due to their bulk and transportation costs. Thus, generally speaking, cattle feeders utilize those roughages that are most readily available and lowest in price. Among the most common roughages used in fattening rations are: legume hays, silages, grass-legume mixed or grass hays, corn cobs, cereal straws, and various stovers and fodders. Where good legume hays are home grown or are available at a reasonable cost, they make a most satisfactory forage, supplying the necessary proteins, calcium, and vitamin A for the dry-lot ration. However, such low quality feeds as cereal straw and corn cobs may replace part of the roughage for fattening cattle provided the other feeds supply sufficient protein, calcium, phosphorus, and vitamin A.

Increasing quantities of silage are being fed to fattening cattle. At the present time, it is estimated that 90 per cent of the nation's silage is made from corn and sorghum, and the other 10 per cent from hay and pasture crops, small grains, by-products, etc. However, with increasing interest in grassland agriculture, more and more grass silage is being fed to fattening cattle. The following silage pointers, based on experiments and practical observations, are generally observed by successful cattle feeders:

1. Where cattle are given a liberal amount of grain, any silage that is fed is considered a part of the roughage ration; hence, the silage should be fed in accordance with the well-recognized rules for feeding roughage. Also, it may be assumed that about 3 pounds of silage will replace one pound of hay.

2. The maximum use of silage is best obtained early in the fattening period or with more mature steers that possess a larger digestive capacity.

3. Low grade cattle may be fed either (1) entirely or (2) liberally on silage throughout the fattening period, but cattle grading good or better will usually return more profit if they are full fed on grain during the last half of the feeding period.

4. Cattle can be placed on full feed of silage from the beginning of the feeding period without any detrimental effects.

5. When fed on silage alone, cattle on full feed will consume 5 to 6 pounds per 100 pounds weight.

6. Sorghum silage has 85 to 90 per cent of the value of corn silage and should be supplemented in the same manner as corn silage.

7. Grass silage should be supplemented with additional energy feeds, such as cereal grain or molasses, to be of the same value as corn silage.

The choice of the concentrate ration should be determined largely by the availability and price of feeds. The experienced Corn Belt cattle feeder generally figures that it takes 40 to 50 bushels of corn (or an equivalent amount of another grain) and one-half ton of good quality legume hay to fatten a steer to Choice grade regardless of his age. Young animals require a longer time in which to consume this amount of feed and reach approximately the same degree of finish. Although corn is by far the most common grain used in fattening steers, such small grains as barley, rye, oats, and wheat are used in many sections of the northern and Pacific Coast states, and in Canada. The small grains are excellent for fattening cattle when properly used. In comparison with corn-feeding, (1) barley-fed cattle are more susceptible to bloat (for this reason, it is best not to use a straight legume hay along with a grain ration high in barley; also, a mixture of barley and dried beet pulp is commonly used in the West), (2) barley- or wheat-fed animals are more apt to tire of their feed during a long feeding period, (3) rye should not constitute more than one-third of the grain ration because it is unpalatable, (4) more care is necessary to prevent wheat-fed cattle from going off feed, and (5) oats should not constitute more than one-half of the ration, and preferably not more than one-third, because of its bulk. Fortunately, these limitations can be lessened considerably by mixing these feeds together, or by mixing the cereal grain with beet pulp, silage, or chopped hay. Also, it is important that the small grains be coarsely ground or rolled. It is recognized that wheat and oats are frequently too expensive to include in cattle fattening rations.

In the Southwest, the grain sorghums predominate, both as grain and silage. In the sugar-beet areas, beet pulp (dry or wet), beet tops, and molasses are used extensively, whereas in the Cotton Belt cottonseed meal and hulls make up the standard cattle-fattening ration.

Beet by-products are notoriously low in phosphorus. For best results, therefore, a suitable phosphorus mineral supplement, such as steamed bone meal, should be provided where these feeds are used extensively.

Whenever either a non-legume dry forage or silage is used in fattening steers, a protein supplement should be added to the ration. Generally speaking, the choice of a protein supplement should be determined by the comparative prices of a pound of protein in the available supplements. As protein supplements of animal origin are usually more expensive and no more effective for steers than proteins of plant origin, the latter are usually fed. The leading protein supplements for fattening cattle are linseed oil meal, cottonseed oil meal, and soybean oil meal. When a good quality legume roughage is used, it is not necessary to add protein supplement to the ration of fattening cattle or even to that of calves. When non-legume roughages are used, however, a protein supplement should be added to the ration, the exact amount depending upon the kind of roughage and grain and the age of the cattle (see Table 26). Naturally, calves have a higher protein requirement. As protein concentrates are usually expensive, normally one should not add more than is required to balance the ration.

Fig. 120. Steers eating beet tops in feed yard near Torrington, Wyoming. In the sugar-beet areas, beet tops, beet pulp (dry or wet), and beet molasses are used extensively. (Courtesy, C. B. & Q. Railroad Co.)

Cottonseed meal and hulls are very deficient in vitamin A. When cattle are fed heavily on these products, they may develop serious deficiency symptoms, formerly known as "cottonseed meal poisoning." This condition may be averted by adding a good source of carotene—such as green, leafy alfalfa hay or yellow corn—to rations high in cottonseed by-products.

Cattle fattening in the dry-lot should have free access to salt. Also, when a non-legume is used, a mineral source of calcium should be provided. Phosphorus is not likely to be deficient in fattening rations, except when liberal quantities of beet by-products are being fed.

Occasionally vitamin A is lacking in dry-lot rations. This is especially true under conditions when bleached roughages or cereal straws are fed or the ration contains liberal amounts of cottonseed by-products. Yellow corn and green, leafy hays are good feed-lot sources of vitamin A.

Pasture Fattening

Where grazing land is extensive and not too high in price, pastures no doubt will continue to be utilized in finishing cattle for market. Cattle finished on grass may not make quite such rapid gains or reach the same high degree or quality of finish as cattle fattened on grain. Moreover, grass-finished cattle do not command the values of grain-finished cattle. Yet when grass is plentiful and cheap, one can usually afford to sacrifice in gain, finish, and selling price because of the much lower cost of production.

In farming districts where there is much rough waste-land unsuited to tillage and where high grain prices prevail (because of shipment from distant areas), the fattening of cattle on grass (with or without supplements) is common for pastures are then utilized to the maximum. On the other hand, in districts where there is but little untillable land, where more feed can be produced on an acre of tilled crops than on an acre of pasture, or where land is high in price, dry-lot fattening is more common. Even in the so-called dairy sections of the United States, there are many cheap, isolated pasture areas that are not now being effectively utilized for dairy production or other enterprises but which seem admirably adapted to a system of beef production in which pastures may be utilized to the maximum.

Generally speaking, no cheaper method of harvesting forage crops has been devised than is afforded by harvesting directly by

Fig. 121. Yearling Hereford steers from Texas, fattening on bluestem grass in the famous grazing area in the Kansas Flint Hills. (Courtesy, Dr. A. D. Weber, Kansas State College)

grazing animals. Moreover, even most seeded pastures last several years; thus seeding costs may be distributed over the entire period. Naturally the cash income to be derived from pastures will vary from year to year and from place to place depending upon such factors as market price levels, class of animals, soil, season, and the use of adapted varieties.

ADVANTAGES AND DISADVANTAGES
OF GRAIN FEEDING ON PASTURE:

The **advantages** of grain feeding cattle on pasture, compared to strictly dry-lot fattening, are:

1. Pasture gains are cheaper because: (1) Less grain is required per one hundred pounds gain; (2) grass is a cheaper roughage than hay or silage; and (3) less expensive protein supplement is required. Generally speaking, feeding grain on pasture results in saving ¼ to ½ of the cereal grain and protein supplement and ¾ to all of the hay that would be required in the dry lot.

2. Less labor is required because the cattle gather their own roughage and the labor required for feeding roughage is eliminated. In brief, grass-fattened cattle do their own harvesting. Furthermore, it may be possible to get satisfactory results with but one grain feeding each day in fattening on pasture, or the animals may be self fed, with the caretaker merely filling the feeder at intervals.

3. Pigs following steers on pasture make better gains than pigs following steers under dry-lot conditions.

4. The maximum fertility value of the manure is conserved, and handling of the manure is eliminated. When pastures are utilized by livestock, approximately 80 per cent of the plant nutrients of the crop is returned to the soil.

5. Pasture fattening eliminates any requirement for buildings.

The **disadvantages** of fattening cattle on pasture, compared to strictly dry-lot fattening, are:

1. Most feeder cattle are marketed in the fall rather than in the spring. Therefore, feeder steers purchased in the spring and intended for pasture fattening are usually scarce and high in price.

2. Though less labor is required, less labor is available. The cropping season is a rush season.

3. During the midsummer, the combination of heat and flies may cause much discomfort to the animals and reduce the gains made.

4. Pastures may become dry and parched, reducing the gains made during dry seasons.

5. The manure is usually dropped on permanent pastures year after year, which may result in the neglect of the other fields.

6. In many pastures, availability of shade and water does not present a problem. However, some areas are less fortunate in this regard.

After both the advantages and the disadvantages of pasture fattening are considered, the availability of cheap, rough pasture land and the price of concentrates will usually be the determining factors in deciding upon the system to follow.

SYSTEMS OF PASTURE FATTENING:

When cattle are finished on pasture, any one of the following systems may be employed:

1. Fattening on pastures alone—no concentrates being fed.

2. Limited grain allowance during the entire pasture period.

3. Full feeding during the entire pasture period.

4. Full or limited grain feeding on pasture following the period of peak pasture growth.

5. Short feeding (60 to 120 days) in the dry lot at the end of the pasture period.

The system of pasture finishing that will be decided upon will depend upon the age of the cattle, the quality of the pasture, the price of concentrates, the rapidity of gains desired, and the market conditions.

BASIC CONSIDERATIONS IN UTILIZING PASTURES FOR FATTENING CATTLE:

The following points are basic in utilizing pastures for fattening cattle:

1. **Moderate winter feeding makes for most effective pasture utilization.**—The more liberally beef cattle are fed during the winter, the less will be their effective utilization of pasture the following summer. Generally speaking, for maximum utilization of pasture, stocker calves should be fed for winter gains not in excess of $\frac{3}{4}$ to 1 pound per head daily, and yearlings not in excess of 1 to $1\frac{1}{4}$ pound.

2. **Early pastures are "washy" but high in protein.**—Cattle should not be turned to pasture too early. The first growth is extremely "washy," possessing little fattening property. However, the crude protein content of the forages is high during the early stages of growth and rapidly decreases as the forages mature. This would indicate the importance of pasturing rather heavily during the period of maximum growth in the spring and early summer.

3. **Sudden changes are to be avoided.**—Changes from dry lot to pastures or from less succulent to more succulent pastures should be made with care; for grass is a laxative, and the cattle may shrink severely. Also, bloat may occur.

4. **Time of starting grain feeding on pastures is determined by condition of cattle and quality of pastures.**— Cattle that have been fed grain rather liberally through the winter and are in good condition should usually be fed grain from the beginning of the grazing period. On the other hand, if they have been roughed through the winter, it may be just as well to feed the grain only during the last 80 to 120 days of the grazing season, after the season of peak pasture growth. The latter recommendation is made because it is sometimes difficult to get animals to consume grain when an abundance of palatable forage is available. At peak pasture growth, the animals should be started on feed and brought to full feed as rapidly as possible.

5. **Grain supplements on pastures usually make for larger daily gains, earlier marketing, and higher prices.**—The addition of a grain supplement for cattle on pasture makes for larger daily gains and earlier marketing—either directly off grass or with a shorter dry-lot finishing period—and the cattle usually bring a higher price. The owner thus avoids late fall competition and lower prices of strictly grass-fed cattle. Also, because cattle that are grain fed on pasture can be marketed over a wider period of time, there is greater flexibility in the operations.

6. **Protein supplements on pasture should be considered.**— Corn is the most common grain supplement fed to cattle on pasture. However, because of availability and price, cottonseed cake is commonly used in the South and wheat and barley in the West. The quality of pasture, the relative price of corn and protein supplements, and the grade of cattle are factors that will determine whether the addition of a protein supplement will increase the profit. Generally, when grass pastures approach

maturity—when they become dry in the late summer and fall, and consequently lower in protein—it will pay to feed a protein supplement. At this time, it may be good business to add 1 pound of protein supplement to each 8 to 12 pounds of grain. Usually this will increase the rate and efficiency of gain.

7. **Carrying capacity of pastures will vary.**—The carrying capacity of pastures will vary with the amount of grain supplement, the quality of pasture, and the age and condition of the cattle. Because of these factors, the acreage per steer will vary all the way from one to ten.

8. **Age is a factor.**—Young cattle (yearlings) tend to grow as well as to fatten. Thus older cattle (two years or older) will reach a high degree of finish on pastures alone. As fine as the pastures are, it must be remembered that grass is still a roughage.

9. **Salt for cattle on pasture.**—Salt is especially necessary when grass is being utilized. Fattening steers consume from three-fourths to one and one-half ounces of salt per head daily.

10. **Species of grasses or legumes will vary.**—The best species of grasses or legumes or grass-legume mixtures to be seeded will vary according to the area, especially according to the soil and climatic conditions. Pasture yields vary greatly from area to area and season to season.

11. **Grass versus grass-legume mixtures should be considered.**—In general, where adapted legumes can be successfully grown—either alone or with grass mixtures—the results are superior to yields obtained from pure stands of the grasses. At Pullman, Washington, in a study of pure species of smooth brome and crested wheatgrass versus grass-alfalfa mixtures, it was found that: (1) The grasses produced an average of 87 pounds of beef per acre, whereas the grass-alfalfa mixtures averaged 223 pounds of beef per acre; (2) when based on forage yields at monthly intervals, the same mixtures produced three times as much oven-dry forage per acre as the pastures seeded to grasses alone; (3) the grass-legume mixtures provided a slightly longer grazing season; (4) the grass-legume mixtures provided a higher carrying capacity in terms of animals per acre; (5) the erosion-resisting characters of the soil were improved by the fibrous grass roots, both while the crop was growing and after the seeding had been plowed under; and (6) the addition of grasses to legumes tended to keep out cheatgrass and other undesirable

plants.[1] The two latter points are based merely on careful observation, whereas the rest of the points were proved experimentally.

12. **Grain feeding will lengthen the grazing season.**—At the Washington Agricultural Experiment Station, grain feeding cattle on pasture lengthened the grazing season by an average of fifty-seven days.

13. **Self-feeding versus hand feeding on pasture.**—Self-feeding grain on pasture has generally proved superior to hand feeding, as the animals consume more feed, make more rapid gains, and return more profit.

14. **Economy of grain feeding on pasture.**—Whether or not it will be profitable to feed grain on pasture will depend primarily upon the price of grain, the premium paid for cattle of higher finish and grade, the season in which it is desired to market, and the area and quality of pasture.

15. **Amount of grain to feed.**—The amount of grain to feed on pasture will depend upon the quality of the pasture.

16. **Size of pasture area.**—Grain feeding on pasture is most feasible when the area for grazing is limited.

17. **Quality of beef.**—In general, cattle finished with grain on pasture dress and grade slightly higher and have a slightly lower shrinkage than cattle finished on pasture with no supplement. Perhaps any such differences as exist are due to the higher fat and lower water content of the carcass and the decrease in yellowness of fat present.

18. **Body form affected by early fattening.**—Supplemental feed on pasture at an early date, in comparison with delayed finishing in the dry lot, results in young animals having greater development in the late maturing and most valuable parts of the carcass, such as the loin and hindquarters.

19. **Effect of grain feeding on digestibility.**—The digestibility of pasture grass supplemented with grain or other concentrates is greater than that of pasture alone.

20. **Grass-sweetclover adapted in short-time rotation.**— When adapted, grass-sweetclover mixtures can be used as short-time pastures. They fit especially well into rations when cash crops predominate.

21. **Amount of pasture consumed.**—Cattle on good pasture without a grain supplement will eat approximately one hundred

[1]Ensminger, M. E., *et al.* Wash. Agri. Expt. Sta. Bul. No. 444, June, 1944.

pounds of green forage daily per one thousand pounds live weight.

22. Grain and young pastures constitute a balanced ration.—As immature grass is high in protein, grain and lush pastures usually make a well-balanced ration for fattening cattle and even for calves soon after weaning. The rate of gain can usually be increased slightly, however, by feeding one pound of protein supplement to each ten to twelve pounds of grain. Whether this will increase the profit will depend primarily upon the relative price of grain and the protein supplement. Usually, the benefit from the addition of a protein supplement will be much greater after the period of peak pasture growth is past.

LESSENING BLOAT ON PASTURES:

There is always a possibility that bloat will occur when appreciable amounts of legumes are grazed. Even so, the high productivity of grass-legume mixtures usually makes their use profitable—especially for commercial cattle—provided that proper precautions are taken to minimize the danger from bloat.

The following practices will be helpful in reducing the bloat hazard:

1. Give a full feed of hay or other dry roughage before the animals are turned to legume pastures, to prevent the animals from filling up too rapidly on the green material.

2. If possible, after the animals are once turned to pasture, they should be left there continuously. If they must be removed over night or for longer periods, they should be filled with dry roughage before they are returned to pasture.

3. Mixtures that contain approximately half grasses and half legumes should be used.

4. Water and salt should be conveniently accessible at all times.

5. The animals should not be allowed to become empty when they congregate in a dry lot for shade or insect protection and then be allowed to gorge themselves suddenly on the green forage.

6. Many practical cattlemen feel that the bloat hazard is reduced by mowing alternate strips through the pasture, thus allowing the animals to consume the dry forage along with the pasture. Others keep in the pasture a rack well filled with dry hay or straw.

7. Because of the many serrations on the leaves, Sudan hay

appears especially effective in preventing bloat when fed to cattle on legume pastures.

8. Use a salt-antibiotic mixture as directed by a competent authority.

Although the cause of bloat has not been scientifically established, it appears that anything that will tickle the animal's belching mechanism—thus causing it to belch rather than permitting it to blow up like a balloon—will reduce the hazard. Coarse dry roughages appear to have this effect.

The Feeder's Margin

By "margin" is meant the difference between the cost per hundredweight of the feeder animals and the selling price per hundredweight of the same animal when fattened. Gains made in the feed lot are expensive. They generally cost more per pound to produce than the selling price per pound obtained at marketing time. To cover this loss and secure a profit on the operations, the cattle must sell at a higher price per pound than was paid for them. This spread in price is commonly referred to as the "necessary margin."

FACTORS DETERMINING THE NECESSARY MARGIN:

The cost of feed and the cost of cattle are the two major capital expenses in any cattle feeding venture. Likewise, these same two factors are the most important ones in determining profits and losses. How the cost of feed and the cost of cattle influence the necessary margin for the feeder to break even on his operations is indicated in Fig. 122.

Generally speaking, about 80 per cent of the cost of fattening cattle (exclusive of the initial purchase price for animals) is for feed. Another 6 per cent is usually absorbed by interest on the purchase price of the cattle. Then labor costs, taxes, purchasing and marketing charges, shrinkage losses, and death losses (about 1 to 2% of the animals) make up most of the remaining expenses. Of course, the value of the manure compensates for part of these costs.

In summary form, the factors that determine the necessary margin are as follows:

1. The better the grade of cattle and the younger the animals, the smaller the necessary margin. This is so because better grades and younger cattle generally bring a higher selling price, and, therefore, a higher price is obtained on their gains made in the feed lot. This point is well illustrated in Fig. 122.

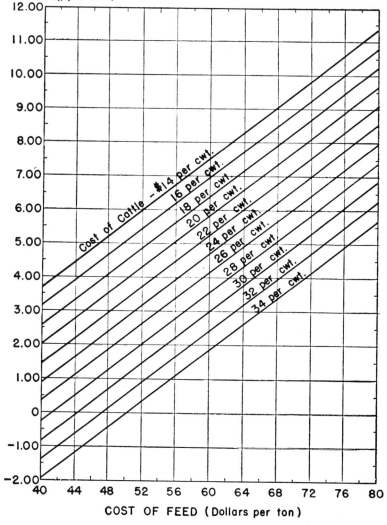

BREAK-EVEN MARGINS

Margin required to
break even ($ per cwt.)

COST OF FEED (Dollars per ton)

Fig. 122. This chart indicates the relation of the cost of the feed and the cost of feeder cattle to the necessary margin required to break even on the feeding operation. It is based upon a 700-pound feeder steer fed to a slaughter weight of 1,000 pounds in 150 days, with an average weight of 850 pounds during the feeding period and an average daily feed consumption of 3 pounds per Cwt. The costs include interest at 6% on the purchase price of cattle (for 5 mo.) but no other production costs. A reading of the vertical scale at the point of intersection between a given cost line for cattle and a given cost line for feed indicates the necessary margin required to break even on the feeding operations. (Computations by Wm. Goodin and Jean Sandborn; drawing by Steve Allured; photo by Washington State University)

2. The higher the cost of feed, the greater the necessary margin. This is so because of the high cost of gains as compared to their selling price. Also, this point is well illustrated in Fig. 122.

3. The heavier the initial weight of the cattle, the smaller the necessary margin. This is due to the fact that the lower cost initial weight makes up a larger proportion of the higher priced finished market weight than would be the case when starting with a lighter animal.

4. The longer the feeding period and the greater the gains necessary to get the cattle in a finished condition, the greater the margin. This is also due to the fact that gains made in the feed lot are expensive, generally costing more to produce than can be realized in selling on the market.

Considering all the above factors collectively, it may be understood why less margin is necessary in the case of heavy, mature steers carrying considerable flesh when purchased as compared with thin, light-weight yearlings. Calves usually require the smallest margin of all because of their efficiency of gains and their higher value per hundredweight.

The computations upon which Fig. 122 is based may best be illustrated by the following example, keeping in mind that a reading of the vertical price scale at the point of intersection between a given cost line for cattle and a given cost line for feed indicates the necessary margin required to break even on the feeding operation under the conditions previously indicated: *If feeder cattle cost $20.00 per Cwt. and feed costs $50.00 per ton, what margin is necessary in order to break even?*

A reading of the vertical price scale at the point of intersection between the cost line for cattle (in this case $20.00) and the cost line for feed (in this case $50.00) indicates that a margin of nearly $4.00 per hundred is necessary (actually, $3.91).

Step by step, the computations back of this direct reading are obtained as follows:

1. Cost of each steer (700 lbs. @ $20. per Cwt.)   =$140.00
2. Cost of feed:
   The amount of feed consumed is calculated by multiplying the average weight of the steer during the feeding period (850 lbs.) by the daily feed consumption (3 lbs. per Cwt.) which is then multiplied by the length of the feeding period (150 days). (In this case 1.9125 tons @ $50 per ton)= 95.625
3. Interest (6% on $140. for 150 days)   = 3.50

4.   Total cost $239.125
5. Thus, a sale price of $23.91 per Cwt., or a margin of $3.91 per Cwt., is required to break even (1,000 lbs. @ $23.91 per Cwt.)   = 239.10

Fattening Cattle of the Various Market Grades

The most profitable grade of cattle to feed will generally be that kind of cattle in which there is the greatest spread of margin between their purchase price as feeders and their selling price as fat cattle. As can be readily understood, one cannot arrive at this decision by merely comparing the existing price between the various grades at the time of purchase. Rather, it is necessary to project the differences that will probably exist, based on past records, when the animals are fat and ready for market.

As very few grain-fed cattle are marketed in the summer and fall, the spread in price between Good and Choice fat cattle and those of the lower grades is usually the greatest during this season. On the other hand, the spread between these grades is likely to be least in late winter and early spring, when a large number of well-fattened cattle are coming to market from the feed lots.

The length of the feeding period and the type of feed available should also receive consideration in determining the grade of cattle to feed. Thus for a long feed and when a liberal allowance of grain is to be fed, only the better grades of feeders should be purchased. On the other hand, when a maximum quantity of coarse roughage is to be utilized and a short feed is planned, cattle of the medium or lower grades are most suitable. In other words, successful cattle feeders match the quality of the cattle selected with the quality of the available feed; the better the feed the higher the grade of cattle.

Cattle of the lower grades should be selected with very special care to make certain that only thrifty animals are bought. Ordinarily, death losses are much higher among low-grade feeder cattle, especially when the low-grade animals are calves. The death loss in handling average or high-grade feeders seldom exceeds 1 to 2 per cent; whereas with "cull" or "dogie" cattle, it frequently is twice or three times this amount. Many low-grade cattle are horned, and dehorning further increases the death risk—in addition to the added labor and shrinkage resulting therefrom.

No given set of rules is applicable under any and all conditions in arriving at the particular grade of cattle to feed, but the following factors should receive consideration.

1. The feeding of high-grade cattle is favored when:

(1) The feeder is more experienced.

(2) A long feed with a maximum of grain in the ration is planned.

(3) Conditions point to a wide spread in price between grades at marketing time. Such conditions normally prevail in the late summer or early fall.

2. The feeding of average or low-grade cattle is favored when:

(1) The feeder is less experienced.[1]

(2) A short feed with a maximum of roughage or cheap by-products is planned.

(3) Conditions point to a narrow spread in price between grades at marketing time. Such conditions normally prevail in the spring.

3. In addition to the profit factors enumerated above, it should be pointed out that with well-bred cattle the following conditions prevail:

(1) Well-bred cattle possess greater capacity for consuming large quantities of feed than steers of a more common grade, especially during the latter part of the feeding period.

(2) The higher the grade of cattle, the higher the dressing percentage and the greater the proportionate development of the high-priced cuts.

(3) The higher the grade of the cattle, the greater the opportunities for both profit and loss.

(4) There is a greater sense of pride and satisfaction in feeding well-bred cattle. To top the market with a load of Prime steers is frequently more gratifying and means more to an experienced and self-respecting feeder than any greater profits that might be derived from feeding low-grade cattle.

Certainly the producer who raises his own feeder cattle should always strive to breed high grade cattle regardless of whether he fattens them out himself or sells them as feeders. On the other hand, the purchaser of feeder steers can well afford to appraise the situation fully prior to purchasing any particular grade.

---

[1] In general, the inexperienced feeder should stick to the middle kind and leave the extremes—the fancy and the plain cattle—to the man with experience.

The Value of Breeding and Type in Fattening Cattle

Although the supporting data are rather limited, it is fully realized that there is considerable difference between individual animals insofar as rate and economy of gain is concerned. It is to be emphasized that these differences are greater within breeds than between breeds.

In studies at the Wisconsin Experiment Station, feeding trials were conducted with purebred Aberdeen-Angus, purebred Holstein, and cross-bred Angus-Holstein calves of approximately the same age. The Wisconsin investigators found that the Holsteins used produced slightly more rapid and economical gains than were obtained with the purebred Aberdeen-Angus, with the cross-breds intermediate between the two. However, the beef-type animals had a higher dressing percentage and a more desirable quality of carcass, with a greater proportion of valuable cuts of meat. Thus the animals of beef type and breeding brought a higher market price. The average selling price for the Aberdeen-Angus steers was $13.00 in comparison with $12.16 for the cross-breds and $10.08 for the Holsteins.[1]

The Wisconsin studies would again lend credence to the statement that the breeder should always strive to produce beef-type cattle of good breeding. On the other hand, where replacement calves are not needed in the dairy herd, it may often be advantageous to use a beef-type bull as a "cow freshener"—thus producing a calf which is more valuable either as a veal or as a potential feeder. There may, however, be sufficient spread in price between the grades to warrant that the purchaser of feeder steers shop about when considering the particular grade of cattle to choose.

Age as a Factor in Fattening Cattle

A generation ago the term feeder steer signified to both the rancher and the Corn Belt feeder a two-and-one-half to three-year-old animal weighing approximately one thousand pounds. Today, feeder steers are referred to by ages as "feeder calves," "yearlings," and "two-year-olds." This shift to younger cattle has been brought about primarily by the consumer demand for smaller and lighter cuts of meat and improved feeding and management practices.

---

[1]Fuller, J. G., Wisc. Agri. Expt. Buls. Nos. 396, 405, and 410; see also Fuller, J. G., Soc. Anim. Prod., Proc. 1930.

The age of cattle to feed is one of the most important questions to be decided upon by every practical cattleman. The following factors should be considered in reaching an intelligent decision on this point:

1. **Rate of gain.**—When cattle are fed liberally from the time they are calves, the daily gains will reach their maximum the first year and decline with each succeeding year thereafter. On the other hand, when in comparable condition, thin but healthy two-year-old steers will make more rapid gains in the feed lot than yearlings, and likewise yearlings will make more rapid gains than calves.

2. **Economy of gain.**—Calves require less feed to produce one hundred pounds of beef than do older cattle. This may be explained as follows:

(1) The increase in body weight of older cattle is largely due to the deposition of high-energy fat, whereas the increase in body weight of young animals is due, in part at least, to the growth of muscles, bones, and organs. Thus the body of a calf at birth usually consists of more than 70 per cent water, whereas the body of a fat two-year-old steer will only contain 45 per cent moisture. In the latter case, a considerable part of the water has been replaced by fat deposition.

(2) Calves consume a larger proportion of feed in proportion to their body weight than do older cattle.

(3) Calves masticate and digest their feed more thoroughly than older cattle. Despite the fact that calves require less feed per one hundred pounds gain—because of the high-energy value of fat—older cattle store as much energy in their bodies for each one hundred pounds of total digestible nutrients consumed as do younger animals.

3. **Flexibility in marketing.**—Calves will continue to make satisfactory gains at the end of the ordinary feeding period, whereas the efficiency of feed utilization decreases very sharply when mature steers are held past the time that they are finished. Therefore, under unfavorable market conditions, calves can be successfully held for a reasonable length of time, whereas prolonging the fattening period of older cattle is usually unprofitable.

4. **Length of feeding period.**—Calves require a somewhat longer feeding period than older cattle to reach comparable finish. To reach Choice to Prime condition, steer calves must be full fed from eight to nine months, yearlings six to seven months, and two-year-olds only from five to six months. The longer fattening period required for calves is due to the fact that they are growing as well as fattening.

5. **Total gain required to finish.**—In general calves must put on slightly more total gains in the feed lot than older animals to attain the same degree of finish. In terms of initial weight, calves practically double their weight in the feed lot; yearlings increase in weight approximately 70 per cent; and two-year-olds increase their initial feed lot weight by from 40 to 50 per cent.

6. **Total feed consumed.**—The daily feed consumption of calves is considerably less than for older cattle, but as calves must be fed for a slightly longer feeding period, the total feed requirement for the entire fattening period is approximately the same for cattle of different ages.

7. **Experience of the feeder.** — Young cattle are bovine "babies." As such, they must be fed more expertly. Thus the amateur feeder had best feed older cattle.

8. **Kind and quality of feed.**—Because calves are growing, it is necessary that they have more protein in the ration. Normally, protein supplements are higher in price than carbonaceous feeds, thus making for a more expensive ration. Also, because of the smaller digestive capacity, calves cannot utilize as much coarse roughage, pasture, or cheap by-product feeds as older cattle.

Calves also are more likely to develop peculiar eating habits than older cattle. They may reject coarse, stemmy roughages or moldy or damaged feeds that would be eaten readily by older cattle. Calves also require more elaborate preparation of the ration and attention to other small details designed to increase their appetite.

9. **Pigs following cattle.** — Because calves masticate and digest their feed more thoroughly than older cattle, the amount of pork obtained from pigs following fattening cattle varies directly with the age of the cattle.

10. **Comparative costs and selling price.**—Calves usually cost more per one hundred pounds as feeders than do older cattle.

They also usually sell for a higher price per hundredweight as finished cattle.

11. Dressing percentage and quality of beef.—Older cattle have a slightly higher dressing percentage than fat calves or baby beef. Moreover, many consumers have a decided preference for the greater flavor of beef obtained from older animals.

From the above discussion, it should be perfectly clear that there is no best age of cattle to feed under any and all conditions. Rather, each situation requires individual study and all factors must be weighed and balanced out.

Heifers versus Steers

On the market, cattle are divided into five sex classes: steers, heifers, cows, bulls, and stags. The sex of feeder cattle is important to the producer from the standpoint of cost and selling price (or margin), the contemplated length of feeding period, quality of feeds available, and ease of handling. The consumer is conscious of sex differences in cattle and is of the impression that it affects the quality, finish, and conformation of the carcass.

Steers are by far the most important of any of the sex classes on the market, both from the standpoint of numbers and their availability throughout the year, whereas heifers are second.

The relative merits of steers versus heifers, both from the standpoint of feed lot performance and the quality of carcass produced, has long been a controversial issue. Based on experiments[1] and practical observations, the following conclusions and deductions seem to be warranted relative to this question:

1. Length of feeding period.—Heifers mature earlier than steers and become fat sooner, thus making for a shorter feeding period. In general, heifers may be ready for the market thirty to forty days earlier than steers of the same age started on feed at the same time. Usually a short feed of 60 to 120 days is preferable with heifers.

2. Market weight.—The most attractive heifer carcasses are obtained from animals weighing 650 to 900 pounds on foot, showing good condition and finish but not so fat as to be patchy and wasty.

3. Rate and economy of gain.—Because of their slower rate of growth, the feed lot gains made by heifers are usually some-

---

[1] Bull, Sleeter, F. C. Olson, and John H. Longwell, Ill. Agri. Expt. Sta. Bul. No. 355, 1930.

what smaller and more costly than those made by steers of the same age. This point, however, is usually of little practical importance, as steers must be fed for a longer period to reach the same degree of finish.

4. **Price.**—Because of existing prejudices, feeder heifers can be purchased at a lower price per pound than steers, but they also bring a lower price when marketed. Thus the net return per head may or may not be greater with heifers.

5. **Carcass quality.**—In England, there is no discrimination in price against well-finished heifers. In fact, the English argue that the grain of meat in heifer carcasses is finer and the quality superior. On the other hand, the hotels, clubs, and elite butcher shops in the United States hold a decided prejudice against heifer beef.

Carefully controlled experiments have now shown conclusively that when heifers are marketed at the proper weight and degree of finish sex makes no appreciable difference in the dressing percentage, in the retail value of the carcasses, or in the color, tenderness, and palatability of the meat.

6. **Ease of handling in the feed lot.**—Because of disturbances at heat periods, many feeders do not like to handle heifers in the feed lot.

7. **Flexibility in marketing.**—If the market is unfavorable, it is usually less advisable to carry heifers on feed for a longer period than planned because of (1) possible pregnancies and (2) the fact that animals become too patchy and wasty.

8. **Effect of pregnancy.**—Packer buyers have long insisted that they are justified in buying fat heifers at a lower price than steers of comparable quality and finish because: (1) Most heifers are pregnant and have a lower dressing percentage, and (2) pregnant heifers yield less desirable carcasses. In realization that the packer will lower the price anyway, many feeders make it a regular practice to turn a bull with heifers about three to four months before the market period. Such feeders contend that the animals are then quieter and will make better feed-lot gains.

In a carefully controlled experiment designed to ferret out the facts of this controversy, the Illinois Experiment Station[1] compared open and bred heifers in a five-month feeding period with the following pertinent results:

-----

[1]Snapp, R. R., and Sleeter Bull, Ill. Expt. Sta. Bul. No. 508, 1944.

(1) The bred heifers were quieter and easier to handle in the feed lot.

(2) The bred heifers possessed keener appetites.

(3) The young pregnant heifers grew less and put on more fat.

(4) When kept at the same level of feed consumption, pregnancy had no appreciable effect on average daily gain.

(5) Pregnancy did not affect dressing percentage. This was probably due to the higher finish and the lighter hides, heads, shanks, stomach and smaller "fill" of the pregnant heifers. These factors were sufficient to overcome the weight of the three to four months' fetus which averaged thirty pounds.

(6) The carcasses of the bred heifers were noticeably better finished.

(7) The flank, loin-end, and round were lighter in the bred than in the open heifers, but the other wholesale cuts were practically the same in each group.

The results of the Illinois experiment would indicate that the producer is entirely justified in breeding full-fed heifers three to four months prior to the time of marketing. It would also seem that packers are not justified in buying such bred heifers at a lower price because of any alleged lower dressing percentage or difference in carcass quality.

The trade in feeder cows and heifers assumes considerable volume only in the fall and early winter—at the close of the grazing season when the farmer or rancher is culling his herd and prior to the start of the wintering operations. When market conditions are favorable and an abundance of cheap roughage is available, cows may often be fed at a profit.

When there is considerable demand for cheap meats, the feeder may find it profitable to fatten bulls and stags. Usually it is difficult to purchase such animals in large numbers. Here, as with the fattening of cows, the feeder should plan to utilize the maximum of cheap roughage.

Spayed Heifers

Spaying prevents the possibility of heifers becoming pregnant and eliminates the necessity of separating heifers from bulls or steers. Also, some buyers pay a slight premium for spayed heifers. However, most experiments have shown that spayed heifers make less rapid gains and require more feed per

100 pounds gain than open (control) heifers.[1] The latter facts, plus the attendant danger of the operation, generally do not justify spaying unless the selling price is sufficiently higher.

It is noteworthy that stilbestrol-fed spayed heifers gain about as rapidly and efficiently as non-spayed heifers.[2]

Buildings and Equipment for Fattening Cattle

The equipment should be adequate and durable, but in no case should it be elaborate, expensive, or of such type as to contribute to a high overhead for maintenance. From the standpoint of shelter, it is difficult if not impossible to improve upon a barn

Fig. 123. A paved corral lot used for fattening steers. Note that the cattle are clean and free from mud and manure. (Courtesy, Dale Woolson-croft, Iowa State College)

in which the major portion of the first floor is given over to cattle and which has grain storage bins along one side, silo and scales at either end, hay and straw storage above, and open sides

[1]Dinusson, W. E., F. N. Andrews, and W. M. Beeson, *Journal of Animal Science*, 1950, Vol. 9, p. 321.

Gramlich, H. J. and R. R. Thalman, Nebr. Agri. Expt. Sta. Bul. 252, 1930.

Hart, G. H., H. R. Guilbert, and H. H. Cole, Calif. Agri. Expt. Sta. Bul. 645, 1940.

Langford. L. H., R. J. Douglas and M. L. Buchanan, N. Dak. Agri. Expt. Sta. Bimonthly Bul., 1955, Vol. XVIII, No. 2.

[1 & 2]Smith, E. F., D. Richardson, B. A. Kocy, D. L. Mackintosh, and W. E. Stitt; Kan. Agri. Expt. Sta. Circ. 349, 1957, p. 53; and unpublished report from Dr. Smith, covering the 1956-57 experiment.

to the south or away from the direction of strong prevailing winds.

Even in cold climates the shelter for fattening cattle need not be constructed for warmth. Protection from wind, rain, and snow is all that is necessary. Fattening cattle on full feed unavoidably produce ample heat—through the mastication, digestion, and assimilation of their feed—to keep their bodies warm under all ordinary conditions without in the least diminishing the amount of nutrients available for fattening. In many western sections, especially where there is little winter rainfall, cattle are often fattened in open yards with no shelter whatsoever. At the most, only a natural windbreak or a solid fence windbreak is provided. In humid sections with mild winters, it may not pay to provide any shelter for fattening cattle.

In dry-lot feeding during the summer months, shelters provide desirable coolness and protection from insects. They also protect the animals from exposure to blistering sun. Without such protection, the coats of the cattle are likely to become harsh and sunburned, thus lessening the attractiveness of the animals and lowering their sale value.

Covering the windows and draping the openings of the shed with burlap reduces trouble from flies.

Providing dry bedding makes for comfort of the animals and helps to conserve the manure, especially the urine.

Excess Fattening

During World War II, excess fattening was discouraged on the basis that it represented a needless waste of feed—and grains were desperately needed for human consumption for our fighting allies and in rehabilitating the war-torn countries. In order to reduce such waste of grains, the Prime grade of beef was eliminated. Moreover, meat controls were designed to favor the Good and Medium grades of beef rather than the Choice grade.

Excessive fattening is undesirable, both from the standpoint of the producer and the consumer. Feed-lot gains are always expensive, and experienced cattle feeders are fully aware of the fact that to carry fattening cattle to an unnecessarily high finish is usually prohibitive from a profit standpoint. This is true because the gains in weight then consist chiefly of fat and contain but little water. In addition, a very fat animal eats less heartily, with the result that a small proportion of the nutrients, over and above the maintenance requirement, are available for making body tissue.

Beef should carry ample finish to make the meat attractive, juicy, and well flavored but any fat in excess of these requirements is usually trimmed off. Because of this situation, one of the real challenges to the beef cattle producer of the future is to produce animals which, from a genetics standpoint, are predisposed to produce marbling without excessive exterior fat.

Hogs Following Cattle

During normal years, many good Corn Belt cattle feeders feel amply repaid if they are able to: (1) market the grain through cattle at prevailing prices, (2) retain the manure to put back upon the land, and (3) obtain as profit the gains made by pigs following cattle.

The cattle feeder should plan for one pig to follow every one to three steers. The number of pigs will vary with the kind and preparation of the feed and the age of the cattle being fed.

Fig. 124. Hogs following cattle. One pig should follow every one to three steers, the ratio of pigs varying with the kind and preparation of the feed and the age of the cattle. Sometimes the only profit obtained is in the gains made by pigs following cattle. (Courtesy, The Corn Belt Farm Dailies)

Younger cattle masticate their feed better than older cattle do, thus providing less feed for pigs. Moreover, from one-third to one-half as many pigs are needed when ground grains rather than whole grains are fed. The best pigs weigh from 50 to 150 pounds and are active and not too fat.

Contract (or Custom) Feeding Cattle[1]

Contract feeding is not new. It increases in importance (1) during periods of financial stress, (2) when animals and feed are high in price, and (3) when feeders do not wish to take the risk of ownership. But these three factors alone do not explain the magnitude of today's contract feeding of cattle. Two additional factors, which generally accompany large contract feed yards, are primarily responsible for their expansion since World War II; namely, (1) increased mechanization, and (2) increased know-how. Also, increased integration has made for more contract feeding.

The contract feeding of cattle made rapid development after 1929, reaching a maximum during the severe drought of 1934. From this time to World War II, contract feeding declined with improved feed conditions on the western range, higher prices for feeder animals, and the availability of more credit to both the producer and the feeder through federal and private loan agencies.

In recent years (during and since World War II), some feeders have developed highly mechanized and most efficient plants, with capacities ranging up to 30,000 cattle at one time. Some of the larger establishments have on their staffs highly trained nutritionists who are charged with the responsibility of formulating rations and of obtaining maximum gains and feed efficiency at the lowest possible cost. Through contract feeding, they sell the use of their facilities and their services to cattle owners, usually with profit to each party.

As a competitive measure, some of the larger and better financed yards are currently going so far as to finance up to 80 per cent of the cost of cattle and transportation—usually at 6 per cent, and to finance the entire cost of the feed without interest.

The experience of owners and feeders with contract feeding and the difficulties encountered suggest opportunities for improvement in methods and practices along the following three

---

[1]This section was authoritatively reviewed by Mr. James C. Nofziger, formerly with California Cattle Supply Co., Artesia, Calif.; now in the Department of Animal Science, Washington State University.

principal lines, which, if carried out, would make for greater success in the handling of feeder cattle under contract:

1. Use of contracts that are fair to both owners and feeders.[1]
2. Utilization of proper feeding methods and rations.
3. Employment of experienced and efficient help.

In general, there are the following five types of contracts:

1. **The guaranteed feeder's margin contract.**—With this type of contract, the animals are weighed to the feeder at an agreed price per hundred weight, but with the seller then and there contracting for their delivery at a certain price at an agreed approximate date and weight. Thus the margin is definitely known at the time of the transaction, and there is no gamble that it will be either greater or less. The risk is minimized, and with it chances for either great profits or losses.

2. **The gain-in-weight contract.**—In this arrangement, the feeder is reimbursed on the basis of the gain in weight put on the cattle, at an agreed price of so many dollars per hundred. This type of contract has decreased in importance in recent years, because it frequently results in poor owner-feeder relations—due primarily to the following reasons: (1) It is impossible in advance of feeding to detect those lots of animals that will be poorer "doers" because of such factors as nervousness, nutritional deficiencies, diseases, and/or parasites, (2) the longer the feeding period the greater the cost of gains, and the length of the feeding period is seldom stipulated in such contracts, and (3) the amount of fill or shrinkage when weighing animals in and out the feed lot is of great importance to both the owner and the feeder, and a source of argument.

   At the present time, use of the gain-in-weight contract is confined largely to cattle that are being fed predominantly on pasture, green chop, or silage.

3. **The cooperative investment contract.**—Sometimes this is referred to as the "going-in-pardners contract." In this arrangement, after the marketing costs and freight have been deducted from the gross proceeds of the sale

---

[1]Many contracts are verbal, rather than written; for possession of the animals is usually considered a satisfactory guarantee against liabilities which will accrue to the account of the owner.

of the animals, the remaining sum is divided by the contracting parties according to the percentage of their respective investments in the finished animals. Usually the owner's investment consists of the total value of the feeder cattle plus the interest on the investment; whereas the feeder inventories the feeds, labor, and other overhead costs.

4. **The stipulated fee per head per day and/or price per ton of feed contract.**—In this type of contract, charges are on a fixed basis (usually so many cents per head per day and/or so many dollars per ton handling charge on feed). The feeder does not assume any risk whatsoever; it merely is his intent to sell feed, equipment, and services for an agreed price.

Contracts with fixed charges are the most satisfactory and the most common, primarily because there is less room for misunderstanding. Based on information which the author collected from different sections of the country, it appears that the following pertinent provisions are incorporated in most cattle contracts with fixed charges:

(1) The feeder charges 1 to 7 cents per head per day for corrals, shelter, equipment, and labor and other services; the amount charged depends chiefly upon (a) the milling and handling charges made on the feed, (b) the number and size of cattle, and (c) the shelter, equipment, and labor necessary. In addition, the feeder charges from $1.50 to $9.00 per ton above ingredient cost for the feed[1]; this added charge to cover (a) milling costs (ranging from $2.50 to $5.50 per ton[2]), and (b) other operating costs plus profit.

(2) The owner furnishes the cattle delivered to the feed lot, and moves them from the feed lot when finished.

(3) The owner pays for all feed on a cost basis. Where the feeder produces feeds that are sold to the owner, such feeds are sold at prevailing market prices for their respective kinds and grades.

Where minerals are self-fed, the feeder may absorb the charges; where they are incorporated in

---

[1]Silage and root crops are usually handled on the basis of $1.00 to $3.00 per ton; wet beet pulp may be converted to a dry basis.

[2]Milling costs—including labor, power, insurance, maintenance of the mill, and part of the yard—run between $2.50 and $5.50 per ton.

the ration, they are charged to the cattle owner on the same basis as other feed ingredients.

Some custom feeders use whatever ration is requested by the owner; others insist that the ration be at the feeder's discretion. The latter arrangement appears to be most satisfactory because (1) the feeder usually knows what feeds are cheapest and most satisfactory under his conditions, and (2) feed storage and handling costs mount as the number of rations increases.

(4) Generally the owner pays for all veterinary services and medication; in other cases the feeder stands these costs. The feeder brands, sorts, weighs and hospitalizes sick stock.

(5) The owner assumes all death losses and other risks.

(6) The feeder retains the manure. In the case of those establishments located in areas where the sale of manure to truck gardeners is especially remunerative, it is common for the feeder to furnish such straw and other bedding as may be necessary.

The above six points are specific, fair, and easily understood. Although some deviations from them can and should be made, such feeding contracts result in a minimum of misunderstanding.

Generally, those who charge the higher yardage rates per head daily (up to 7 cents) add little or no feed-handling costs above actual ingredient prices; conversely, those who charge the lower yardage rates per head per day (1 cent daily, or no charge at all) make a higher feed charge over and above actual ingredient cost. As a rule of thumb, those charging yardage generally lower their feed cost by $1.00 per ton for each 1 cent of yardage charged. At the present time, it appears that the lower yardage cost and the higher feed handling charge is the favored basis; primarily because (1) the owner of the cattle is less inclined to object to such charges, and (2) increased competition has driven custom feeders to make their charges on the least conspicuous basis.

Where charges are made only for the milling and

handling of the feed, the custom feeder is, in essence, operating as a feed manufacturer; processing and delivering feed to his customers—the owners of the cattle.

The method of computing the feed consumption varies from yard to yard; some actually weigh it over the scales; others estimate it on a predetermined basis—such as 3 per cent of the incoming body weight plus 7 pounds per day (for example, the daily feed consumption of a steer weighing 700 pounds at the time of delivery to the yard would be estimated at 28 pounds).

5. **The incentive basis contract.**—This is another system of charging on a per-head per-day basis that some cattle owners like, because it gives an incentive for the feeder to produce rapid daily gains. It consists in paying the feeder for all feed plus a charge arrived at by "multiplying the average daily gain times itself, or times some factor." Thus, if the cattle being fattened should average 2½ pounds gain daily over the entire feeding period, the per-head, per-day basis of payment to the feeder would be as follows:

2½ (gain) X 2½^1 = 6¼ cents per head per day

If the average daily gain per head over the entire period is 2 pounds, then the basis of payment would be as follows:

2 (gain) X 2^1 = 4 cents per head per day

The incentive basis isn't desirable from the standpoint of the feeder if the cattle are "poor doers" or if, because of disease or other factors beyond the feeder's control, poor gains are obtained. For understandable reasons, however, this type of contract does have a very strong appeal to the cattle owner.

Some custom feeders honor more than one type of contract, thereby according the cattleman a selection.

It is likely that there will always be many cases of dispute and disagreement in any method of contract feeding. In such cases, it is customary that arbitration

---

[1] This factor might be varied in keeping with economic conditions. There is no reason why it must be identical to the average daily gains. It may be higher or lower according to economic conditions.

be conducted by a committee of three—each party to the contract choosing a representative and these two then choosing a third party, to study the case and recommend a settlement.

FEED ALLOWANCE AND SOME SUGGESTED RATIONS FOR BEEF CATTLE[1]

Some general rules of feeding may be given, but it must be remembered that *"the eye of the master fattens his cattle."* Nevertheless, the beginner may well profit from the experience of successful feeders. It is with this hope that the suggested rations are herewith presented.

TABLE 25—HANDY BEE

SUGGESTED RATIONS

W th all rations and for all classes and ages of cattle, provide free access in separate containers to (1) salt (iodized salt in iodine-deficient areas) and (2) a mixture of ⅓ salt and ⅔ steamed bone meal.	Wintering Mature Beef Breeding Cows (Av. Wt. 1,100)	Wintering Replacement Heifers (weighing 400 to 500 lbs. start of wintering).
	(lbs. per day)	(lbs per day)
1. Legume hay or grass-legume mixed hay, good quality.........	18–26	12–18³
Grain............	....	2–4
Protein supplement............	....	....
2. Grass hay or other non-legume dry roughage....................	18–28	12–18³
Grain............	....	2½–4½
Protein supplement............	½–1	1¼–1½
3. Legume hay or grass-legume mixed hay, good quality......	7–11	8–12³
Grass hay or other non-legume dry roughage....................	11–17	4 6
Grain............	....	2½–4
Protein supplement............	....	½–¾
4. Silage............	55–60	25–40⁴
Grain............	....	....
Protein supplement............	½–1½	1½–1¾
5. Silage............	40–45	16–28
Legume hay or grass-legume mixed hay, good quality......	5–6	3–4
Grain............	....	....
Protein supplement............	....	1¼–1½
6. Silage............	40–45	16–28
Grass hay or other non-legume dry roughage....................	5–6	3–4
Grain............	....	....
Protein supplement............	½–1	1¾–2

[1]If stocker calves are late or the roughage is fair to poor in quality, it may be desirable to add 2 to 4 pounds of grain per head daily. If farm scales are available, monthly weights may be used as the criterion for grain feeding. Keep in mind that the calves should gain ¾ to 1 pound daily.

[2]In general, the experienced feeder plans that cattle on full feed shall consume (1) feeds in amounts (daily; air-dry basis) equal to about 3.0% of their live weight, (2) 70 to 75% concentrates, and (3) a minimum of 0.5 to 0.8 lbs. roughage for each 100 lbs. live weight. In areas where roughage is more abundant and comparatively cheaper than grain, as in the irrigated valleys of the West, the proportions of roughage to grain should be somewhat higher than indicated. In computing roughage consumption three pounds of silage are considered equivalent to one pound of hay.

[1]Where possible, these rations were computed from the requirements as reported by the National Research Council and interpreted by the author.

Table 25 is a handy beef cattle feeding guide for different classes and ages of cattle.[1] All of these are merely intended as general guides. Variations can and should be made in the rations used. The feeder should give consideration to (1) the supply of home-grown feeds, (2) the availability and price of purchased feeds, (3) the class and age of cattle, (4) the health and condition of the animals, and (5) the length of the grazing season.

In using Table 25 as a guide, it is to be recognized that feeds of similar nutritive properties can and should be interchanged as price relationships warrant. Thus, (1) the cereal grains may consist of corn, barley, wheat, oats, and/or sorghum; (2) the protein supplement may consist of soybean, cottonseed, peanut,

CATTLE FEEDING GUIDE

Wintering stocker alves; roughed through winter, and generally razed the following ummer. Fed for winter ain of ¾ to 1 lb. per head daily (weighing 0 to 500 lbs. start of wintering).[1]	Fattening calves in dry lot, generally in winter. (Weighing 400 to 500 lbs. start of feeding, and 750 to 850 lbs. at marketing.[2])	Wintering Yearlings; roughed through the winter, and generally pasture fattened the following summer. Fed for winter gains of 1 to 1¼ lbs. per head daily (weighing about 600 lbs. start of wintering).	Fattening yearlings in dry-lot, generally in winter (weighing about 600 lbs. start of feeding, and 850 to 1000 lbs. at marketing).[2]	Fattening two-year-old steers in dry-lot, generally in winter (weighing about 800 lbs. start of feeding and 1,000 to 1,100 lbs. at marketing).[2]
(lbs. per day) 12–18[3]	(lbs. per day) 4–6 12–15 1–1½	(lbs. per day) 16–24	(lbs. per day) 4–8 15–19½ 1 1½	(lbs. per day) 6–12 16–22 ....
12–18[3] 1¼–1½	4–5 12–15 1¾–2	16–24 .... 1½–1¾	4–8 15–20 1½–2	6–12 16½–22¾ 1½–1¾
8–12[3] 4–6 .... ¼–½	2–3 2–3 12–15 1½–1¾	6–8 10–16 .... 1–1½	2–4 2–4 15–19¾ 1¼–1¾	3–6 3–6 16–22 ½–¾
25–40[4] 1–1¼	12–15 8–12 2–2¼	45–55 .... 1¼–1½	18–24 11–16 2–2½	24–36 15–21 1¼–1½
20–30 2–4 .... ¾–1[5]	6–8 2–3 8–12 1¾–2	40–50 2–4 .... ¾–1	12–18 2–3 11–16 ¾–1¾	16–24 3–4 15–21 ¼–½
20–30 2–4 .... 1¼–1½	6–8 2–3 8–12 2–2¼	40–50 2–4 .... 1¼–1½	12–18 2–3 11–16 1¼–2	16–24 3–4 15–21 1–1¼

[3]With calves (both replacement heifers and stockers) an extra 2 lbs. of hay daily, over and above requirements is herewith indicated to allow for wastage. Practical operators generally feed stemmy or other hay left over by calves to the cow herd.

[4]Practical operators report scouring and unsatisfactory gains where grass or legume silage only is fed to young stock. On the other hand, corn or sorghum silage properly balanced with a protein supplement appear to be entirely satisfactory for young animals.

A protein supplement is not necessary for wintering stocker and feeder calves when good quality silage and good quality legume hay are fed free choice.

[1]Recommendations relative to feeding show animals are included in Chapter XVI of this book.

and/or linseed meal or cake; (3) the roughage may include many varieties of hays and silages; and (4) a vast array of by-product feeds may be utilized.

FEEDING AS AN ART

The feed requirements of animals do not necessarily remain the same from day to day or from period to period. The age and size of the animal, the kind and degree of activity, climatic conditions, the kind, quality, and amount of feed, the system of management, and the health, condition, and temperament of the animal are all continually exerting a powerful influence in determining the nutritive needs. How well the feeder understands, anticipates, interprets, and meets these requirements usually determines the success or failure of the ration and the results obtained. Although certain principles are usually followed by all good feeders, no book knowledge or set of instructions can substitute for experience and born livestock intuition. Skill and good judgment are essential to the feed lot. Indeed, there is much truth in the old adage that "the eye of the master fattens his cattle."

The discussion that follows will primarily be directed at the fattening operations of cattle. The maintenance of the breeding herd has already received special attention.

Starting Animals on Feed

In cattle feeding operations, it is important that the animals be accustomed to feed gradually. In general, upon arriving at the feed lot, the animals may be given as much non-legume roughages as they will consume. On the other hand, it is necessary that they be gradually accustomed to high-quality legumes which may be too laxative. The latter can be accomplished by slowly replacing the non-legume roughage with greater quantities of legumes. Of course, as the grain ration is increased the consumption of roughages will be decreased.

Starting cattle on grain requires care and good judgment. It is usually advisable first to accustom them to a bulky type of ration, a starting ration with considerable oats or beet pulp being excellent for this purpose. A common "rule of thumb" in starting cattle on feed is to give them two pounds per head the first day; increase the ration by from one-half to one pound daily until they reach approximately the halfway mark of what is anticipated will be a full feed; and then increase the ration by one pound every third day until full feeding is obtained.

The keenness of the appetites and the consistency of the droppings of the animals are an excellent index of their capacity to take more feed. In all instances, scouring, the bane of the feeder, should be avoided.

Frequency, Regularity, and Order of Feeding

In general, fattening animals are fed twice daily. With animals that are being fitted for show, where maximum consumption is important, it is not uncommon to find three or even four feedings daily. When self-fed, animals eat at more frequent intervals, though they consume smaller amounts at each feeding.

Animals learn to anticipate their feed. Accordingly, they should be fed *with great regularity*, as determined by a time piece. During warm weather, they will eat better if the feeding hours are early and late, in the cool of the day.

Usually, the grain ration is fed first, with the roughage following. In this manner, the animals eat the bulky roughages more leisurely.

Feeds Should Not Be Changed Abruptly

Sudden changes in diet are to be avoided, especially when changing from a less-concentrated ration to a more-concentrated one. When this rule of feeding is ignored, digestive disturbances result, and animals go "off feed." In either adding or omitting one or more ingredients, the change should be made gradually. Likewise, caution should be exercised in turning animals out to pasture or in transferring them to more lush grazing. If it is not convenient to accustom them to the new pasture gradually, they should at least be well filled with hay (or with the former pasture) before being turned out.

Selection of Feeds

In general, the successful feeder balances out the ration through selecting those feeds which are most readily available at the lowest possible cost. In addition, consideration is given to supplying quality proteins, the proper minerals, and the necessary vitamins. Attention is also given to the laxative or constipating qualities of feeds and palatability of the ration. Furthermore, the relation of the feeds to the quality of product produced should not be overlooked.

Attention to Details Pays

The successful feeder pays great attention to details. In addition to maintaining the health and comfort of the animals and filling their feed troughs, consideration is also given to their individual likes and temperaments.

It is important to avoid excessive exercise, which results in loss of energy by the animals through unnecessary muscular activity. Rough treatment, excitement, and noise usually result in nervousness and inefficient use of feed. Fattening animals should not be required to exercise any more than is deemed necessary for the maintenance of health. Dehorning is usually necessary to reduce fighting and possible bruises or injury. Likewise, all males should be castrated; for they will be much quieter, and the quality of the meat will be enhanced.

BALANCED RATIONS FOR BEEF CATTLE[1]

A balanced ration is one which provides an animal the proper proportions and amounts of all the required nutrients for a period of 24 hours.

Several suggested rations for different classes of livestock are listed in Table 25 of this chapter. Generally these rations will suffice, but it is recognized that rations should vary with conditions, and that many times they should be formulated to meet the conditions of a specific farm or ranch, or to meet the practices common to an area. Thus, where cattle are on pasture, or are receiving forage in the dry lot, the added feed (generally grains, by-product feeds, and/or protein supplements), if any,

---

[1]The author gratefully acknowledges the helpful suggestions of the following authorities who reviewed this section: Dr. Timothy H. Blosser, Nutritionist, Dairy Science Department, Washington State University, Pullman, Wash.; Mr. Charles Kyd, Manager, Climbing Arrow Ranch, Bozeman, Mont.; Dr. J. Wesley Nelson, Research Director, Nutrena Mills, Inc., Minneapolis, Minn.; Mr. James C. Fritz, Director of Nutrition Research, Dawe's Laboratories, Inc., Chicago, Ill.; Dr. P. R. Record, Director of Research, Security Mills, Inc., Knoxville, Tennessee; Dr. O. Burr Ross, Head, Department of Animal Science, University of Illinois, Urbana, Ill.; Dr. H. Ernest Bechtel, Director of Research, General Mills, Inc., Indianola, Iowa; Dr. J. W. Hayward and Mr. Roy C. Elrod, Nutrition Research Department, Archer-Daniels-Midland Company, Minneapolis, Minn.; Dr. R. R. Spitzer, Director of Research, Murphy Products Co., Burlington, Wis.; Dr. W. N. McMillen, Director of Feed Nutrition, A. E. Staley Manufacturing Co., Decatur, Ill.; Mr. Russ Lindstrom, Albers Milling Company, Los Angeles, California; Mr. Ralph McCall and Dr. R. O. Nesheim, The Quaker Oats Company, Chicago, Ill.; Dr. J. L. Krider, Vice President and Director of Feed Sales, McMillen Feed Mills, Fort Wayne, Ind.; Dr. Otto Hill, Assistant Manager, Feed Department, Washington Cooperative, Seattle, Wash.

should be formulated so as to meet the nutritive requirements not already provided by the forage. Rations may be formulated by the method which follows, but first the following pointers are noteworthy:

1. In computing rations, more than simple arithmetic should be considered, for no set of figures can substitute for experience.

2. Before attempting to compute a ration, one should have clearly in mind the general requirements of satisfactory rations for the particular class of livestock under consideration, preferably as determined by controlled feeding experiments.

3. In addition to providing the proper quantity of feed and to meeting the protein and energy requirements, a well balanced and satisfactory ration should meet the following requisites:

(1) It should be palatable and digestible.

(2) It should be economical. Generally speaking, this calls for the maximum use of home-grown feeds, especially forages.

(3) It should not be higher in protein content than is actually needed, for, generally speaking, medium and high protein feeds are in scarcer supply and higher in price than high energy feeds. In this connection, it is noteworthy that the newer findings in nutrition indicate (a) that much of the value formerly attributed to proteins, as such, was probably due to the vitamins and minerals which they furnished, and (b) that lower protein content rations may be used successfully provided they are fortified properly with the needed vitamins and minerals.

(4) It should be well fortified with the needed vitamins.

(5) It should be well fortified with the needed minerals, or free access to suitable minerals should be provided; but mineral imbalances should be avoided.

(6) It should so nourish the billions of bacteria in the paunch of ruminants (cattle and sheep) that there will be satisfactory (1) digestion of roughages, (2) utilization of lower quality and cheaper proteins and other nitrogenous products (thus, it is possible to use urea to constitute up to one-third of the total protein of the ration of ruminants, provided care is taken to supply

enough carbohydrates and other nutrients to feed properly the rumen bacteria), and (3) synthesis of B vitamins.

This means that rumen microorganisms must be supplied adequate (1) energy, including small amounts of readily available energy such as sugars or starches, (2) ammonia-bearing ingredients such as proteins, urea, and ammonium salts, (3) major minerals especially sodium, potassium, and phosphorus, (4) cobalt and possibly other trace minerals, and (5) unidentified factors found in certain natural feeds rich in protein or non-protein nitrogenous constituents.

(7) It should enhance, rather than impair, the quality of meat or milk produced.

How to Balance a Ration by the Square Method

The so-called "square method" (or the Pearson Square Method) is one of several methods that may be employed to balance rations.

The square method is simple, direct, and easy. Also, it permits quick substitution of feed ingredients in keeping with market fluctuations, without disturbing the protein content. The latter virtue is of particular value to the feed manufacturer.

In balancing rations by the square method, it is recognized that protein content alone receives major consideration. Correctly speaking, therefore, it is a method of balancing the protein requirement, with only incidental consideration given to the vitamin, mineral, and other nutritive requirements.

With the instructions given herein, the square method may be employed to balance rations by both stockmen and feed manufacturers.

To compute balanced rations by the square method, or by any other method, it is first necessary to have available both feeding standards and feed composition tables. Several feeding standards can be and are used, (for example, the Morrison standards are excellent), and there is practically no limit to the number of nutrients that can be listed in feed composition tables.

For purposes of simplification, the author has prepared Table 26, Handy Beef Cattle Feeding Recommendations. Then, the crude protein content of most common feeds can be obtained from Table I of the Appendix. These two tables are adequate for balancing most rations by the square method.

In using Tables 26 and Appendix Table I, the following points should be noted[1]:

1. Under "Description of Animals"—column No. 1 of Table 26—are sufficient groups to cover the vast majority of cattle found on the nation's farms and ranches.

2. Columns 2 to 8 give pertinent recommendations relative to both forages and concentrates. These recommendations are in keeping with those advocated by scientists, and with the actual practices followed by successful operators.

In particular, it should be noted that all protein recommendations are in terms of *crude protein* content,[2] rather than digestible protein. This innovation was decided upon because (1) this is what the feed manufacturer wants to know as he plans a feed formula, and (2) this is what the stockman sees on the feed tag when he purchases feed.

3. It is recognized that most farmers and ranchers generally grow their own forages, and purchase part or all of the concentrates. Thus, they generally wish to know what crude protein content of concentrate alone (including grains, by-product feeds, and/or protein supplements) they need to feed to balance out the forage which is available. Likewise, feed manufacturers have need for this information in compounding mixes. For these reasons, harvested forages are classified as (1) high protein forages, (2) medium protein forages, and (3) low protein forages; and specific recommendations are made for each. Similar classifications and recommendations are made for (1) excellent, (2) fair to good, and (3) poor pastures.

4. It is often hazardous to formulate rations for "excellent" pastures that are different from those for "poor" pastures, because (1) stockmen may be in error in appraising the quality of their pastures, and (2) pastures are generally excellent in the

---

[1] In addition, see pertinent footnotes which accompany Table 26.

[2] No attempt is made to recommend crude protein content of total ration (including both forage and concentrate) for beef cattle, because (1) they consume a large proportion of forage, and (2) the percentage digestibility of protein of forages differs tremendously—for example, the per cent digestibility of protein of wheat straw is 8, whereas for alfalfa hay it is 71. On the other hand, the grains do not differ greatly in per cent digestibility of protein. The National Research Council (Bulletin No. IV, revised 1958) expresses digestible protein as 60 per cent of total protein in high roughage rations and 75 per cent for high concentrate rations.

TABLE 26
HANDY BEEF CATTLE FEEDING RECOMMENDATIONS

| Description of Animals (1) | Recommendations[1] (2) | Recommendations Relative to Concentrate Only (Including grain, by-product feeds, and/or protein supplements) | | | | | |
| | | In dry lot, with following types of forages: | | | On pasture of the following grades: | | |
		Legume and/or legume-non-legume mixed forages of high quality; consisting of dry forages and/or silage (high protein forages) (3)	Legume and non-legume forages mixed; consisting of dry forages and/or silage (medium protein forages) (4)	Non-legume forage; consisting of dry forages and/or silage (low protein forages) (5)	Excellent (6)	Fair to good (7)	Poor; including winter pasture consisting of dry grass cured on the stalk[2] (8)
Mature beef breeding cows (av. wt. 1100 lbs.)	Forage per head daily, in lbs. Concentrate: (1) Supplement allowance of soybean oil meal (or equivalent 41–45% crude protein) per head daily, in lbs.[3]	18–26	18–28	18–28 ½–1½	....	....	.... ½–3
Replacement heifers (weighing 400–500 lbs.)	Forage per head daily, in lbs. Concentrate: (1) Total concentrate allowance per head daily, in lbs. (2) Supplement allowance of soybean oil meal (or equivalent 41–45% crude protein) per head daily, in lbs.[3,4] (3) Crude protein composition of total concentrate in %.	12–18 2–4 .... 9–13 (Cereal grains only will suffice)	12–18 2½–4 ½–1 14–18	12–18 2½–4½ 1¼–1½ 17–22	....	....	2½–4½ 1¼–1½ 17–22
Stocker calves: roughed through the winter and generally grazed the following summer. Fed for winter gains of ¾ to 1 lb. per head daily (weighing 400–500 lbs. start of period).	Forage per head daily, in lbs. Concentrate: (1) Supplement allowance of soybean oil meal (or equivalent 41–45% crude protein) per head daily, in lbs.[3]	12–18	12–18 ¼–1	12–18 1¼–1½	....	....	.... 1¼–1½

TABLE 26 (Continued)

Fattening calves (weighing 400–500 lbs. start of feeding, and 750–850 lbs. at marketing).	Forage per head daily, in lbs.	4–6	4–6	4–5	....	....	....
	Concentrate: (1) Total concentrate allowance per head daily, in lbs.	12–15	12–15	12–15	10–12	11–13	12–14
	(2) Supplement allowance of soybean oil meal (or equivalent 41–45% crude protein) per head daily in lbs.[3], [4].	1–1½	1½–1¾	1¾–2¼	....	1½–1¾	1¾–2¼
	(3) Crude protein composition of total concentrate, in %	10–12 (Cereal grains only will suffice)	12–13	13–15	10–12 (Cereal grains only will suffice)	12–13	13–15
Yearlings: roughed through the winter, and generally pasture fattened the following summer. Fed for winter gains of 1 to 1¼ lbs. per head daily (weighing about 600 lbs. start of wintering).	Forage per head daily, in lbs.	16–24	16–24	16–24	....	....	....
	Concentrate: (1) Supplement allowance of soybean oil meal (or equivalent 41–45% crude protein) per head daily, in lbs.[3], [4].	....	1–1½	1½–1¾	....	....	0–2
Fattening yearlings (weighing about 600 lbs. start of feeding, and 850 to 1000 lbs. at marketing).	Forage per head daily, in lbs.	4–8	4–8	4–8	....	....	....
	Concentrate: (1) Total concentrate allowance per head daily, in lbs.	15–19½	15–19¾	15–20	12–18	13–19	14–20
	(2) Supplement allowance of soybean oil meal (or equivalent 41–45% crude protein) per head daily, in lbs.[3], [4].	1–1½	1¼–1¾	1½–2½	....	1¼–1¾	1½–2½
	(3) Crude protein composition of total concentrate, in %.	10–11 (Cereal grains only will suffice)	11–12	12–13	10–11 (Cereal grains only will suffice)	11–12	12–13

[1]The daily forage recommendations given herein are based on dry forage. When silage is included in the ration, figure 3 lbs. of silage equivalent to 1 lb. of dry forage, due to the higher moisture content of silage. Many cattlemen do not winter feed as liberally as herein recommended. In general, these operators feel that it is more profitable (1) to let cattle "hold their own" or even lose in condition during the winter months (so long as they remain healthy), to keep winter feed and labor costs at a minimum, and (2) to make all or most of the gains on grass.

[2]On a dry basis, the crude protein content of mature, weathered grasses may be 3 per cent or less. The upper limit of the concentrate allowance recommended in column No. 8 should be fed on winter range when (1) the grass is less abundant, and/or (2) the grass is relatively low in protein.

[3], [4] See footnotes on following page.

TABLE 26 (Continued)

Description of Animals	Recommendations[1]	Recommendations Relative to Concentrate Only (Including grain, by-product feeds, and/or protein supplements)					
		In dry lot, with following types of forages:			On pasture of the following grades:		
		Legume and/or legume-non-legume mixed forages of high quality; consisting of dry forages and/or silage (high protein forages)	Legume and non-legume mixed; consisting of dry forages and/or silage (medium protein forages)	Non-legume forage; consisting of dry forages and/or silage (low protein forages)	Excellent	Fair to good	Poor; including winter pasture consisting of dry grass cured on the stalk[2]
(1)	(2)	(3)	(4)	(5)	(6)	(7)	(8)
Fattening 2-yr.-old steers (weighing about 800 lbs. start of feeding and 1,000 to 1,100 lbs. at marketing).	Forage per head daily, in lbs.	6-12	6-12	6-12	......	......	......
	Concentrate: (1) Total concentrate allowance per head daily, in lbs.	16-22	16-22	16½-22¾	13-19	14-20	15-21
	(2) Supplement allowance of soybean oil meal (or equivalent 41-45% crude protein) per head daily, in lbs.[3],[4]	......	½-¾	1½-1¾	......	½-¾	1½-1¾
	(3) Crude protein composition of of total concentrate, in %.	9-10 (Cereal grains only will suffice)	10-11	11-12	9-10 (Cereal grains only will suffice)	10-11	11-12

[1] and [2] See preceding page footnotes.

[3]Soybean oil meal, which ranges from 41 to 45 per cent protein content, is herein used as a standard merely because it is the leading U. S. protein supplement. It is to be emphasized, however, (1) that other protein supplements, including numerous commercial products, may be used, (2) that, in general, those supplements should be purchased which provide a unit of protein at the lowest cost, and those feeds which are highest in protein content are usually the most economical, and (3) that where other protein feeds are substituted for the soybean oil meal recommended herein (41-45% protein), an equivalent amount of crude protein should be provided—for example approximately 2 lbs. of a 20 per cent crude protein supplement should be provided to replace each 1 lb. of soybean oil meal, (although it is recognized that 2 lbs. of a 20 per cent crude protein feed will generally provide more energy, and may supply more of certain other important nutrients, than 1 lb. of soybean oil meal).

[4]The recommended supplement allowance is based on the assumptions (1) that cereal grains, averaging 9 to 13 per cent crude protein content, comprise the major part of the concentrate mix, and (2) that the forage is not comprised entirely or predominantly of non-legume silage. Naturally, less protein supplement will need to be added where feeds of higher protein content than the cereal grains predominate. Also less protein supplement is required to balance a ration consisting predominantly of barley (of 12.7% crude protein content) than one consisting mostly of corn (of 8.7% crude protein content). Likewise, the upper limit of protein supplement recommended herein (or even a higher figure) is required to balance a ration where the forage is comprised entirely or largely of non-legume silage (corn silage has a crude protein content of 2.3%, whereas Timothy hay, for example, has a crude protein composition of 6.6%).

early spring, but become progressively poorer as the season advances unless they are irrigated.

For purposes of illustration, let us refer to Table 26. Under column 5, it is noted that a mature beef breeding cow (av. wt. 1,100 lbs.) that is being fed a daily ration of somewhere between 18-28 lbs. of a forage of grass hay or other non-legume dry roughage should receive, in addition, ½ to 1½ pounds daily of a protein supplement of soybean oil meal (or some other protein supplement which will provide an amount equivalent to 41 to 45% crude protein). To be sure, it is entirely proper to meet this recommended crude protein content of concentrate by feeding double the allowance of some protein supplement with approximately 20 per cent crude protein content. Many times the latter may be more economical, and even advisable—for example, when the forage is of poor quality and added energy feed is needed. In general, however, those feeds should be purchased which furnish a unit of protein at the lowest cost, and those feeds which supply the protein in the most concentrated form are the most economical.

Under column No. 2 of Table 26, additional information, of value to both the feed manufacturer and the stockman who mixes his own rations, is given. For example, in Table 26, under "Fattening 2-yr.-old steers............," recommendations are given relative to the following:

"(3) Crude protein composition of total concentrate, in %."

The application of the square method will be illustrated by solving some practical problems.

Problem No. 1:

A cattleman wishes to compute a balanced ration for 800 pound yearling fattening steers in dry lot. Timothy hay is on hand, and corn (No. 2 grade) and soybean oil meal (solvent process) are the cheapest concentrate feeds available. The cattleman wishes to know (1) the pounds each of forage and of concentrate to feed daily, and (2) the proportions of corn and of soybean oil meal to put in the concentrate mixture.

Step by step, the answers may be calculated as follows:

1. Table 26, Handy Beef Cattle Feeding Recommendations, gives the following requirements for 800 pound fattening steers in dry lot:

(1) Forage per head per day=4 to 8 lbs.

(2) Concentrate per head per day = 15 to 20 lbs.

(3) Crude protein content of the concentrate alone where a grass hay is fed = 12 to 13%.

2. Thus, when on full feed the steers should receive daily feed allowances of somewhere between 4 and 8 lbs. of the Timothy hay, and between 15 and 20 lbs. of the concentrate mixture. A range is given, because (1) individual animals and different lots of cattle differ in feed capacity, (2) feeds differ in composition and feeding value, and (3) the proportion of forage should decrease whereas the proportion of concentrate should increase as the fattening period advances.

3. The proportions of corn and of soybean oil meal to put in the concentrate mixture may be obtained by the square method as follows:

(1) Place in the center of the square the percentage of crude protein needed in the mixture; in this case 13% (using the upper limit).

(2) Place at the upper left hand corner of the square the percentage of crude protein in the soybean oil meal; in this case 45.8% (see Appendix Table I).

(3) Place at the lower left-hand corner of the square the percentage of protein in the corn; in this case 8.7% (see Appendix Table I).

(4) Connect the diagonal corners of the square with lines, and subtract, diagonally across the square, the smaller figure from the larger. Place the answers at the opposite corners. This gives the following:

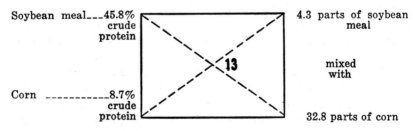

Soybean meal___45.8% crude protein — 4.3 parts of soybean meal

13

mixed with

Corn _____8.7% crude protein — 32.8 parts of corn

(5) Thus, a mixture of 4.3 parts of soybean meal and 32.8 parts of corn (37.1 parts total) will provide a concentrate mix with the desired 13% crude protein content.

(6) The proportions of soybean meal and corn can be converted to 100 pounds of mixture as follows (or to a ton basis by using 2,000 instead of 100):
4.3 (4.3 parts soybean meal) ÷ 37.1 (37.1 = 4.3 parts soybean meal and 32.8 parts corn) × 100 = **11.6 lbs. soybean meal**
32.8 (32.8 = parts corn) ÷ 37.1 (37.1 = 4.3 parts soybean meal and 32.8 parts corn) × 100 = **88.4 lbs. corn.** Total = 100 lbs. mix.

(7) Thus, to make a 13% crude protein concentrate mixture from corn and soybean meal, the cattleman will need to mix 11.6 lbs. of soybean meal and 88.4 lbs. of corn for each 100 lbs. of mix.

Problem No. 2:

A cattle feeder is planning to fatten 2-yr.-old steers in the dry lot. He has on hand corn silage and alfalfa hay, but wishes to purchase the entire concentrate mixture from a commercial feed manufacturer. What per cent crude protein content (as shown on the feed tag) is needed in the commercial concentrate?

This can be readily and directly answered simpy by referring to Table 26, Handy Cattle Feeding Recommendations. As noted in Table 26, where corn silage and a legume hay constitute the forage ration, 10 to 11% crude protein concentrate is recommended.

EFFECT OF UNDER-FEEDING ON CATTLE

Many cattle throughout the United States are under-fed all or some part of the year. In fact, lack of sufficient total feed is probably the most common deficiency suffered by beef cattle, although it is recognized that under-feeding is frequently complicated by concomitant shortage of protein and other nutrients. Restricted rations often occur during periods of drought, when pastures or ranges are overstocked, or when winter rations are skimpy. Also, many range cattlemen regularly plan that cows in good flesh should lose some condition during the winter months; they feel that it is uneconomical to feed sufficient to retain the fleshy condition. Fortunately, during such times of restricted feed intake, animals have nutritive reserves upon which they can draw. Although they may survive for a considerable period of time under these conditions, there is an inevitable loss in body weight and condition; and, varying with the degree of under-feeding, there may be a slowing or cessation of growth (including skeletal growth), failure to conceive, and increased mortality. Low feed intake also commonly results in increased deaths from toxic plants and from lowered resistance to parasites and diseases.

Research workers of the U.S. Department of Agriculture conducted an experiment[1] to determine some of the economic effects and possible harm to animals of limited rations. Identical twin calves were used and the following planes of nutrition were studied: (1) full feed—gains of more than 1.5 pounds daily, (2) 75 per cent of full feed—gains of 1.0 pound per day, (3) 62 per cent of full feed—gains of 0.5 pound a day, and (4) a maintenance ration of about 50 per cent of full feed—they neither gained nor lost in weight.

All animals—including those on the low energy rations—received ample protein, vitamins, minerals, and other nutrients. At the end of the period of retarded feeding, the steers were fed liberally until they reached a slaughter weight of 1,000 pounds.

Although the low-plane-of-nutrition animals reached slaughter weight from 10 to 20 weeks later than did their co-twins, the former attained their weight on approximately the same total feed intake as the latter; which means that, after limited feeding ended, the retarded animals made more economical gains than did their co-twins. Carcass quality, amount of lean meat, and grade were not affected.

This experiment showed that, under conditions of feed scarcity, beef cattle between the ages of 6 and 12 months can be carried on a maintenance ration—where they will neither gain nor lose in weight—provided the nutrient needs other than energy are supplied—without subsequent loss in feed efficiency, carcass quality, or quantity of lean meat.

NUTRITIONAL DISEASES AND AILMENTS OF CATTLE

More animals (and people) throughout the world suffer from hunger—from just plain lack of sufficient feed—than from the lack of one or more specific nutrients. Therefore, it is recognized that nutritional deficiencies may be brought about by either (1) too little feed, or (2) rations that are too low in one or more nutrients.

---

[1]Winchester, C. F. and Paul E. Howe; U.S.D.A. Tech. Bul. No. 1108.

Also, forced production (such as very high milk yields and marketing of animals at early ages) and the feeding of forages and grains which are often produced on leached and depleted

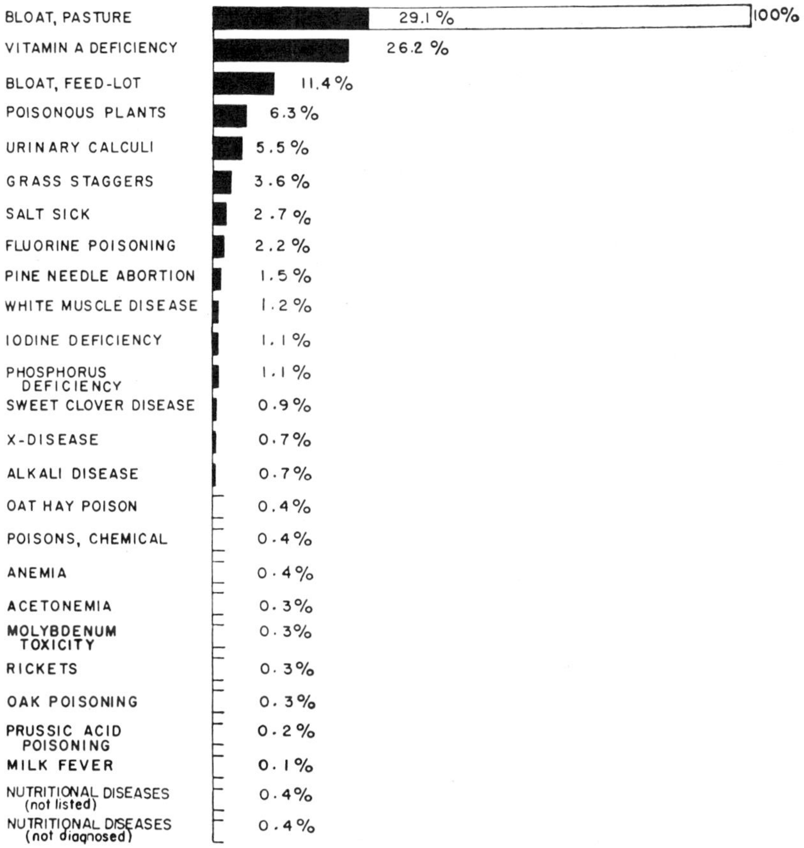

BLOAT, PASTURE	29.1 %
VITAMIN A DEFICIENCY	26.2 %
BLOAT, FEED-LOT	11.4%
POISONOUS PLANTS	6.3%
URINARY CALCULI	5.5%
GRASS STAGGERS	3.6%
SALT SICK	2.7%
FLUORINE POISONING	2.2%
PINE NEEDLE ABORTION	1.5%
WHITE MUSCLE DISEASE	1.2%
IODINE DEFICIENCY	1.1%
PHOSPHORUS DEFICIENCY	1.1%
SWEET CLOVER DISEASE	0.9%
X-DISEASE	0.7%
ALKALI DISEASE	0.7%
OAT HAY POISON	0.4%
POISONS, CHEMICAL	0.4%
ANEMIA	0.4%
ACETONEMIA	0.3%
MOLYBDENUM TOXICITY	0.3%
RICKETS	0.3%
OAK POISONING	0.3%
PRUSSIC ACID POISONING	0.2%
MILK FEVER	0.1%
NUTRITIONAL DISEASES (not listed)	0.4%
NUTRITIONAL DISEASES (not diagnosed)	0.4%

(100% scale shown at top of chart)

Fig. 125. Relative frequency of beef cattle nutritional diseases and ailments. This figure, taken from Wash. Agri. Expt. Sta. Bul. 562, is based on a 24-state survey which covered over a half million cattle. It is recognized that cattlemen may not always have been accurate in their diagnosis; nevertheless, this is the most complete record of its type available.

Bloat accounted for 40.5 per cent of all nutritional disease and ailments; vitamin A deficiency ranked second. The survey also brought out some area difference; vitamin A deficiency and poisonous plant losses were relatively higher in the West, bloat was higher in the South, urinary calculi was higher in the Great Plains, and white muscle disease was higher in the Pacific Northwest.

During the course of a year, 1.33 per cent of the nation's cattle were afflicted by nutritional deficiency diseases and ailments, of which 0.32 per cent died therefrom. Of the death losses due to nutritional deficiency diseases and ailments, 36 per cent were attributed to bloat, 22 per cent to poisonous plants, and 13 per cent to urinary calculi. (Photo, courtesy Washington State University)

TABLE 27—NUTRITIONAL DISEASES

Disease	Species Affected	Cause	Symptoms (and age or group most affected)	Distribution and Losses Caused By
Acetonemia in Cattle (see Ketosis)				
Alkali Disease (see Selenium poisoning)				
Anemia, nutritional	All warm-blooded animals and man	Commonly an iron deficiency, but it may be caused by a deficiency of copper, cobalt, and/or certain vitamins (riboflavin, pyridoxine, pantothenic acid and folic acid).	Loss of appetite, progressive emaciation, and death. Most prevalent in suckling young.	World-wide Losses consist of slow and inefficient gains, and deaths.
Aphosphorosis	Cattle, and sheep to lesser extent.	Low phosphorus in feed.	Depraved appetite; chewing bones, wood, hair, rags, etc. Stiff joints and fragile bones.	World-wide; in S. W. United States.
Bloat	Cattle, Sheep	Unknown. Most common on lush legume pastures.	Greatly distended paunch noticeable on the left side in front of the hip bone.	Widespread, although some areas appear to have more bloat than others. Often results in death. 36% of all mortality due to nutritional diseases and ailments is attributed to bloat.[1]
Fluorine poisoning (Flucrosis)	All farm animals, poultry, and man.	Ingesting excessive quantities of fluorine through either the feed or water.	Abnormal teeth (especially mottled enamel) and bones, (bones become thickened and softened), stiffness of joints, loss of appetite, emaciation, reduction in milk flow, diarrhea and salt hunger.	The water in parts of Arkansas, California, South Carolina, and Texas has been reported to contain excess fluorine. Occasionally throughout the U. S. high fluorine phosphates are used in mineral mixtures.
Founder	Cattle, Horses, Sheep, Goats	Overeating, over-drinking, or from inflammation of the uterus following parturition. Also intestinal inflammation.	Extreme pain, fever (103° to 106°F.) and reluctance to move. If neglected, chronic laminitis will develop, resulting in a dropping of the hoof soles and a turning up of the toe walls.	World-wide Actual death losses from founder are not very great.
Goiter (see Iodine Deficiency)				
Grass tetany (Grass staggers) —a highly fatal nutritional ailment	Cattle, especially lactating cows.	Exact cause unknown, but it does appear to be nutritional.	Generally occurs during first 2 weeks of pasture season. Nervousness, twitching of muscles (usually of head and neck), head held high, accelerated respiration, high temperature, gnashing of the teeth, and abundant salivation. Slight stimulus may precipitate a crash to the ground, and finally death.	Reported in Nebraska, Kentucky, Missouri, Iowa, Washington, and other states. Also found in New Zealand, England and Holland. Highly fatal if not treated quickly.

¹Ensminger, M. E., M. W. Galgan, and

AND AILMENTS OF CATTLE

Treatment	Control and Eradication	Prevention	Remarks
Provide dietary sources of the nutrient or nutrients the deficiency of which is known to cause the condition.	When nutritional anemia is encountered, it can usually be brought under control by supplying dietary sources of the nutrient or nutrients the deficiency of which is known to cause the condition.	Supply dietary sources of iron, copper, cobalt, and certain vitamins. Levels of iron in feed believed to be ample, since feeds contain 40 to 400 milligrams/lb.	Anemia is a condition in which the blood is either deficient in quality or quantity (a deficient quality refers to a deficiency in hemoglobin and/or red cells).
	Controlled by feeding phosphorus.	Free access to a phosphorus supplement, or 0.1 lb. of a phosphorus supplement added to the daily ration.	Generally caused by lack of P. in the pasture. P. fertilizing may help.
Time permitting, severe cases of bloat should be treated by a veterinarian. Puncturing of the paunch should be a last resort. Mild cases may be home-treated by (1) keeping the animal on its feet and moving, and (2) drenching either with (a) ½ to 1 pt. of mineral oil or (b) a mixture of 1 tbl. of turpentine, 1 tbl. of aromatic spirits of ammonia, and 1 qt. of water. (A mature cow may be given the full dosage of either).	When there is high incidence of bloat, it may be desirable to change the feed.	No sure way of preventing bloat is known. The incidence is lessened by (1) avoiding straight legume pastures, (2) feeding dry forage along with pasture, (3) avoiding a rapid fill from an empty start, (4) keeping animals continuously on pasture after they are once turned out, (5) keeping salt and water conveniently accessible at all times, and (6) avoiding frosted pastures. Some are advocating the use of a salt-antibiotic mixture, but more study needs to be made relative to this preventive measure.	Legume pastures, alfalfa hay and barley appear to be associated with a higher incidence of bloat more than many other feeds.
Any damage may be permanent, but animals which have not developed severe symptoms may be helped to some extent, if the sources of excess fluorine are eliminated.	Discontinue the use of feeds, water, or mineral supplements containing excessive fluorine.	Avoid the use of feeds, water, or mineral supplements containing excessive fluorine. Limit the upper level of fluorine to not more than 65 ppm in the ration of cattle to be slaughtered and 30 ppm for breeding animals to be kept a long period of time.	Fluorine is a cumulative poison. Undefluorinated rock phosphate often contains 3.5 to 4.0 per cent fluorine.
Pending arrival of the veterinarian, the attendant should stand the animal's feet in a cold water bath. Unless foundered animals are quite valuable, it is usually desirable to dispose of them following a case of severe founder.	Alleviate the causes, namely (1) overeating, (2) overdrinking, and/or (3) inflammation of the uterus following parturition.	Avoid overeating and overdrinking (especially when hot).	Swine do not founder, because they can unload their stomachs by vomiting.
Intravenous injection of a solution of calcium and/or magnesium salt by a veterinarian.	(See Prevention.)	Grass tetany can be prevented by not turning animals to pasture, but this is not practical. Feeding hay at night during the first 2 weeks of the pasture season is helpful. A salt lick of 10 parts each of magnesium sulfate and calcium diphosphate with 80 parts of salt will aid in prevention.	Affected animals show low blood Mg., often low serum Ca. Treated cattle may be aggressive on arising; so watch out!

W. L. Slocum, Wash. Agri. Expt. Sta. Bul. 562, p. 18.

TABLE 27

Disease	Species Affected	Cause	Symptoms (and age or group most affected)	Distribution and Losses Caused By
Iodine Deficiency (Goiter)	All farm animals and man	A failure of the body to obtain sufficient iodine from which the thyroid gland can form thyroxin (an iodine-containing compound).	Goiter (big neck) is the most characteristic symptom in humans, calves, lambs, and kids. Also, there may be reproductive failures and weak offspring that fail to survive. Pigs may be born hairless, and foals may be weak.	Northwestern U.S. and and the Great Lakes region.
Ketosis (Acetonemia in cattle, or Pregnancy Disease in Sheep)	Cattle, Sheep, Goats	A metabolic disorder, thought to be a disturbance in the carbohydrate metabolism.	In cows, ketosis or acetonemia is usually observed within first 6 months after calving. Affected animals show loss in appetite and condition, a marked decline in milk production, and the production of a peculiar, sweetish, chloroform-like odor of acetone that may be present in the milk and pervade the barn. In sheep, ketosis or pregnancy disease generally strikes during the last 2 weeks of pregnancy, and usually the affected ewes are carrying twins or triplets. Symptoms include grinding of the teeth, dullness, weakness, frequent urination, and trembling when exercised—with the final stage being complete collapse, followed by death in 90% of the cases.	World-wide Ketosis or acetonemia affects dairy cattle throughout the U. S. Ketosis or pregnancy disease of sheep affects farm flocks more than range bands, the losses in the former sometimes being as high as 25%.
Milk Fever	Cattle, Sheep, Goats, Swine	The actual cause of milk fever is unknown. It is characterized by an acute fall in blood calcium concentration together with a possible unbalanced condition of other minerals.	Commonly occurs soon after calving and in high-producing cows. Rarely occurs at first calving. First symptoms are loss of appetite, constipation, and general depression. This is followed by nervousness and finally collapse and complete loss of consciousness. The head is usually turned back.	A common, widespread disease of dairy cows. Losses are not great, although untreated animals are likely to die.
Molybdenum toxicity (commonly called teartness)	Ruminants especially calves and cows in milk.	As little as 10 to 20 ppm in forages result in toxic symptoms.	Toxic levels of molybdenum interfere with copper metabolism thus increasing the copper requirement and producing typical copper deficiency symptoms. The physical symptoms are anemia and extreme diarrhea, with consequent loss in weight and milk yield.	England, and in Florida, California, and Manitoba.
Oat hay poisoning (actually nitrite poisoning)	Cattle, principally	Ingestion of large amounts of nitrate, sometimes present in oat hay, which is changed into nitrite in the rumen and causes nitrite poisoning.	Trembling, staggering, rapid respiration and prostration.	U. S., and Canada in certain areas.
Osteomalacia	All species	Lack of vitamin D. Inadequate intake of calcium and phosphorus, and/or Incorrect ratio of calcium and phosphorus.	Phosphorus deficiency symptoms are: depraved appetite (gnawing on bones, wood, or other objects, or eating dirt); lack of appetite, stiffness of joints, failure to breed regularly, decreased milk production, and an emaciated appearance. Calcium deficiency symptoms are: fragile bones, reproductive failures, and lowered lactations. Mature animals most affected. Most of the acute cases occur during pregnancy and lactation.	Southwestern U. S. is classed as a phosphorus-deficient area whereas calcium-deficient areas have been reported in parts of Florida, Louisiana, Nebraska, Virginia, and West Virginia.

(Continued)

Treatment	Control and Eradication	Prevention	Remarks
Occasionally borderline cases may survive; in these the moderate thyroid enlargement disappears in a few weeks.	At the first signs of iodine-deficiency, iodized salt should be fed to all farm animals.	In iodine-deficient areas, feed iodized salt to all farm animals throughout the year. Stabilized iodized salt containing 0.01% potassium iodide is recommended.	The enlarged thyroid gland (goiter) is nature's way of attempting to make sufficient thyroxine under conditions where a deficiency exists.
One of the following is commonly used by the veterinarian in the treatment of ketosis: (1) glucose injection, (2) chloralhydrate in warm water, (3) cortisone, (4) ACTH, or (5) sodium propionate.	When ketosis is encountered in cattle, sheep, or goats, add molasses to the ration to stimulate appetite.	No sure prevention, but the following will help: Ketosis (Acetonemia) in cattle: —Feed a well-balanced ration, and, for high producing cows, add 1 quart of molasses to the ration daily.	The clinical findings are similar in the case of affected cattle and sheep, but it usually strikes ewes just before lambing, whereas cows are usually affected within the first 6 months after calving.
Treatment consists of (1) having the veterinarian give an intravenous injection of a calcium salt, or (2) inflating the udder with filtered air.	(See Prevention)	The best preventive appears to consist in feeding 20 to 30 million units of vitamin D daily starting about eight days before calving. Scientists of the Calif. Station have effectively prevented milk fever by feeding grass hay and phosphorus to cows a month before calving; but further studies are needed relative to prevention of milk fever by this method.	The name "milk fever" is a misnomer, because the disease is not accompanied by fever; the temperature really being below normal.
One gram of copper sulfate per head daily will cure symptoms of molybdenum toxicity.		One gram of copper sulfate per head daily will prevent molybdenum toxicity.	When feeds are high in sulfate, toxic symptoms will be produced on lower levels of molybdenum and, conversely, higher levels of molybdenum can be tolerated with low levels of sulfate.
	Don't feed oat hay to ruminants in affected areas.	(See Control)	Oat hay which produces this disease contains 3 to 7% KNO_3 content; normally only a trace of potassium nitrate is present.
Increase the calcium and phosphorus content of feed through fertilizing the soils. Select natural feeds that contain sufficient quantities of calcium and phosphorus. Feed a special mineral supplement or supplements. If this disease is far advanced, treatment will not be successful.	(See Treatment)	Feed balanced rations, and allow animals free access to a suitable phosphorus and calcium supplement.	Calcium deficiencies are much more rare than phosphorus deficiencies in cattle.

TABLE 27

Disease	Species Affected	Cause	Symptoms (and age or group most affected)	Distribution and Losses Caused By
Pine Needle Abortion	Cattle	Needles of Yellow Pine (*Pinus ponderosa*); commonly called Yellow Pine, British Columbia Pine, or Jack Pine. It is suspected that the high turpentine content of Yellow Pine needles actually causes the abortion, for there is evidence that turpentine can cause abortion in the human female.	Pregnant cows, free of brucellosis, abort.	British Columbia, Canada, and in the states of Washington, Idaho, and Oregon.
Rickets	All farm animals and man	Lack of either calcium, phosphorus, or vitamin D, or An incorrect ratio of the two minerals.	Enlargement of the knee and hock joints, and the animal may exhibit great pain when moving about. Irregular bulges (beaded ribs) at juncture of ribs with breastbone, and bowed legs. Swine are frequently paralyzed in the hind legs. Rickets is a disease of young animals —of calves, foals, pigs, lambs, kids, pups, and chicks.	World-wide It is seldom fatal.
Salt Deficiency (Sodium chloride)	All farm animals and man	Lack of salt (Sodium chloride).	Loss of appetite, retarded growth, loss of weight, a rough coat, lowered production of milk, and a ravenous appetite for salt.	World-wide, especially among grass-eating animals and the pig.
Salt Sick	Cattle, Sheep, Goats	Probably cobalt deficiency, associated with copper and perhaps iron deficiencies.	Loss of appetite, depraved appetite, scaliness of skin, listlessness and lack of thrift.	Florida; on sandy soils.
Selenium Poisoning (Alkali Disease)	All farm animals and man	Consumption of plants grown on soils containing selenium.	Loss of hair from the mane and tail in horses, from the tail in cattle, and a general loss of hair in swine. In severe cases, the hoofs slough off, lameness occurs, food consumption decreases, and death may occur by starvation.	In certain regions of western U. S. — especially certain areas in South Dakota, Montana, Wyoming, Nebraska, Kansas, and perhaps areas in other states in the Great Plains and Rocky Mountains. Also in Canada.
Sweet Clover Disease	Cattle; rarely affects sheep, horses	Usually produced only by moldy or spoiled sweet clover hay or silage. Caused by presence of dicumarol which interferes with vitamin K in blood clotting.	Loss of clotting power of the blood. As a result, blood forms soft swellings beneath skin on different parts of body. Serious or fatal bleeding may occur at time of dehorning, docking, castration, parturition or following injury. All ages affected. A newborn animal may also have the condition at birth.	Wherever sweet clover is grown.

(Continued)

Treatment	Control and Eradication	Prevention	Remarks
No treatment known		Keep pregnant cows away from Yellow Pine trees	Lodgepole Pine (*Pinus contorta*) —Commonly called Black Pine, Jack Pine, Western Jack Pine, White Pine, or Cypress—does not appear to cause abortion in cattle. Pregnant cows will consume quantities of pine needles even though fed an adequate ration.
If the disease has not advanced too far, treatment may be successful by supplying adequate amounts of vitamin D, calcium, and phosphorus, and/or adjusting the ratio of calcium to phosphorus.	(See Prevention)	Provide (1) sufficient calcium, phosphorus and vitamin D, and (2) a correct ratio of the two minerals.	Rickets is characterized by a failure of growing bone to ossify, or harden, properly.
Salt-starved animals should be gradually accustomed to salt; slowly increasing the hand-fed allowance until the animals may be safely allowed free access to it.	(See Treatment and Prevention)	Provide plenty of salt at all times, preferably by free-choice feeding.	Common salt is one of the most essential minerals for grass-eating animals, and one of the easiest and cheapest to provide. Excessive salt intake can result in toxicity.
		Mix 0.2 oz. of cobalt chloride or cobalt sulfate/100 lbs. of either (1) salt, or (2) the mineral other than salt.	
	(Control measures based on Prevention)	Abandon areas where soils contain selenium, because crops produced on such soils constitute a menace to both animals and man.	Chronic cases of selenium poisoning occur when cattle consume feeds containing 8.5 ppm of selenium over an extended period; acute cases occur on 500 to 1,000 ppm.
Remove the offending materials and administer mena dione (vitamin K3). The veterinarian usually gives the affected animal an injection of plasma or whole blood from a normal animal that was not fed on the same fe	When a case of sweet clover disease is observed in the herd, either (1) discontinue feeding the damaged product or (2) alternate it with a better quality hay, especially alfalfa.	Properly cure any sweet clover hay or ensilage.	The disease has also been produced from feeding moldy lespedeza hay.

TABLE 27

Disease	Species Affected	Cause	Symptoms (and age or group most affected)	Distribution and Losses Caused By
Urinary Calculi (Gravel, Stones)	Cattle, Sheep, Horses, Man	Unknown, but it does seem to be nutritional. Experiments have shown a higher incidence of urinary calculi when there is (1) a high potassium intake, (2) an incorrect Ca-P ratio, or (3) a high proportion of beet pulp or grain sorghum in the ration.	Frequent attempts to urinate, dribbling or stoppage of the urine, pain and renal colic. Usually only males affected, the females being able to pass the concretions. Bladder may rupture, with death following. Otherwise, uremic poisoning may set in.	World-wide Affected animals seldom recover completely.
Vitamin A deficiency (Night Blindness and Xerophthalmia)	All farm animals and man	Vitamin A deficiency.	Night blindness, the first symptom of vitamin A deficiency, is characterized by faulty vision, especially noticeable when the affected animal is forced to move about in twilight in strange surroundings. Xerophthalmia develops in the advanced stages of vitamin A deficiency. The eyes become severely affected, and blindness may follow. Severe diarrhea in young calves and intermittent diarrhea in advanced stages in adults. In fattening cattle, generalized edema or anasarca with lameness in hock and knee joints and swelling in the brisket area.	World-wide. Especially prevalent in western U. S. where one of the following conditions frequently prevails; (1) extended drought, and (2) winter feeding on bleached grass cured on the stalk or on bleached hay.
White Muscle Disease	Cattle	Lack of vitamin E; or perhaps for some as yet unknown reason the vitamin E of the ration is not available to the animal due to an inhibitor.	Symptoms range from mild "founder-like" stiffness to sudden death. Calves continue to nurse as long as they can reach the cow's teats. Many calves stand or lie with protruded tongue, fighting for breath against a severe pulmonary edema. It seems that more calves than lambs develop fatal heart damage. Affected calves show pathological lesions similar to those of "stiff lambs" (white muscle disease in lambs); namely, whitish areas or streaks in the heart and other muscles. Affects calves from birth to 3 months of age.	Throughout the U.S., but the incidence appears to be highest in the inter - mountain area, between the Rocky and Cascade mountains.

(Continued)

Treatment	Control and Eradication	Prevention	Remarks
Once calculi develop, dietary treatment appears to be of little value. Surgery may save the animal, but such treatment will result in bulls becoming non-breeders. When the condition strikes in feed-lot cattle, increase the salt content of the diet if the animals are not ready to market.	If severe outbreaks of urinary calculi occur in fattening steers, it is usually well to dispose of them if they are carrying acceptable finish.	Good feed and management appear to lessen the incidence. Delayed castration (castration of bull calves at 4–5 mo. of age) and high salt diets of feed-lot cattle (1–3% salt in the grain ration; using the upper limits in the winter months) in order to induce more water consumption are effective preventive measures.	Calculi are stone-like concretions in the urinary tract which almost always originate in the kidneys. These stones block the passage of urine.
Treatment consists of correcting the dietary deficiencies.	(See Prevention and Treatment)	Provide good sources of carotene (vitamin A) through green, leafy hays; silage; lush, green pastures; yellow corn or green and yellow peas; whole milk; or fish oils.	
Confine affected animals to a stall, and give plenty of rest. The veterinarian may administer alpha tocopherol.	Unknown.	Unknown, but perhaps the feeding of a good ration will help. Incidence appears to be lower when cows receive 2–3 lbs. of grain during last 60 days of pregnancy.	White muscle disease is often overlooked in calves. Calves require 40 milligrams of alpha-tocopherol/100 lbs. wt./day.

soils has created many problems in nutrition. This condition has been further aggravated through the increased confinement of stock, many animals being stall-fed all or a large part of the year. Under these unnatural conditions, nutritional diseases and ailments have become increasingly common.

Although the cause, prevention, and treatment of most of these nutritional diseases and ailments are known, they continue to reduce profits in the livestock industry simply because the available knowledge is not put into practice. Moreover, those widespread nutritional deficiencies which are not of sufficient proportions to produce clear-cut deficiency symptoms cause even greater economic losses because they go unnoticed and unrectified. Table 27 contains a summary of the important nutritional diseases and ailments affecting cattle.

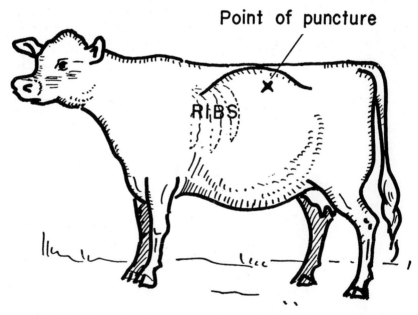

Fig. 126. When bloat is encountered, puncturing of the paunch should be a last resort. However, if such treatment must be administered in order to save the life of an animal, the stockman should know where to make the puncture. As noted in the above drawing, it should be made on the left side at the location shown. (Drawing by R. F. Johnson)

Fig. 127. Calf with sweet clover disease. Note the collection of blood at the point of the left shoulder. (Courtesy, Dept. of Veterinary Pathology and Hygiene, College of Veterinary Medicine, University of Illinois)

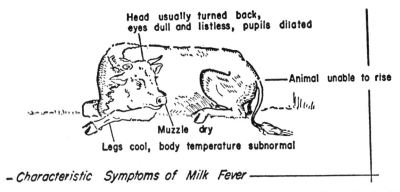

Fig. 128. The typical symptoms of milk fever in a cow. (Drawing by R. F. Johnson)

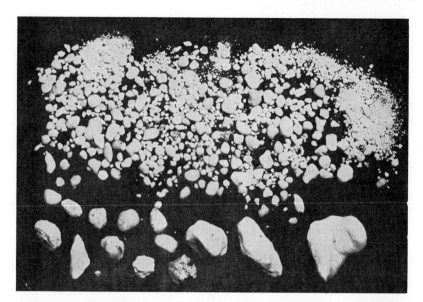

Fig. 129. Concretions or stones obtained from a $6,500 imported Short-horn bull that died from urinary calculi. The cause of urinary calculi is unknown, but it does seem to be tied up with nutrition. (Courtesy, Washington State University)

Fig. 130. Selenium toxicity in cow grazing on forage produced on alkali soil containing excessive selenium. Note emaciated condition, curvature of back and deformed hoofs. (Courtesy, Harold Eppson, Wyoming Agricultural Experiment Station)

QUESTIONS FOR STUDY AND DISCUSSION

1. Why is knowledge of beef cattle feeding so important?
2. Compare the nutritive needs of beef cattle with those of the pig.
3. In Washington Experiment Station Bulletin 562, it is reported that 78.3 per cent of the cattlemen fed a commercial mineral mix. Is this good, bad, and/or economical? Why do so many use a commercial mineral rather than a home-mixed mineral?
4. For beef cattle, list the vitamins most apt to be deficient; then (1) list some of the deficiency symptoms, and (2) give practical sources of each vitamin for use on your farm or ranch.
5. Compare silage with hay as a roughage for beef cattle.
6. Discuss the utilization of fibrous roughages by beef cattle.
7. Discuss the use of urea and other non-protein nitrogenous products by beef cattle.
8. What recent (within the past two decades) nutritional discovery has had the greatest impact on the beef cattle industry? Justify your answer.
9. When would you use each (1) stilbestrol, (2) antibiotics, and/or (3) other feed additives in the beef cattle ration; when wouldn't you?
10. Use Fig. 122, page 368 of this book to estimate the necessary margin on cattle that you have bought or sold this season, or on cattle sales with which you are acquainted.
11. What age, grade, and sex of cattle should you feed on your farm or ranch? Give the reasons.
12. Is the cattle feeder justified in breeding fattening heifers 3 to 4 months prior to marketing? Is the packer justified in buying such bred heifers at a discount?
13. Discuss contract feeding as it relates to integration of the beef cattle business.
14. In order to feed beef cattle efficiently and economically, one must understand thoroughly the nutrients furnished by the available feeds, the extent to which cattle can utilize each feed, and the actual feeding value of these feeds. This can be accomplished only through careful and thorough study of the different feeds.

    Table 24 of this chapter is a summary of the comparative values of the most common U. S. feeds. Also, two different methods (the tabular method and the chart method) of arriving at the best buy in feeds are presented in Section II, Feeding Livestock, of *The Stockman's Handbook*. However, the following exercises are designed better to acquaint the student with the feeds commonly fed to beef cattle:

(1) **A study of available roughages.**—Table 15 shows that 83.1 per cent of the feed of beef cattle is derived from roughages. Also, it is well known that a relatively large portion of the feed consumed by beef cattle is used in meeting the energy needs. Thus, a convenient and reasonably accurate way of determining which roughages are most economical under the conditions existing in a particular area at any given time is to compute the cost at which each of the available roughages furnishes 100 pounds of total digestible nutrients. This is a measure of the economy with which the various feeds furnish fuel or energy. Refer to Table I in the Appendix of this book (or the Appendix of *Feeds and Feeding*) for analyses, and obtain prices of available roughages locally. Then fill out the following table:

TABLE I—AVAILABLE ROUGHAGES

Feed	Farm Price Per Ton	Total Protein Per 100 lbs.	Digestible Protein Per 100 lbs.	T. D. N. Per 100 lbs.	Cost Per 100 lbs. T. D. N.	Carotene mg. Per lb.	Calcium Content (%)	Phosphorus Content (%)

The student should also become familiar with the protein, calcium, phosphorus, and carotene content of the different roughages. The above table is so designed.

(2) **A study of available grains and by-products.**—At least one of the cereal grains is grown in almost every section of the country, and all of them are used quite widely as beef cattle feeds. As a group, the cereals and their by-products are high in energy. However, they possess certain nutritive deficiencies which may prove to be quite limiting if they are not properly used. Refer to Table I in the Appendix of this book (or the Appendix of *Feeds and Feeding*) for analyses, and obtain prices of available grain and by-product feeds locally. Then fill out the following table:

TABLE II—AVAILABLE GRAIN AND BY-PRODUCT FEEDS

Feed	Retail Price Per Cwt.	Total Protein Per 100 lbs.	Digestible Protein Per 100 lbs.	T. D. N. Per 100 lbs.	Cost Per 100 lbs. Digestible Protein	Cost Per 100 lbs. T.D.N.	Carotene mg. Per lb.	Calcium Content (%)	Phosphorus Content (%)

In addition to considering the cost per 100 pounds of each T.D.N. and digestible protein, give consideration to calcium, phosphorus, and carotene content of each of these feeds. Also, in studying the by-product feeds, be sure to understand the source of the feed and just what part of the original grain or seed goes into the by-product.

15. Select a specific class of beef cattle and prepare a balanced ration, using those feeds that are available at the lowest cost.

SELECTED REFERENCES

Title of Publication	Author(s)	Publisher
Animal Nutrition	L. A. Maynard	McGraw-Hill Book Co., New York, 1956.
Applied Animal Nutrition	E. W. Crampton	W. H. Freeman and Co., San Francisco, Calif., 1956.
Composition of Cereal Grains and Forages	Publication 585	National Academy of Sciences, National Research Council, Washington 25, D. C.
omposition of Concentrate By-Product Feeding Stuffs	Publication 449	National Academy of Sciences, National Research Council, Washington 25, D. C.
Better Feeding of Livestock	Farmers' Bul. 2052	U. S. Department of Agriculture, Washington, D. C.
Feed Bag, Red Book The	Annual	Editorial Service Co., 1712 West St. Paul Ave., Milwaukee 3, Wis.
Feeder's Guide and Formulae for Meal Mixtures	Quebec Provincial Feed Board	Department of Agriculture, Quebec, Canada.
Feeding Cattle for Beef	Farmers' Bul. 1549	U. S. Department of Agriculture, Washington 25, D. C.
Feeding Practices	Educational Service	National Cottonseed Products Assn., 618 Wilson Bldg., Dallas, Tex.
Feed Mixer's Handbook, The	R. M. Sherwood	Interstate Printers & Publishers, Inc. Danville, Ill., 1951.
Feeds and Feeding, Abridged	F. B. Morrison	Morrison Publishing Co., Ithaca, N. Y.
Feeds and Feeding, 22nd. edition	F. B. Morrison	Morrison Publishing Co., Ithaca, N. Y.
Feeds of the World	B. H. Schneider	Agri. Exp. Sta., West Virginia Univ., Morgantown, W. Va., 1947.
Feed Trade Manual		National Miller Publications, Inc., 6 E. McDonald Rd., Prospect Heights, Ill.

SELECTED REFERENCES (Continued)

Title of Publication	Author(s)	Publisher
Handbook of Feedstuffs, The	Rudolph Seiden W. H. Pfander	Springer Publishing Co., New York, 1957.
How to Make Money Feeding Cattle	L. H. Simerl Bruce Russell	United States Publishing Company, Indianapolis, Ind., 1958.
Minerals for Livestock	Gus Bohstedt	Circ. 297, Univ. of Illinois, Extension Service, Urbana, Ill., 1957.
Minerals in Livestock Feeding	H. H. Mitchell	Circ. 688, Univ. of Illinois, Extension Service, Urbana, Ill., 1951.
Nutrient Requirements of Beef Cattle	Revised 1958	NAS-NRC Pub. 579, National Research Council, 2101 Constitution Ave., Washington 25, D. C.
Nutritional Deficiencies in Livestock	R. T. Allman T. S. Hamilton	Food and Agriculture Organization Studies No. 5, Rome, Italy.
Practical Explanation of Some Terms in Animal Nutrition	M. J. Brinegar	E. C. 252, Revised, 1951, Extension Service, Univ. of Nebraska, Lincoln, Neb.
Problems and Practices of American Cattlemen	M. E. Ensminger M. W. Galgan W. L. Slocum	Wash. Agri. Expt. Sta. Bul. 562, State College of Washington, Pullman, Wash., 1955.
Proteins and Amino Acids in Animal Nutrition	H. J. Almquist	U. S. Industrial Chemicals Co., 99 Park Ave., New York 16, N. Y.
Salt in Animal Nutrition		Salt Institute, 33 North LaSalle Street, Chicago 2, Ill., 1957.
Scientific Feeding of Farm Animals		Armour and Co., Chicago 9, Ill.
Stockman's Handbook, The	M. E. Ensminger	Interstate Printers & Publishers, Inc. Danville, Ill., 1959.
Through the Leaves	E. J. Maynard	Great Western Sugar Co., Denver, Colo.

In addition to the above selected references, valuable publications on feeds for and feeding beef cattle can be obtained from:

1. Division of Publications
   Office of Information
   U.S. Department of Agriculture
   Washington 25, D.C.
2. Your state agricultural college
3. Various feed manufacturers and pharmaceutical houses

CHAPTER X

BEEF CATTLE MANAGEMENT

Contents   Page

Fortunes have been made and lost in the beef cattle industry. Although it is not possible to arrive at any over-all, certain formula for success, in general those operators who have made money have paid close attention to the details of management.

SOME BEEF CATTLE MANAGEMENT PRACTICES

The almost innumerable beef cattle management practices vary widely between both areas and individual farmers and ranchers. In a general sort of way, the principles of good management of farm and range herds are much alike. The main differences arise from the sheer size of the range cattle enterprise, which means that things must be done in a big way. Without attempting to cover all management practices, some facts relative to—and methods of accomplishing—some simple beef cattle management practices will follow.

Dehorning

Although the presence of well-trained and properly polished horns may add to the attractiveness of the horned breeds in the show-ring or of the purebred herd, horns are objectionable on animals in the commercial herd and should always be removed.

The chief reasons for dehorning are:

1. Less shed and feeding space is required for dehorned cattle.

2. Dehorned cattle are less likely to inflict injury upon other cattle or upon the attendant.

3. Dehorned cattle are quieter and easier to handle.

4. Feeders prefer to buy dehorned cattle.

5. Dehorned cattle suffer fewer bruised carcasses and damaged hides in shipment to market, thus commanding a premium of 50 to 75 cents a hundredweight more than horned cattle of similar market class and grade.

Although the advantages in dehorning commercial cattle far outweigh the disadvantages, and progressive farmers and ranchers regularly dehorn their calf crop, there are certain unfavorable aspects. The disadvantages are:

1. Dehorning gives animals a set-back, especially when the operation is performed on older animals. With yearling steers, the South Dakota Station found[1] (1) that about two weeks were needed for dehorned steers to equal their initial weight, and (2) that dehorned steers failed to catch up with horned animals; that, due to shrink at dehorning time, dehorned steers weighed slightly less at marketing time than horned steers.

2. Labor and equipment are required in dehorning.

3. There are some death losses which result from excessive bleeding, screwworms, or infection.

4. Scurs may result if the operation is not carefully done.

5. Diseases may be spread unless equipment (except the hot iron) is disinfected between animals.

AGE AND SEASON TO DEHORN:

Cattle should be dehorned as early in life as possible. Young calves are easier to handle, lose less blood, and suffer less set-back. The danger of screwworm trouble and infection is also reduced when calves are dehorned while young.

In a study[2], which included more than a half million cattle in a 24-state area, it was found that, on the average, calves are dehorned at 5.2 months of age, which is considerably later in life than is desirable.

---

[1]Luther, Richard M., South Dakota Farm and Home Research, Feb., 1958, Vol. IX, No. 2, pp. 16-19.

[2]Ensminger, M. E., M. W. Galgan, and W. L. Slocum; Wash. Agri. Expt. Sta. Bul. 562.

Less insect trouble is encountered when dehorning is done in the early spring or late fall—an especially important consideration in dehorning animals in an area where screwworms exist.

METHODS OF DEHORNING:

Dehorning is accomplished in the ways shown in Fig. 131; which also shows the percentage of cattlemen using each method. As noted, most cattle are dehorned by means of saws and clippers, with the use of chemicals and polled bulls almost tied for second position. Because of the screwworm problem, the use of polled bulls is especially popular in the South.

When using a mechanical method to dehorn, most stockmen (96%)[1] routinely do their own work; others (4%)[1] call upon the veterinarian. Perhaps the most important thing is that it be done at the proper time.

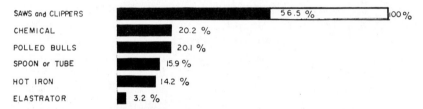

SAWS and CLIPPERS   56.5 %   100%
CHEMICAL   20.2 %
POLLED BULLS   20.1 %
SPOON or TUBE   15.9 %
HOT IRON   14.2 %
ELASTRATOR   3.2 %

Fig. 131. Methods of dehorning and the percentage of cattlemen using each. (From Wash. Agri. Expt. Sta. Bul. 562; courtesy, Washington State University)

Breeding Polled Cattle

The use of polled bulls is the most humane method of securing cattle without horns. If such a bull is "pure" polled (carrying in his blood no tendency to produce horns), practically all of his calves will be polled, even though their dams have horns.[2] This system of securing hornless calves saves labor and avoids pain and possible set-back to the calves. Without doubt, the breeding of polled calves will increase in popularity as more *good* polled bulls become available.

Use of Chemicals

With small herds kept under close supervision, newborn calves may be dehorned satisfactorily by the use of caustic pot-

[1] Ensminger, M. E., M. W. Galgan, and W. L. Slocum; Wash. Agri. Expt. Sta. Bul. 562.
[2] This applies to cattle of European extraction. See section in this book relative to "Dominant and Recessive Factors," p. 131 and the footnote therewith, for a more complete treatment of this subject.

ash (potassium hydroxide) or caustic soda (sodium hydroxide). These chemicals can be purchased at almost any drug store and come in the form of a stick, paste, or a lacquer base (the accompanying use of petroleum jelly is not necessary with the lacquer base). This method really prevents horn growth and does not actually remove the horns. The treatment should be applied when the calf is from three to ten days old and when only small buttons are present. After the hair around the buttons has been clipped or sheared closely, smear a ring of heavy grease or petroleum

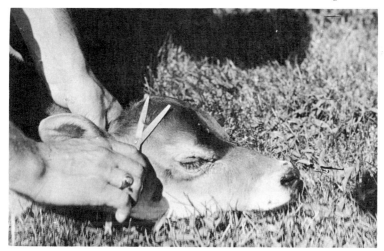

Fig. 132. Use of chemicals in dehorning. First the hair around the "button" is clipped (upper), following which caustic material should be rubbed over the little horn until blood appears (lower). (Courtesy, USDA)

jelly around the clipped area to keep the caustic from running into the calf's eyes. Then rub the caustic material over the button or little horn until the blood appears. This should be done carefully, for otherwise some of the horn cells may not be destroyed and a scur may develop. The caustic should be wrapped in a cloth or paper to protect the operator's hands from serious burns. Within a week or ten days, the thick scab that appears over the horn button will drop off, and the calf will suffer little inconvenience. Calves treated with caustic should be protected from rain for a day following the application, for the caustic may wash down and injure the side of the face. It is best not to turn the calves back with the dams for a few hours following the application of the caustic.

SAWS AND CLIPPERS

Saws or various forms of shears and clippers are used almost exclusively for dehorning in the range country. Even on the general livestock farms of the central and eastern states, mechanical methods are more generally used than chemicals. Whatever the instrument used (saws or clippers), it is necessary to remove the horn with about one-fourth to one-half inch of the skin around its base to make certain that the horn-forming cells are destroyed. The skin should then be allowed to grow over the wound. Dehorning of young animals can be done with greater ease, and there is less shock to the animals. However, some attention must be given to the season.

Ordinarily, clippers are satisfactory for removing the horns of younger cattle; but the hard, brittle horns of mature cattle can best be removed with a saw. With older animals, clippers are likely to sliver or crack the bone that forms the horn core. Moreover, the saw results in less loss of blood, for the action of the saw blade produces a lacerating of the blood vessels rather than a clean-cut cross section. On the other hand, the ragged wound made by a saw heals more slowly, and the operation is less rapid.

While the dehorning operation with older cattle is being performed, it is necessary to have some device for confining or restraining animals. For this purpose, various types and arrangements of dehorning chutes, pinch gates, squeeze pens, and cattle stocks have been devised. Calves may be handled by throwing or snubbing them to a fence post and tying one side of the

Cattle Dehorning Equipment

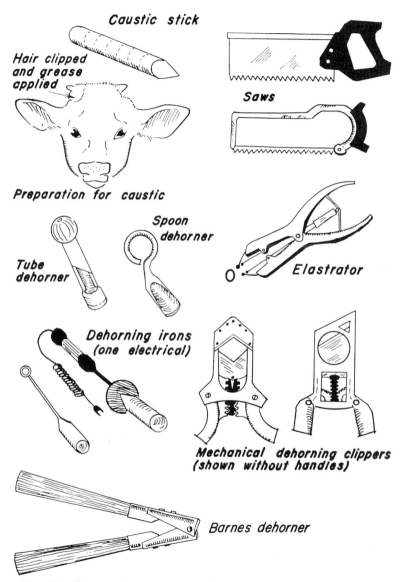

Fig. 133. Common instruments used for dehorning cattle. (Drawing by R. F. Johnson)

body against a strong fence or solid wall. Such methods are more difficult, however, for both man and beast.

THE HOT IRON

The hot-iron method of dehorning consists of the application of a specially designed hot iron to the horn of young calves. The iron is fashioned with one end cupped out so that it fits over the small horn button. Some ranchers first cut out the horn with a sharp knife before applying the hot iron; whereas others use a larger iron and fit it over the small horn. This system of dehorning is bloodless and may be used any time of the year, but it can be used on young calves only — preferably calves under five months of age.

Where electricity is available, the electric hot iron may be used. It keeps an even temperature, without getting too hot or too cold.

THE DEHORNING SPOON AND DEHORNING TUBE

The dehorning spoon (or gouge) is a small instrument with which the horns of young calves can be gouged out. In the hands of an experienced operator, it is both fast and effective. The use of the spoon leaves the head slightly rounded, and very seldom do scurs occur.

The dehorning tube is a newer instrument than the dehorning spoon. In comparison with the spoon, the tube is easier, faster, and less tiresome to use, and more certain to avoid regrowth.

Dehorning tubes come in four sizes, varying in diameter from three-fourths of an inch for the smallest to one and one-eighth inches for the largest. All four sizes should be available.

The steps and directions for using the dehorning tube are as follows:

1. Restrain the calf.

2. Select a sharp tube of proper size to fit over the base of the horn and include about one-eighth of an inch of skin all the way around.

3. Place the cutting edge straight down over the horn and then push and twist, first one way and then the other, until the skin has been cut through. A cut from one-eighth to three-eighths of an inch deep is required, the greater depth being

necessary with calves about three months of age. Going deeper than necessary will cause excessive bleeding.

4. Turn the tube to about a 45-degree angle and rapidly shove and turn the cutting edge until the button comes off.

Most ranchers who use the dehorning spoon or tube do so at the time of branding, thus avoiding extra handling. Either instrument can be used on calves up to sixty days of age.

THE ELASTRATOR

The elastrator is an instrument for use in stretching a specially made rubber ring over the horns, well down into the hair line. It is reported that this system may be used on cattle with horns from 2½ to 6 inches long. Small horns drop off in 3 to 6 weeks; large horns may take 2 months. Some cattlemen report that they have obtained good results when using the elastrator for dehorning; others report that they have been disappointed.

TREATMENT AFTER DEHORNING:

If dehorning is done in cool weather (spring or fall), when there are no flies, no treatment is required. On the other hand, if the operation is performed when flies are present, it is important that a good repellent be applied to the wound. Pine-tar oil or a mixture of pine-tar oil and tannic acid is very satisfactory for this purpose. As a rule, there will be no danger from excess bleeding. The danger of infection will be materially reduced if cleanliness is practiced and the instruments (except hot irons) are disinfected at intervals.

Castrating

It is advisable to castrate all male calves that are not to be used for breeding purposes. This operation results in more desirable beef development (a better balance between front and hind quarters), and improvement in the texture, flavor, and tenderness of the meat. It also makes the animals quieter and easier to handle.

AGE AND SEASON FOR CASTRATING:

Castration is best done when calves are from four to ten weeks of age, rather than at 2.5 months of age as is the general practice[1]; but bulls of any age can be desexed. The

---

[1]Ensminger, M. E., M. W. Galgan, and W. L. Slocum; Wash. Agri. Expt. Sta. Bul. 562.

older the animal at the time of the operation, the greater the shock and risk. Moreover, if a bull calf is not castrated before he is ten to twelve months old, he may become "staggy"—a very objectionable characteristic in the feeder or fat steer.

As in dehorning, it is best to perform this operation in the early spring or late fall so as to avoid infestation from flies. Moreover, it is unwise to castrate during periods of inclement weather. If castration is performed in an area where screwworms exist, a fly repellent should be applied to the wound and the animal should be kept under close observation until the wound has healed over; or a bloodless method of castration should be used.

METHODS OF CASTRATING:

Fig. 134 shows the common methods of castrating and the percentage of cattlemen using each. As noted, the vast majority of cattlemen use the knife.

As is true in dehorning, most stockmen routinely castrate their calves (94.9%)[1]; others call upon the veterinarian (5.1%).[1] Perhaps the most important thing is that it be done at the proper time.

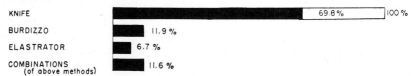

Fig. 134. Methods of castrating and the percentage of cattlemen using each. (From Wash. Agri. Expt. Sta. Bul. 562; courtesy Washington State University)

REMOVAL OF LOWER END OF SCROTUM

In this method, approximately the lower third of the scrotum is removed (exposing the testicles from below); the membrane covering each testicle is slit (if desired, the membrane need not be slit; simply remove it along with the testicle) and the testicles are removed by pulling them out. In older cattle, excessive bleeding may be prevented through severing the partially withdrawn cord by scraping with a knife or clamping with an emasculator. Although the removal of the end of the scrotum allows for excellent drainage, this method is not recommended for calves intended for show purposes because the cod will not be so large and shapely. Most ranchers castrate calves by this method.

---

[1]Ensminger, M. E., M. W. Galgan, and W. L. Slocum; Wash. Agr. Expt. Sta. Bul. 562

SLITTING SCROTUM DOWN THE SIDES

In this method, one testicle is pulled down at a time and is held firmly to the outside so that the skin of the scrotum is tight over the testicle. With a sharp knife, an incision is then made on the outside of the scrotum next to the leg. It is important that the incision extend well down to the end of the scrotum to allow for proper drainage and that it extend both through the scrotum and membrane, (if desired, the membrane need not be slit; simply remove it along with the testicle). The testicle may be removed as previously indicated.

THE BURDIZZO PINCERS

"Burdizzo" pincers (named after their inventor, Dr. Burdizzo, and manufactured in Italy) are sometimes used in making a "bloodless castration." In this method, the cords and associated blood vessels are crushed or severed so completely that the testicles waste away from want of circulation. After the animal is thrown, the cord is worked to the side of the scrotum, and the Burdizzo is clamped on about 1½ to 2 inches above the testicle, where it is held for a few seconds. Then repeat this operation on the same cord at a location about ¼ inch removed from the first one. The same procedure is then followed on the other testicle. In using the Burdizzo, it is important that the cord not slip out, that only one cord be clamped at a time, and that there be no interference with the circulation of the blood through the central portion of the scrotum.

This method is a satisfactory means of castration if done properly and by an experienced operator. But if the operation is not performed correctly, the cord may be incompletely crushed and the animal may develop stagginess later. This is especially disturbing when discovered in experimental or show animals or fat steers that are nearly ready for market or show. Because there is no break in the skin with this type of castration, there is no external bleeding. Nor can there be any trouble from screw worms—an important consideration in the South. Furthermore, steers so castrated usually develop very large and shapely cods, a characteristic that is very desirable in well-finished steers.

THE ELASTRATOR

The elastrator (developed in New Zealand) may be used in stretching a specially made rubber ring over the scrotum to

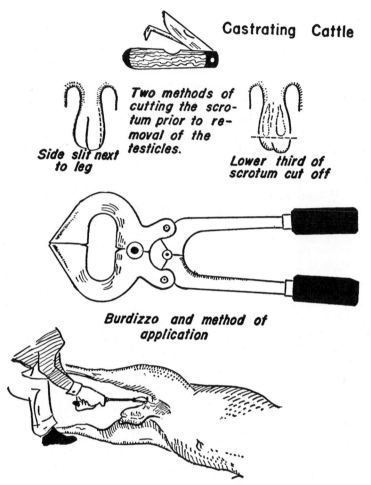

Fig. 135. Two common pieces of castrating equipment (the Knife and the Burdizzo), and method (s) of using each. (Drawing by R. F. Johnson)

castrate young calves. It works best on calves under two months of age. The directions are as follows: (1) Hold the calf in either a sitting or lying position, and (2) press both testicles through the ring and to the lower end of the scrotum, then release the rubber ring.

POSITION AND TREATMENT IN CASTRATING:

Young animals are usually thrown to be castrated, whereas animals eight months of age or older may be more easily operated on in a standing position.

Before making any incision, the hands of the operator and the knife should be thoroughly cleaned and washed in a good disinfectant. With these precautions, there is usually little danger of infection in castrating under range conditions; for normally the calves are turned back on the range where there is plenty of sunshine, fresh air, and no contamination. If the operation is performed in fly season and in an area where screw worms are prevalent, a good repellent should be applied. Pine-tar oil is most commonly used for the latter purpose.

Spaying

In females, the operation corresponding to castration is known as spaying. Under most conditions, desexing of the heifers is not recommended because: (1) The operation is more complicated and difficult, requiring a very experienced man; (2) spaying is attended with more danger than castration; (3) it eliminates the heifers for possible replacement purposes or sale as breeding stock; and (4) experiments and practical operations with spayed heifers have generally shown that the selling price obtained is not sufficiently higher to compensate for the lower and less efficient gains plus the attendant risk of the operation (see p. 377). On the other hand, spaying does prevent the possibility of heifers becoming pregnant, and eliminates the necessity of separating heifers from bulls or steers.

In a survey[1] made by the author, it was found that 9 per cent of cattlemen spayed heifers, that they spayed an average of 67.5 heifers each, and that they spayed at an average of 8.9 months of age. Also, it was reported that 80.5 per cent of the owners did their own spaying, while 19.5 per cent had the work done by the veterinarian.

Marking or Identifying

It is of historical interest to note that one of the first uses of branding in many countries of the world was to identify permanently human criminals. Also of interest is the fact that the noun "Maverick," meaning unbranded cattle, and now a recognized part of the American language, originated with lawyer-cattleman Samuel A. Maverick (1803-1870). Maverick, who accepted 600 head of cattle as an attorney's fee, failed to brand his young stock. As a result, year after year, his unbranded

---

[1] Ensminger, M. E., M. W. Galgan, and W. L. Slocum; Wash. Agri. Expt. Sta. Bul. 562.

yearlings fell into the hands of other cattlemen who promptly placed their brands on them. After 10 discouraging years of such operation, Maverick sold his depleted herd for the amount of the original fee.

Ranchers take pride in their brands, for to them it is much more than a sign of ownership; it is a symbol of service—a pledge of integrity of the man behind it and a mark of courage, character, and wisdom. It is indicative of the quality of stock that the owner raises, the class of bulls used, the condition of the range, and the kind of cowhands connected with the outfit.

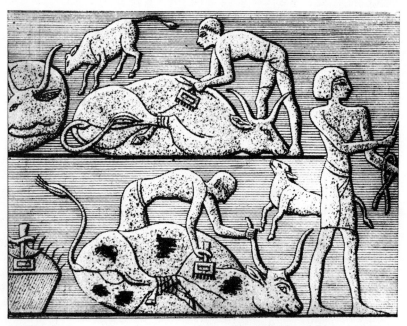

Fig. 136. Branding is a very old management practice. This picture made from an Egyptian tomb shows Egyptian drivers branding their cattle. (Courtesy, The Bettmann Archive)

On the western range, marking or branding is primarily a method of establishing ownership and/or age. In the small herd, particularly in the purebred herd, it is a means of ascertaining ancestry or pedigree. The method of marking employed will depend primarily upon the objective sought and the area.

The common methods of identification are shown in Fig. 137 and Table 28. As indicated, the three leading methods of identification, by rank, are: hide brands, ear marks, and tattoos. However, there are some differences between areas and between purebred and commercial herds (Table 28). Hide brands and ear marks are popular in the West and in commercial herds; and

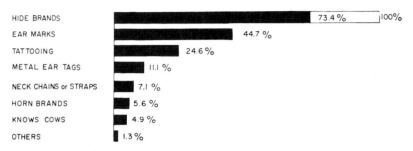

Fig. 137. Methods of identification and the percentage of cattlemen using each. (From Wash. Agri. Expt. Sta. Bul. 562; courtesy Washington State University)

TABLE 28. METHOD OF IDENTIFICATION

Method of Identification	Cattlemen Using the Method[1]					Purebred vs. Commercial	
	In West	In South	In Great Plains	In Pacific Northwest	All Respondents	Purebred Herds	Commercial Herds
	(%)	(%)	(%)	(%)	(%)	(%)	(%)
Hide Brands	78.8	66.7	77.2	69.4	73.4	30.0	86.0
Ear Marks	52.6	39.8	38.6	52.0	44.7	5.7	52.2
Tattooing	22.0	26.5	24.7	29.5	24.6	84.9	6.0
Metal Ear Tags	14.3	5.4	13.9	15.0	11.1	10.8	9.4
Neck Chains or Straps	3.6	11.0	5.0	2.9	7.1	14.2	2.3
Horn Brands	5.5	4.8	7.3	5.8	5.6	12.6	0.0
Knows Cows	4.7	7.1	1.5	4.6	4.9	2.7	5.6
Others	2.3	0.4	1.2	2.9	1.3	0.0	1.5

[1]From Wash. Agri. Expt. Sta., Bul. 562. The columns will total over 100 per cent because several cattlemen reported using more than one method of identification.

tattooing is a requisite to registration in most beef cattle registry associations. In this same study,[1] it was found that 42.8 per cent of the cows were individually identified and 36.2 per cent of the calves were individually identified before weaning.

HIDE BRANDS:

When properly applied, hide brands are permanent. Throughout the range country, the hide brand is recognized as the cattleman's trademark. Most of the western states require that each brand be recorded as to both type and location in order to avoid duplication. When stock are run close to a state boundary, the same brand may be recorded in two states.

[1]Ensminger, M. E., M. W. Galgan, and W. L. Slocum; Wash. Agri. Expt. Sta. Bul. 562.

In addition to the regular brand, many ranchers identify the age of the females by adding the last number of the year. Thus, heifer calves born in 1955 might be identified by adding the number 5 to the regular brand. At the end of ten years, the numbers are used over again, for there is seldom any difficulty in determining ages where there is a ten-year spread. In those states where brands are recorded, these added numbers or

Fig. 138. Branding Time. The assignments of each cowhand are: 1, using syringe to vaccinate against blackleg; 2, branding number on jaw to indicate year of birth—for example "O" would indicate born in 1960; 3, using a dehorning spoon to remove horn buttons; 4, holding front end of calf securely; 5, side branding—the "trademark" of each ranch; and 6, holding rear end of calf securely. (Courtesy, National Cottonseed Products Association)

brands must also be approved by and recorded with the Registrar of Brands.

Hide brands have the disadvantage of being unsightly, and of lowering the market value of the hide. For these reasons, they are not recommended except when necessary for identification purposes. Even then, it is desirable that their size be as small as possible, consistent with serving the primary objective of the brand.

The pertinent facts relative to branding are:

1. **Time.**—In the range country, the usual practice is to brand calves at the same time they are castrated and vaccinated against blackleg.

2. **Location on animal.**—The brand is located on a body area where it may be easily seen and where it will do the least possible damage.[1] Hips and thighs are favorite body areas for brands.

3. **Preparation.**—Usually calves are thrown for branding— roped by the hind legs and dragged to the place of branding. Older cattle, however, are restrained in a chute. Some ranchers now prefer to use the specially designed branding chutes for calves.

4. **Two methods of applying brands are:**

(1) *The hot iron.*—Most ranchers prefer this method. They heat the irons to a temperature that will burn sufficiently deep to make the scab peel but which will not leave deep scar tissue. The proper temperature of the hot iron is indicated by a yellowish color. Branding is accomplished by placing the heated branding iron firmly against the body area which it is desired to mark and by not allowing it to slip for the few seconds when the hide is burned. The branding iron should be kept free from dirt and adhering hair at all times.

Where electricity is available, the electric iron may be used; it keeps an even temperature, and if properly used, makes a clear, uniform brand.

(2) *Branding fluids.*—Branding fluids, which are less widely used in making hide brands, consist of caustic material applied by means of a cold iron. Best results are secured if the area is first clipped. The chemical method of producing hide brands is slower; the results are generally less satisfactory, particularly if the operator is inexperienced with the method; and the resulting brand is less permanent.

5. **Characteristics of a good brand.**—A good brand is one that is easily read, that is of simple design and yet cannot be easily changed or tampered with, that has no welds or thick points in the iron, and that interferes with the circulation as little as possible. Thick points mean deeper burning

---

[1] In arriving at both the kind and the location of the brand, the owner should first check with the brand inspector or the local county agent to determine if any part of the animal is reserved for state or federal disease control programs; for example, the cheek of cattle is used for brucellosis reactor identification.

and slower healing; whereas small enclosed areas, such as a small "O," will slough out entirely.

EAR MARKS:

Ear marks are permanent and easily recognized but unsightly. They may be administered with either a sharp knife or a regular ear notcher. Sometimes polled animals are individually identified through ear notches. In such instances a definite value is assigned to each area location. When ear marks are used in commercial operations, however, they are uniform and recorded for any given ranch. Some of the more common earmarks are "crops," "swallow forks," "bobs," "over-bits," "under-bits," and "splits."

METAL EAR MARKERS (TAGS AND BUTTONS):

Metal ear markers are easily attached but easily lost. They also frequently rub and scratch the skin, thus making openings for screwworm infestation—an important consideration in the South.

NECK CHAINS OR STRAPS:

Neck chains or straps are the most frequently used means of identifying polled cattle. Occasionally, chains or straps may be lost, but this is not particularly serious if the caretaker is on the alert and immediately replaces each one that is lost, without allowing several losses to accumulate before taking action. Neck chains or straps must be adjusted, for young animals grow, or animals change in condition.

HORN BRANDS:

Horn branding for individual identification is commonly used among breeding or sale animals of the horned breeds. Usually horn brands are made by heating small copper numbers with a blow torch or charcoal burner. On mature animals, this method of branding works fairly well, but it cannot be used on young animals while the horns are still growing, unless it is repeated at intervals.

TATTOOS:

Most purebred beef cattle registry associations require that registered animals be individually tattooed. This method of marking consists of piercing the skin with instruments equipped

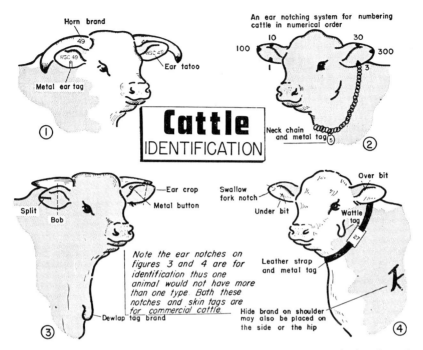

Fig. 139. Composite drawings showing a number of methods of cattle identification. It is unlikely that any individual animal will carry more than one or two of these methods of identification. (Drawing by R. F. Johnson)

with needle points which form letters or numbers. This operation is followed by rubbing indelible ink into the freshly pierced area. On dark-skinned animals, tattoos are difficult to read. It is well carefully to disinfect the tattooing instrument between each operation in order to alleviate the hazard of spreading warts to the pierced area. Warts make it impossible to read the tattoo.

OTHER MARKS:

Other identification marks used on the range include: (1) "buds" formed by making a strip incision through the nose, (2) "wattles" made by cutting down a strip of skin on the jaw bone, and (3) "dewlaps" formed by cutting down a strip of skin on the brisket.

MARKING PUREBRED CATTLE:

Table 29, Handy Marking or Identifying Guide for Registered Beef and Dual-Purpose Cattle, summarizes the pertinent regulations of the beef and dual-purpose cattle registry associations relative to marking or identifying.

TABLE 29

HANDY MARKING OR IDENTIFYING GUIDE FOR REGISTERED
BEEF AND DUAL-PURPOSE CATTLE

Breed	Association Rules Relative to Marking
Aberdeen-Angus	Each animal, for which application for registry is submitted, must be tattooed alike in both ears. Each breeder may devise his own tattooing system. Each animal to be registered by any one breeder must be tattooed differently.
Brahman	A holding brand (a symbol, letter, combination of letters and/or symbols, numerals, replica of some object, etc. to denote ownership or breeder) and private herd number (branded by fire) are required on a calf before it may be registered.
Brangus	Each animal for which application is submitted must be fire branded on the body with the owner's holding brand and a private herd number. The application for registration or enrollment must show where this brand is located on the body. The Association suggests starting with the number '1' on the private herd number and numbering consecutively. The holding brand is any mark, initial, or number, or combination of all three which the breeder chooses to use.
Charbray	No association rules relative to marking. The breeder may devise his own system.
Charolais	Animals must be identified by a (1) holding brand (owner brand) or tattoo, and (2) private herd number (animal no.) tattooed or branded.
Devon	Each breeder is assigned a herd tattoo code of three letters, which must be applied to the right ear. The individual herd number plus the letter code for the year of birth must be tattooed in the left ear.
Herefords	Each animal, for which application for registry is submitted, must be tattooed in one ear. Tattooing in both ears is recommended. The Association recommends (1) starting with number '1' in each ear and proceeding upward in regular order to 999, (2) limiting numbers to 3 digits, and (3) using the tattoo number as the horn brand number also.
Indu Brazil	Because of the dark pigmentation of the skin of Zebu (Indu Brazil) cattle, tattoos are not commonly used for their identification. Accordingly, the Association recognizes only identification numbers branded upon the animal.

TABLE 29 (Continued)

Breed	Association Rules Relative to Marking
Milking Shorthorn......	Milking Shorthorn cattle cannot be registered unless they have been tattooed in the ear with an identification number.
	The tattoo number should be different from the number used for any other animal of the same sex in the same herd, except that two or more animals of the same sex, if born in different years, may be marked with the same serial numbers if they are also marked with numbers designating different years of birth.
Polled Hereford...........	Each animal, for which application for registry is submitted, must be tattooed with a number in one or both ears (the Association recommends tattooing in both ears).
	Application for registry must (1) give the tattoo number, and (2) indicate in which ear or both ears, as the case may be, that it appears. Each animal registered by any one breeder should be tattooed differently.
Red Poll.......................	Owners select their own marking system. However, identifying numbers must be tattooed in both ears, but either the same or different marks may be used in each ear (if different marks are used, they must be so specified on application for registry). Each animal must be tattooed with a different number.
Santa Gertrudis..........	Each animal must carry breeders' holding brand. Each animal to be registered must carry individual number brand or tattoo.
Scotch Highland.........	Each animal for which application for registry is submitted must be tattooed, ear tagged or hip or horn branded. The method of marking shall be determined by the owner, but it must appear on the application for registry.
	The Association recommends (1) that the left ear carry the two letters for herd designation, followed by the year (thus, a calf in 1958 on the Double X ranch might be marked XX58), and (2) that individual animal numbers appear in the right ear.
Shorthorn.....................	Each animal, for which application for registry is submitted, must be tattooed with a number in one ear. A letter or initial may or may not precede the number. The application for registry must show whether the tattoo appears in the calf's right or left ear. Duplication of numbers in the same sex and herd is not permissible.

Weaning

Early spring calves should be weaned in the fall, preferably before the forage becomes dry or just before moving the breeding herd to the winter range or into winter quarters. Calves are usually weaned when they are six to eight months of age,[1] but animals intended for show purposes may be continued on milk (by using a nurse cow) for a much longer period. Usually a cow will wean her calf by the time it reaches ten to eleven months of age, even if the two animals are not separated.

If creep feeding has been practiced, weaning will cause very little disturbance or set-back. Otherwise, the calves may well be taught to eat grain when the weaning process is initiated. The weaning separation should be complete and final, preferably with no opportunity for the calf to hear or see its dam again. It is well to check over the udders of the cows every day or two and to milk them out partially if necessary. In no event, however, should the cows and calves be turned together once the separation has been made. Such a practice will only prolong the weaning process and also may cause digestive disorders in the calf.

Bedding Cattle

Bedding or litter is used primarily for the purposes of keeping animals clean and comfortable. But bedding has the following added values from the standpoint of the manure:

1. It soaks up the urine which contains about one-half the total plant food of manure.

2. It makes manure easier to handle.

3. It absorbs plant nutrients, fixing both ammonia and potash in relatively insoluble forms that protects them against losses by leaching. This characteristic of bedding is especially important in peat moss, but of little signifiance with sawdust and shavings.

KIND AND AMOUNT OF BEDDING:

The kind of bedding material selected should be determined primarily by (1) availability and price, (2) absorptive capacity, and (3) plant nutrient content. In addition, a desirable bedding should not be dusty, should not be excessively coarse, and should remain well in place and not be too readily kicked aside. Table

---

[1]On the average, beef calves are weaned at 7.3 months of age (Wash. Agri. Expt. Sta. Bul. 562).

30 summarizes the characteristics of some common bedding materials.

In addition to the bedding materials listed in Table 30, many other products can be and are successfully used for this purpose, including low quality hays, peanut hulls, leaves of many kinds, spent tanbark, tobacco stalks, buckwheat hulls, oat hulls, and cocoa shells.

Naturally the availability and price per ton of various bedding materials vary from area to area, and from year to year. Thus, in the New England states shavings and sawdust are available, whereas other forms of bedding are scarce, and straws are more plentiful in the central and western states.

Table 30 shows that bedding materials differ considerably in their relative capacities to absorb liquid. Thus 45 pounds of wheat straw will absorb about 100 pounds of liquid, whereas 10 pounds of peat moss has the same absorptive capacity. This means that, on the average, 1 pound of peat moss will absorb as much liquid as 4½ pounds of wheat straw. Also, it is noteworthy that cut straw will absorb more liquid than long straw; ordinary long straw will take up to 2 to 3 times its weight in water, whereas cut straw will absorb about 5 times its weight in water. But there are disadvantages to chopping; chopped straws do not stay in place, and they may be dusty.

TABLE 30

CHARACTERISTICS OF BEDDING MATERIALS[1]

	Bedding Required to Absorb 100 Pounds of Liquid	Ability to Absorb Ammonia Nitrogen Per Ton of Bedding	Plant Food Content Per Ton of Air-Dry Materials		
			Nitrogen	Phosphoric acid (P_2O_5)	Potash (K_2O)
	(lbs.)	(lbs.)	(lbs.)	(lbs.)	(lbs.)
Wheat straw	45	4.5	11	4	20
Oat straw	35	7.1	12	4	26
Rye straw	45	3.4	12	6	17
Chopped straw	20-30	....	....	....	....
Cornstalks (shredded)	25-35	5.3	15	8	18
Sawdust	25	0	4	2	4
Wood shavings	25-45	0	4	2	4
Peat moss (Sphagnum)	10	40	16	2	3

[1]From Yearbook of Agriculture, 1938, *Soils and Men*, Table III, p. 451.

Table 30 also shows that bedding materials contain valuable plant foods, and that there is considerable difference between them in this respect. From the standpoint of the value of plant food nutrients per ton of air dry material, peat moss is the most valuable bedding, and wood products (sawdust and shavings) the least valuable.

The suspicion that sawdust or shavings will hurt the land is rather widespread, but unfounded. It is true that these products decompose slowly. But this process can be expedited by the addition of nitrogen fertilizers.

The minimum desirable amount of bedding to use is the amount necessary to absorb completely the liquids in manure. Some helpful guides to the end that this may be accomplished follow:

1. With 24-hour stabling, the minimum daily bedding requirements, based on uncut wheat or oats straw, of cattle is as follows: Cows, 9 pounds; steers, 7 to 10 pounds. With other bedding materials, these quantities will vary according to their respective absorptive capacities (see Table 30). Also, more than these minimum quantities of bedding may be desirable where cleanliness and comfort of the animal are important. Comfortable animals lie down more and utilize a higher proportion of the energy of the feed for productive purposes (cattle require 9 per cent less energy when lying down than when standing).

2. Under average conditions, about 500 pounds of bedding are used for each ton of excrement.

3. Where the liquid excrement is collected separately in a cistern or tank—as is the common practice in Denmark, Germany, and France, and on some dairy farms in the United States—less bedding is required than where the liquid and solid excrement are kept together.

CATTLE MANURE FOR MAKING AND KEEPING THE SOIL PRODUCTIVE[1]

Making and keeping the soil productive is the very foundation of a successful agriculture, of national prosperity. It has been well said that good soils, good farms and ranches, and good living go hand in hand. At its best, this necessitates an animal

[1]The author gratefully acknowledges the helpful suggestions of Dr. H. M. Reisenauer, Soil Specialist, Washington State University, Pullman, Wash., who very kindly reviewed this material.

agriculture; one in which the manure is carefully conserved and properly applied, and in which supplements of commercial fertilizers and lime are intelligently used where and when they are needed.

Despite all the recent developments in the use of commercial fertilizers and soil-building crops, manure still is the first and most logical way for stockmen to keep their soils fertile and productive.

The term "manure" refers to a mixture of animal excrements (consisting of undigested feeds plus certain body wastes) and bedding. From the standpoint of soils and crops, barnyard manure contains the following valuable ingredients:

1. **Organic matter.**—It supplies valuable organic matter which cannot be secured in commercial fertilizers. Organic matter—which constitutes 3 to 6 per cent, by weight, of most soils—improves soil tilth, increases water-holding capacity, lessens water and wind erosion, improves aeration and has a beneficial effect on soil microorganisms. It is the "lifeblood" of the land.

2. **Plant food.**—It supplies plant food or fertility—especially nitrogen, phosphorus, and potash. A ton of well-preserved manure, including bedding, contains plant food nutrients equal to about 100 pounds of 10-5-10 fertilizer. Thus, when manure is spread at the rate of 8 tons per acre, it is like applying 800 pounds of 10-5-10 commercial fertilizer.

Amount of Manure Produced

It is conservatively estimated that one billion tons of manure are produced annually on the farms and ranches of the United States; sufficient to add nearly one ton each year to every acre in the nation's farms and ranches.

Although the quantity of manure produced per animal is materially affected by the amount of bedding used, on the average the production on any farm or ranch can be estimated from Fig. 140.

The data in Figure 140 are based on animals confined to stalls the year around. Actually, the manure recovered and available to spread where desired is considerably less than indicated because (1) animals are kept on pasture and along roads and lanes much of the year, where the manure is dropped, and (2) losses in weight often run as high as 60 per cent when manure is exposed to the weather for a considerable time.

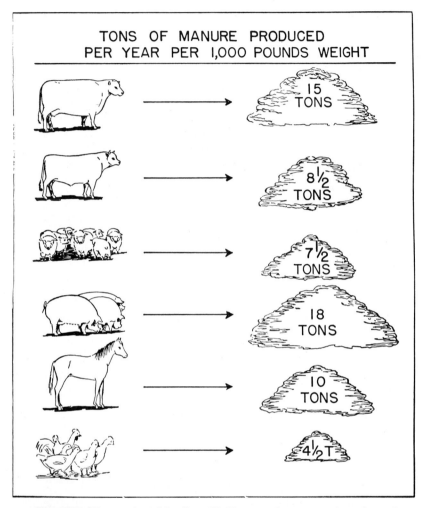

Fig. 140. Manure is a big "crop"! How much manure does your farm or ranch produce? On the average, each class of stall-confined animals produces per year per 1,000 pounds weight the tonnages shown above. (Drawing by Steve Allured; courtesy Washington State University)

Composition of Manure

As shown in Figure 141, about 75 per cent of the nitrogen, 80 per cent of the phosphorus, and 85 per cent of the potash contained in animal feeds are returned as manure. In addition, about 40 per cent of the organic matter in feeds is excreted as manure. As a rule of thumb, it is commonly estimated that 80

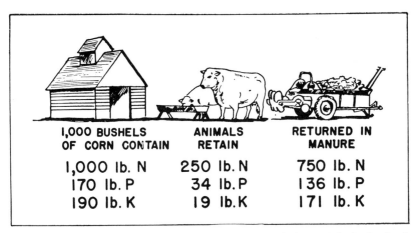

1,000 BUSHELS OF CORN CONTAIN	ANIMALS RETAIN	RETURNED IN MANURE
1,000 lb. N	250 lb. N	750 lb. N
170 lb. P	34 lb. P	136 lb. P
190 lb. K	19 lb. K	171 lb. K

Fig. 141. Animals retain about 20 per cent of the nutrients in feed; the rest is excreted in manure. (Drawing by Steve Allured; courtesy Washington State University)

per cent of the total nutrients in feeds are excreted by animals as manure.

Naturally, it follows that the manure from well-fed animals is higher in nutrients and worth more than that from poorly-fed ones. For example, the manure produced from cattle liberally fed on nutritious concentrates is more valuable than that produced from cattle wintered on straw.

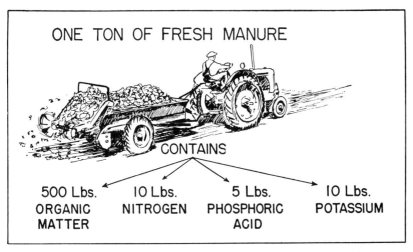

ONE TON OF FRESH MANURE

CONTAINS

500 Lbs. ORGANIC MATTER	10 Lbs. NITROGEN	5 Lbs. PHOSPHORIC ACID	10 Lbs. POTASSIUM

Fig. 142. The contents of one ton of fresh manure. (Drawing by Steve Allured; courtesy Washington State University)

Although varying with (1) the kind of feed, (2) the class of animal, (3) the age, condition, and individuality of the animal, and (4) the kind and amount of bedding used, a ton of average barnyard manure has approximately the composition shown in Figure 142.

Figure 143 gives the nutrients, by classes of animals, in one ton of fresh manure. As shown, in terms of nutrients contained, chicken manure is the most valuable, with sheep manure ranking second, horse manure third, swine manure fourth, and cattle manure last, with little actual difference in the last two. Of course, cattle and swine account for a far greater tonnage of manure than other classes of animals.

The urine makes up 20 per cent of the total weight of the excrement of horses, and 40 per cent of that of hogs; these

PLANT NUTRIENTS IN ONE TON OF DIFFERENT MANURES
(includes solid, liquid and bedding)

	Nitrogen (N) pounds	Phosphoric Acid (P_2O_5) pounds	Potash (K_2O) pounds	Tons of manure produced per year per 1,000 lbs. weight
 COW (1 cow)	11.4	3.1	9.9	15
 STEER (1 beef steer)	15.0	6.0	8.0	8½
 SHEEP (6 or 7 sheep)	15.8	6.7	18.0	7½
 SWINE (3 sows)	9.9	6.7	9.3	18
 HORSE (1-light horse)	13.2	5.1	12.1	10
 CHICKENS (a flock)	21.0	16.4	10.2	4½

Fig. 143. The composition of manure varies according to the class of animals. Chicken manure is the most valuable; sheep manure ranks second. Nutrient figures from Cornell Extension Bulletin 642, Table 2; courtesy Dr. R. Bradfield, Cornell Department of Agronomy. (Drawing by Steve Allured; courtesy Washington State University)

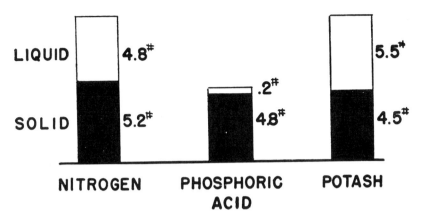

LIQUID 4.8# 5.5#

.2#

SOLID 5.2# 4.8# 4.5#

NITROGEN PHOSPHORIC POTASH
ACID

Fig. 144. Distribution of plant nutrients between liquid and solid portions of a ton of average farm manure. As noted, the urine contains about half the fertility value of manure. (Drawing by Steve Allured; courtesy Washington State University)

figures represent the two extremes in farm animals. Yet the urine, or liquid manure, contains nearly 50 per cent of the nitrogen, 6 per cent of the phosphate and 60 per cent of the potash of average manure; roughly one-half of the total plant food of manure (see Fig. 144). Also, it is noteworthy that the nutrients in liquid manure are more readily available to plants than the nutrients in the solid excrement. These are the reasons why it is important to conserve the urine.

Value of Manure

The value of manure varies according to (1) the class of animals, (2) the kind of feed consumed and the kind of bedding used, (3) the method of handling, (4) the rate and method of application, and (5) the kind of soil and crops on which it is used.

The actual monetary value of farm manure can and should be based upon the following criteria:

1. **Increased crop yields.**—Numerous experimental studies and practical observations have shown the measurable monetary value of manure in increased crop yields.

At the Iowa Experiment Station, beginning in 1915, 8 tons of manure per acre were applied to the sod and plowed under for corn in a 4-year rotation of corn-corn-oats-meadow. For a 10-year period, the following results were obtained from the manure:

Crop	Increased yields from manure	Prevailing prices	Increased value from manure
Corn	15 bu.	$ 1.50/bu.	$22.50
Corn	15 bu.	1.50/bu.	22.50
Oats	9 bu.	0.80/bu.	7.20
Clover	0.7 ton	15.00/ton	10.50
Total increased value from manure			$62.70

Since 8 tons of manure were used, this means an average of $7.84 worth of increased crops from each ton of manure.

At the Ohio Agricultural Experiment Station, in 3 experiments in which barnyard manure was the only source of applied nutrients for a period of 50 years, manure showed an average value of $9.50 per ton, based on increased crop yields.

At the Illinois Experiment Station, extensive experiments with manure were conducted at 20 different locations over the state during a 4-year period. The crop rotations varied somewhat, but corn and hay were common to all fields. The manured fields received an application of one ton of manure for each ton of crops removed from the land, or an average of 2.36 tons per acre annually. In comparison with fields which were not manured, the increased crop yields obtained on the manured plots were sufficient to give manure a value of $10.11 per ton, when the value of the increased yields was computed on the basis of the average prices received by farmers during the same 4-year period.

2. **Equivalent cost of a like amount of commercial fertilizer.**—A ton of average barnyard manure contains about 10 pounds of nitrogen, 5 pounds of phosphoric acid, and 10 pounds of potash.

At 16 cents per pound for nitrogen, 9 cents per pound for phosphoric acid and 5 cents per pound for potash (approximate commercial fertilizer prices), the plant food alone—exclusive of the valuable organic matter—in the ton of manure would cost $2.55 if purchased in commercial fertilizers.

Thus, in terms (1) of increased crop yields, and (2) of equivalent cost of a like amount of commercial fertilizer, at the present time manure has a value of from $2.55 to $10.11 per ton; or $6.33 per ton based on the average of the figures presented and the two methods of evaluating. This is considerably higher than the often quoted pre-World War II figure of $3.00 per ton. But manure increased in value with higher prices for crops and for commercial fertilizers.

Therefore, if manure is assigned a value of $6.33 per ton and it is assumed that the yearly production of each class of animals is as shown in Figure 140, each farm animal has a yearly manure producing potential about as follows: one cow, $95.00; one steer, $54.00; one sheep, $8.00; one sow, $38.00; and one horse, $64.00.

Of course, the value of manure cannot be measured alone in terms of increased crop yields and equivalent cost of a like amount of commercial fertilizer. It has additional value for the organic matter which it contains, which almost all soils need, and which farmers and ranchers cannot buy in a sack.

Also, it is noteworthy that, due to the slower availability of its nitrogen and to its contribution to the soil humus, manure produces rather lasting benefits, which may continue for many years. Approximately one-half of the plant nutrients in manure are available to and effective upon the crops in the immediate cycle of the rotation to which the application is made. Of the unused remainder, about one-half, in turn, is taken up by the crops in the second cycle of the rotation, one-half of the remainder in the third cycle, etc., etc. Likewise, the continuous use of manure through several rounds of a rotation builds up a back-log which brings additional benefits, and a measurable climb in yield levels.

Stockmen sometimes fail to recognize the value of this barnyard crop because (1) it is produced whether or not it is wanted, and (2) it is available without cost.

How to Lessen Manure Losses

Since manure is both valuable and perishable, it is important that the stockman take precautions to lessen its losses. It is worth more the day it is produced than at any subsequent date. Manure exposed to the weather will, under average conditions, lose one-third of its plant food and organic matter value in three months; half in six months; and even more with a longer period. Despite these facts, it is estimated that each year farmers and ranchers lose half of the value of the nation's one billion tons of manure through careless handling. But there are other losses; losses incurred because (1) about one-half the excrement is dropped on pasture, and its full value is not realized because of improper distribution, and (2) of the small but indeterminate amounts dropped on lanes and roads. All in all, it is probably safe to assume that not more than one-third of the potential value of the manure resources of the nation are now realized. This is shocking, indeed, when it is realized that the annual loss of ⅔ of the billion tons of manure produced would have had a total monetary value of nearly 4¼ billion dollars.

When manure is exposed to the weather, nitrogen goes into the air as eye-stinging ammonia gas, washes away with rain water, and leaches into the ground; phosphorus is washed or

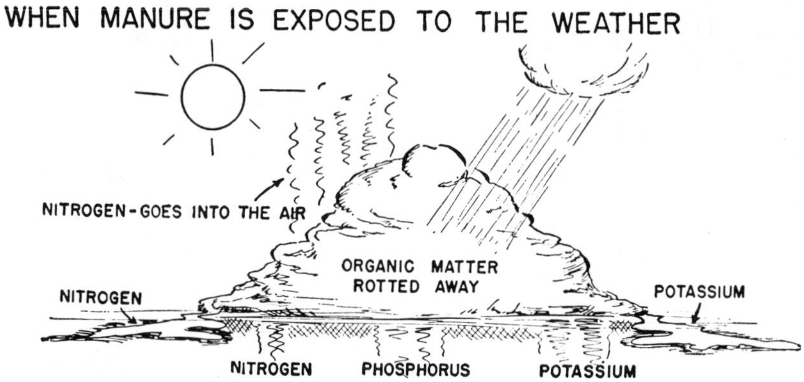

WHEN MANURE IS EXPOSED TO THE WEATHER

NITROGEN-GOES INTO THE AIR

ORGANIC MATTER
ROTTED AWAY

NITROGEN   POTASSIUM

NITROGEN   PHOSPHORUS   POTASSIUM

Fig. 145. Here is how the fertility value of manure is lost when it is exposed to the weather. (Drawing by Steve Allured; courtesy Washington State University)

drained away with the liquid portion; potassium is washed away by rain or carried off in wasted urine; and organic matter is rotted away (see Fig. 145). Based on this knowledge of how manure loses its value, the following practical ways in which to lessen manure losses are recommended:

1. **Use ample bedding to absorb the liquid manure.**—In addition to making for comfort and cleanliness of animals, bedding (1) retains the valuable liquid manure, and (2) adds to the fertility of the soil because of its own nutrient and humus content. The stockman should use sufficient bedding to absorb all the liquid manure.

Wheat or oats straw will soak up about twice their own weight of water. Thus, about 300 pounds bedding of either of these products will absorb the approximately 600 pounds of liquid

in each ton of manure.[1] Chopped bedding will absorb more moisture than coarse bedding. But not all kinds of bedding are as
absorbent as wheat or oats straw and relatively little litter is
chopped. Under average conditions, about 500 pounds of bedding
is used for each ton of excrement.

2. **Construct watertight floors.**—Urine drained into the
ground is lost. Thus, watertight floors are an important adjunct,
along with ample bedding, in saving the valuable liquid manure.

3. **Pave feedlots and corrals.**—Paved feedlots and corrals
prevent manure from being tramped into the mud and lost. In
addition, they save in feed and labor, and make for increased
animal comfort, cleanliness, and faster gains. For these reasons,
paved feedlots and corrals soon pay for themselves.

Where feedlots and corrals are not paved, the manure should
be hauled early in the spring or as soon as animals have gone
to market.

4. **Construct overhead protection.** — Rainwater quickly
washes away manure's soluble plant nutrients. That is why overhead protection lessens manure losses and should be provided
where practicable.

5. **Provide adequate but not excessively large feedlots.**—
Feedlots should be of adequate size to provide animal comfort
(see Table 32, p. 520), but not so large that they will be either
wash basins for the loss of manure or too expensive to pave.

6. **Use deep litter and let manure accumulate in feeding and
loafing sheds.**—Wherever possible, it is recommended that manure be left to accumulate in feeding and loafing sheds until it
can be hauled and spread directly on the fields; perhaps once or
twice each season. On top of a well-bedded manure pack, animals
stay clean and warm and thrive. Under such conditions, manure
is tramped on and kept well packed and moist; thus minimizing
the losses in both nitrogen and organic matter.

The manure from stalls can also be added to the manure in
feeding and loafing sheds thus conserved.

7. **Haul from stalls to fields daily if practicable.**—Since manure is perishable, daily spreading on the land is recommended
wherever practicable. Of course, this is impossible when the soil

---

[1]Actually, the moisture content of fresh animal excrements will average
60 to 80 per cent, but it is impossible and unnecessary that all the moisture
be taken up in the bedding.

is wet or there is deep snow, or when there is a peak labor load. But fresh manure may be spread on frozen ground with little loss in value.

When manure is spread promptly and regularly, its plant nutrients pass directly into the ground, where they are securely trapped or "fixed." Also, daily hauling distributes the work so that it never becomes a major task.

8. **Spread thinly on fields.**—A modest even application of manure over a large acreage gives higher returns than a heavy application over a small acreage. In general, the application of manure should not exceed 8 to 12 tons per acre for row crops or 4 to 6 tons for other crops, thus covering as much acreage as possible.

9. **Store properly in a concrete pit or place in straight-sided, well-packed piles.**—If manure cannot be hauled to the fields daily or left to accumulate as deep litter in a shed, it should be stored properly in a concrete pit or packed in straight-sided piles. The manure pit should have a watertight floor and sidewalls. A roof is also preferable, for rain adds nothing but weight to the manure and will leach out the plant food unless the storage is watertight. The pit should be located some distance from the house and the dairy barn for sanitary reasons, yet it should be conveniently accessible, both from the standpoint of filling and emptying.

Whether manure is stored in a pit or outside, it should be packed in straight-sided, deep piles in order to reduce air circulation through it and the leaching action of rain or snow; conditions conducive to losses of nitrogen and destruction of organic matter by decay. Moist, tight piles retard the loss of nitrogen as ammonia gas.

Manure that has been stored and fermented loses nitrogen rapidly after spreading, unless it is either plowed under or disked in within one to three hours after spreading.

10. **Keep livestock on pasture as much as practical.**—Animals on pasture spread their own manure with little loss of its fertilizing value. Where the area permits, the droppings should be spread by harrowing at intervals (at least every fall) to distribute fertility and to prevent accumulations which result in uneven grazing.

11. **Add phosphate to trap nitrogen.**—Manure ferments and

Manure leaching out by the barn door

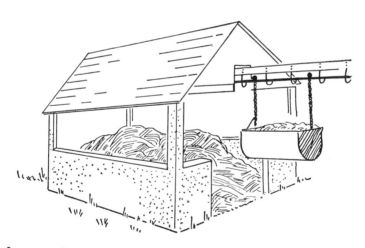

A nutrient saving manure pit

Fig. 146. Manure should be stored properly. Upper drawing shows a wrong way—manure piled out the barn door. Lower picture shows a right way—a concrete pit with a roof over it. (Drawing by R. F. Johnson)

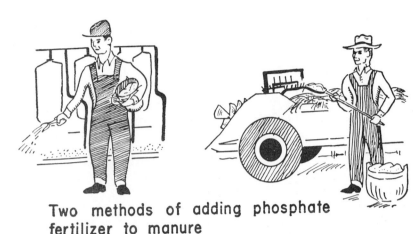

Two methods of adding phosphate fertilizer to manure

Fig. 147. When added to manure, superphosphate will trap the nitrogen and correct the phosphorus deficiency. This can be accomplished either by (1) scattering daily in the stall or shed 1 to 2 lbs. of 20 per cent superphosphate for each mature cow (or equivalent animal unit), or (2) adding 40 to 50 lbs. of 20 per cent superphosphate to each ton of manure on the spreader. (Drawings by R. F. Johnson)

thereby releases ammonia gas (containing nitrogen) into the atmosphere.

The addition of superphosphate will lessen this loss (the superphosphate unites with the ammonia to form a more stable compound of nitrogen), and also correct the phosphorus deficiency of manure. These purposes can be accomplished by the addition of 40 to 50 pounds of 20 per cent superphosphate to each ton of manure. On a daily basis, this calls for the spreading in the stall or shed of 1 to 2 pounds of superphosphate for each mature cow or horse; with amounts for other livestock in proportion to their weights.

Where the deep litter system is used, as in feeding and loafing sheds, the phosphorus treatment is usually given just before rebedding the shed, which generally means once or twice each week. With horses the application is best made just before cleaning the stable. With dairy cattle kept in stanchions, the superphosphate is usually dusted in the gutter either before or after cleaning the barn. Where a manure pit is used, the superphosphate should be added to the pile at the same time that manure is added.

Where manure is either produced or piled out in the open, superphosphate should not be added until at the time of hauling and spreading on the fields; otherwise too much of it will be wasted.

Modern Ways of Handling Manure

Modern handling of manure involves the use of such equipment and buildings as will make for (1) expediency, (2) efficiency of labor, and (3) a minimum loss of nutrients. This includes the following:

1. **The spreader.**—A modern manure spreader is the key machine in almost any efficient system of handling barnyard manure. It (1) makes daily spreading practical, (2) provides uniform application on the land, (3) saves time and labor, and (4) works well with all modern loading methods (carriers, loaders, or automatic cleaners).

2. **Overhead carrier.**—Where the barn design does not permit direct loading into the spreader, an efficient litter carrier system reduces the labor of daily cleaning, such as is required in a dairy barn.

If possible, the carrier should be dumped directly into the spreader and the manure hauled daily or as soon as practicable. Where manure must be stored before hauling, the carrier should be dumped into a suitable pit.

3. **Automatic gutter cleaner.**—Automatic gutter cleaners offer a way of eliminating much of the hand labor in stanchioned dairy barns, but they are expensive in the first cost. They are usually designed to carry the manure directly into a spreader located just outside the barn. With such a cleaner, the sprockets and chains must be adequately shielded to prevent injury to animals and men, and the whole system designed to permit a high standard of sanitation in the barn.

4. **Drive-through barns.**—The simplest method of handling manure in the stanchioned dairy barn consists in having a wide enough alley behind the cows to permit the spreader to be driven through the barn, for direct loading from the gutters. With such an arrangement, the manure is handled only once; the spreader is loaded each day as the barn is cleaned. If the spreader cannot be filled each day, the partial load should be parked under a shed roof until the following day.

5. **Power loader.**—Wherever manure is allowed to accumulate in sheds or feed lots or is stored, the power loader provides

The modern manure spreader

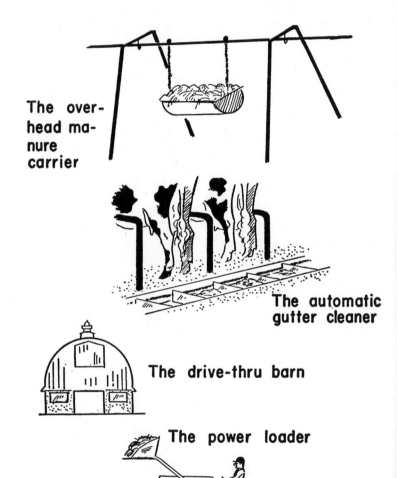

**The over-
head ma-
nure
carrier**

**The automatic
gutter cleaner**

The drive-thru barn

The power loader

Fig. 148. Modern ways of handling manure; each designed to attain (1) expediency, (2) efficiency of labor, and (3) a minimum loss of nutrients. (Drawings by R. F. Johnson)

a fast, labor-saving way of moving it into a spreader. Sheds, feedlots, and storage pits should be designed so as to permit the effective use of such a machine.

Objectionable Features of Manure

Despite the recognized virtues of manure, it does possess the following objectionable features:

1. **It may propagate insects.**—Unless precautions are taken, often manure is the preferred breeding place for flies and other insects. It is noteworthy, however, that comparatively few house flies are reared in cow manure.

2. **It may spread diseases and parasites.**—Where animals are allowed to come in contact with their own excrement there is always danger of infections from diseases and parasites.

3. **It may produce undesirable odors.**—Where manure is stored improperly, there may be a nuisance from odors.

4. **It may scatter weed seeds.**—Even when fermented, manure usually contains a certain quantity of viable weed seeds which may be scattered over the land.

MANAGEMENT OF SUB-HUMID, HUMID, AND IRRIGATED PASTURES

Many good pastures have been established only to be lost through careless management. Good pasture management in the sub-humid, humid, and irrigated areas involves the following practices (The management of arid and semi-arid pastures is covered in Chapter XI of this book):

1. **Controlled grazing.**—Nothing contributes more to good pasture management than controlled grazing. At its best, it embraces the following:

(1) **Protection of first year seedings.**—First year seeding should be grazed lightly or not at all in order that they may get a good start in life. Where practical, instead of grazing, it is preferable to mow a new first year seeding about 3 inches above the ground and to utilize it as hay or silage, provided there is sufficient growth to so justify.

(2) **Rotation or alternate grazing.**—Rotation or alternate grazing is accomplished by dividing a pasture into fields (usually 2 to 4) of approximately equal size, so

that one field can be grazed while the others are allowed to make new growth. This results in increased pasture yields, more uniform grazing, and higher quality forage.

Generally speaking, rotation or alternate grazing is (1) more practical and profitable on rotation and supplemental pastures than on permanent pastures, (2) more productive with high-producing dairy cows than with other farm animals, and (3) more beneficial where parasite infestations are heavy—as is usually the case with sheep—than where little or no parasitic problems are involved.

(3) **Shifting the location of salt, shade and water.**—Where portable salt containers are used, more uniform grazing and scattering of the droppings may be obtained simply by the practice of shifting the location of the salt to the less grazed areas of the pasture. Where possible and practical, the shade and the water should be shifted likewise.

(4) **Deferred spring grazing.**—Allow 6 to 8 inches of growth before turning out to pasture in the spring, thus giving grass a needed start. Anyway, the early spring growth of pastures is high in moisture and washy.

(5) **Avoiding close late fall grazing.**—Pastures that are closely grazed late in the fall start late in the spring. With most pastures, 3 to 5 inches of growth should be left for winter cover.

(6) **Avoiding overgrazing.**—Never graze more closely than 2 to 3 inches during the pasture season. Continued close grazing reduces the yield, weakens the plants, allows weeds to invade and increases soil erosion. The use of temporary and supplemental pastures, such as Sudan, may "spell off" regular pastures through seasons of drought and other pasture shortages and thus alleviate overgrazing.

(7) **Avoiding undergrazing.**—Undergrazing seeded pastures should also be avoided, because (a) mature forage is unpalatable and of low nutritive value, (b) tall-growing grasses may drive out such low-growing plants as white

clover due to shading, and (c) weeds, brush and coarse grasses are more apt to gain a foothold when the pasture is grazed insufficiently. It is a good rule, therefore, to graze the pasture fairly close at least once each year.

2. **Clipping pastures and controlling weeds.**—Pastures should be clipped at such intervals as necessary to control weeds (and brush) and to get rid of uneaten clumps and other unpalatable coarse growth left after incomplete grazing. Pastures

Fig. 149. Clipping to control weeds and brush increases yields and improves quality of pastures. (Drawing by R. F. Johnson)

that are grazed continuously may be clipped at or just preceding the usual haymaking time; rotated pastures may be clipped at the close of the grazing period. Weeds and brush may also be controlled by chemicals, by burning, etc.

3. **Topdressing.**—Like animals, for best results grasses and legumes must be fed properly throughout a lifetime. It is not sufficient that they be fertilized (and limed if necessary) at or

Fig. 150. In most areas, it is desirable and profitable to topdress pastures with fertilizer annually, and at less frequent intervals with reinforced manure and lime. (Drawing by R. F. Johnson)

prior to seeding time. In addition, in most areas it is desirable and profitable to topdress pastures with fertilizer annually, and, at less frequent intervals, with reinforced manure and lime (lime to maintain a pH of about 6.5). Such treatments should be based on soil tests, and are usually applied in the spring or fall.

4. **Scattering droppings.**—The droppings should be scattered at the end of each grazing season in order to prevent animals from leaving ungrazed clumps and to help them fertilize a larger area. This can best be done by the use of a brush harrow or chain harrow.

5. **Grazing by more than one class of animals.**—Grazing by two or more classes of animals makes for more uniform pasture

Fig. 151. At the end of each grazing season, it is recommended that the droppings be scattered by the use of a harrow. (Drawing by R. F. Johnson)

utilization and less weeds and parasites, provided the area is not overstocked. Different kinds of livestock have different habits of grazing; they show preference for different plants and graze to different heights.

6. **Irrigating where practical and feasible.**—Where irrigation is practical and feasible, it alleviates the necessity of depend· ing on the weather.

Extending the Grazing Season

In the South, year-round grazing is a reality on many a successful farm. By careful planning, and by selecting the proper combination of crops, other areas can approach this desired goal.

In addition to lengthening the grazing season through the selection of species, earlier spring pastures can be secured by avoiding grazing too late in the fall and by the application of a nitrogen fertilizer in the fall or early spring. Nitrogen fertilizers will often stimulate the growth of grass so that it will be ready for grazing ten days to two weeks earlier than unfertilized areas.

QUESTIONS FOR STUDY AND DISCUSSION

1. By what method and at what age and season would you dehorn cattle in your area? Give reasons for your answers.
2. By what method and at what age and season would you castrate cattle in your area? Give reasons for your answers.
3. Are there any circumstances under which you would recommend that heifers be spayed? Justify your answer.
4. Under your conditions, what method of marking or identifying cattle would you select? Justify your selection and tell how you would apply this method.
5. What type of cattle bedding is commonly used on your farm or ranch (or on a farm or ranch with which you are familiar)? Would some other type of bedding be more practical? If so, why?
6. For your farm or ranch (or one with which you are familiar) is it preferable and practical to apply manure to the land, or should commercial fertilizers be used instead?
7. How would you improve upon the current pasture management practices followed on a farm or ranch with which you are familiar?

SELECTED REFERENCES

Title of Publication	Author(s)	Publisher
Beef Cattle	R. R. Snapp	John Wiley & Sons, New York, 1952.
Dehorning, Castrating, Branding, and Marking Beef Cattle	Farmer's Bul. 1600	U. S. Department of Agriculture, Washington 25, D. C.
Problems and Practices of American Cattlemen	M. E. Ensminger M. W. Galgan W. L. Slocum	Wash. Agri. Expt. Sta. Bul. 562, Washington State University, Pullman, Wash. 1955.

CHAPTER XI

RANGE CATTLE MANAGEMENT

Contents   Page

Because of the magnitude of the range beef cattle industry
and the fact that it is a highly specialized type of operation, considerable space will be given to the range area and the care and
management of cattle in the range method.

THE WESTERN RANGE

The range area of the United States, as used herein, com-
prises parts or all of seventeen states west of an irregular line

461

extending south through the Dakotas, Nebraska, Kansas, Oklahoma, and Texas. The total land area of these states approxi-
mates 1,160,000,000 acres, of which about 765 million acres are
used for grazing—including about 65 million acres of improved
pasture and 700 million acres of range land. Thus, the range area
alone represents 37 per cent of the total land area and two-thirds
of the total grazing lands of continental United States. A considerable portion of the range area of the West is publicly owned
and unenclosed (See Fig. 152). Its chief economic value is in
terms of commercial cattle and sheep production.

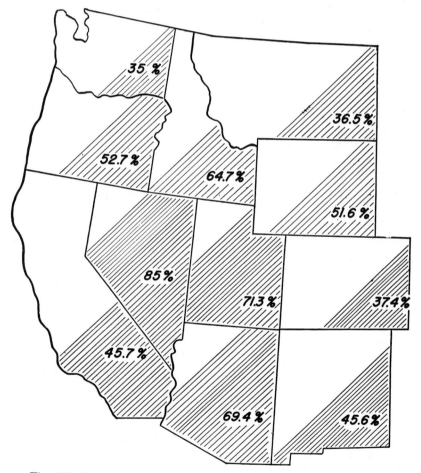

Fig. 152. A map showing the eleven western states and the proportion
of land in each of these states that is owned by the U.S. Government

The carrying capacity of much of the western range is low, and little of it provides year-long grazing. Moreover, variation in vegetative types, climate, and topography in the range country is accompanied by great diversity in the seasonal use made of it. As a result, range lands are usually grazed during different parts of the year, and the herds and flocks migrate with the season, moving to the mountains and higher elevations in summer and returning to the lower ranges in winter.

Geographical Divisions of the Range

Various geographical divisions are assumed in referring to the western range area. Sometimes reference is made to the seventeen range states, whereas at other times this larger division is broken down, chiefly on the basis of topography, into: (1) the Great Plains area (the six states of North Dakota, South Dakota, Nebraska, Kansas, Oklahoma, and Texas) and (2) the eleven Western states (Arizona, California, Colorado, Idaho, Montana, Nevada, New Mexico, Oregon, Utah, Washington, and Wyoming).

In addition to these major and commonly referred to geographical divisions, there are numerous other groupings. These are of importance to the cattleman in that they affect the type of management and, to some extent, the kind of animals kept.

Wild Animals of the Range

While stockmen were expanding to the West, they had to compete for forage with great herds of wild grazing animals, the most numerous of which were buffalo, wild horses, and elk. Contrary to many present-day opinions, these animals were so numerous as to be a major factor in the utilization of the available forage. For example, it has been estimated by those competent to judge, that there were 15 million buffalo in the West in 1864 and that the combined number of buffalo, wild horses, and elk in 1873 amounted to not less than 100 million. It is reasonable to assume, therefore, that the forage consumed annually by wild animals exceeded the amount utilized by the cattle and sheep grazed on these same ranges today. Except for the heavy and destructive grazing which occurred in the vicinity of strategic watering places and near salt licks, these wild animals alone were not particularly destructive to the virgin vegetation, primarily because their normal seasonal migrations permitted recovery of

Fig. 153. Herd of elk at feed. It has been estimated by those competent to judge that the combined number of buffalo, wild horses, and elk on
the western ranges in 1873 amounted to not less than 100 million. (Courtesy,
U. S. Forest Service)

the range. But when cattle and sheep were added, overgrazing
and range deterioration were inevitable.

History of the Range Cattle Industry

Animals of Spanish extraction served as sturdy foundation
stock for the great cattle herds which were eventually to popu-
late the western range. Although cattle have grazed intermittent-
ly on the southern plains of the United States since 1540, at
which time they were introduced by Coronado, the period of continuous grazing accompanied the establishment of several Jesuit
missions in Arizona, New Mexico, and Texas in the period from
1670 to 1690.

The growth of the industrial East and the subsequent development and extension of the railroads provided the necessary
stimulus for further expansion of the range cattle industry. The
grass supply of the vast ranges seemed unlimited, and the region
was regarded as a permanent paradise for cattle. About 1880, the
lure of the grass bonanza fired the imagination of investors, big
and little. Cowboys, lawyers, farmers, merchants, laborers, and
bankers—many of them English and Scotch investors in great
companies—rushed in to seek their fortunes. The number of
cattle increased rapidly, and soon the range was overstocked.

Regulations were few, and the guiding philosophy was "to get what you can while the getting is good, and let the devil take the hindmost."

Then, suddenly, it became apparent that greed had taken its toll. The supply of tall grass was exhausted. Even more tragic, the winter of 1886-87 was unusually severe, and few owners had made provisions for winter feed. Cattle perished by the thousands. In some herds, 85 per cent of the animals starved. But this was not all! The prolonged drought of 1886-95 brought further losses to the cattle companies, and the inroads of the homesteaders on the range and the growth of the range sheep industry contributed other difficulties. These circumstances marked the beginning of the end of the large cattle companies, the gradual growth of smaller operators, and increased attention to management.

Types of Range Vegetation[1]

Cattlemen and students alike—whether they reside in the East, West, North, or South—should be well informed concerning range grasslands, the very foundation of the range livestock industry. This is so because this vast area, comprising 37 per cent of the total land area and two-thirds of the total grazing lands of the United States, is one of the greatest cattle countries in the world and a potential competitor of every American cattle producer. Since cattle and sheep compete successfully with each other in utilizing most range forages, both classes of animals necessarily will be mentioned in the discussion which follows relative to types and uses of range vegetation.

Chiefly because of climate, topography, and soil, the character and composition of native range vegetation is quite variable. Ten broad types of vegetation native to the western ranges of the United States are discussed in this chapter.

TALL-GRASS TYPE:

It is estimated that about 20 million acres of tall-grass range remain, most of which is in the eastern Great Plains region, in a rainfall area varying from 20 to 40 inches. Although differing

---

[1]In the preparation of this section, including the sub-sections relative to each of the ten types of range vegetation, the author had the benefit of the authoritative review and suggestions of Mr. Joseph F. Pechanec, Superintendent, Southeastern Forest Experiment Station, U. S. Forest Service, Asheville, N. C.

with the soil, topography, and rainfall, the dominant native tall-grass species include the bluestem (big and little), Indiangrass, switchgrass, side oats grama, and slough grass. Such famous

Fig. 154. Steers on tall-grass type range in the famous Flint Hills area of Kansas.

grazing areas as the Flint Hills of Kansas, the Osage Pastures of Oklahoma, and the Sand Hills of Nebraska belong to the tall-grass type of vegetation. For the most part, this type of range is utilized by cattle, although sheep do graze some of it. Each fall, thousands of fat cattle are marketed after being fattened on tall-grass vegetation without a grain supplement. The carrying capacity of these ranges is very high.

SHORT-GRASS TYPE:

The short-grass range represents the largest and most important grassland type in the United States, embracing an area of approximately 280 million acres. This extends from the Texas Panhandle to the Canadian border and from the foothills of the Rocky Mountains eastward midway into the Dakotas. The common grasses of this area include the grama grasses, buffalograss, and western wheatgrass, all of which are well adapted to making their growth during the time of favorable moisture conditions in the late spring and early summer. Although they become bleached and cured on the stalk, because of the small amount of leaching in the fall and winter months, these plants retain sufficient nutrients to furnish valuable winter grazing. Because the forages in

Fig. 155. Short-grass type range in Montana. Cow-and-calf operations predominate throughout this area, which represents the largest and most important grass land type in the U. S. (Courtesy, U. S. Forest Service)

the short-grass area are dry during much of the year and droughts are rather frequent, cow-and-calf operations predominate in the cattle industry of the area; and most of the calves and older steers are finished in Corn Belt feed lots or in irrigated valleys prior to slaughter. The smaller fine-wool breeds of sheep are also most numerous, and most of the lambs go the feeder route.

SEMIDESERT-GRASS TYPE:

The semidesert-grass type—which predominates in an area characterized by low rainfall, frequent droughts, and mild winters—embraces about 93 million acres of grasslands in central and southwestern Texas, Arizona, and New Mexico. It provides year-around grazing. Because of great differences in climate and soil, the vegetation is quite variable. The most common grasses are grama, curly-mesquite, and black grama. Scattered among the more or less sparse grasses are many scraggly shrubs, dwarf trees, yuccas, and cacti. Some of these—especially saltbush, mesquite, ratany, and scrub oak—are rather palatable and are browsed effectively by goats. For the most part, the semidesert-grass area is utilized by commercial cattle as a cow-and-calf proposition. But bands of breeding sheep are found throughout the area. Both sheep and goats are common in southwestern

Fig. 156. Semidesert-grass type range in New Mexico, showing dry cows owned by New Mexico State University on excellent grama grass. Generally this type of range provides year-around grazing for commercial cow-and-calf enterprises, although some of it is utilized by sheep and goats. (Courtesy, U. S. Forest Service)

Texas. The sheep of this area are kept primarily for wool production, and production of feeder lambs is secondary.

PACIFIC BUNCHGRASS TYPE:

The Pacific bunchgrass area embraces about 60 million acres in western Montana, eastern Washington and Oregon, northern and southwestern Idaho, and central California. Much of the original bunchgrass area, including the famous Palouse area of eastern Washington and northern Idaho, is now devoted to the production of wheat and peas. Though well adapted to the dry summers and moist winters of the area, the native tall bunch or tuft-growing grasses of this area—bluebunch wheatgrass, Idaho fescue, Sandberg bluegrass, and California needlegrass—did not withstand overgrazing and have largely been replaced by such annuals as alfileria, bur-clover, and cheatgrass (in the Northwest), and wild oatgrasses (in California). These ranges furnish excellent grazing in the spring and fall months but are too dry for summer use. The Pacific bunchgrass area is best adapted for spring, fall, and winter grazing by cattle and sheep.

SAGEBRUSH-GRASS TYPE:

The sagebrush area, which is the third largest of all range types, embraces between 90 and 100 million acres extending from northern New Mexico and Arizona northwestward into Montana and to the east slope of the Cascades in the Pacific Northwest. This type of vegetation is characteristic of low rainfall areas where most of the meager precipitation occurs during the winter and spring seasons. Interspersed among the ever-present sagebrush, of which there are several kinds, are many species of native grasses among which are bluebunch and western wheatgrasses, needle-and-thread, Indian ricegrass, Sandberg bluegrass, and numerous species of weeds. The sagebrush, which varies

Fig. 157. Sagebrush-grass type range in Idaho, showing big sagebrush with excellent understory of bluebunch wheatgrass, bluegrass, and palatable perennial weeds. Generally, this type of range is used for early spring and late fall grazing for cattle and sheep. (Courtesy, U. S. Forest Service)

from 2 to 7 feet in height, provides little forage except when winter snows blanket the grasses. For the most part, the sagebrush type of vegetation is used for early spring and late fall grazing for cattle and sheep. It furnishes interim pasture until more distant summer and winter grazing areas may be used. In recent years, studies have shown that the carrying capacity of sagebrush areas may be increased by destruction of the sagebrush, which encourages greater growth of the grasses.

SALT-DESERT-SHRUB TYPE:

About 40 million acres in central Nevada, Utah, southwestern Wyoming, western Colorado, and southern Idaho are covered with a mixture of low shrubs and scattered grasses. The common browse species of the area are shadscale, saltbrush, black sagebrush, winterfat, rabbit-brush, greasewood, spiny hop-sage, and horsebrush; and the rather sparse grass species include blue grama, sand dropseed, galleta, and Indian ricegrass. Because there is not any dependable source of water and because of the high temperature and dryness during the summer months, the use of much of this area by cattle and sheep is restricted to the winter months when there is snow. Other areas cannot be grazed because of the high alkali content of the soil.

SOUTHERN-DESERT-SHRUB TYPE:

Approximately 50 million acres, located chiefly in southeastern California, southern Nevada, and southwestern Arizona, are classed as southern-desert-shrub vegetation. The common shrubs are the creosotebush and different kinds of cacti. Normally, the scant rainfall, extremely high temperatures and sparse vegetation of this area make it rather poor grazing for cattle or sheep. However, when moisture conditions are favorable, there is growth of such annuals as alfileria, Indian-wheat, burclover, black grama, tobosa, dropseed, and six weeks fescue. When forage and water are available, nearby ranchers make use of the southern-desert-shrub area, primarily for winter grazing, although it is used for spring and fall grazing and in a few cases throughout the year.

PINYON-JUNIPER TYPE:

The pinyon-juniper type of vegetation forms the transition zone from the shrub and grass areas of the lower elevations to the forests of the mountains. The 76 million acres in this general type area extend all the way from southwest Texas to south central Oregon. As the name would indicate, pinyon and juniper trees are common to the area. These scattered trees range in height from 20 feet to 40 feet, and interspersed among them are such low-growing shrubs as sagebrush, bitterbrush, mountain-mahogany and cliff-rose, and grasses like the gramas, bluebunch and bluestem wheat-grass, and galleta. For the most part, this area is used for spring and fall grazing by cattle and sheep; but in the Southwest, where the forage cures on the ground and retains much of its nutritive value through the winter, year-long grazing is prevalent.

Fig. 158. Pinyon-Juniper type range in Arizona, showing young juniper trees encroaching on the area. For the most part, this type of range is used for spring and fall grazing by cattle and sheep; although in the Southwest year-long grazing is prevalent. (Courtesy, U. S. Forest Service.)

WOODLAND-CHAPARRAL TYPE:

This type of vegetation is characteristic of parts of California and Arizona. It varies all the way from an open forest of park-like oak and other hardwood trees with an undergrowth of herbaceous plants and shrubs to dense "chaparral" thickets of no value to animals. Alfileria, slender oat-grass, and bur-clover have been introduced in the more open areas. Though somewhat restricted, woodland-chaparral is used for fall, winter, and spring grazing by cattle and sheep.

OPEN FOREST TYPE:

The 130 million acres of open forests, found scattered in practically all the mountain ranges, constitute the second largest range-type vegetation. This is the summer range of the West, which provides grazing for large numbers of cattle, sheep, and big game. Many grass-fat cattle and lambs are sent to market directly off these cool, lush, high-altitude ranges. For the most part, the tree growth common to the area consists of pine, fir, and spruce; and the grasses include blue grama, fescues, blue-

Fig. 159. Open forest type range in ponderosa pine timber of Oregon. (Courtesy, U. S. Forest Service)

stem, wheatgrasses, timothy, bluegrasses, sedges, and many others. More than half of these mountain ranges are federally owned as national forest lands. In addition to serving as valuable grazing areas, the open forests are important for lumbering and recreational purposes.

Grazing Publicly Owned Lands

The ownership of U. S. land is summarized in Table 31.

About 89 per cent of the federal holdings are located in the eleven western states of Arizona, California, Colorado, Idaho, Montana, Nevada, New Mexico, Oregon, Utah, Washington and Wyoming. Also it is noteworthy that federal lands comprise 48 per cent of the total land area of these eleven states (see Fig. 152).

Much of the publicly owned land is effectively used by private farmers and ranchers for livestock production under grazing permit or lease systems. For example, each year about two-thirds of the federal land is grazed some part of the year by approximately 20 million head of livestock.

AGENCIES ADMINISTERING PUBLIC LANDS:

Because much of the grazing land that ranchers rely upon to maintain their cattle and sheep enterprises is built up into

TABLE 31

OWNERSHIP OF U. S. LAND

Ownership	Acreage	Percentage of Total
	(million acres)	(%)
1. Private ownership	1,342	70.5
2. Indian land	57	3.0
3. Public ownership	495	26.0
(1) Federal	398	20.9
(2) State and local governments	97	5.1
4. Roads and unaccounted for areas	10	.5

operating units by leasing or by obtaining use permits from several federal and state agencies, private corporations, and individuals, it is imperative that the owner have a working knowledge of the most important of these agencies. Some range operators are placed in the position of using range rented from as many as six landlords; either private, state, and/or federal.

The bulk of federal land is administered by the following six agencies: the Bureau of Land Management, the U. S. Forest Service, the Bureau of Indian Affairs, the Department of Defense, the National Park Service, and the Bureau of Reclamation. The most important federal lands from the standpoint of grazing permits and utilization of grazing areas by animals are administered by the first three of these agencies.

1. **Bureau of Land Management.**—Forty-four per cent of the present public domain is administered by the Bureau of Land Management of the Department of the Interior. From the standpoint of the stockman, the most important function of the Bureau of Land Management is its administration of the grazing districts established under the Taylor Grazing Act of 1934 and of the unreserved public land situated outside of these districts which are subject to grazing lease under Section 15 of the Act. This federal act and its amendments authorize the withdrawal[1] of public domain from homestead entry and its organization into grazing districts administered by the Department of the Interior. Also, this legislation, as amended, allows the Bureau of Land Management to administer state and privately-owned lands under a cooperative arrangement.

[1] On May 28, 1954, a bill was signed by President Eisenhower lifting the 142 million acre limitation on public domain lands that can be included in Taylor Grazing Act districts.

In 1956, the Bureau of Land Management had 59 grazing districts, operating in the 10 western states and totaling 158.5 million acres of public lands. In these districts, 18,758 operators were granted privileges to graze 8,590,276 head of livestock for an average of about 4½ months each year. These operators paid the United States, as grazing fees for this range use, a total of $2,443,747. In addition to this livestock use, in 1956 the grazing districts supported, for approximately 5 months of the year, an estimated 957,404 big game animals, most of which were deer.

In addition to, and outside of, the grazing districts, in 1956 the Bureau of Land Management supervised 17.7 million acres of public domain in the Western States, most of which was leased to 9,517 stockmen for 2,699,234 head of livestock for about 1¾ months. These operators paid rentals in the amount of $358,509 for the use of these lands.

Each grazing district is administered by a range manager, who is a technically trained employee of the Bureau of Land Management. He is responsible to the state bureau office for the proper use, management, and welfare of the range resources of his district. In turn, the state office is responsible to an area office, and the area office to the director's office in Washington, D. C.

In each of the grazing districts, local groups of stockmen elected by the users serve in an advisory capacity in allocating grazing privileges and supervising details of administration.

Grazing privileges are allocated to individual operators, associations and corporations on the basis of (1) priority of use, (2) ownership or control of base property dependent on grazing district land for forage during certain seasons of the year, or control of permanent water needed to graze district land, (3) proximity of home ranch to the grazing district, and (4) adequate property to supply the feed needed along with grazing privileges, to maintain throughout the year the livestock permitted on public range. All of these lands are subject to classification and disposal under Sections 7 and 14 of the Taylor Grazing Act, for any higher use or other appropriate purpose. Grazing privileges may, therefore, be cancelled whenever such lands are determined to be more suitable for other purposes.

A nominal grazing fee is charged for grazing privileges. In 1956, this charge was equivalent to 15 cents per animal unit month; or 15 cents per cow month, 30 cents per horse month, and 3 cents per sheep or goat month.

The Bureau of Land Management has been responsible for many changes, not all of which have been popular. Some stockmen complain about the loss of their ranges; others tell of increased costs; and there are those who resent government controls, and, above all, the confusion which results from dealing with several agencies. Without doubt, many of these criticisms are justified, and some errors in administration should be rectified; but those who would be fair are agreed that the ranges as a whole have improved under the supervision of the Bureau of Land Management and that further improvements are in the offing.

2. **U. S. Forest Service.**—About 62 million acres of the national forests are used for grazing under a system of permits issued to local farmers and ranchers by the Forest Service of the U. S. Department of Agriculture. In 1956, about 2,740,000 mature sheep and goats and 1,135,000 mature cattle and horses (mostly cattle), owned by 19,860 paid permit operators, were grazed on national forests for some part of the year. In addition, there were many calves and lambs for which no fee is charged and additional stock that were grazed under free permits to local settlers. This made an estimated total of 7⅓ million domestic animals grazed on the national forest ranges in the year 1956.

The Forest Service issues ten-year term permits to stockmen who hold preferences and annual permits to those who hold temporary use. Among other things, the permit prescribes the boundaries of the range which they may use, the maximum number of animals allowed, and the season when grazing is permitted.

Preferences may be acquired through prior use, through a grant, or through purchase of land or livestock, or both, of a user who already holds a preference.

The requisites in order to qualify for a permit are:

1. **Ownership.**—The ownership of both the livestock and commensurate ranch property.

2. **Dependency.**—The need for forest range in order to round out an operation to obtain proper and practical use of commensurate property.

3. **Commensurability.**—The ability of the land to support livestock during the period when not on forest land.

A grazing preference is not a property right. Rather, it is approved for the exclusive use and benefit of a person to whom allowed. Preferences or permits may be revoked in whole or in part for a clearly established violation of the terms of the permit, the regulations upon which it is based, or the instructions of forest officers issued thereunder.

A ranger administers the grazing use on each National Forest Ranger District. Several districts (usually 3 to 6 or more) comprise a national forest. A forest supervisor, with his staff, administers the national forest. Several national forests, under the direction of a regional forester and staff, comprise a forest region. The chief administers the Forest Service from Washington, D. C., under the supervision of the Secretary of Agriculture.

As is true in the administration of Taylor grazing districts, local farmers and ranchers act in an advisory capacity in the allocation of grazing privileges and in details of administration of the national forests. About 750 such livestock associations and advisory boards are recognized and in operation.

Forest Service grazing fees are based on a formula which takes into account livestock prices over the past ten years, the quality of forage on the allotment, and the cost of ranch operation. In 1956, average charges were 35 cents per head per month for mature cattle and 8¾ cents for sheep.

Although shortcomings exist in the management of the national forests, it is generally agreed that these ranges have been vastly improved under the administration of the Forest Service. Many of them now approach the quality that existed in their virgin state. Perhaps the most heated arguments between stockmen and the Forest Service arise over the relative importance attached to the multiple use of big game and other wildlife, recreation, etc. For example, it was estimated that in 1956 there were 2,680,000 big game animals (85 per cent of which were deer) in the national forests. As would be expected, these wild animals compete with domestic animals for use of the range, thus creating a most difficult problem.

3. **Bureau of Indian Affairs.**—Indian lands, comprising nearly 57 million acres, are really not public lands. But 55 million acres of these lands are held in trust for the benefit or use of the Indians and are merely administered by the Bureau of Indian Affairs of the Department of the Interior. Because over 80 per cent of Indian lands are in the range area of the West, they are

suited primarily to livestock. Thus, it is noteworthy that the sale of livestock and animal by-products regularly account for two-thirds of the total Indian agricultural income. Although the Indians themselves own most of the stock grazed on these lands, animals owned by non-Indians utilize one-fourth of the 44 million acres of Indian lands devoted to grazing. Provision for such use is handled under lease agreement jointly approved by the Indian owners and the Bureau of Indian Affairs.

Many of the Indian lands have suffered serious vegetative depletion, but a concerted effort is now being made to decrease livestock numbers in keeping with available feed supplies and to improve the quality of animals produced. It is reported, however, that overstocking continues to be a difficult problem on the Navajo, Hopi, and Papago Reservations.

4. **State and local government-owned lands.**—Of the national total of 1,020,000,000 acres of pasture and grazing land, 65 million acres are owned by state and local governments. For the most part, the management of such areas may be considered diverse and confused, each state and local government having established different regulations relative to the lands under its ownership. In general, however, such lands are operated on a stipulated lease arrangement. On many such areas, range depletion has been severe.

5. **Railroad-owned lands.**—Recognizing that the main deterrent to rapid settlement and development of the West was the lack of adequate transportation facilities, the federal government very early encouraged the construction and westward extension of the railroads by means of large grants of land. It was intended that the railroads should sell or otherwise utilize these lands in financing their costs of construction. These initial grants, totaling 94,149,866 acres, consisted of alternate sections extending in a checkerboard fashion for a distance of from 10 to 40 miles on each side of the right of way. Today, less than 20 million acres of these lands are held by railroads. Many of these holdings are leased to stockmen; but because of inconvenience, past abuses, or other reasons, some of these lands are considered worthless for grazing. In general, railroad lease agreements do not restrict the number of stock to be grazed or the season during which the land may be so used.

Seasonal Use of the Ranges

A prime requisite of successful range management for both cattle and sheep is that there shall be as nearly year-around grazing as possible and that both the animals and the range shall thrive. In some areas, especially in the southwestern Great Plains region, these conditions are met without necessitating extensive

SEASONAL USE OF WESTERN RANGE, 1947

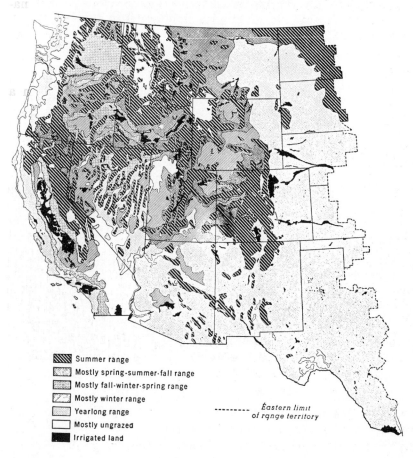

Summer range
Mostly spring-summer-fall range
Mostly fall-winter-spring range
Mostly winter range
Yearlong range   ‒‒‒‒‒‒‒‒   Eastern limit
Mostly ungrazed   of range territory
Irrigated land

BUREAU OF AGRICULTURAL ECONOMICS IN COOPERATION WITH THE U S FOREST SERVICE

Fig. 160. Seasonal use of the western range. In general, the most desirable management, both from the standpoint of animals and vegetation, consists of the proper seasonal use of the range. (Courtesy, USDA)

migration of animals. The winter climate is mild, and the native forages cure well on the stalk, thus providing nutritious dry feed at times when green vegetation is not available. Generally speaking, however, most of the cattle and sheep from such areas are marketed via the feeder route rather than as grass-fat slaughter animals.

In general, the most desirable management, both from the standpoint of the animals and the vegetation, consists of the proper seasonal use of the range. Although there is wide variety in the customs and requirements for seasonal use of the range—because of the spread in climate, topography, and vegetative types included in the vast expanse of range country—seasonal-use ranges are usually placed in four major classes: (1) spring-fall, (2) winter, (3) spring-fall-winter, and (4) summer.

Because a range band of sheep can be moved and herded on unenclosed areas with greater ease than a herd of cattle and because investigations in range livestock management have been

Fig. 161. Trailing cattle from a winter range in Utah. Calves are from one day to several weeks of age. (Courtesy, U. S. Forest Service)

conducted more extensively with sheep, greater seasonal use of ranges is made with sheep. On the other hand, the more progressive cattlemen are finding ways and means of adopting many of the same methods.

Despite the values of year-long grazing, it is recognized that the prevalence of severe winters in some parts of the West precludes winter grazing except to a limited degree, and stock must be fed during at least a part of the winter season. Where these conditions prevail, cattle and sheep are usually wintered in the irrigated valleys, close to the feed supply, especially a supply of alfalfa or meadow hay.

Some pertinent points in determining the proper season of use of the range follow:

1. **Elevation.**—Generally speaking, vegetative development is delayed 10 to 15 days by each 1,000 feet increase in elevation. Also, severe storms occur later in the spring and earlier in the fall at higher altitudes than at low, desert locations.

2. **Availability of water.**—Certain desert areas are so poorly watered that only the occurrence of winter snows makes their use practical.

3. **Early forage "washy."**—Early spring forage is extremely "washy," and may be incapable of supporting stock.

4. **Soil tramping.**—Soil tramping may be serious in early spring.

5. **Poisonous plants grow early.**—Most poisonous plants are very early growers and cause their greatest damage when animals are turned out too early. Larkspur, which affects cattle, and death camas, which affects sheep, are two examples. Poisoning losses from these two plants are usually negligible if stock are detained until the best forage plants have made suitable growth.

6. **Winter range should be saved.**—If stock are allowed to remain on winter ranges too long after spring growth begins, the next winter's feed will be reduced, because the forage produced on these ranges grows mainly during spring and early summer.

SPRING-FALL RANGE:

The foothills and plateaus, lying between the plains or desert sections and mountains, furnish desirable spring and fall grazing for both cattle and sheep. Areas of this type are, therefore, commonly referred to as spring and fall range. The sagebrush-grass type is the leading range vegetation used for spring and fall range. Compared with the vegetation of the plains and desert regions, that growing on the foothills and plateaus in season is more luxuriant and succulent and better suited to milk production and fattening. Although spring and fall ranges are accessible most of the year—because such areas are not too extensive— usually they are not grazed for a very extended period. Some-

Fig. 162. Cattle on rich fall range in Oregon. (Courtesy, Bureau of Land Management, Department of the Interior)

times fall grazing for the herd or flock is provided through using owned or leased stubble fields and meadow aftermath.

WINTER RANGE:

Areas adapted to year-long grazing possess desirable climatic and vegetative conditions for winter range. Many such areas are used only during the winter season because of their proximity to more desirable spring-fall and summer ranges. Desert areas, such as the salt-desert-shrub type, which would otherwise be suited to year-long grazing, must be restricted to use as winter range. This is due to the absence of any reliable water supply except that secured from the snow or rain during the winter months. In some sections, winter wheat is used for late fall and winter grazing.

SPRING-FALL-WINTER RANGE:

In general, spring-fall-winter-type ranges are adapted to year-around grazing. But because of their proximity to more lush mountain ranges, they are not used during the summer months.

Fig. 163. Cattle on winter range in New Mexico. (Courtesy, U. S. Forest Service)

On typical spring-fall-winter ranges, the annual grass species dry up during the summer months.

SUMMER RANGE:

The most desirable summer ranges are located in the cooler and higher altitudes of the mountains where the vegetation is lush, palatable, and nutritious during the three to six summer months. Usually there is a bountiful supply of water. Much of this range is of the open-forest type on national forest lands, where the average grazing period for cattle is 5.6 months and for sheep 3.1 months. Although summer range is usually very rugged, the conditions are generally ideal for fattening, so that year after year it is the most consistent type of range area for the production of grass-fat cattle and lambs. Sheep are sometimes trailed or shipped a distance of 200 miles in order to have access to a desirable summer range, but cattle are usually not moved so far. These summer ranges supplement the lower spring, fall, and winter ranges (either publicly or privately owned). Thus they hold a key position in the year-long operations of many livestock producers. Sometimes seeded grass-legumes or irrigated pastures are used for summer grazing instead of mountain ranges.

THE RANGE CATTLE HERD

The range herd may be owned by an individual, a cattle company, or a corporation. Usually the ranch headquarters consists of

Fig. 164. A summer range for cattle in the Sawtooth National Forest of Idaho. (Courtesy, U. S. Forest Service)

a ranch-type house, bunk house, sheds, corrals, and a water supply and there is ownership of sufficient adjacent land for the production of winter forage and a limited amount of grain. Additional and more distant range land is either owned or leased.

Size of Herd and Carrying Capacity

Range herds vary in size from about a hundred head up to several thousands. In general, the most important single criterion in determining the size of herd is the number of aimals that the unit will support each season over a period of years without injury to the range. When the range is stocked more heavily than its true grazing capacity, usually three conditions become evident: (1) The animals fail to thrive as they should; (2) the vegetation gets thinner and of less desirable species; and (3) erosion and soil losses occur. Practical observations and controlled experiments would indicate that somewhere between 20 and 30 per cent of the palatable growth of the more important forage species should be left ungrazed each year. Additional considerations in arriving at the size of herd and carrying capacity are: (1) available reserve feed supply for drought and winter feeding, (2) the long-range economic conditions, and (3) the topography, water supply, and poisonous plants of the area.

Conservative Stocking

The key to successful long-term operation of range land lies in a good estimate of the grazing capacity of the individual units. Too light stocking wastes forage, while too heavy stocking results in a change of forage plant cover from an abundance of valuable forage plants to an abundance of worthless plants.

Of course, the stocking rate for any given unit may vary widely from year to year, depending on the forage production as affected by weather and other factors. For this reason, stocking should either be adjusted to forage yield each year, or set at a constant rate that will assure a sustained yield of the most valuable forage plants (constant stocking at about 25 per cent below average capacity will usually achieve the latter).

Recognition must also be given to the fact that animals do not graze uniformly over a range unit—that certain areas are more attractive to them. Consequently, some areas produce most of the grazed forage, while others may go practically unused. Cattle tend to congregate on fairly level creek bottoms, ridge tops, and around water and shade; whereas sheep, especially if herded, can be moved more uniformly over a unit. But even sheep graze some areas more heavily than others if not herded properly. For the purpose of determining grazing capacity, the key areas—those rather extensive parts of the range which are most heavily grazed—must be given greatest consideration. If preferred or key areas are maintained in good condition, the whole unit will generally remain in good condition. Conversely, if key areas are allowed to deteriorate, the grazing capacity of the whole unit will be endangered.

Grazing capacity determinations are relatively complex and require careful study over a period of several years. They are arrived at most simply and accurately by observing soil conditions and changes in plant cover. If the best plants are being destroyed and soil movement is observed, numbers of animals or season of use should be reduced; conversely, if excessive forage remains at the end of the grazing season, numbers should be slowly increased until a balance is struck.

The following rule of thumb, applied to the more heavily grazed key areas, may be used in arriving at the proper stocking rate: "Use half and save half, and the half you save will grow bigger and bigger." The rule refers to half the weight, which is concentrated at the bottom of the plant, and not to half the height. Thus, when the 50 per cent rule of thumb is applied to bluebunch wheatgrass, a common range plant, it means that approximately 75 per cent of the bunches have been grazed to an average stubble height of about four inches, and the remaining 25 per cent of the plants left relatively ungrazed.

In arriving at grazing capacity determinations, it is generally wise to seek assistance from county agents, soil conservation service technicians, or other trained specialists.

The commonly used terms for describing range condition are: (1) excellent, (2) good, (3) fair, and (4) poor. If the range is covered almost entirely with high value forage plants, it is classified as being in excellent condition. If the best plants are scarce, it is classified as being in poor condition. Good and fair classifications are intermediate. The trend in condition is also important; if the range condition is improving, the trend is upward, and vice versa. Actually, the range condition reflects the kind of management practiced in the past.

The Water Supply

Cattle should always be provided with a dependable and adequate supply of good water. On some ranges, this problem presents a difficult, costly, or even impossible situation. The source or sources of water vary between ranges and areas, with reservoirs or ponds, streams, deep wells, and springs being utilized.

Some cattlemen haul water to the range. Although there is considerable variation in the equipment, the better outfits use the following: (1) a main storage tank that will hold at least one week's supply, (2) a 1,000 gallon tank truck, and (3) galvanized rectangular troughs, approximately 8 feet long and 2 feet wide, with sloping sides so as to permit nesting and easy transportation. On unwatered ranges, hauling can make the difference between grazing and no grazing. Also, hauling helps obtain more uniform use of forage, reduces trailing damage, permits grazing at the most appropriate time, and makes for more animal weight gains. It generally costs $1.00 to $1.50 per animal per month to truck water where hauling distances do not exceed 15 miles for the round trip.

For cattle, the ideal arrangement consists of having sufficient watering places distributed over the range so that the ani-

Fig. 165. A cattle water supply on TO Ranch, Raton, New Mexico. Deep wells and concrete tanks are becoming more common on the western range. (Courtesy, National Cottonseed Products Association, Inc.)

mals never have to travel over two miles to water and even a shorter distance where the topography is rough or broken. Sheep can travel about twice as far to water as cattle. If cattle must travel great distances to water, the amount of walking will use up much of the energy which would otherwise be available for the production of meat or milk. They also will water infrequently and overgraze and tramp out the grass near the water supply.

The Grazing System

Consciously or unconsciously, cattle ranchers follow one of the following grazing systems: (1) deferred grazing, (2) rotation or alternate grazing, or (3) continuous grazing.

DEFERRED GRAZING:

In deferred grazing, the range usually is divided into three to five units. The grazing on at least one unit is deferred each year until after the seed crop has matured. The next year a sec-

Fig. 166. A cattle water hole in New Mexico. (Courtesy, Bureau of Land Management, Department of the Interior)

ond area is deferred and the grazing on the first area is delayed as late as possible to afford opportunity for the young seedlings to become established. By so treating a new unit each year, the entire area is rested, allowed to reseed itself, and grazed in rotation.

ROTATION OR ALTERNATE GRAZING:

Rotation or alternate grazing is that system in which the grazing of areas is alternated at intervals throughout the season. A heavy concentration of animals is placed on a given area for a few weeks, after which all the stock are moved on to another area or areas and are finally returned to the first field when the growth is sufficient to withstand another period of grazing. This system is best adapted to the utilization of cultivated pastures in the irrigated valleys of the West or to the humid regions of the United States. On arid ranges, such heavy grazing for even a short interval is likely to produce erosion or may permanently destroy certain plants.

CONTINUOUS GRAZING:

Perhaps most ranges of the West are grazed more or less continuously, although some rest is given them through the use of seasonal ranges (such as in migrating to summer ranges in the mountains). Where continuous grazing is *moderate*, it is perhaps more suitable and practical than deferred or alternate grazing under the following conditions: (1) when the construction of fences or barriers is very costly, (2) when the important forage species are not dependent upon reseeding for reproduction, and (3) when seasonal ranges are available and used.

Until and unless research studies reveal that rotation grazing is superior, from the standpoint of both stock and vegetation, continuous grazing will be followed most extensively.

Distribution of Animals on the Range

Next to the proper rate of stocking and proper seasonal use, distribution of the animals on the range is the most important feature in range management. Proper distribution of animals is reflected in more even utilization of the forage. This assignment is more difficult with cattle than with sheep, especially on rough or mountainous land. Cattle have more of a tendency to utilize the flatter areas and to congregate around watering places. Better distribution of cattle on the range may be accomplished through: (1) fencing or riding the range (or herding), (2) providing water at short intervals (under ideal conditions, the distance between water in rough country should not exceed one-half mile for cattle; in level country 2 to 2½ miles. Water hauling on the range is increasing), (3) systematically locating salt grounds away from watering areas and salting at the proper intervals and in the right quantities, and (4) building trails into inaccessible parts of the range.

Fig. 167. Showing how systematically locating salt grounds away from watering areas may be used as a means of obtaining better distribution of cattle on the range. (Courtesy, U. S. Forest Service)

Range Riding

In a cattle spread, the range rider is the counterpart of the sheep herder. Riders prevent straying, force better distribution of animals on the range and more even utilization of forage, provide salt, service watering facilities, give minor repairs to fences, herd the animals away from areas infested with poisonous plants, see that "bogged down" animals are removed and cared for, dispose of dead carcasses, administer such assistance as may be required when animals are injured and at calving time, and warn the owner of any unusual parasite or disease problems. The number of cattle cared for by one rider and his saddle and pack animals will vary from 150 to 1,200 head. The number will be determined chiefly by the character of the country and the carrying capacity of the range.

Fencing on the Range

Some fences are essential to the improvement of both cattle and ranges. Cattle fences are less costly than sheep fences. Moreover, cattle are less well adapted to herding methods than sheep. For these reasons, cattle ranges are more frequently fenced than sheep ranges.

Fig. 168. A drift fence on the Uncompahgre National Forest of Colorado's western slope. Drift fences are not intended as enclosures, but serve as barriers to retain animals within a certain area and to prevent drifting into an area where it is not desired that the animals shall travel. (Courtesy, The Record Stockman)

The cattle rancher commonly refers to two types of fences: (1) drift fences and (2) division fences. Drift fences are those that are not intended as enclosures, but which serve as barriers to retain animals within a certain area and to prevent drifting into an area where it is not desired that the animals shall travel. Usually drift fences extend between such natural barriers as steep ridges, ravines, etc. Frequently drift fences are useful for such things as preventing animals from following the snow line back in the spring, avoiding poison infested areas, confining animals to the area owned or leased by the operator, and holding stock during the round-up.

Division fences are those which enclose the boundaries of the range or field. They are usually used in keeping animals on the area owned or leased, in segregating different age and sex groups, and in conducting deferred or alternate systems of grazing.

Breeding Season and Calving Time

The breeding season on the range is usually timed so that the calves will be dropped in the spring of the year with the coming of mild weather and green forage. Quite naturally, therefore, the calendar date of calving will vary in different sections of the United States. It is earlier on the ranges of the Southwest (February to April) and later in the Northwest (April to June).

Some range producers let the bulls run with the cows throughout the year, reasoning that a calf born out of season is better than no calf at all. The vast majority of the better producers, however, prefer to have the calves born in the shortest possible time. They make every effort to get calving over within two to three months.

Winter Feeding Cattle on the Range

Cattle must be given rather close supervision when on the winter range, and usually some supplemental feeding is desirable. Unless they are on fenced range or herded, they are inclined to drift great distances during blizzards and in cold weather. Unlike horses, they seldom learn to paw snow off the ground in search of forage.

Fig. 169. Winter feeding cattle on the range. (Courtesy, U. P. Railroad Company)

In the early days of the range cattle industry, the animals were usually moved to the lower winter ranges and turned loose to get their feed as best they could. There was precious little feeding of supplemental forage or concentrates. If the winter happened to be mild and if a reasonable amount of grass had cured on the stalk, the herd came through in pretty good shape. During an exceedingly cold winter, however, the losses were severe and often disastrous. Today, the practical and successful rancher winter feeds. He generally provides 1 to 2 pounds daily of a protein supplement and has an adequate supply of fodder or hay for those periods when the range is covered with snow. Young animals and cows with calves are more liberally fed than mature animals.

The progressive rancher is also equipped to meet emergency feeding periods, of which droughts are the most common in the West. Concentrates and roughages should be available for such emergencies.

The Round-up

Because of the large territory over which range cattle graze, it is common practice to gather them together at least twice each year, in the spring and again in the fall, for the purpose of carrying out certain routine assignments.

Fig. 170. Cattle round-up on a Nevada ranch. Note animals trailing in from several directions. (Photo by Pennett, Reno, Nevada, through the courtesy of The Western Horseman)

The spring round-up takes place between April and June, the exact time depending upon the earliness of the forage and the time of calving. The objects of this round-up are: (1) to get an accurate count on the stock; (2) to castrate, brand, and vaccinate calves against blackleg; and (3) to separate the breeding animals from the steers and heifers.

The fall round-up, which usually takes place in September and October, is for the purpose of: (1) castrating, branding, and blackleg vaccinating calves born since the spring round-up; (2) culling out and marketing barren, old, or otherwise undesirable breeding stock which it is not desired to winter; and (3) weaning the calves.

QUESTIONS FOR STUDY AND DISCUSSION

1. Why is so much of the range area of the West publicly owned and unenclosed? Is it good or bad to have so much public domain?

2. Do you concur in the policy which permits a sizeable number of wild animals to feed on privately owned land?

3. If you live in the West, classify the range grass of your ranch or area as to (1) type (which of the ten broad types) and (2) dominant native species.

4. What similarities and differences characterize the various agencies administering public lands?

5. Discuss the seasonal use of western ranges.

6. How can you detect if a given range has been overstocked? If overstocking is apparent, how would you rectify the situation?

7. Would you change the grazing system followed on your ranch, or in your area? Justify your answer.

8. Wherein does a modern cattle roundup differ from the roundup portrayed in most western movies?

9. How has the handling of cattle on the western range been mechanized? What further automation and mechanization of the western range can you suggest?

SELECTED REFERENCES

Title of Publication	Author(s)	Publisher
Beef-Cattle Production in the Range Area	Farmers' Bul. 1395	U. S. Department of Agriculture, Washington 25, D. C.
Problems and Practices of American Cattlemen	M. E. Ensminger M. W. Galgan W. L. Slocum	Wash. Agri. Expt. Sta. Bul. 562, Washington State University, Pullman, Wash., 1955.
Hauling Water for Range Cattle	Leaflet No. 419	U. S. Department of Agriculture, Washington 25, D. C.

CHAPTER XII

BUILDINGS AND EQUIPMENT FOR BEEF CATTLE[1]

Contents   Page

The economical production of beef cattle in most sections of
the United States depends largely upon the investment in practical, durable, and convenient buildings and equipment, as well as
upon the care, feeding, and management of the herd. As would

[1]The author acknowledges his indebtedness to the following authorities
who reviewed Chapter XII: Professor June Roberts, Chairman, Department
of Agricultural Engineering, Washington State University, Pullman, Wash.;
Professor J. C. Wooley, Head, Department of Agricultural Engineering,
University of Missouri, Columbia, Mo.; Professor K. B. Huff, Department of
Agricultural Engineering, University of Missouri, Columbia, Mo.; and Professor C. H. Zuroske, Associate Professor, Department of Agricultural Economics, Washington State University, Pullman, Wash.

be expected in a country so large and diverse as the United States, there is wide difference in the systems of beef production. In a broad general way, a major difference in management exists between the farm herd method and the range cattle method. In addition, further management differences exist within each area according to whether the enterprise is commercial or purebred, whether it is a cow-and-calf proposition or is devoted to one of the many methods of growing stockers and feeders or cattle for fattening, or whether it is a combination of two or more of these systems of beef production. Climatic differences also vary, all the way from nearly year-around grazing in the deep South to a long winter-feeding period in the northern part of the United States. Then, too, the size of the herd may vary all the way from a few animals up to an operation involving many thousands of head. Finally, there is the matter of availability of materials and labor and individual preferences.

Except for the classic experiment conducted by the University of Missouri, little experimental work has been done on the basic building requirements of beef cattle.

Brody, of the Missouri station,[1] placed cattle in "climatic chambers," in which the temperature, humidity, and air movements were regulated as desired. The ability of the animals to withstand different temperatures was then determined by studying the respiration rate and body temperature, the feed consumption, and the productivity in growth, milk, beef, etc. Out of these experiments came the following pertinent findings: The most comfortable temperature for Shorthorns was within the range of 30° to 60° F.; for the Brahmans it was 50° to 80° F. (20° higher); and for the Santa Gertrudis (⅝ Shorthorn X ⅜ Brahman) it was intermediate between the ideal temperatures given above. Translated into practicality, the Missouri experiment proved what is generally suspected; namely:

1. That there are breed differences; that Brahman and Santa Gertrudis cattle can tolerate more heat than the European breeds—thus, they are better equipped to withstand tropical and subtropical temperatures.

2. That acclimated European cattle do not need expensive, warm barns—they merely need protection from wind, snow and rain.

---

[1]Brody, Samuel; Mo. Agri. Expt. Sta. Journal Series No. 1607.

3. That more attention needs to be given to providing summer shades and other devices to assure warm weather comfort for cattle.

No standard set of buildings and equipment can be expected to be adapted to all the diverse conditions and systems of beef production. In presenting the discussion and illustrations that follow, it is intended, therefore, that they be considered as guides only. Detailed plans and specifications for buildings and equipment can usually be obtained through the local county agricultural agent, FFA instructor, or lumber dealer, or through writing the college of agriculture in the state.

The right kind of beef cattle buildings and equipment can materially lower the work required to do the job. Although beef cattle normally require a relatively small amount of labor, a great deal can be done to lower costs and shorten the hours of work.

BEEF CATTLE BUILDINGS

Beef cattle are not as sensitive to extremes of temperature—heat and cold—as are dairy cattle or swine. In fact, mature beef animals will withstand extremely cold weather if kept dry. It is not necessary, therefore, that this building requisite be accorded the same degree of attention as certain other requisites of cattle buildings.

It is especially noteworthy that fattening steers, whose bodies generate considerable heat from the digestion and assimilation of their rations, do not need a warm shelter even during the cold winter months. Their chief need is for a dry bed and protection against cold winds, rains, and snow. About the same thing can be said about the sheltering of dry cows and stockers and feeders. Young stock require more protection. A shelter also permits the feeder to do his work in greater comfort. In the deep South and in the Southwest, barns are not necessary for cattle, except on rare occasions.

Beef cattle shelters are of two kinds, natural and artificial. The former includes hills and valleys, timber, and other natural windbreaks. The artificial shelters include those man-made structures (solid fences, stacks, barns, and sheds) designed to protect cattle against the elements—heat, cold, wind, rains, and snows.

It is with beef cattle barns and sheds that this discussion will deal.

Fig. 171. Cattle shelter and equipment on the farm of Ed Reiter, Cascade, Iowa. With fattening cattle, whose bodies generate considerable heat from the digestion and assimilation of their rations, an open shed is best. (Courtesy, The Corn Belt Farm Dailies)

In addition to protecting the animals during severe cold and stormy weather and at winter calving time, these structures should (1) provide a reasonably dry bed for the animals, (2) simplify feeding and management, (3) provide storage for feed and bedding when necessary, (4) protect young calves, and (5) conserve the fertility value of the manure.

Although the discussion describes beef cattle barns and sheds, it must be recognized that on the average general farm which has only a small number of beef cattle the cattle are usually housed in a general-purpose barn or shed or in extensions to other barns rather than in separate and specially designed beef cattle structures.

Beef Cattle Barns

Barns are more substantial structures than sheds and provide more complete protection for stock in the colder areas. In addition to housing the animals, such structures usually provide adequate facilities for all of the roughage and bedding needed during the winter season and for a considerable proportion of the concentrates. Stalls, pens, and storerooms may also be included— additions which are especially important where a breeding herd is to be served. In general, beef cattle barns effect a saving of labor and time in feeding, and save feed.

KINDS OF BEEF CATTLE BARNS:

The type of barn is determined by the kind of stock and the method of handling and management. In general, the following two types of beef cattle barns, or modifications thereof, are in common use:

1. **The pen, stall, or general utility barn.**—These barns range up to 40 feet in width and may be either one- or two-story, the only essential difference between the two being the overhead loft for hay and bedding storage in the latter. If feeding is done inside, mangers are placed along the alley and hay racks along the side walls; or the location of the racks and bunks may be reversed. Frequently, especially in a feeder cattle operation, hay is fed inside the barn and grain and silage outside. If this type of barn is to be used for breeding stock, the plan usually provides grain bins and stalls and pens for calves, cows, and bulls. The barn may be an oblong structure; or it may have wings or extensions to form an L, T, or U shape.

2. **The central storage type with attached sheds or livestock sections.**—This is a popular and economical type of cattle barn. These barns vary in width, but perhaps the average structure is about 60 feet wide and consists of a 24-foot center and two 18-foot wings. Sometimes the wings may extend around three sides

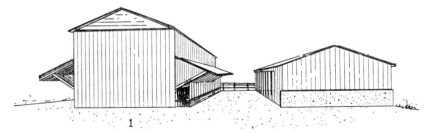

Fig. 172. A modern low-cost, labor-saving (1) hay feeding shed and (2) shelter. The shelter may have some boxed-in maternity stalls if desired, and the corral may be paved. (Drawing prepared especially for this book by H. E. Wichers, Specialist Rural Architecture, and James H. Hubenthal, Draftsman, Agricultural Extension Service, Washington State University, Pullman, Wash.)

Central Storage with Cattle Sheds Attached on Sides

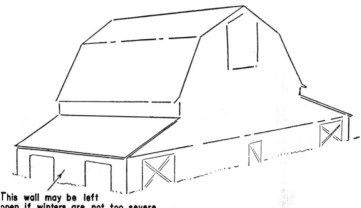

This wall may be left
open if winters are not too severe

Fig. 173. A central storage barn with attached sheds. Where considerable hay storage is desired, the central storage barn with attached sheds is
popular. (Sketch by R. F. Johnson)

of the building, thus providing more shelter space in relation to
storage. The general floor plan for this type of barn consists of
ground-to-roof storage for hay and bedding in the center and
cattle sheds on each side. Racks for hay are adjacent to the central storage area. Troughs for grain and silage may be along the
outside wall of the barn or outside in the lot.

Beef Cattle Sheds

Sheds are the most versatile and widely used beef cattle
shelters throughout the United States. They are used for cattle
in the feed lot, as a range shelter for dry cows with calves, and
for housing young stock. They usually open to the south or east,
preferably opposite to the direction of the prevailing winds and
toward the sun. They are enclosed on the ends and sides. Some-

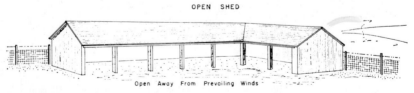

Fig. 174. An open shed. Sheds are the most versatile and widely used
beef cattle shelters throughout the United States. (Drawing by H. E.
Wichers, Specialist Rural Architecture, and James H. Hubenthal, Draftsman, Agricultural Extension Service, Washington State University, Pullman, Wash.)

Fig. 175. A modern low-cost, labor-saving (1) feed bunker (which may be equipped with a chain or belt feeder) and (2) open shed. (Drawing prepared especially for this book by H. E. Wichers, Specialist Rural Architecture, and James H. Hubenthal, Draftsman, Agricultural Extension Service, Washington State University, Pullman, Wash.)

Fig. 176. A practical shelter for the herd bull, on the farm of O. C. Allen, McComb, Miss. Note the hay rack and feed storage loft in the shelter and the grass and shade trees in the paddock. Such an arrangement is most important in keeping the sire thrifty and virile. (Courtesy, National Cottonseed Products Association, Inc.)

times the front is partially closed, and in severe weather drop-doors may be used. The latter arrangement is especially desirable when the ceiling height is sufficient to accommodate a power manure loader.

So that the bedding may be kept reasonably dry, it is important that sheds be located on high, well-drained ground; that eave troughs and down spouts drain into suitable tile lines, or surface drains; and that the structures have sufficient width to prevent rain and snow from blowing to the back end. Sheds should be a minimum of 24 feet in depth, front to back, with depths up to 36 feet preferable. As a height of 8½ feet is necessary to accommodate some power-operated manure loaders, when this type of equipment is to be used in the shed, a minimum ceiling height of 9 feet is recommended. The extra 6 inches allow for the accumulation of manure. Lower ceiling heights are satisfactory when it is intended to use a blade or pitch fork in cleaning the building.

The length of the shed can be varied according to needed capacity. Likewise, the shape may be either a single long shed or in the form of an L or T. The long arrangement permits more corral space. When an open shed is contemplated, thought should be given to feed storage and feeding problems.

Sometimes hay racks are built along the back wall of sheds, or next to an alley, if the shed is very wide or if there is some hay storage overhead. Most generally, however, hay racks, feed bunks, and watering troughs are placed outside the structure.

A Modern Multiple-Use Barn

The two-story red barn, long a traditional American trade-

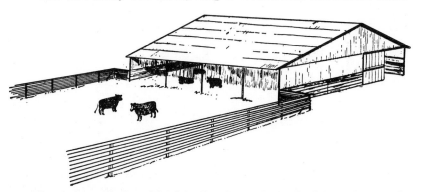

Fig. 177. A Modern Multiple-Use Barn. It is flexible and versatile. (Drawing by Steve Allured)

mark, is fast giving way to cheaper one-story structures of more flexible design and lower operating costs.

Figures 177 and 178 show a modern low-cost, labor-saving, multiple-use barn. It may be used for beef cattle, for dairy cattle (as a loafing barn), for sheep, for swine, for horses, and/or for storage of feed, seed, fertilizer, and machinery. This barn is flexible and versatile. Figure 179 shows how this barn can be adapted to hillside construction, thereby obtaining a gravity feeding arrangement.

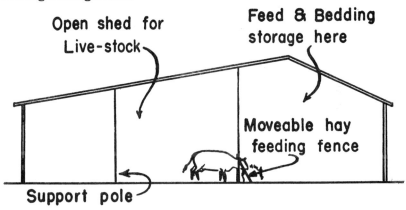

Fig. 178. Cross-section of the Modern Multiple-Use Barn shown in Fig. 177. Note the movable hay feeding fence which makes it possible (1) to decrease the feed and bedding storage area and to increase the animal area as winter advances, and (2) to keep the feed and bedding in close proximity to the supply, thereby lessening labor and drudgery. (Drawing by Steve Allured)

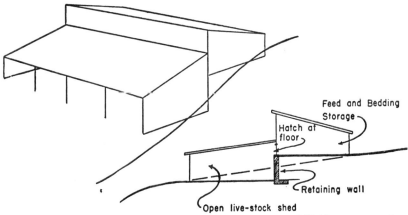

Fig. 179. Modern Multiple-Use Barn adapted to hillside construction. This design alleviates costly leveling of the building site and provides for easy gravity handling of the feed and bedding. (Drawing by Steve Allured)

IT HAS DESIRABLE FEATURES:

If properly designed and constructed, this Modern Multiple-Use Barn should possess the following desirable features:

1. **Meet needed animal space and feed storage requirements.**—It should meet the specific animal space and feed storage requirements of the farm or ranch.

2. **Face in the right direction.**—Except in the deep South, it should open to the south or east, preferably opposite the direction of the prevailing winds and toward the sun.

3. **Be relatively dry.**—It should be constructed to assist in providing a reasonably dry bed for animals.

4. **Be of proper height.**—A minimum ceiling height of 9 feet is recommended in order to accommodate a power-operated manure loader.

5. **Possess movable equipment.**—Wherever possible, barn equipment should be as movable as the furniture in a home. Thus, where the entire floor of the barn is on the same ground level, movable feed facilities make it possible (1) to decrease the feed and bedding storage area and to increase the animal area as winter advances, and (2) to keep the feed and bedding in close proximity to the supply, thereby lessening labor and drudgery.

6. **Promote animal health.**—This is most important, for healthy animals are the profitable and efficient ones. Today, it is recognized (1) that animals of all kinds need much less shelter than was formerly deemed necessary, (2) that too close confinement may be as detrimental as lack of proper shelter, (3) that open sheds provide the cheapest type of ventilation, and usually the best, and (4) that, except for newborn or sick animals, the inside temperature of the barn should be as close to the outside temperature as possible. The modern multiple-use type of barn shown in Figure 177 meets these requisites.

7. **Be flexible.**—The need for flexibility is best illustrated by referring to the great number of obsolete draft horse and mule barns throughout the country, usually two-story structures with built-in stalls and permanent feed mangers. With the passing of the draft animal, many of these old barns have either remained unused or have been modernized at high cost. But this is not the end of such changes! Who can predict, with certainty for example, what the future holds relative to methods of harvesting, curing, and storing hay? Thus it is important that buildings be

of such flexible design that they can be easily and inexpensively modernized to meet changes in a changing world.

This desired flexibility is best obtained by constructing a single-story building with movable equipment—features of the modern barn shown in Figure 178.

8. **Gravity feed if on a hillside.**—In a hilly area, it is recommended that the design of the barn be adapted as shown in Figure 179. This alleviates costly leveling of the building site and provides for easy gravity handling of the feed and bedding.

9. **Possess such added rooms and stalls as are needed.**— Maternity stalls, feed, seed, or fertilizer rooms, a milking room, and/or a tack room may be incorporated in this type of barn if they are needed.

10. **Possess adjacent corrals and a loading chute.**—Suitable corrals and a loading chute should be provided adjacent to the building.

IT IS REASONABLE IN COST:

On many livestock establishments, the cost of the improvements is about equal to the value of the land alone. Thus, it is important that every consideration should be given to affecting savings in the construction of buildings and equipment. Among the most important reasons why the modern type barn shown in Figure 177 is reasonable in cost, are the following:

1. **It is of simple pole-frame construction.**—It is supported by poles chemically treated under pressure and set like fence posts 4 to 5 feet in the ground and spaced at least 12 feet apart. This barn (1) eliminates scaffolding, for even the highest points can be reached from ladders, trucks, or wagons, (2) lessens bracing, and (3) saves labor, for this simple type of construction can be built with any farm labor capable of building a movable hog house.

2. **It uses the ground to support feed and bedding;** instead of requiring heavy construction to support this weight overhead.

3. **It is built low to the ground,** thus making for less wind pressure to resist and requiring less bracing.

4. **It leaves one side open.**—This saves on material, and desirable ventilation is obtained without cost.

IT SAVES LABOR:

The importance of designing farm buildings for efficiency of operation becomes apparent when it is realized that the average stockman spends more than half his working hours in and around the farm buildings.

The type of barn shown in Figure 177 is labor-saving in comparison with conventional two-story barns for the following reasons:

1. **Feed is stored on the ground level.**—The truck, or other vehicle, may be driven directly into the ground-level storage area and unloaded without hoisting or elevating.

2. **Feed and bedding are stored where used.**—A movable hay and feed bunk can be so designed that it can be moved back as the animals eat the feed and use the bedding. This eliminates the necessity of climbing into mows, poking feed and bedding down a chute, and carrying it some distance to where it is to be used. Instead, the feed may be tossed directly and easily into the rack or bunk and the bedding into the area where it is used.

3. **Overflow feed and bedding storage is convenient.**—If the farm production of feed and bedding is higher than normal, the added tonnage may be temporarily stored in the animal area. Then as it is used, more and more of the animal space becomes available as winter advances. With a conventional two-story barn, such flexibility is not easily obtained.

4. **Manure may be removed by power loader.**—The ceiling height and open shed arrangement make for ease in operating a manure loader and in getting in and out with a spreader. No hand labor is required.

BEEF CATTLE EQUIPMENT

It is not proposed that all of the numerous types of beef cattle equipment will be described herein but only those articles that are most common. Suitable equipment saves feed and labor, conserves manure, and makes for increased production.

Hay Racks

Various sizes and designs of racks are used in feeding hay and other forages. In general, these structures are of two types: Overhead racks, and low mangers. Overhead racks are easily moved, but they are difficult to clean; and often there is considerable wastage especially when cows have horns and do considerable fighting. Low mangers result in less wastage of the leaves and other fine particles than overhead racks because the cattle must work down from the top. Low mangers may be satis-

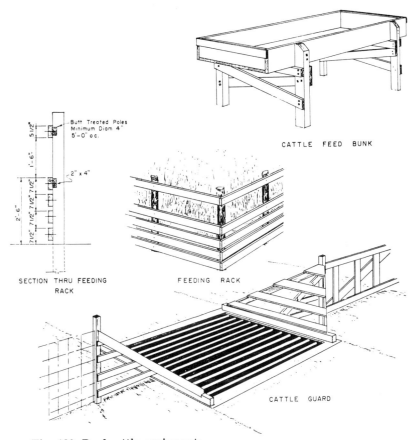

CATTLE FEED BUNK

Butt Treated Poles
Minimum Diam 4"
5'-0" o c.

2" x 4"

SECTION THRU FEEDING
RACK

FEEDING RACK

CATTLE GUARD

Fig. 180. Beef cattle equipment:
The **feed bunk** is usually placed out in the open and used for feeding silage and grain.
The **feeding rack** offers a convenient and labor-saving method of feeding stacked hay.
Cattle **guards** (lower picture) may be set in a fence to permit convenient passage of automobiles and trucks but deter cattle, hogs, sheep, and most horses and mules.
Detailed plans and specifications for such equipment can usually be obtained through the local county agricultural agent, vocational agriculture instructor, lumber dealer, or through writing the college of agriculture in the state. (The feeding rack and the bunk were drawn from sketches provided by Roland A. Glaze, Rilco Laminated Products, Inc., Tacoma, Wash. All drawings prepared especially for this book by H. E. Wichers, Specialist Rural Architecture, and James H. Hubenthal, Draftsman, Agricultural Extension Service, Washington State University, Pullman, Wash.)

factorily used also in the feeding of kaffir and other coarse forages.

It is preferable that racks be of sufficient size so that one filling will last several days, thus lessening the labor requirements. It is desirable also that the rack be mounted on runners or wheels, thus making it convenient to move it from place to place.

Feed Troughs or Bunks

Feed troughs or bunks are used for feeding both grain and silage. Figure 180 shows a common and desirable type of cattle bunk that is well braced, free from sharp corners, portable, and made so as to prevent cattle from throwing feed out. It could be made stationary by extending the posts into the ground or by setting the posts on concrete foundations. Stationary troughs should be located on a well-drained site, or, preferably, placed on a concrete or other hard-surfaced platform. The dimensions of the feed bunk or trough should be in keeping with those given

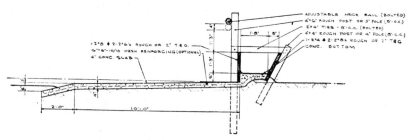

Fig. 181. A cattle feed bunk and concrete apron for fattening cattle. (Specifications developed by the author, and based on actual inspection of many large and modern feeding establishments; drawing by Glenn Wegner, WSC Architect; photo courtesy Washington State University)

in Table 32. Bunks of a height for mature cattle may be used for calves by digging holes for the legs or runners. In many large cattle feeding yards, especially in the West, a "manger-type" trough forms a part of the enclosure and is filled from outside the corral along a service lane or road (see Fig. 181). Stationary troughs in barns should be provided with adjustments for height, thus making it possible to adjust for cattle of different ages and for the accumulation of manure.

Self-Feeders

Most cattle are hand-fed, but the use of self-feeders for fattening cattle is increasing. A self-feeder does a better job of feeding than a careless man. Self-feeders may either be stationary or portable. The latter are usually equipped with runners or are mounted on low wheels. The most desirable cattle self-feeders have feed troughs along both sides, have a capacity adequate to hold a feed supply that will last ten days to two weeks, and are easily filled.

Fig. 182. A self-feeder for fattening cattle. Note door in the roof for filling and runners for moving. (Courtesy, Washington State University)

Watering Facilities

Water is more essential than feed, for animals will subsist longer without feed than without water. As indicated in Table 32, on the average, mature cattle consume approximately twelve gallons of water per head daily, with variations according to size of animal, season, and type of feed. Cattle are frequently watered from reservoirs, springs, lakes, and streams; but if surface water is not available, labor can be saved by having reliable power for pumping and by piping water under pressure to tanks or troughs where it will be available at all times. When wells are used as a source of supply, windmills are the most commonly used power unit, although electric motors and gas engines are sometimes used. In cold areas, outside tanks are generally provided with tank heaters or covers during the winter months.

Regardless of the source of the water supply—wells, springs, streams, or surface-storage supplies—it is important that it be abundantly available at all times. It should also be fresh and well protected. When watering tanks and troughs are used, they

Fig. 183. A good concrete water tank for cattle. Note fence over top of tank to keep animals out. (Courtesy, USDA)

should be of adequate size, and there should be provision for keeping animals out of the tank. In areas in which mud is a problem, it is desirable that tanks be surrounded by a pavement at least six feet in width, and provision should be made to pipe the overflow away from the vicinity of the tank.

Shades

Cattle should be provided with suitable shade during the hot, summer months. An unshaded cow standing in an air temperature of 100° F. has to dispose of enough heat in a 10-hour period to bring 9 gallons of ice water to the boiling point. At the Imperial Valley Field Station, El Centro, Calif., it was found (1) that the difference in heat load in an animal under a shade 10 to 12 feet high at 100° F., and one in the sun was 1,334 b.t.u. per hour, and (2) that to make 100 pounds gain during midsummer required 200 to 300 pounds more feed without shade than with shade.

The most satisfactory cattle shades are (1) located with an east-west placement, because a greater proportion of the shadow lies to the north of the shade than in a north-south placement (the latter are drier underneath, however, because the sun can get underneath to dry out the manure and urine), (2) at least 10 to 12 feet in height (in addition to being cooler, high shades allow a truck to be driven under and cattle to be worked by a man on a horse), and (3) open all around.

Corrals

No equipment adds more to the ease and pleasure of handling cattle than a convenient system of well-constructed corrals. In addition, such a system saves money by reducing the shrinkage resulting from sorting and handling cattle. On the western range, this type of equipment is considered a virtual necessity. To be sure, it is not presumed that each operator will have need for the same size, number, and arrangement of lots. These will vary according to the size of the herd, management practices, and individual preferences. There are, however, certain salient features that should be observed in planning a system of corrals: (1) They should be large enough to accommodate easily the

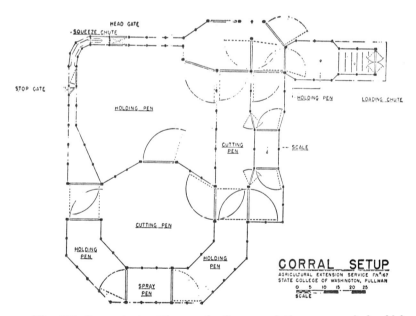

Fig. 184. Convenient cattle corrals. Some variations can and should be made in keeping with (1) the number of animals to be worked, (2) the size and topography of the area available, and (3) the facilities adjacent thereto. (Courtesy, H. E. Wichers, Rural Architecture Specialist, Washington State University)

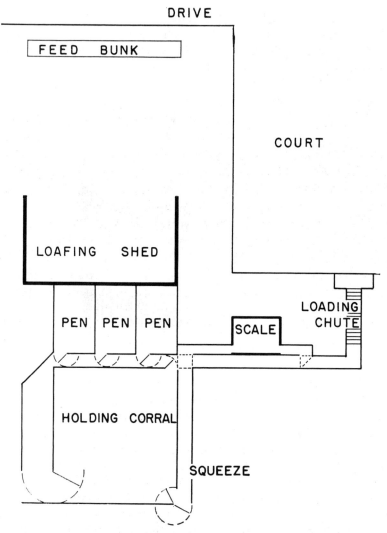

Fig. 185. Convenient and adequate cattle corral for a small operation. (Drawing prepared especially for this book by H. E. Wichers, Specialist Rural Architecture, and James H. Hubenthal, Draftsman, Agricultural Extension Service, Washington State University, Pullman, Wash.)

number of cattle involved; (2) they should be conveniently located with respect to the range and a nearby water supply; and (3) they should include at least one large pen for holding the herd, a chute or alley to be used for separating or crowding work, and two smaller pens in which to put the separated cattle.

Fig. 186. A paved corral lot used for fattening steers. Note that the cattle are clean and free from mud and manure. (Courtesy, Dale Woolson-croft, Iowa State University)

Loading Chute

The extensive use of trucks makes it desirable that the stock farm and ranch be equipped with a chute for loading and unloading stock. Such equipment may be either portable or stationary. In the latter case, it is usually desirable to attach the chute to the corrals or feed lot. A loading chute of sufficiently durable construction for cattle is equally satisfactory for sheep and swine. The main essentials are: (1) that the chute have proper height for the truck commonly served (or preferably have an adjustable height arrangement), (2) that it have adequate width to accommodate animals, and (3) that it have sufficient slope and cleating to the platform approach to prevent slipping. Most chutes are about 28 to 30 inches in width and 46 inches high.

Squeeze

A squeeze for handling cattle can be profitably used on any farm or ranch for dehorning, branding, castrating, testing for tuberculosis, vaccinating, or in performing minor surgical opera-

Cattle Squeeze

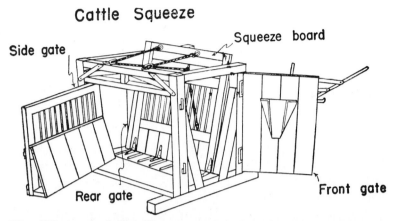

Fig. 187. A practical cattle squeeze. Detailed plans and specifications for such equipment can usually be obtained through the local lumber dealer, county agricultural agent or FFA instructor, or through writing the college of agriculture in the state. (Drawing by R. F. Johnson)

tions. Lack of such equipment usually entails a great deal of labor in catching and throwing animals and is hard on both man and beast. Numerous designs of homemade and commercial cattle squeezes are available, but the essential features of all of them are: (1) durability, (2) thorough restraint of the animal, and (3) convenience for the operator. When cattle corrals are constructed, the cattle squeeze is normally a part of the pen arrangement.

Stocks

Cattle stocks are primarily an item of equipment for the purebred herd and the feed lot. Usually they are so located that animals must be led into them rather than driven, thus limiting their use to cattle that may be rather easily handled. Cattle stocks may be used for trimming and treating hoofs, dehorning, horn branding, drenching, ringing bulls, removing of ties, swinging injured animals, and restraining animals during surgical operations. The essential features of cattle stocks are (1) durability, (2) thorough restraint of the animal, (3) convenience for the operator, (4) a canvas sling to place under the animal to prevent him from lying down while in the stocks (the sling may be wound up on side rollers by means of turning rods), and (5) wooden sills that extend along either side at a height of 15 inches from the floor and on which the feet may be rested and tied while being trimmed or treated.

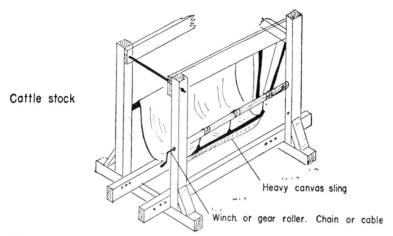

Cattle stock

Heavy canvas sling

Winch or gear roller. Chain or cable

Fig. 188. Cattle stock. Detailed plans and specifications for such equipment can usually be obtained through the local lumber dealer, county agricultural agent or FFA instructor, or through writing the college of agriculture in the state. (Drawing by R. F. Johnson)

Breeding Rack

Breeding racks are sometimes used by purebred operators who desire to breed young heifers to mature, heavy bulls. Fig. 189 shows a very satisfactory type of breeding rack.

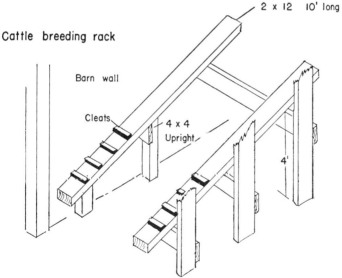

2 x 12 10' long

Cattle breeding rack

Barn wall

Cleats

4 x 4
Upright

4'

Fig. 189. Cattle breeding rack. Detailed plans and specifications for such equipment can usually be obtained through the local lumber dealer, county agricultural agent or FFA instructor, or through writing the college of agriculture in the state. (Drawing by R. F. Johnson)

Dipping Vat and Spraying Equipment

Dipping vats have long been used successfully and rather extensively on the western range in treating cattle, sheep, and sometimes horses, for external parasites. The vat is usually built at one side of the corral system. The chief virtue of the dipping vat lies in the fact that animals so treated are thoroughly covered. On the other hand, the vats are costly to constuct and lack mobility and flexibility; and there is always considerable leftover dip at the finish of the operation. Frequently, dipping vats are built as a cooperative enterprise by a group of producers rather than by an individual operator. With the development of modern insecticides and improved spraying equipment, it appears probable that in the future spraying operations will increase and that fewer expensive dipping vats will be constructed.

Other Beef Cattle Equipment

There is hardly any limit to the number of different articles of beef cattle equipment, and the design of each. In addition to those already listed, Figs. 190, 191, and 192 show a calf creep, a salt-mineral feeder, and scales, respectively.

CALF CREEP:

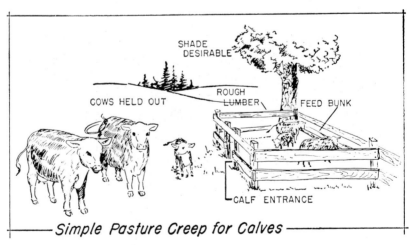

Fig. 190. A calf creep. Note the small entrance for the calves. (Drawing by R. F. Johnson)

SALT-MINERAL FEEDER:

Fig. 191. A salt-mineral feeder for cattle. Note that it is a two-compartment arrangement, and that the feeder is enclosed except for the feeding side. (Drawing by Steve Allured)

SCALES:

Fig. 192. Scales take the "guess" out of many farm and ranch operations. (Courtesy, Swift & Company)

Silos

The general kinds of silos are: tower silos, pit silos, trench silos, self-feeder or bunker silos, above ground temporary silos, and plastic silos. The kind of silo decided upon and the choice of construction material should be determined primarily by the cost and by the suitability to the particular needs of the farm or ranch.

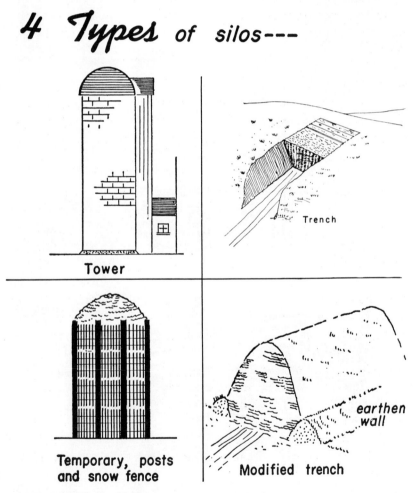

4 Types of silos---

Tower

Trench

Temporary, posts and snow fence

Modified trench

earthen wall

Fig. 193. Four kinds of silos: (1) tower silo (upper left), (2) trench silo (upper right), (3) enclosed stack silo (lower left), and (4) modified trench-stack silo (lower right). The latter two are both above-ground temporary silos. (Drawing by R. F. Johnson)

SPACE REQUIREMENTS OF BUILDINGS AND EQUIPMENT FOR BEEF CATTLE

One of the first and frequently one of the most difficult problems confronting the farmer or rancher who wishes to construct a building or item of equipment for beef cattle is that of arriving at the proper size or dimensions. Table 32 contains some conservative average figures which, it is hoped, will prove helpful. In general, less space than indicated may jeopardize the health and well-being of the animals, whereas more space may make the buildings and equipment more expensive than necessary.

Recommended Minimum Width of Service Passages

In general, the requirements for service passages are similar, regardless of the kind of animals. Accordingly, the suggestions contained in Table 33 are equally applicable to cattle, sheep, swine, and horse barns.

Storage Space Requirements for Feed and Bedding

The space requirements for feed storage for the livestock enterprise—whether it be for cattle, hogs, sheep, or horses, or as is more frequently the case, a combination of these—vary so widely that it is difficult to provide a suggested method of calculating space requirements applicable to such diverse conditions. The amount of feed to be stored depends primarily upon: (1) length of pasture season, (2) method of feeding and management, (3) kind of feed, (4) climate, and (5) the proportion of feeds produced on the farm or ranch in comparison with those purchased. Normally, the storage capacity should be sufficient to handle all feed grain and silage grown on the farm and to hold purchased supplies. Forage and bedding may or may not be stored under cover. In those areas where weather conditions permit, hay and straw are frequently stacked in the fields or near the barns in loose, baled, or chopped form. Sometimes poled framed sheds or a cheap cover of water-proof paper or wild grass is used for protection. Other forms of low-cost storage include temporary upright silos, trench silos, and temporary grain bins.

TABLE 32

SPACE REQUIREMENTS OF BUILDING AND EQUIPMENT FOR BEEF CATTLE

Class, age and size of animals	BARN OR SHED			FEED LOT		HAY MANGER OR RACK					FEED BUNK OR TROUGH (FOR GRAIN OR SILAGE)				SELF FEEDER	WATER	
	Floor area per animal (sq. ft.)	Height of ceiling (ft.)	Window space, (not including open sheds) (sq. ft.)	Area if ordinary dirt lot (sq. ft.)	Area if paved lot (sq. ft.)	Length per animal (in.)	Width if feeds from 1 side (in.)	Width if feeds from 2 sides (in.)	Width if attached side of barn (in.)	Height at throat (in.)	Length per animal (in.)	Width if feeds from 1 side (in.)	Width if feeds from 2 sides (in.)	Height at throat (in.)	Trough length if feeder is kept filled (in.)	Water per animal per day (gal.)	Water trough space
Cow or steers, 2 years or over	25–45	8½–10	1 sq. ft. window space to 35 sq. ft. floor space	300–1000	35–100	24–30	30	36–40	30	30	24–30	30	36–40	30	9–12 per animal	12	For animals in feed lot or where water under pressure is near by, space sufficient to accommodate 5 to 10 per cent of animals simultaneously. For animals on the range or where water is not convenient the water space should be adequate to accommodate 10 to 20 per cent of the animals simultaneously.
Yearlings	20–40	"	"	250–800	30–80	20	"	"	"	24	20–26	"	"	28	"	10	
Calves, 350 to 550 lbs.	15–30	"	"	150–500	25–50	18	"	"	"	20	18–24	"	"	24	"	8	
Cows in maternity stall	100–150	"	"	1–2 acre pasture paddock		30	…	…	…	26	30	…	…	30	…	15	
Herd bulls	100–150	"	"	"		"	30	36–40	30	"	"	30	36–40	"	…	"	

Remarks: Animals with horns require about one linear foot more manger or trough space per animal than the figures given in this table. Movable hay racks or feed bunks are usually 12 to 16 feet in length.

TABLE 33

RECOMMENDED MINIMUM WIDTHS FOR SERVICE PASSAGES

Kind of Passage	Use	Minimum Width
Feed alley......................	For feed cart	4' – 0"
Driveway.......................	For wagon, spreader, or truck	9' – 0"
Doors and gate..............	Drive-through	9' – 0"
Doors and gate............	To small pens	4' – 0"

Table 34 gives the storage space requirements for feed and bedding. This information may be helpful to the individual operator who desires to compute the barn space required for a specific livestock enterprise. This table also provides a convenient means of estimating the amount of feed or bedding in storage.

How to Determine the Size Barn to Build

The length and depth of the barn (its size) may be varied according to needs. The size barn to build for any given farm or ranch may be determined as follows:

1. Estimate the number and kind of animals to be quartered and compute their total animal space requirements (see Table 32).

2. Compute the yearly feed requirements of the animals to be fed and quartered by referring to Table 25, p. 386, giving consideration to the length of the pasture season and the quantity and quality of the grass.

3. Estimate the farm production of feeds and bedding to be stored in the barn. In most operations this should coincide reasonably close to the total animal requirements (point No. 2), but there may be circumstances where the feed and bedding storage requirements are more or less than the animal feed requirements.

4. Estimate the total tonnage of feed and bedding to be stored by correlating the animal feed needs and the farm or ranch production. (Correlate the results of points 2 and 3). Then determine the total storage space requirements for feed and bedding from Table 34.

5. Determine the size of barn to build from the total animal space requirements and the total yearly feed and bedding storage requirements (Points 1 and 4).

TABLE 34

STORAGE SPACE REQUIREMENTS FOR FEED AND BEDDING

Kind of Feed or Bedding		Pounds per cubic feet (approx.)	Cubic feet per ton (approx.)	Pounds per bushel of grain	Cubic feet per bushel
Hay[1]	Timothy, loose	3	625–640		
	Wild Hay, loose	3–4	450–600		
	Alfalfa, loose	4	470–485		
	Clover, loose	4	500–512		
	Chopped hay	10	210–225		
	Baled hay (closely stacked)	10	150–200		
Straw and Shavings	Straw, baled[1]	10	200		
	Straw, loose[1]	2–3	600–1000		
	Shavings, baled	20	100		
Silage	Corn or sorghum silage in tower silos	40	500		
	Corn or sorghum silage in trench silos	35	510		
Mill Feed	Bran	13	154		
	Middlings	25	80		
	Linseed or soybean meal	35			
Grain	Corn, shelled	45	45	56	1.25
	Corn, ear	28	72	70	2.50
	Corn, snapped	25	81	80	3.25
	Oats	26	77	32	1.25
	Barley	39	51	48	1.25
	Wheat	48	42	60	1.25
	Rye	45	44	56	1.25
	Grain sorghum	45	44	56	1.25

[1]From *Doane Agricultural Digest*, Table 1, p. 532, courtesy, Mr. Howard Doane. Under hay and loose straw, a range is given under the columns "pounds per cu. ft." and "cubic feet per ton"; the higher figures being for hay and loose straw settled 1 to 2 mo., and the lower figure for hay or loose straw settled over 3 mo.

In general, modern multiple-use barns of the type shown in Fig. 177 are 52 feet deep, with 26 feet devoted to feed and bedding storage and 26 feet to animals; although both the depth and the length can be varied to meet specific needs.

How to Determine the Size Silo to Build[1]

The size of silo to build should be determined by needs. With tower type and pit silos, this means (1) that the diameter should be determined by quantity of silage to be fed daily, and (2) that the height (depth in a pit silo) should be determined by the length of the silage feeding period. Similar consideration should be accorded with trench silos.

SIZE OF TOWER SILO:

If the diameter is too great, the silage will be exposed too long before it is fed; and unless a quantity is thrown away each day, spoiled silage will be fed.

The minimum recommended rate of removal of silage varies with the temperature. In most sections of the United States, it is desirable that a minimum of 1½ inches of silage be removed from tower silos daily during the winter feeding period, with the quantity increased to a minimum of 3 inches when summer feeding is practiced. Of course, the total daily silage consumption on any given farm or ranch will be determined by (1) the class and size of animals, (2) the number of animals, and (3) the rate of silage feeding. Some suggestions on how much silage to feed cattle are found in Table 25, p. 386.

Silo height should be determined primarily by the length of the intended feeding period. In general, however, the height should not be less than twice, nor more than three and one-half times the diameter. The greater the depth, the greater the unit capacity. Extreme height is to be avoided because (1) of the excessive power required to elevate the cut silage material, and (2) of the heavier construction material required. Also it is noteworthy that, with silos of the larger diameters, more labor is required in carrying the silage to the silo door for removal.

Table 35 may be used as a guide in computing the proper diameter of tower silo for any given farm or ranch.

Fig. 194 shows capacities of tower silos of different heights and diameters. It is based on well-eared corn silage harvested in the early dent stage, cut in ¼″ lengths, well-tramped when filled, and with the silo refilled once after settling for a day.

Figure 194 can be adapted for corn silage of different stages

---

[1]The author is very grateful to Mr. Thomas E. Long, Manager, Farm Bureau, Portland Cement Association, Chicago, Illinois, who very kindly reviewed this section and made many helpful suggestions.

TABLE 35

MAXIMUM DIAMETER OF TOWER SILO TO BUILD IF SILAGE IS TO BE KEPT FRESH

Inches of Silage Removed Daily	Total Silage Removed Daily With An Inside Silo Diameter of—					
	10 feet	12 feet	14 feet	16 feet	18 feet	20 feet
	(lbs.)	(lbs.)	(lbs.)	(lbs.)	(lbs.)	(lbs.)
Summer: 3" daily will remove[1]	786	1,312	1,539	2,010	2,545	3,142
Winter: 1½" daily will remove[1]	393	656	770	1,005	1,272	1,571

[1]The pounds listed in each of the columns to the right are approximations based on an average constant weight of 40 lbs. of silage per cubic foot.

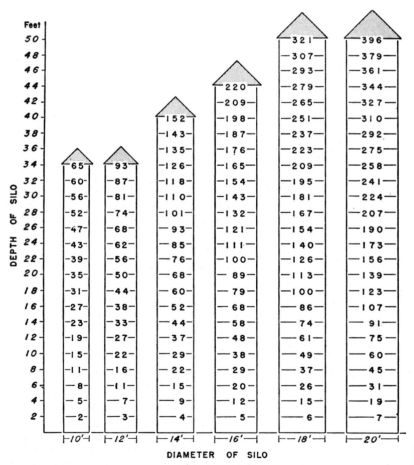

Fig. 194. Capacity in tons of settled corn silage in tower silos of varying sizes (based on data reported in USDA Circ. 603; drawing by R. F. Johnson)

of maturity and grain content, and for other kinds of silage, by applying the following rules of thumb:

Kind of Silage:	Changes to Be Made in the Number of Tons Shown in Fig. 194
1. For corn silage ensiled when less mature than usual	Add 5 to 10%
2. For corn ensiled when dry or over-ripe	Deduct 5 to 10%
3. For corn very rich in grain	Add 5 to 10%
4. For corn with very little grain	Deduct 5 to 10%
5. For sorghum silage	Use the same weights as used for corn silage of comparable grain and maturity.
6. For sunflower silage	Add 5 to 10%
7. For grass silage	Add 10 to 15%[1]

[1]For this reason, a stronger structure is necessary where grass silage is stored.

The following example will serve to illustrate how to determine the size tower silo to build:

Over a period of years, a farmer plans to winter 34 head of 425-pound stocker calves on a ration of corn silage and protein supplement. There is a 240-day wintering period. No increase in the herd is planned. What size tower silo should be built?

The answer is obtained as follows:

1. First, here are the silage requirements:

   (1) Table 25, Handy Beef Cattle Feeding Guide, indicates that 425 pound stocker calves on a ration of corn silage and protein supplement should receive about 30 lbs. of silage per head per day.

   (2) 34×30=1020 lbs. of silage required daily for the 34 calves.

   (3) 1020 × 240=244,800 lbs., or 122.4 tons, of silage required for the 240-day wintering period for the 34 calves.

2. Next, here is the size silo to build:

   (1) Table 35 shows that in order to remove 1005 lbs. of silage daily (which is only slightly less than the 1020 lbs. needed daily), with 1½" removed from the top of the silo each day, the diameter of the silo should not be greater than 16'.

   (2) Fig. 194 can now be used as a guide in determining both the proper height (or depth) and diameter of the silo. Fig. 194 shows that a silo 16 ft. in diameter and 27 ft. high will hold 127 tons of silage; which would allow for 4.6 tons spoilage in excess of the required 122.4 tons. However, the height of a silo should not be less than twice the diameter. It appears best, therefore, to plan on a 14 ft. diameter silo. As noted in Fig. 194, 34 ft. of settled silage in a 14 ft. diameter silo will provide 126 tons of silage; which would allow for 3.6 tons spoilage in

excess of the required 122.4 tons. To allow for settling, an additional 4 to 6 ft. should be added to the height, thus making a 38 to 40 ft. height.

(3) The size silo to build to meet the needs outlined in this example, therefore, is one that is 14 ft. in diameter and 38 to 40 ft. high.

SIZE OF TRENCH SILO:

As in an upright silo, the cross-sectional area of a trench silo should be determined by the quantity of silage to be fed daily. The length is determined by the number of days of the silage feeding period. The only difference is that generally greater allowance for spoilage is made in the case of trench silos, though this factor varies rather widely.

Under most conditions, it is recommended that a minimum 4″ slice be fed daily from the face (from the top to the bottom of the trench) of a trench silo during the winter months, with a somewhat thicker slice preferable during the summer months.

The dimensions, areas, and capacities given in Table 36 are based on the assumption that the silage weighs 35[1] lbs. per cubic foot, which is an average figure for corn or sorghum silage. Thus a trench silo 8 ft. deep, 6 ft. wide at the bottom, and 10 ft. wide at the top has a cross sectional area of 64 ft. This size silo will hold 747 lbs. of silage for each 4″ slice, or 2,240 lbs. of silage for each 1-foot slice, or 112 tons in a trench 100 feet long.

For illustrative purposes, let us use the same example and silage requirements as given on page 525, but this time determine the size trench silo to build rather than the size tower silo. Briefly, the requirements are for 1020 lbs. of silage daily for a 240-day wintering period. As noted in Table 36, one day's feed or 1020 lbs. of silage (1062 lbs. to be exact) can be obtained in each 4″ slice of a trench silo 8 ft. wide at the bottom, 14 ft. 8 in. wide at the top, and 8 ft. deep; or a 91 sq. ft. cross-sectional area. The cross-sectional area should not be larger than

[1]Because the silage in trench silos is generally not so deep and well-packed as the silage in tower silos, an average figure of 35 lbs. per cubic foot is used herein for trench silos and 40 lbs. for upright silos. With all types of silos—including above-ground and below-ground types—the weight of a cubic foot of silage varies with the kind and maturity of the material, moisture content, length of cut, rate of filling, and depth of the silo. Corn silage harvested when about 74% of the grain has passed the milk stage and containing approximately 70% moisture is considered average silage. Volume for volume, sorghum silage weighs about the same as corn silage. Grass or grass-legume silage is 10 to 15% heavier than corn silage.

TABLE 36

DIMENSIONS, CROSS-SECTION AREA OF TRENCH SILO, AND
WEIGHT OF SILAGE IN 4-INCH SLICE AND PER LINEAL FOOT[1]

Side Slope Per Foot of Depth	Depth	Bottom Width	Top Width		Cross Sectional Area	Weight of Silage	
						4-inch slice	1-foot slice
(in.)	(ft.)	(ft.)	(ft.)	(in.)	(sq. ft.)	(lbs.)	(lbs.)
3	4	5	7	0	24	280	840
4	4	6	8	8	29	338	1,015
5	4	7	10	4	33	385	1,155
3	6	6	9	0	45	525	1,575
4	6	7	11	0	54	630	1,890
5	6	8	13	0	63	735	2,205
3	8	6	10	0	64	747	2,240
4	8	7	12	4	77	898	2,695
5	8	8	14	8	91	1,062	3,185
3	10	6	11	0	85	992	2,975
4	10	8	14	8	113	1,318	3,955
5	10	10	18	4	142	1,657	4,970

[1]*Silos, Types and Construction*, USDA, Farmers' Bulletin No. 1820, Revised 1948, p. 55.

this if a 4″ slice is to be removed daily in order to alleviate spoilage.

In order to obtain a 240-day feed supply, the filled trench must be 80 ft. long (240 by ⅓; the ⅓ representing ⅓ ft. or 4″). The size trench silo to build to meet the specified needs, therefore, is one that is 8 ft. wide at the bottom, 14 ft. 8 in. wide at the top, 8 ft. deep, and 80 ft. long. In order to take care of spoilage and to provide a measure of safety, it is recommended that the actual length be from 85 to 90 ft.

About 8 ft. for a trench silo is the most economical depth from the standpoint of cost and feeding. Of course, in filling it is desirable to pile silage 3 feet higher over the center of the trench and round it off. This provides for settlement.

FENCES FOR CATTLE

Good fences (1) maintain farm boundaries, (2) make livestock operations possible, (3) reduce losses to both animals and crops, (4) increase land values, (5) promote better relationships between neighbors, (6) lessen accidents from animals getting on roads, and (7) add to the attractiveness and distinctiveness of the premises.

The discussion which follows will be limited primarily to wire fencing, although it is recognized that such materials as rails, poles, boards, stone, and hedge have a place and are used under certain circumstances. Also, where there is a heavy concentration of animals, such as in corrals and feed yards, there

Fig. 195. Fences for cattle. (Drawing by Steve Allured)

is need for a more rigid type of fencing material than wire. Moreover, certain fencing materials have more artistic appeal than others; and this is an especially important consideration on the purebred establishment.

The kind of wire to purchase should be determined primarily by the class of animals to be confined. Tables 37 and 38 are suggested guides.

The following additional points are pertinent in the selection of wire:

1. **Styles of woven wire.**—The standard styles of woven wire fences are designated by numbers as 958, *1155*, 849, *1047*, 741, *939*, *832* and *726* (the figures in italic are most common).

TABLE 37

HANDY WOVEN WIRE FENCE CHART

Kind of Stock	Recommended Woven Wire Height	Recommended Weight of Stay Wire	Recommended Mesh or Spacing Between Stays	Number Recommended Strands of Barbed Wire to Add to Woven Wire	Comments
	(inches)	(gauge)	(inches)		
Cattle	47, 48 or 55	9 or 11	12	1 strand on top, with points 3 or 4 inches apart.	Also satisfactory for all farm animals, except young pigs.
Sheep	32	11 or 12½	12	2 strands on top.	12" mesh is best for sheep as they will not get their heads caught if they attempt to reach through.
Swine	26, 32, or 39	9 or 11	6	1 strand on bottom.	Barbed wire on bottom prevents rooting.
Horses	55 or 58	9 or 11	12	2 strands on top; top strand with points 3 or 4 inches apart.	Also satisfactory for all farm animals, except young pigs.
All farm animals	26 or	9 or 11	6	{3 strands on top; {1 strand on bottom.	
	32	9 or 11	6	{2 strands on top; {1 strand on bottom.	

TABLE 38

HANDY BARBED WIRE FENCE CHART

Kind of Stock	Recommended Number of Points	Recommended Spacing Between Points	Recommended Weight of Strands	Recommended Number of Lines of Barbed Wire to Install	Comments
		(inches)	(gauge)		
Cattle or horses; in farm pastures..	2 or 4	4 or 5	12½	5	2-point barbs are generally 4″ apart; 4-point are 5″ apart.
Cattle or horses; on the range......	2 or 4	4 or 5	12½	2 or 3	Not all animals will be restrained by 2 or 3 strands.
Sheep................	Barbed wire is not considered suitable for sheep because it tears the fleece.				
Swine................	2 or 4	4 or 5	12½	6 .	A 6-strand barbed wire fence for swine may cost more to build and maintain than a woven wire fence.

The first one or two digits represent the number of line (horizontal) wires; the last two the height in inches; i.e., 1155 has 11 horizontal wires and is 55 inches in height. Each style can be obtained in either (1) 12-inch spacing of stays (or mesh), or (2) 6-inch spacing of stays.

2. **Mesh.**—Generally, a close-spaced fence with stay or vertical wires 6 inches apart (6 in. mesh) will give better service than a wide-spaced (12-in. mesh) fence. However, some fence manufacturers believe that a 12-inch spacing with a No. 9 wire is superior to a 6-inch spacing with No. 11 filler wire (about the same amount of material is involved in each case).

3. **Weight of wire.**—A fence made of heavier weight wires will usually last longer and prove cheaper than one made of light wires. Heavier or larger size wire is designated by a smaller gauge number. Thus, No. 9 gauge wire is heavier and larger than No. 11 gauge. Woven wire fencing comes in Nos. 9, 11, 12½ and 14½ gauges—which refers to the gauge of the wires other than the top and bottom line wires. Barbed wire is usually 12½ gauge.

Heavier or larger wire than normal should be used in those areas subject to (1) salty air from the ocean, (2) smoke from close proximity industries which may give off chemical fumes into the atmosphere, (3) rapid temperature changes, or (4) overflow or flood.

Heavier or larger wire than normal should be used in fencing (1) small areas, (2) where a dense concentration of animals is involved, and (3) where animals have already learned to get out.

4. **Styles of barbed wire.**—Styles of barbed wire differ in the shape and number of the points of the barb, and the spacing of the barbs on the line wires. The two-point barbs are commonly spaced 4 inches apart while four-point barbs are generally spaced 5 inches apart. Since any style is satisfactory, selection is a matter of personal preference.

5. **Standard size rolls or spools.**—Woven wire comes in 20 and 40 rod rolls; barbed wire in 80 rod spools.

6. **Wire coating.**—The kind and amount of coating on wire definitely affects its lasting qualities.

Three kinds of material are commonly used for fence posts: wood, metal, and concrete. The selection of the particular kind of posts should be determined by (1) the availability and cost of each, (2) the length of service desired (posts should last as long as the fencing material attached to it, or the maintenance cost may be too high), (3) the kind and amount of livestock to be confined, and (4) the cost of installation.

Wood posts.—Osage orange, black locust, chestnut, red cedar, black walnut, mulberry, and catalpa—each with an average life of 15 to 30 years without treatment—are the most durable wood posts, but they are not available in all sections. Untreated posts of the other and less durable woods will last 3 to 8 years only, but they are satisfactory if properly butt treated (to 6 to 8 in. above the ground line) with a good wood preservative.

The proper size of wood posts varies considerably with the strength and durability of the species used. In general, however, large posts last longer than small ones. Satisfactory line posts of osage orange may be as small as 2½ inches in diameter; whereas line posts of other woods should be 4 to 8 inches in diameter at the smaller end. Split posts should be a minimum of 5 inches in diameter. Line posts are generally 7 to 8 feet in length, depending on the height of the fence to be constructed.

Wood corner, end, and gate posts should be substantial, usually not less than 10 to 12 inches in diameter. Also they should be long enough so that they can be set in the ground to a depth of at least 36 inches.

The less durable types of fence posts will last about 5 times longer when treated than when untreated. This effects yearly savings in two ways: (1) in the cost of posts, and (2) in the labor involved in fence construction.

Although the relative durability of posts does not materially affect initial fencing costs, the length of life of the posts is the greatest single factor in determining the cost of a fence on an annual basis.

Some recommended preservatives are: creosote, pentachlorophenol, zinc chloride, and chromated zinc chloride. Creosote and "penta" should be used only on dry seasoned posts; the others are effective on green posts with the bark left on.

Metal posts.—Metal posts (made of steel or wrought iron) last longer, require less storage space when not in use, and require less labor in setting than wood posts. Also they may give protection against lightning by grounding the current. However, such protection is questionable in dry weather or in areas with a low water table. But they are usually higher in price than wood posts.

Metal line posts are made in different styles and cross sections. Heavier studded "Y" section posts are most popular for livestock, although lighter channel posts may be used for temporary and movable fences. Line posts are available in lengths of 5 to 8 feet in increments of 6 inches. Metal corner, end, and gate posts are commonly made from angle sections, and come in 7 to 9 feet lengths.

Concrete posts.—When properly made, concrete posts give excellent service over many years. In general, however, they are expensive.

Electric Fences

Where a temporary enclosure is desired or where existing fences need bolstering from roguish or breachy animals, it may be desirable to install an electric fence, which can be done at minimum cost.

The following points are pertinent in the construction of an electric fence:

1. **Safety.**—If an electric fence is to be installed and used, (1) necessary safety precautions against accidents to both persons and animals should be taken, and (2) the farmer or rancher should first check into the regulations of his own state relative to the installation and use of electric fences. *Remember that an electric fence can be dangerous.* Fence controllers should be purchased from a reliable manufacturer; homemade controllers may be dangerous.

2. **Wire height.**—As a rule of thumb, the correct wire height for an electric fence is about three-fourths the height of the animal; with two wires provided for sheep and swine. Following are average fence heights above the ground for cattle and calves:

> Cattle: 30 to 40 inches
> Calves: 12 to 18 inches
> Mixed Livestock,
>   three wires—8, 12, and 32 inches

3. **Posts.**—Either wood or steel posts may be used for electric fencing. Corner posts should be as firmly set and well braced as required for any non-electric fence so as to stand the pull

necessary to stretch the wire tight. Line posts (1) need only be heavy enough to support the wire and withstand the elements, and (2) may be spaced 40 to 50 feet apart for cattle.

4. **Wire.**—In those states where barbed wire is legal, new four point hog wire is preferred. Barbed wire is recommended, because the barbs will penetrate the hair of animals and touch the skin, but smooth wire can be used satisfactorily. Rusty wire should never be used, because rust is an insulator.

5. **Insulators.**—Wire should be fastened to the posts by insulators and should not come into direct contact with posts, weeds, or the ground. Inexpensive solid glass or porcelain in-

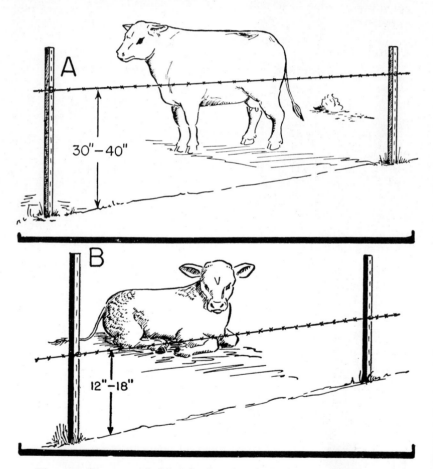

Fig. 196. Recommended height for electric fence for, A, cattle, and B, calves. (Drawing by R. F. Johnson)

sulators should be used, rather than old rubber or necks of bottles.

6. **Grounding.**—One lead from the controller should be grounded to a pipe driven into the moist earth. *An electric fence should never be grounded to a water pipe, because it could carry lightning directly to connecting buildings.* A lightning arrestor should be installed on the ground wire.

Guards or Bumper Gates

Cattle guards or bumper gates set in a fence permit convenient passage of automobiles and trucks but deter cattle, hogs, sheep, and most horses and mules (see Fig. 180, p. 507). Where cattle guards are installed, gates should be constructed nearby in order to allow for the movement of animals.

QUESTIONS FOR STUDY AND DISCUSSION

1. Make a critical study of your own beef cattle barn(s), or one with which you are very familiar, and determine its (1) desirable and (2) undesirable features.
2. One of the first and frequently one of the most difficult problems confronting the cattleman who wishes to construct a building or item of equipment is that of arriving at the proper size or dimensions. In planning to construct new buildings and equipment for beef cattle, what factors and measurements for buildings and equipment should be considered?
3. List and discuss the factors determining the type and size of beef cattle buildings.
4. List and discuss the steps in determining the size beef cattle barn to build on any given farm or ranch.
5. List and discuss the steps in determining the size silo to build on any given farm or ranch.
6. List and discuss the needed and desirable features of a modern multiple-use barn such as shown in Figs. 177-179.
7. In the selection of woven wire fence, what is meant by the following number: 1155? What other factors should be considered in the selection of woven wire? What specifications may be used in ordering barbed wire?

SELECTED REFERENCES

Title of Publication	Author(s)	Publisher
Automatic Livestock Waterers	Leaflet No. 395	U. S. Department of Agriculture, Washington 25, D. C.
Beef Cattle Housing	Bulletin No. 382	Agri. Expt. Sta., South Dakota State College, Brookings, S. D.
Beef Handling and Feeding Equipment	Reuben Albaugh C. F. Kelly H. L. Belton	Circ. 414, College of Agriculture, University of California, Davis, Calif.
Cattle Shelters and Equipment for Southern States	Agri. Handbook No. 81	U. S. Department of Agriculture, Washington 25, D. C., 1955.
Doane Ideas on Farm Buildings		Doane Agricultural Service, Inc., 5144 Delmar Blvd., St. Louis 8, Mo.
Equipment for Handling Beef Cattle	O. J. Trenary P. S. Pattengale	Bul. 441-A, Colorado State University, Fort Collins, Colo.
Farm Book, The		Doane Agricultural Digest, 5144 Delmar Blvd., St. Louis 8, Missouri.
Farm Buildings	D. G. Carter W. A. Foster	John Wiley & Sons, New York, 1947.
Farm Buildings	J. C. Wooley	McGraw-Hill Book Co., New York, 1946
Farm Service Buildings	H. E. Gray	McGraw-Hill Book Co., New York, 1955.
Farm Structures	H. J. Barre L. L. Sammet	John Wiley & Sons, Inc., New York, 1950.
Feed-Lot and Ranch Equipment for Beef Cattle	Farmers' Bul. No. 1584	U. S. Department of Agriculture, Washington 25, D. C.
Plans of Farm Buildings for Southern States	Misc. Pub. No. 360	U. S. Department of Agriculture, Washington 25, D. C.
Plans of Farm Buildings for Western States	Misc. Pub. No. 319	U. S. Department of Agriculture, Washington 25, D. C.

*   *   *   *   *

Plans and specifications for beef cattle buildings and equipment can also be obtained from the local county agricultural agent, your state college of agriculture, and materials and equipment manufacturers and dealers.

CHAPTER XIII

BEEF CATTLE HEALTH, DISEASE PREVENTION, AND PARASITE CONTROL[1]

Contents

[1]In the preparation of this chapter, the coauthorship of Dr. Leo Bustad, D.V.M. and M.S., General Electric, Richland, Washington is gratefully acknowledged.

The authors are indebted to the following veterinarians and the entomologist who reviewed Chapter XIII: Dr. A. J. Durant, D.V.M., Professor, Department of Veterinary Bacteriology, University of Missouri, Columbia, Mo.; Dr. Dean C. Lindley, D.V.M., Glendora Veterinary Clinic, Glendora, Calif.; Dr. Nyles Van Hoosen, D.V.M., Tacoma, Wash.; Dr. John R. Gorham, Associate Professor of Veterinary Pathology, Washington State University, Pullman, Wash.; and Mr. David H. Brannon, Extension Entomologist, Washington State University, Pullman, Wash.

In the revision of this chapter for the third edition of *Beef Cattle Science*, an authoritative review was accorded by Dr. James L. Palotay, D.V.M., College of Veterinary Medicine, Washington State University, Pullman, Wash.

It is to be emphasized that the review accorded by these eminent authorities does not constitute either full approval or full agreement of the reviewers and the authors on the contents of this chapter.

537

Without doubt, one of the most serious menaces threatening the livestock industry is animal ill-health, of which the largest loss is a result of the diseases that are due to a common factor transmitted from animal to animal. Today, with modern rapid transportation facilities and the dense livestock population centers, the opportunities for animals to become infected are greatly increased compared with a generation ago.

Each year, cattlemen suffer staggering losses from diseases and parasites. Death takes a tremendous toll. Even greater economic losses result from the decreased growth, gains, or production among the living and from the increased production costs. Also, considerable cost is involved in keeping out diseases that do not exist in the United States; and quarantine of a diseased area may cause depreciation of land values or even restrict whole agricultural programs. It has been conservatively estimated that annual U.S. losses from the more important diseases, parasites, and pests of livestock and poultry aggregate $2.4 billion dollars.[1]

Cattlemen should also be well informed relative to the relationship of cattle diseases and parasites to other classes of ani-

---

[1]USDA, The Yearbook of Agriculture 1956, *Animal Diseases*, p. 11.

mals and to man, because many of them are transmissible between species. For example, over ninety different types of infectious and parasitic diseases can be transmitted from animals
to human beings.[1] Of most concern in the latter respect are such
animal diseases as brucellosis (undulant fever), anthrax, Q fever,
rabies, trichinosis, tuberculosis, and tularemia. Thus, rigid meat
and milk inspection is necessary for the protection of human
health. This is an added expense which the producer, processor,
and consumer must share.

Fortunately for the producer, beef animals are out in the
open much of the time, with a minimum of confinement in shelters and small enclosures and close contact with each other.
This results in their having less infection with diseases and parasites than normally is encountered with dairy cattle. On the other
hand, the very fact that beef herds usually are inspected less
frequently than dairy herds may result in serious and widespread losses before the ravages of diseases or parasites are
observed and control measures instituted.

NORMAL TEMPERATURE, PULSE RATE, AND BREATHING RATE OF FARM ANIMALS

Table 39 gives the normal temperature, pulse rate, and
breathing rate of farm animals. In general, any marked and
persistent deviations from these normals may be looked upon as
a sign of animal ill health.

Every stockman should provide himself with an animal
thermometer, which is heavier and more rugged than the ordinary human thermometer. The temperature is measured by inserting the thermometer full length in the rectum, where it
should be left a minimum of 3 minutes. Prior to inserting the
thermometer, a long string should be tied to the end.

In general, infectious diseases are ushered in with a rise in
body temperature, but it must be remembered that body temperature is affected by stable or outside temperature, exercise, excitement, age, feed, etc. It is lower in cold weather, in older animals
and at night.

---

[1]Hull, Thomas G., *Diseases Transmitted from Animals to Man*, third
edition, Charles C. Thomas, Publisher, Springfield, Ill., Table 67, 1947.
Only about 20 of these 90 maladies are important to public health in the
United States.

TABLE 39

NORMAL TEMPERATURE, PULSE RATE, AND BREATHING RATE
OF FARM ANIMALS

Animal	Normal Rectal Temperature		Normal Pulse Rate	Normal Breathing Rate
	Average	Range		
	(degrees F)	(degrees F)	(rate/minute)	(rate/minute)
Cattle _____	101.5	100.4 - 102.8	60-70	10-30
Sheep _____	102.3	100.9 - 103.8	70-80	12-20
Goats _____	103.8	101.7 - 105.3	70-80	12-20
Swine _____	102.6	102 - 103.6	60-80	8-18
Horses _____	100.5	99 - 100.8	32-44	8-16

The pulse rate indicates the rapidity of the heart action.
The pulse of cattle is taken either on the outside of the jaw just
above its lower border, on the soft area immediately above the
inner dewclaw, or just above the hock joint. It should be pointed
out that the younger, the smaller, and the more nervous the animal, the higher the pulse rate. Also, the pulse rate increases with
exercise, excitement, digestion, and high outside temperature.

The breathing rate can be determined by placing the hand
on the flank, by observing the rise and fall of the flanks, or, in the
winter, by watching the breath condensate in coming from the
nostrils. Rapid breathing due to recent exercise, excitement, hot
weather or poorly ventilated buildings should not be confused
with disease. Respiration is accelerated in pain and in febrile
conditions.

A PROGRAM OF BEEF CATTLE HEALTH,
DISEASE PREVENTION, AND PARASITE CONTROL

Although the exact program will and should vary according
to the specific conditions existing on each individual farm or
ranch, the basic principles will remain the same. With this
thought in mind, the following program of beef cattle health,
disease prevention, and parasite control (based on the program
followed at Washington State University) is presented with
the hope that the beef cattle producer will use it (1) as a yardstick with which to compare his existing program, and (2) as a
guide post so that he and his local veterinarian, and other ad-
visors, may develop a similar and specific program for his own
enterprise:

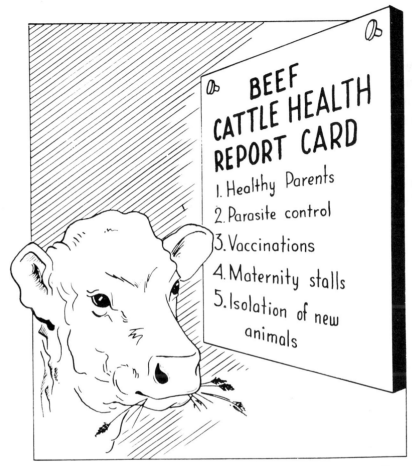

Fig. 197. Drawing by Steve Allured; print courtesy Washington State University.

I. GENERAL BEEF CATTLE PROGRAM

1. Breed only healthy cows to healthy bulls.

2. Avoid either an overfat or a thin, emaciated condition in all breeding animals.

3. Provide plenty of exercise for bulls and pregnant cows, preferably by allowing them to graze in well-fenced pastures in which plenty of shade and water are available.

4. Keep lots and corrals well drained and as dry as practical to prevent breeding places for foot rot and other diseases. Fence cattle out of pasture mudholes for the same reason.

5. If possible, divert drainage from adjacent infected premises and avoid across-the-fence contact with the neighbors' cattle unless they are definitely disease free. Do not visit farms where infectious diseases exist, as the germs may be brought home on shoes, clothing, or vehicles. For the same reason, feeds should not be bought from such farms, and one should beware of used feed bags.

6. If rented pastures must be used, avoid areas on which cattle have over-wintered; and, preferably, use only those rented pastures that have not had cattle on them for one year or that have been plowed in the interim.

7. Test the entire herd for tuberculosis and brucellosis each fall or at the time they are brought in from pasture and placed in winter quarters.

8. Eliminate the breeding ground of parasites as far as practical and use the proper insecticide or vermifuge for their control.

9. Keep commercial cattle—such as stocker and feeder cattle, and fattening cattle—in isolated quarters away from breeding animals.

10. When disease troubles are encountered, isolate affected animals and follow the instructions and prescribed treatment of a veterinarian.

II. CALVING TIME

1. When weather conditions permit, allow parturient cows to calve in a clean, uncontaminated, open pasture. During inclement weather, place the cows in isolated, roomy, light, well-ventilated maternity stalls—which should first be carefully cleaned and thoroughly disinfected with Lysol or a cresol disinfectant manufactured by a reputable company (following the mixing directions printed on the container) and provided with clean bedding for the occasion. After calving, all wet, stained, or soiled bedding should be removed and the floor sprinkled with lime; the afterbirth should be burned or buried deep in lime; and, if there has been trouble, the cows should be kept isolated until all discharges have ceased.

2. Unless the calves are born on a clean pasture away from possible infection, treat the navel cord of each newborn animal with tincture of iodine.

III. SUCKLING CALVES

1. If the baby calves are confined to stalls, scrub stalls thoroughly twice each week with warm soap solution and disinfect the walls and feed bunks and/or mangers.

2. Immunize for brucellosis all heifer calves at 4 to 12 months of age, observing the state regulations relative to age for vaccination.

3. Vaccinate all winter- and spring-born calves with blackleg and malignant edema bacterin, at approximately one month of age and again in the fall or in the following spring.

IV. NEW STOCK

1. Where your veterinarian feels that it is indicated, and preferably 10 days to 2 weeks before taking delivery on new animals, administer (1) a 10 cc. dose of pasteurella-corynebacterium bacterin (or, if this is not available, use hemorrhagic septicemia bacterin), and (2) a booster shot (according to the directions found on the bottle) of blackleg-malignant edema bacterin.

2. Isolate newly acquired animals for a minimum of three weeks, during which time they should be cared for by a separate caretaker.

3. While in isolation, test all newly acquired breeding animals for tuberculosis, brucellosis, leptospirosis, and Johne's disease; first, however, make every reasonable effort to ascertain that they come from herds which are known to be free from these and other diseases.

4. Spray newly acquired animals for lice control; and check them for internal parasites, and treat where indicated.

5. When possible, it is preferable to purchase virgin heifers and bulls, from a disease control standpoint. Isolate "tried" (non-virgin) bulls for a period of three weeks, and then turn them with a limited number of virgin heifers; observe these heifers for 30 to 60 days after breeding, as an aid in preventing the introduction of breeding diseases.

6. Thoroughly clean and disinfect the isolation stall after each animal(s) is removed and before a new animal(s) is placed therein. Disinfect with a hot 3 per cent lye solution, followed by the use of another recommended disinfectant (recommended by your local veterinarian), such as Lysol or sodium ortho phenylphenate.

In Per Cent of All Sick Animals Afflicted

Fig. 198. Relative frequency of non-nutritional beef cattle diseases and ailments. This figure, from Wash. Agri. Expt. Sta. Bul. 562, p.6, is based on a 24-state survey which covered over a half million cattle. It is recognized that cattlemen may not always have been accurate in their diagnosis; nevertheless, this is the most complete record of its type available. The five most common beef cattle diseases, in order of frequency—pink eye, calf scours, shipping fever, foot rot, and pneumonia—accounted for 77.2 per cent of all sick cattle (non-nutritional). During the course of a year, 8 per cent of the nation's cattle were afflicted by one or more non-nutritional diseases, and 0.59 per cent of all cattle died from such diseases. By rank, four diseases—pneumonia, calf scours, shipping fever, and blackleg—accounted for 60 per cent of all death losses from non-nutritional diseases. (Photo, courtesy Washington State University)

DISEASES OF BEEF CATTLE

It is not intended that this book shall serve as a source of home remedies. Rather, the enlightened cattleman will institute a program designed to assure herd health, disease prevention, and parasite control. When animal disease troubles are encountered, he will not attempt to diagnose or treat but will call upon his local veterinarian in exactly the same manner as he calls upon the family doctor when human ill health is encountered.

This chapter is limited to non-nutritional diseases and ailments; the nutritional diseases and ailments of cattle are covered in Table 27, Chapter IX.

Anthrax (Splenic Fever or Charbon)

Anthrax, also referred to as splenic fever or charbon, is an acute, infectious disease affecting all warm-blooded animals and man; but mature cattle are most susceptible. It usually occurs as scattered outbreaks or cases, but hundreds of animals may be involved. Certain sections are known as anthrax districts because of the repeated appearance of the disease. Grazing animals are particularly subject to anthrax, especially when pasturing closely following a drought or on land that has been recently flooded. In the United States, most human infections of anthrax result from handling diseased or dead animals on the farm or from handling hides, hair, and wool in factories.

Historically, anthrax is of great importance. It was one of the first scourges to be described in ancient and Biblical literature; it marked the beginning of modern bacteriology, being described by Koch in 1876; and it was the first disease in which immunization was effected by means of an attenuated culture, Pasteur having immunized animals against anthrax in 1881.

SYMPTOMS:

The mortality is usually quite high. It runs a very short course and is characterized by a blood poisoning (septicemia). The first indication of the disease may be the presence of severe symptoms of colic accompanied by high temperature, loss of appetite, muscular weakness, depression, and the passage of blood-stained feces. Swellings may be observed over the body, especially around the neck region. Milk secretion may turn bloody or cease entirely.

Fig. 199. Cow dead of anthrax. Local swellings, which frequently occur, are seen in the left flank. (Courtesy, USDA, Agricultural Research Administration)

CAUSE, PREVENTION, AND TREATMENT:

The disease is identified by a microscopic examination of the blood in which will be found the typical large, rod-shaped organisms causing anthrax. The bacillus can survive for years in a spore stage, resisting most destructive agents. As a result, it may remain in the soil for extremely long periods.

This disease is one that can largely be prevented by immunization. In the so-called anthrax regions, vaccination should be performed annually, usually in the spring, and well in advance of the time when the disease normally makes its appearance. At least nine types of biologics (serums, bacterins, and vaccines) are now available for use in anthrax vaccination. The choice of the biologic is dependent upon the local situation and should be left to the veterinarian or state livestock sanitary officials. Also, in the infected areas, adequate fly control should be obtained by spraying animals duing the insect season.

Herds that are infected should be quarantined, and all milk and other products should be withheld from the market until the danger of disease transmission is past. The farmer or rancher should never open the carcass of a dead animal suspected of having died from anthrax; instead the veterinarian should be summoned at the first sign of an outbreak.

When the presence of anthrax is suspected or proved, all carcasses and contaminated material should be completely burned or deeply buried and covered with quick-lime, preferably on the spot. This precaution is important because the disease can be spread by dogs, coyotes, buzzards, and other flesh eaters, and by flies and other insects.

When an outbreak of anthrax is discovered, all sick animals should be isolated promptly and treated. All exposed healthy animals should be vaccinated; pastures should be rotated; the premises should be quarantined; and a rigid program of sanitation should be initiated. These control measures should be carried out under the supervision of state or federal regulatory officials.

Early treatment of affected animals, with either antianthrax serum or massive doses of penicillin, may be effective if given soon enough.

Bacillary Hemoglobinuria (or Red Water Disease)

Bacillary hemoglobinuria, which is an acute, infectious disease, is often confused with other cattle diseases in which bloody urine is seen. The disease usually occurs in cattle over one year of age that are pastured on meadows or irrigated lands where drainage is poor, and during the summer and early fall months. Sheep are also affected, but to a lesser degree than cattle. A mortality up to 100 per cent occurs in untreated cases.

SYMPTOMS:

The course of the disease is usually a couple of days or less. Appetite, rumination, and milk flow suddenly cease. The animal hesitates to move and stands apart from the herd. The eyes are sunken, bloodshot, and may appear yellow. Breathing is rapid, and the temperature is high. The urine and feces are usually both blood tinged. It must be understood, however, that bloody urine (red water) may also be one of the symptoms in such conditions and diseases as lack of phosphorus, leptospirosis, Texas fever, plant poisoning, and anthrax. As red water disease can easily be confused with other conditions producing bloody urine, laboratory assistance is usually indicated in the event of unknown hemoglobinuria (bloody urine). All ages are affected, but most losses occur in cows over one year of age.

CAUSE, PREVENTION, AND TREATMENT:

An anaerobic bacteria called *Clostridium hemolyticum* is the primary causative agent, and its toxin causes the blood break-down. It is found in moist alkaline soils, especially in the low lying valley land of the Sierra Nevada, and the Coast and Cascade ranges in Nevada, California, and Oregon.

Inoculations with a bacterin or toxoid to stimulate immunity is valuable in communities where annual losses occur. This vaccination should occur two weeks prior to the time of the previous annual outbreak. Unless unavoidable, cattle should not be pastured on areas of known infection. Pools of stagnant water should be drained as such areas provide a favorable environment for the growth of the causative agent.

Anti-serum from hyper-immunized animals, in conjunction with antibiotics, is the only known treatment for animals showing symptoms of the disease, but suitable medical treatment in the way of stimulants may be a valuable adjunct. Since the disease may be confused with shipping fever, leptospirosis, and plant poisoning, it would be well to consult the local veterinarian.

Blackleg (Black Quarter or Symptomatic Anthrax)

This is a very infectious, highly fatal disease of cattle, and less frequently of sheep and goats. The disease is widespread, especially in the western range states. It occurs at almost any season, predominating in the spring and fall months among pastured cattle; but it may occur in the winter in stabled cattle. Once prevalent in a community, the disease remains there as a permanent hazard, the infected territory being referred to as a "hot area." It is seen most frequently in cattle ranging in age from three months to two years, but it may occur in older animals.

SYMPTOMS:

The incubation period is from one to five days, and its course is from one to three days. The first symptom noted is lameness, usually accompanied by or followed by swellings over the neck, shoulder, flanks, thighs, and breast which crackle under pressure. High fever, loss of appetite, and severe depression accompany the symptoms. Although there are a few recoveries, death is the usual termination, occurring within three days of the onset of symptoms.

CAUSE, PREVENTION, AND TREATMENT:

This disease is caused by an anaerobic bacterium, called *Clostridium feseri* (formerly called *chauvoei*), although it is often accompanied by other of the *Clostridia* genus. Infection is

Fig. 200. Heifer with blackleg, six hours before death. Note the lameness and the swelling over the neck and shoulder. (Courtesy, Veterinary Research Laboratory, Montana State College)

usually the result of wound contamination or ingestion of the organisms.

Prevention consists of vaccination of all animals at approximately three to four months of age,[1] using one of the approved vaccines. The immunity stimulated by proper vaccination usually lasts from twelve to eighteen months or longer, and a natural immunity tends to develop when the animal is about two years of age. Animals that die from blackleg should not be cut open unless under the direction of a qualified veterinarian. The carcasses should be burned or deeply buried and the contaminated area disinfected. Eradication of blackleg from pastures is difficult if not impossible.

When in the hands of a veterinarian, medicinal treatment for older animals is sometimes successful.

Brucellosis (Bang's disease)

Brucellosis, which occurs throughout the world, is an in-

[1] A second, or booster, vaccination at one year of age will give added protection.

sidious (hidden) disease in which the lesions frequently are not evident. Although the medical term "brucellosis" is used in a collective way to designate the disease caused by the three different but closely related *Brucella* organisms, the specie names further differentiate the organisms as: (1) *Br. abortus*, (2) *Br. suis*, and (3) *Br. melitensis.*

The disease is known as *Brucella abortus*, Bang's disease (after Professor Bang, noted Danish research worker, who, in 1896, first discovered the organism responsible for bovine brucellosis), or contagious abortion in cattle; *Brucella suis*, Traum's disease, or infectious abortion in swine; *Brucella melitensis*, Malta fever, or abortion in goats; and Malta fever, Mediterranean fever, or undulant fever in man. The causative organism is often associated with fistulous withers and poll-evil of horses.

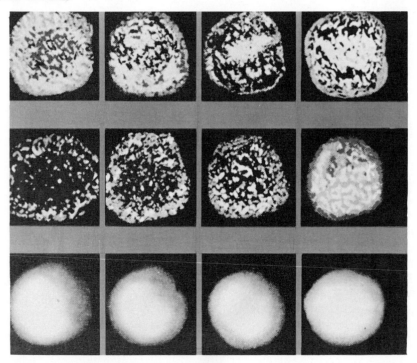

Fig. 201. Microscopic picture showing the blood (agglutination) test for diagnosis of brucellosis. Top row shows clumping (agglutination), indicating brucellosis. Center row shows complete clumping in the first 3 dilutions and partial clumping in the 1:200 dilution. Bottom row shows a negative test, indicating brucellosis free. (Courtesy, Lederle Laboratories)

Brucellosis is one of the most serious and widespread diseases affecting the livestock industry. For the nation as a whole, slightly over 2.5 per cent of all cattle tested (including both beef and dairy animals) react.[1] Control and eradication of the disease is important for two reasons: (1) the danger of human infection; it being the most important U. S. animal-human disease and (2) the economic loss in the form of fewer live calves, more retained placenta, more breeding trouble, more arthritis, more mastitis, and lowered milk production.

The blood (agglutination) test is a safe, reliable (though not perfect), and practical method for the diagnosis of brucellosis in all farm animals. Either the tube test method or the rapid (stained antigen) plate method is satisfactory when conducted by an experienced technician. There is nothing mysterious about the blood test. It is simply based on the following phenomenon: The blood stream of an infected animal contains an antibody, known as agglutinin. When blood serum containing this substance is brought in contact with a suspension of *Brucella* organisms (called an antigen), it causes the organisms to adhere to one another and form clumps.

This action, known as agglutination, constitutes a simple test for diagnosing brucellosis in the living animal. The blood test of swine is unquestionably the most readily available diagnostic method for this species, but it is not considered as reliable as the similar test with cattle or goats.

The milk fat or ring test is a satisfactory method of detecting brucellosis-infected dairy herds.

SYMPTOMS:

Unfortunately, the symptoms of brucellosis are often rather indefinite. While the act of abortion is the most readily observed symptom in cows, goats, and sows, it should be borne in mind that not all animals that abort are affected with brucellosis and that not all animals affected with brucellosis will necessarily abort. On the other hand, every case of abortion should be regarded with suspicion until proved noninfectious.

The infected animal may prematurely give birth to a dead fetus two to four months following conception. On the other hand, the birth may be entirely normal; but the calf may be

[1]Ensminger, M. E., M. W. Galgan, and W. L. Slocum, Wash. Agri. Expt. Sta. Bul. 562, p. 15.

Fig. 202. Cow with aborted fetus. Every case of abortion should be regarded with suspicion until proved noninfectious. (Courtesy, Dr. B. T. Simms, USDA)

weak, or there may be retention of the afterbirth, inflammation of the uterus, and/or difficulty in future conception. The milk production is usually reduced. There may be abscess formation in the testicles of the male and swelling of the joints (arthritis). The observed symptoms in man include weakness, joint pains, undulating (varying) fever, and occasionally orchitis.

CAUSE, PREVENTION, AND TREATMENT:

The disease is caused by a bacteria called *Brucella abortus* in cattle, *Brucella suis* in swine, and *Brucella melitensis* in goats. The suis and melitensis types are seen in cattle, but the incidence is rare; swine are infected with both the suis and melitensis types; and horses may become infected with all three types.

Man is susceptible to all three species of brucellosis. In most areas, the vast majority of undulant fever cases in man are due to *B. abortus*, but it is noteworthy that 70 per cent of such cases in Iowa—the nation's leading hog state—are due to *B. suis*. The swine organism causes a more severe disease in human beings than the cattle organism, although not so severe as that induced by the goat type (*Brucella melitensis*). Fortunately, far less people are exposed to the latter, simply because of the limited number of goats and the rarity of the disease in goats in the United States. Stockmen are aware of the possibility that human

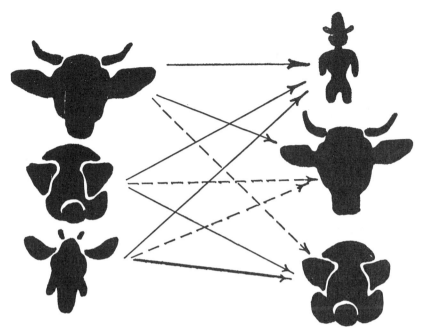

SOURCES OF INFECTION
Dotted lines indicate sometimes a source.

Fig 203. Sources of brucellosis infection. (Drawing by R. F. Johnson)

beings may contract undulant fever from handling affected animals, especially at the time of parturition; from slaughtering operations or handling raw meats from affected animals; or from consuming raw milk or other raw by-products from cows or goats, and eating uncooked meats infected with brucellosis organisms. The simple precautions of pasteurizing milk and cooking meat, however, make these foods safe for human consumption.

The *Brucella* organism is relatively quite resistant to drying but is killed by the common disinfectants and by pasteurization. The organism is found in immense numbers in the various tissues of the aborted young and in the discharges and membranes from the aborted animal. It is harbored indefinitely in the udder and may also be found in the sex glands, spleen, liver, kidneys, blood stream, joints, and lymph nodes.

ROUTE OF BRUCELLOSIS GERMS IN THEIR ATTACK ON CATTLE

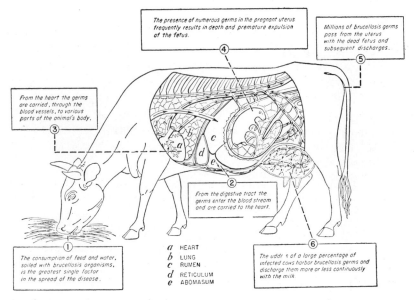

The presence of numerous germs in the pregnant uterus frequently results in death and premature expulsion of the fetus.

Millions of brucellosis germs pass from the uterus with the dead fetus and subsequent discharges.

From the heart the germs are carried, through the blood vessels, to various parts of the animal's body.

From the digestive tract the germs enter the blood stream and are carried to the heart.

The consumption of feed and water, soiled with brucellosis organisms, is the greatest single factor in the spread of the disease.

a HEART
b LUNG
c RUMEN
d RETICULUM
e ABOMASUM

The udder s of a large percentage of infected cows harbor brucellosis germs and discharge them more or less continuously with the milk.

Fig. 204. Diagram showing how cattle become infected with the *Brucella* organism and its route of attack. (Courtesy, USDA)

Brucellosis appears to be commonly acquired through the mouth in feed and water contaminated with the bacteria, or by licking infected animals, contaminated feeders, or other objects to which the bacteria may adhere. Proof that bulls transmit the disease through the act of service is lacking, but there is evidence that boars frequently transmit the disease in this manner.

Freedom from disease should be the goal of all control programs. An annual blood test (and more frequently if the disease is encountered), the removal of infected animals, strict sanitation, proper and liberal use of disinfectants, isolation at the time of parturition and the control of animals, feed, and water brought into the premises is the key to the successful control or eradication of brucellosis.

Where, for various reasons, there is more than ordinary hazard of cattle becoming infected with brucellosis, calfhood vaccination with "strain 19" of heifers at 4 to 12 months of age is advocated. Since the prescribed age for calfhood vaccination varies from state to state, information on this point should be obtained from the local veterinarian. Adult vaccination of negative cows is occasionally recommended in herds where infection is spreading.

Sound management practices, which include either buying replacement animals that are free of the disease or raising all females, are a necessary adjunct in prevention. Drainage from infected areas should be diverted or fenced off, and visitors (man and animal) should be kept away from animal barns and feed lots. Feeds should not be bought from farms that have infected animals, and one should beware of used feed bags. Animals taken to livestock shows and fairs should be isolated on their return and tested thirty days later.

In 1934, a brucellosis control and eradication program was begun in connection with the cattle-reduction program necessitated by the drought of that year. This program has continued to operate, with provision for the slaughter of animals that react positively to the test. Under the slaughter provision, several states pay partial indemnity to farmers whose animals are condemned under the program.

The U. S. Livestock Sanitary Association has outlined a cattle program for guidance of all states, thus unifying the national brucellosis control effort. This calls for the initiation of one of the following plans:

Plan A.—Test and slaughter of reactors, with or without calfhood vaccination of heifers. This program is recommended for infected herds in which the immediate removal of reactors to the brucellosis test will not cause serious economic loss. After a limited number of tests, a lightly infected herd may be freed of the infection. This plan calls for prompt removal of all reactors, thorough cleaning and disinfecting of all reactor-occupied buildings, and retests at frequent intervals (not to exceed thirty days) until the disease has been eradicated. Calfhood vaccination may be practiced in infected herds and areas as a supplement to the above practices.

In order for this (Plan A) to be successful, replacement females must either be raised or the greatest of care must be exercised in introducing them from outside sources. In vaccination, strain 19, which is a modified culture of the causative organism, is being used extensively. Huddleson at Michigan State University, however, reports good results with a mucoid phase vaccine, which consists of a modification of the swine strain of organism.

Plan A will be successful only where rigid sanitary measures are adhered to, where retests are conducted at sufficiently close intervals, and where only disease-free animals are introduced into the herd. The latter precaution is especially to be observed by purebred breeders who buy considerable replacements.

Federal and state agencies often pay the owner of slaughtered animals certain indemnity over and above the market price, when the animals are sold as beef.

Plan B.—Test and segregation of reactors, with calfhood vaccination of heifers. In this plan, the herd is tested, and reactors are retained but carefully segregated until they can be disposed of for slaughter without excessive loss to the owner. This is supplemented by calfhood vaccination of all heifers. It is to be noted that reactors should be disposed of as soon as possible. Cognizance should be taken of the fact that all heifers vaccinated will not be immune.

Although this method is not applicable to a high percentage of farms and ranches, it does offer a possibility of keeping for breeding purposes infected cows of superior breeding or outstanding production. Yet, every effort should be made to reduce the size of the infected herd as rapidly as possible consistent with the breeding and management program; for, as each infected cow goes to the butcher, one possible source of infection is permanently removed from the premises. Though infected at birth, the offspring of brucellosis-infected cows do not remain permanently infected and may, therefore, be added to the clean herd when the blood test indicates that it is safe to do so.

Plan C.—Test with temporary retention of reactors, and calfhood vaccination of heifers. The final aim of this method should always be a brucellosis-free herd, which is established by replacing the infected cows with disease-free vaccinated heifers. Until the herd is free from brucellosis, which should not take longer than four to five years, every precaution should be taken to prevent infection of the disease-free cows in the herd. As infected cows are usually quite dangerous at the time of and for a short while after aborting or calving, they should receive close attention at this time. Separate maternity stalls or paddocks should be provided for the infected cows; the placenta and any aborted or dead calves should be burned or buried; and rigid sanitary measures should be followed. Any milk from such herds should be pasteurized.

Plan C has been popular with dairymen who have an infected herd but who cannot immediately dispose of all reactors because they have certain milk quotas to meet. It has also been popular with cattlemen whose herds are surrounded by infected herds, with those whose farms or ranches do not lend themselves to some other type of enterprise, and with those who, lacking facilities, cannot follow plan B.

Plan D.—Testing and whole-herd vaccination of negative animals. In general, whole-herd vaccination is not recommended in any herd in which it seems reasonable that any one of the former methods may succeed. It is an emergency plan, calling for adult vaccination where there is a rapid spread of virulent infection. Prior to vaccination, however, all animals are tested, and only the negative ones are vaccinated. Animals advanced more than four months in pregnancy are not vaccinated until after calving.

Plan D should be followed only after state and federal cooperating agencies have given written approval; and, in the case of a dairy herd, only after assurance is given that the state or municipal laws or ordinances will not interfere with the sale of milk or other dairy products from reacting cows.

Plan D is sometimes used in problem herds in which storms of abortion are occurring or where the premises do not lend themselves to even partial segregation.

Plan E.—Calfhood vaccination without testing. This plan is rather unscientific and questionable because nothing is initially ascertained as to the brucellosis status of the herd. True enough, the calfhood vaccination of heifers may be helpful in eventually producing a disease-free herd; but as the adult animals are not tested, the disease, if it does exist, may continue to spread among the unvaccinated mature animals. Because of this situation, it is never wise to secure replacement females for a brucellosis-free herd out of a herd following plan E.

Some beef cattle owners have followed plan E, especially when infected cattle were known to be on immediately adjacent premises or when the percentage of infection in the area was known to be high. Most scientists do not recommend this plan.

TABLE 40

GUIDE TO FEDERAL REQUIREMENTS FOR THE INTERSTATE MOVEMENT OF CATTLE WITH RESPECT TO BRUCELLOSIS

[This Guide is NOT a Regulation and is NOT to be used as such. For detailed information relative to each type of Interstate Movement refer to the Regulation which appeared in the July 12, 1956, Issue of the Federal Register (21 F. R. 5183).]

CLASSES OF CATTLE	REQUIREMENTS TO MOVE INTO	
	Modified-Certified Brucellosis Free Areas	All Other Areas
1. Steers, spayed heifers and calves under 8 months	None	None
2. Cattle from brucellosis-free herds and areas.	Official Certificate	Official Certificate
3. Official vaccinates under 30 months of age at time of shipment.	Official certificate and a permit from livestock sanitary official of state of destination.	Official Certificate
4. Official vaccinates over 30 months of age at time of shipment.	Must be tested within 30 days prior to interstate movement and not react over incomplete at 1:100. Negative animals require only an official certificate for movement. Those showing maximum titers of incomplete at 1:100 require a permit from the livestock sanitary official of the state of destination in addition to an official certificate and must be placed under quarantine in state of destination until negative or slaughtered.	Must be tested within 30 days prior to shipment and not react over incomplete at 1:100. Negative animals require only an official certificate for movement. Those showing maximum titers of incomplete at 1:100 require a permit from the livestock sanitary official of the state of destination in addition to an official certificate.
5. Non-vaccinates over 8 months of age.	Negative blood test within 30 days of shipment. Permit from livestock sanitary official of state of destination and an official certificate required. Must be quarantined in state of destination until found negative after 30 days or be slaughtered. If cattle originate in herd under federal-state supervision and a herd blood test within past 90 days revealed no reactors, animals can move without permit and quarantine, providing each animal shipped was negative to another test 30 days from previous test within 30 days of shipment. An official certificate is required.	Negative blood test within 30 days of shipment plus official certificate.
6. Bulls and female cattle of beef type moved for feeding or grazing purposes only.	Can be moved under an official certificate and a permit from livestock sanitary official of state of destination if that state has laws, rules, or regulations providing for the segregating and quarantine of such cattle.	
7. Reactors (CFR Amendment 56-40).	Direct to slaughter at federally inspected plant or one specifically approved by United States Department of Agriculture, or to a public stockyard for sale to such a slaughtering establishment, with "B" brand on left jaw and metal reactor tag in left ear. Official certificate required.	

MOVEMENT OF CATTLE FOR IMMEDIATE SLAUGHTER

Direct to slaughter at federally inspected plant or one specifically approved by U. S. D. A., if accompanied by a waybill or similar document, of a certificate signed by the OWNER or SHIPPER of the cattle.

MOVEMENT OF CATTLE TO PUBLIC STOCKYARDS

Direct to a public stockyard or one specifically approved by U. S. D. A., if accompanied by a waybill or similar document, or a certificate signed by the OWNER or SHIPPER of the cattle.

Also, the following terms and definitions are pertinent to carrying out the provisions of the above referred to requirements:

1. *Certified brucellosis-free herd*——A herd of cattle officially declared by the U. S. D. A. and a state as free from brucellosis and such declaration being evidenced by a currently effective certificate issued jointly by the U. S. D. A. and such state.

2. *Modified certified brucellosis-free areas*——A state, or a political subdivision or portion thereof, in which the percentage of cattle affected with brucellosis has been determined by the U. S. D. A. not to exceed one per cent and the percentage of herds in which brucellosis is present has been determined by such service not to exceed five per cent.

3. *Official vaccinate*——A bovine animal vaccinated against brucellosis for 4 through 8 months of age, or a bovine animal of a beef breed in a range or semirange area, vaccinated against brucellosis from 4 to 12 months of age, under the supervision of a federal or state veterinary official, with a vaccine approved by the U. S. D. A.; permanently identified as such a vaccinate; and reported at the time of vaccination to the appropriate state or federal agency cooperating in the eradication of brucellosis.

In any of the above five plans, certain recommendations are made relative to movement of livestock, branding, tagging, record keeping, slaughtering, etc. It is also to be noted that either slaughter or quarantine of infected cattle, together with rigid sanitation, must be a part of any successful eradication program once the disease has made its appearance. Calfhood vaccination should be restricted to four to twelve months of age. Vaccinated calves are not expected to give a negative reaction to the test until twelve to twenty-four months of age, and some may give a positive test even longer without being infected. Moreover, a few vaccinated heifers—up to 5 per cent—may become permanent reactors. It must also be realized that there is no practical method of differentiating between reactions that follow vaccination and those which follow infection with virulent *Brucella* organisms. The latter point makes it imperative that one regard all reactors with suspicion, unless the honesty of the persons involved is unquestioned. Finally, it is to be emphasized that strain 19 vaccine is a valuable adjunct to, but not a substitute for, sound sanitary measures. Calfhood vaccination is no "cure-all," nor is it 100 per cent effective.

To date, there is no known medicinal agent that is completely effective in the treatment of brucellosis in any class of farm animals. Thus, the farmer and rancher should not waste valuable time and money on so-called "cures" that are advocated by fraudulent operators.

The details relative to federal requirements for the interstate movement of cattle with respect to brucellosis are given in Table 40.

Calf Diphtheria

Calf diphtheria is an acute, infectious disease of housed suckling calves and young feedlot cattle. The disease sometimes attacks these young animals as early as the third or fourth day after birth. If untreated, the mortality is very high. The disease is not to be confused with the virus sore mouth of sheep or the diphtheria of humans, with which it has no relationship.

SYMPTOMS:

The affected animal shows difficulty in breathing, eating, and drinking. Drooling and swallowing movements may also be noted. Inspection of the mouth reveals yellowish crumbling masses and patches of dead tissue (diphtheritic membranes) on the borders of the tongue, adjacent to the molar teeth, and in the throat. Once established and unchecked, it will spread rapidly, eventually causing the death of the animal.

CAUSE, PREVENTION, AND TREATMENT:

The alleged cause of this malady is the soil organism *Actinomyces necrophorus;* the same organism that is often found in foot rot. The organism gains entrance to the tissues through wounds or eruptions in the mouth, and within five days after entrance will develop the symptoms noted above.

Prevention consists of segregating the sick animals from the healthy ones and cleaning and disinfecting the quarters, not only after infection breaks but before the calf is born. After outbreaks, all well animals should be checked daily.

Treatment, which is quite simple and usually very effective, consists of removing the dead tissue and painting the affected areas with tincture of iodine. As in other serious animal diseases, the services of a veterinarian should be sought in handling an outbreak of calf diphtheria. The veterinarian may administer sulfas and/or antibiotics.

Calf Scours (White-Scours or Infectious Diarrhea)

This is an acute, contagious, and often rapidly fatal disease of young or newborn calves, but it is also seen in foals and lambs. Most affected calves are less than five days of age, and the disease is not uncommon in calves less than forty-eight hours old. Outbreaks of calf scours are most common among stabled animals during fall, winter, and early spring. An estimated 20 per cent of all dairy calves die from white scours and associated diseases.[1]

SYMPTOMS:

The affected animal first appears distressed and shows a lack of appetite. The hair coat is rough and the eyes sunken. There is severe diarrhea, with light-colored, foul-smelling, watery, or foamy feces. The animal may bloat, although it may be severely emaciated.

It is sometimes difficult to distinguish this disease from diarrhea caused by other factors—such as overfeeding, irregular feeding, use of unclean utensils, too rapid changes in feed, or exposure to drafts and cold, damp floors. With the infectious type

[1]Ensminger, M. E., M. W. Galgan, and W. L. Slocum, Wash. Agri. Expt. Sta. Bul. 562, p. 15.

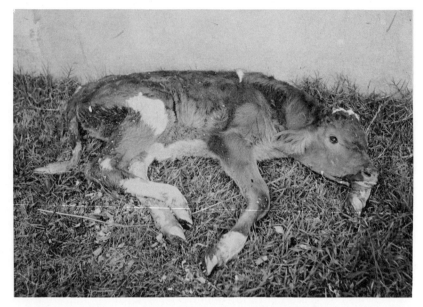

Fig. 205. Young calf with severe calf scours. Note sunken eyes, profuse salivation, and watery bowel discharge; which are characteristic symptoms. (Courtesy, Professor G. H. Weise, University of North Carolina)

of scours, however, several calves are usually affected; and some animals may die quickly. It is reasonable strongly to suspect white-scours if the symptoms appear within the first week after birth.

CAUSE, PREVENTION, AND TREATMENT:

It often seems that the first calf affected was exposed to faulty feeding. Many scientists are of the opinion that the problem is basically of nutritional origin, in that the animal lacks some of the vitamins (A, and some of the B vitamins and ascorbic acid) and perhaps other nutrients and antibodies. This, they say, leaves the calf an easy prey to some of the colon organisms that normally are quite harmless but which may become pathogenic when faulty nutrition exists. Be this as it may, the primary causative agent of the disease is an invasion of the intestinal tract by certain types of microorganisms, particularly varieties of the colon bacillus, which are widely distributed in nature. The infection may enter the body via either the navel cord or mouth. Also, it has been established that some cases of calf scours are caused by a virus.

To keep the disease away from the herd, one must prevent primary infection of the newborn. This rests on the enforcement of strict sanitary measures. Weather conditions permitting, birth should preferably take place in the open on an uncontaminated, sun-exposed pasture. Otherwise a clean, disinfected maternity stall should be provided, and the navel cord of the newborn calf should be treated with tincture of iodine. The newborn animal should be segregated from other animals and the contaminated quarters thoroughly cleaned and disinfected. Prevention should also include proper feeding of pregnant cows and giving colostrum to calves that are subsequently to be raised on a milk replacer. When calf scours appear, infected animals should be segregated and the premises should be thoroughly cleaned and disinfected.

The treatments are legion, although they are often to no avail; and frequently the recovered animal is a "poor doer." With the advent of sulfonamides and antibiotics, many drug combinations have come on the market. The local veterinarian should be consulted for the latest information or treatments.

Circling Disease (Listeriosis)

Circling disease, also called Listerellosis or Listeriosis, is an infectious disease affecting mainly cattle, sheep, and goats; but it has been reported in swine, foals, and other animals and man. All ages of cattle are susceptible. One to seven per cent of the herd may be infected, and the mortality in affected animals is extremely high.

SYMPTOMS:

This disease principally affects the nervous system. Depression, staggering, circling and strange awkward movements are noted. The animal may be seen holding a mouthful of hay for hours. There may be inflammation around the eye, and abortion may occur. The course of the disease is very short, with paralysis and death the usual termination. Positive diagnosis can be made only by laboratory examination of the brain.

CAUSE, PREVENTION, AND TREATMENT:

Circling disease results from the invasion of the central nervous system by bacteria called *Listeria monocytogenes*. The method of transmission is unknown, and there are no known methods of prevention or treatment.

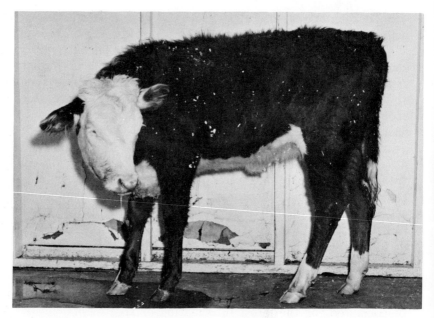

Fig. 206. Calf with circling disease. Note the drooping ear, slobbering and tendency to turn to the left. (Courtesy, Department of Veterinary Pathology and Hygiene, College of Veterinary Medicine, University of Illinois)

Foot-and-Mouth Disease

This is a highly contagious disease of cloven-footed animals (mainly cattle, sheep, and swine) characterized by the appearance of water blisters in the mouth (and in the snout in the case of hogs), on the skin between and around the claws of the hoof, and on the teats and udder. Fever, diminished rumination and reduced appetite are other signs of the disease.

Man is mildly susceptible but very rarely infected, whereas the horse is immune.

Unfortunately, one attack does not render the animal permanently immune, but the disease has a tendency to recur, perhaps because there are several strains of the causative virus. The disease is not present in the United States, but there have been at least nine outbreaks (some authorities claim ten) in this country between 1870 and 1929, each of which was stamped out by the prompt slaughter of every affected and exposed animal. No United States outbreak has occurred since 1929, but the disease is greatly feared. Drastic measures are exercised in preventing the introduction of the disease into the United States, or, in the case of actual outbreak, in eradicating it.

In December, 1946, an outbreak of foot-and-mouth disease was confirmed in Mexico, and the border was closed from that date to Sept. 1, 1952. Then the border remained open from Sept. 1, 1952, until May 23, 1953, at which time another outbreak occurred and it was again closed. The U. S. Secretary of Agriculture again opened the border on Jan. 1, 1955.

On Feb. 25, 1952, an outbreak of foot-and-mouth disease was diagnosed in Saskatchewan, Canada. This resulted in the U. S.— Canada border being closed from this date until March, 1953.

Foot-and-mouth disease is constantly present in Europe, Asia, Japan, the Philippines, Africa, and South America. It has not been reported in New Zealand or Australia.

SYMPTOMS:

The disease is characterized by the formation of blisters (vesicles) and a moderate fever three to six days following exposure. These blisters are found on the mucus membranes of the tongue, lips, palate, cheeks, and on the skin around the claws of the feet, and on the teats and udder.

Fig. 207. Cow with foot-and-mouth disease. The animal is reluctant to stand because of sore feet. The characteristic profuse flow of saliva is caused by blisters in the mouth. (Courtesy, USDA)

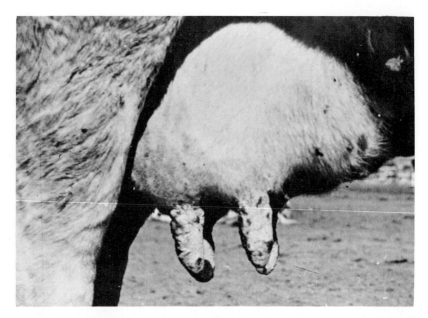

Fig. 208. Blisters (vesicles) on the teats of a cow with foot-and-mouth disease. (Courtesy, USDA)

Presence of these vesicles, especially in the mouth of cattle, stimulates a profuse flow of saliva that hangs from the lips in strings. Complicating or secondary factors are infected feet, caked udder, abortion, and great loss of weight. The mortality of adult animals is not ordinarily high, but the usefulness and productivity of affected animals is likely to be greatly damaged, thus causing great economic loss.

CAUSE, PREVENTION, AND TREATMENT:

The infective agent of this disease is one of the smallest of the filtrable viruses. In fact, it now appears that there are at least six strains of the virus. Infection with one strain does not protect against the other strains.

The virus is present in the fluid and coverings of the blisters, in the blood, meat, milk, saliva, urine and other secretions of the infected animal. The virus may be excreted in the urine for over two hundred days following experimental inoculation. The virus can also be spread through infected biological products, such as smallpox vaccine and hog cholera virus and serum, and by the cattle fever tick.

Except for the nine outbreaks mentioned, the disease has been kept out of the United States by extreme precautions, such as quarantine at ports of entry and assistance with eradication in neighboring lands when introduction appears imminent.

Two methods have been applied in control: the slaughter method and the quarantine procedure. Then, if the existence of the disease is confirmed by diagnosis, the area is immediately placed under strict quarantine; infected and exposed animals are slaughtered and buried, with owners being paid indemnities based on their appraised value. Everything is cleaned and thoroughly disinfected.

Fortunately, the foot-and-mouth disease virus is quickly destroyed by a solution of the cheap and common chemical, sodium hydroxide (lye). Because quick control action is necessary, state or federal authorities should be notified the very moment the presence of the disease is suspected.

Recently, a third method has been tried: use of a newly developed tissue culture vaccine, which contains all the strains of virus. Vaccines have not been used in the outbreaks in the United States because they have not been regarded as favorable to rapid, complete eradication of the infection.

No effective treatment is known.

Foot-Rot (or Foul-Foot)

This disease is an inflammation of the hoofs of cattle, sheep, and goats; but cross-infections of foot rot between cattle and sheep do not occur. It is a potential hazard wherever animals of these species are kept; especially in wet muddy areas.

SYMPTOMS:

A shrewd observer will first notice a reddening and swelling of the skin just above the hoof, between the toes, or in the bulb of the heel. As the infection progresses, lameness will be noted. If not arrested, the infection will invade the soft tissue and cause a discharge of pus from the infected breaks in the skin. At this stage, a characteristic foul odor is present. Later, the joint cavities may be involved, and the animal may show fever and depression characteristic of a general infection. Affected animals lose weight, and, if lactating, produce less milk; and they may die if unattended.

CAUSE, PREVENTION, AND TREATMENT:

Because the feet of animals are continually being exposed to all types of filth containing millions of microorganisms, it is difficult to incriminate the causative agent or agents. The soil organism, *Spherophorus necrophorus* is most frequently recovered from cases of foot rot in cattle; but pus-forming bacteria, colon bacilli, and others may lend support to the destructive process. Similar types of infection may have different causative agents depending on area, soil, and other factors.

The prevention of this disease is much more effective than the treatment, because once established it is difficult to control the spread. Draining of muddy corrals and the segregation of infected and new animals is recommended. If the disease appears, a good cleaning is in order, and unaffected animals should be moved to clean quarters and pastures if possible. Also, effective prevention may be obtained through subjecting animals to (1) a foot bath of 2 to 5 per cent bluestone (copper sulfate) or (2) a walk way of air-slaked lime. In some cases, the inclusion of an organic iodide compound in the feed or salt has markedly reduced the incidence of foot rot in problem herds.

The success of treatment seems to depend on the stage of infection and perhaps on the causative agent. The usual treatment consists of the following:

1. Place in a clean, dry place.
2. If necessary, trim away the affected part of the foot. Also, check for, and if necessary eliminate, foreign bodies in the hoof, or wire that might be wrapped around just above the hoof.
3. Stand in or walk animals through a shallow foot bath of 5 to 20% bluestone for 1 to 5 minutes, treating at 2- to 4-day intervals as required.

If these steps fail, the veterinarian may use intravenous sulfonamide therapy—accompanied by cleaning, disinfecting, and packing the affected area. In advanced stages, best results are obtained by surgical amputation of the affected claw. Animals so treated soon walk as before on the one remaining healthy claw.

Indiana Virus Diarrhea

This disease was first observed and described by Dr. Pritchard in Indiana, in 1954. Since then, it has occurred mostly in the mid-west and west. The greatest losses are in weight, condition, and feed. (See mucosal disease.)

SYMPTOMS:

The symptoms are quite similar to those observed in New York virus diarrhea; high temperature, a mucous diarrhea, nasal and oral discharges, ulceration of the mucous membranes, and lameness in about 10 per cent of the cases. Once the disease appears, almost 100 per cent of the animals are affected; but the death rate is low.

CAUSE, PREVENTION, AND TREATMENT:

As indicated by the name Indiana virus disease is caused by a virus.

The most effective preventive measures consist in avoiding contact with affected animals and in keeping away from contaminated feed and water. Also, all incoming animals should be isolated for at least 30 days. Once the disease makes its appearance, sick animals should be isolated and rigid sanitary measures should be initiated.

There is no known treatment, but antibiotics effectively combat the secondary bacterial invaders that accompany the disease.

Infectious Bovine Rhinotracheitis (IBR or Red Nose)

Infectious bovine rhinotracheitis is a new disease, which was first found in a Colorado feed lot in 1950. It has occurred chiefly in the western United States. The main economic losses from the disease are in time, weight, and drugs. (See mucosal disease.)

SYMPTOMS:

Affected animals go off feed and lose weight; generally cough; may show pain in swallowing; usually slobber and show a nasal discharge; breathe rapidly, with difficulty, and in severe cases through the mouth; show severe inflammation of the nostrils, trachea, and windpipe; have a high fever, 104° to 107° F.; and may remain sick for as long as a week. When the disease breaks out, 51 to 100 per cent of the animals are affected, with an average death loss of about 3 per cent.

CAUSE, PREVENTION, AND TREATMENT:

The disease is caused by a virus.

Infectious bovine rhinotracheitis can be prevented by the

use of a vaccine. For effective control and eradication, one should initiate rigid sanitation and disease preventive measures and isolate sick animals.

There is no known treatment, but antibiotics effectively combat the secondary bacterial invaders that accompany the disease.

Johne's Disease (Paratuberculosis or Chronic Bacterial Dysentery)

This is a chronic, incurable, infectious disease seen chiefly in cattle; also found in sheep and goats, and more rarely in swine and horses. It resembles tuberculosis in many respects. The disease is very widespread, having been observed in practically every country where cattle are raised on a large scale. Apparently, it is increasing in the United States. It is one of the most difficult diseases to eradicate from a herd.

SYMPTOMS:

The disease seems to involve calfhood exposure with no evidence of infection for six to eighteen months. At the end of this time, the animal loses flesh and displays intermittent

Fig. 209. Cow with Johne's disease. Note marked loss of flesh and tucked up flank. Diarrhea is a common symptom of the disease. (Courtesy, Department of Veterinary Pathology and Hygiene, College of Veterinary Medicine, University of Illinois)

diarrhea and constipation, the former becoming more prevalent. Affected animals may retain a good appetite and normal temperature. The diarrheic feces are watery but contain no blood and have a normal odor. The disease is almost always fatal, but with the animal living from a month to two years.

Upon autopsy, the thickening of the infected part of the intestines, covered by a slimy discharge, is all that is evident. This thickening prevents the proper digestion and absorption of food and explains the emaciation.

CAUSE, PREVENTION, AND TREATMENT:

The disease is caused by the ingestion of a bacterium, *Mycobacterium paratuberculosis*. Inasmuch as this organism is acid-fast (that is, it retains certain dyes during a staining procedure), it resembles tuberculosis.

Effective prevention is accomplished by keeping the herd away from infected animals. If it is necessary to introduce new animals into a herd, they should be purchased from reputable breeders; and the owner should be questioned regarding the history of his herd.

It must be borne in mind that apparently healthy animals can spread the disease. Testing at regular intervals of three to six months with "Johnin," removing reactors, disinfecting quarters, and raising young stock away from mature animals should be practiced in infected herds. In using the Johnin test, however, it should be realized that it is not entirely accurate as a diagnostic agent. Some affected animals fail to react to the test.

No satisfactory treatment for Johne's disease has yet been found.

Leptospirosis

Leptospirosis was first observed in man in 1915-16, in dogs in 1931, and in cattle in 1935.

It was first reported in cattle in the U. S. in 1944, although it had been found in dogs in the U. S. since 1939. Bovine leptospirosis has been reported in Europe, Australia, and the U. S.

Human infections may be contracted through skin abrasions when handling or slaughtering infected animals, by swimming in contaminated water, through consuming raw beef or other uncooked foods that are contaminated, or through drinking un-pasteurized milk.

Today, leptospirosis costs 100 million dollars annually.[1]

SYMPTOMS:

The symptoms may vary from herd to herd, or even within a herd. In general, the symptoms noted in cattle are:

1. A large number of abortions, anywhere from the sixth month of pregnancy to term. In a recently infected herd, abortions may approach 30 per cent.

2. Reddish brown color of the urine and milk, accompanied by loss of appetite, heavy breathing, fast pulse, and temperatures between 103° and 107° F. A fever which lasts for 2-7 days may appear after an incubation period of 7-14 days. When fever is present, the animal's red blood cells may be destroyed so that an anemia may be present for several weeks.

3. Chronic type animals that have survived the severe symptoms noted in No. 2 above. The latter animals usually lack thrift, show a rough coat, have a poor appetite, and are thin and in a run-down condition.

4. Mild type animals which show only a slight drop in milk production for several days.

5. Feeder calves, from four months to one year of age, may become sick and die.

All ages of cattle, and both sexes (including steers) are affected. In a recently infected herd, about 10% of all the cattle of all ages may die the first year, but the disease becomes self-limiting and the losses cease.

CAUSE, PREVENTION, AND TREATMENT:

The disease is caused by several species of cork-screw-shaped organisms of the spirochete group.

The following preventive measures are recommended:

1. Blood test animals prior to purchase, isolate for 30 days and then retest prior to adding them to the herd.

2. Do not allow animals to consume contaminated feed or water, or to breathe contaminated urinal mist.

3. Keep premises clean, and avoid use of stagnant water.

4. Vaccinate susceptible animals if the disease is present in the area.

[1]USDA, The Yearbook of Agriculture 1956, *Animal Diseases*, p. 12.

Where a herd is infected, the following control measures should be initiated:

1. Blood test the herd and dispose of reactors either through (1) strict isolation, or (2) sale for slaughter only. Then retest every 30 days until two consecutive clean tests are obtained. The same blood sample used in a brucellosis test may also be used for a leptospirosis test, by simply dividing the serum.

2. Spread the cattle over a large area; avoid congestion in a corral or barn.

3. Do not let animals drink from ponds, swamps, or slow-running streams, and avoid contaminated feed.

4. Clean and disinfect the premises; exterminate the rodents.

5. Vaccinate susceptible animals for protection up to one year.

It should be recognized that carrier animals—animals that have had leptospirosis and survived—may spread the infection by shedding spirochetes in the urine. The infected urine may then either (1) be breathed as a mist in cow barns, or (2) contaminate feed and/or water and thus spread the infection. It is known that such recovered animals may remain carriers for 2 to 3 months or longer after getting over the marked symptoms. Fortunately, the spirochetes seldom survive for more than 30 days outside the animal. However, stagnant water favors their survival.

Antibiotics give fairly good results if cases are promptly treated. It appears that selected antibiotics must be used to eliminate shedders.

Lumpy Jaw and Wooden Tongue

These two infections are chronic diseases affecting mainly the head of cattle—hence the name "big head." They occur most frequently in young cattle during the period of changing teeth. At one time, both of the conditions were referred to as actinomycosis, but now this term is used only for lumpy jaw. Actinobacillosis is the synonym for wooden tongue and soft tissue lesions.

Out of 15 to 20 million cattle killed annually under federal inspection, 200,000 parts of carcasses are condemned from lumpy jaw and wooden tongue, or 1 in 75.[1]

---

[1] Ensminger, M. E., M. W. Galgan, and W. L. Slocum; Wash. Agri. Expt. Sta. Bul. 562, p. 15.

SYMPTOMS:

Because of the area involved in these diseases, there is usually emaciation resulting from the difficulty encountered in chewing and swallowing.

Lumpy jaw only rarely attacks the soft tissue. It is usually confined to the bones of the lower jaw, although the upper jaw and nasal bones may be involved. The affected bone becomes enlarged and spongy and filled with creamy pus. As the disease progresses, inflamed cauliflower masses of tissue spread out and may appear on the surface, discharging pus of foul odor. The surrounding flesh will also show inflammation, and the teeth may become loosened.

The same fungus that causes lumpy jaw occasionally attacks the udder of sows, where it is characterized by many small abscesses filled with calcified granules. There may be fistulous tracts to the outside of the udder, discharging pus. On rare occasions, the organism causing the disease has also been found

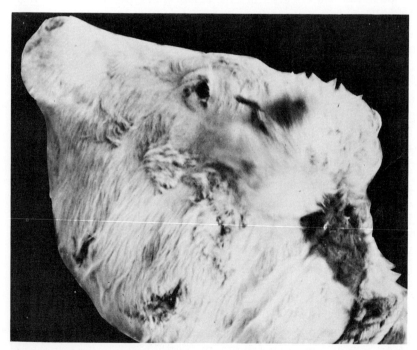

Fig. 210. Head of steer showing a bad case of lumpy jaw. It is usually confined to the bones of the lower jaw, although the upper jaw and nasal bones may be involved. (Courtesy, USDA)

in fistulous withers of the horse, in conjunction with *Brucella* organisms.

Wooden tongue attacks chiefly the tissue in the throat area of cattle, but is also often seen in the tongue, stomach, lungs, and lymph glands. The first lesion usually observed is a movable, tumor-like swelling about the size of a small egg under the skin in the infected area. The enlargements usually break open and discharge a light colored and very sticky pus. An involved tongue may or may not be ulcerated but will show an increase in size and hardness. The tongue may become quite immobile and may protrude from the mouth.

With this wooden tongue condition, there will be constant drooling, and the animal will lose weight and condition through inability to take food. Although any chronic swelling in the region of the head should lead one to suspect the presence of this infection, a positive diagnosis depends upon a microscopic examination of the yellowish, granular pus material that will eventually discharge from the swelling.

The same organism that causes wooden tongue occasionally attacks the lips and face of sheep.

CAUSE, PREVENTION, AND TREATMENT:

The organism of actinobacillosis (wooden tongue) is called *Actinobacillus lignieresei,* and the one causing actinomycosis (lumpy jaw) is called *Actinomyces bovis.* Both may be assisted by secondary invaders. Both organisms lack invasive power, often being found in a normal oral cavity. They are thought to enter the tissue only by wound infections—for example, they may be carried in by the sharp awns of fox tail, barley, rye, bearded wheat, or oats.

Prevention consists of segregation and proper treatment or elimination of infected animals and the restricted feeding of material having sharp awns that might injure the animal's mouth. The latter precaution is important as the fungus is a normal inhabitant of the mucous membranes of the mouth and nasal cavity of animals and man.

For treatment, the veterinarian may, under certain conditions, (1) administer a water solution of an iodine salt of sodium or potassium, (2) prescribe an antibiotic, (3) resort to surgery, or (4) use X-ray therapy.

The first treatment mentioned above consists of daily internal administration of a water solution of an iodine salt until iodism appears. Iodism is characterized by flow of tears, roughness of hair coat, and loss of appetite. Administration should be discontinued until these symptoms disappear, and treatment should then be resumed. Such treatment causes tainted milk and is not recommended for animals in advanced pregnancy.

Treatment of lumpy jaw is not very satisfactory, but most cases of wooden tongue yield readily to treatment.

Superficial abscesses should be opened, drained, and swabbed with tincture of iodine.

Metritis

Metritis is an inflammation of the uterus, which affects cattle, horses, sheep, and swine.

SYMPTOMS:

Metritis usually develops soon after the animal has given birth. It is characterized by a foul smelling discharge from the vulva that becomes thick and yellow, and finally brownish or blood-stained. Also, there is chilling, high temperature, rapid breathing, marked thirst, loss of appetite, and lowered milk production. Pressure on the right flank may produce pain. The animal may lie down and refuse to get up. Affected animals may die in 1 to 2 days; or the acute infection may develop into a chronic form, producing sterility.

CAUSE, PREVENTION, AND TREATMENT:

Metritis is caused by various types of bacteria. Laceration at the time of calving, wounds caused by inexperienced operators and/or retention of the afterbirth are the principal predisposing causes.

Preventive measures consist in alleviating as many of the predisposing factors as possible, including bruises and tears while giving birth, exposure to wet and cold, and the actual introduction of disease-causing bacteria during delivery or the manual removal of the afterbirth. Clean maternity stalls should be provided. If assistance at calving time becomes necessary, the caretaker should first disinfect the hands and arms as well as the external genitals.

Difficult parturition and treatment should be left to the veterinarian. Nothing is so distressing to the veterinarian as a history of long labor and well meaning but ill guided attempts to remove a calf.

Mucosal Disease

This disease was first reported in cattle by Dr. Ramsey of Iowa State University, in 1951. It has also been found in wild deer. It is scattered throughout the United States. The economic losses are in terms of decreases in weight and in deaths.

Collectively, mucosal disease along with infectious bovine rhinotracheitis, New York virus diarrhea, and Indiana virus diarrhea are referred to as the "mucosal disease complex." It is not intended that the latter designation should imply that they are caused by the same virus or organism; rather, it does indicate their similarity in clinical manifestations—that they affect the mucous membranes or tissues that line the digestive and respiratory systems, albeit to different degrees and in different locations.

SYMPTOMS:

The disease is characterized by an initial rise in temperature to 104-106° F., which returns to normal in 2 to 5 days. There may be an increased water intake and a decreased appetite. A mucous exudate hangs from the nose and mouth, and there are ulcerations and erosions of the mouth and tongue. A watery diarrhea occurs about the same time (1) that the mouth and tongue lesions appear, and (2) that the temperature returns to normal. Later, the diarrhea becomes thickened and contains more mucous and flecks of blood. In some cases, lameness occurs. The course of the disease varies from 5 to 30 days. Where the disease appears, 2 to 50 per cent of the animals in the herd may be affected, with the death loss generally above 90 per cent.

CAUSE, PREVENTION, AND TREATMENT:

The disease is probably caused by a virus.

Prevention consists in avoiding contact with affected animals, in using non-contaminated feed and water and in isolating new animals for 30 days. When an outbreak of the disease occurs, sick animals should be isolated and rigid sanitation enforced.

There is no known treatment, but antibiotics effectively combat the secondary bacterial invaders that accompany the disease.

Navel Infection (Joint-Ill or Navel-Ill)

Navel infection is an infectious disease of newborn calves, foals and lambs. It occurs less frequently in calves and lambs than in foals.

SYMPTOMS:

Navel infection is characterized by loss of appetite, by swelling, soreness and stiffness in the joints, by umbilical swelling and discharge, and by general listlessness.

CAUSE, PREVENTION, AND TREATMENT:

Navel infection is caused by several kinds of bacteria.

The recommended preventive measures are: sanitation and hygiene at mating and purturition, painting the navel cord of the new born animal with iodine, and the administration of bacterins.

For treatment, the veterinarian may give a blood transfusion, or he may administer a sulfa, an antibiotic, a serum, or a bacterin.

New York Virus Diarrhea

New York virus diarrhea was first observed and described in New York, in 1946. Since then, it has occurred throughout most of the United States. The greatest losses have been in feed, gains, and milk. (See mucosal disease.)

SYMPTOMS:

The disease is characterized by a high fever, 105 to 108° F.; excessive salivation, with ropy stringy mucous hanging down from the muzzle; ulcers on the mucous membranes of the nose, in the mouth, and on the muzzle; usually a severe diarrhea; there may be rapid breathing and a cough; and abortions may follow an acute attack. Where the disease appears, 5 to 100 per cent of the animals may become sick, often within a short period of time; but the death rate is relatively low (4 to 8 per cent).

CAUSE, PREVENTION, AND TREATMENT:

As indicated by the name, New York virus diarrhea is caused by a virus.

The most effective preventive measures consist in avoiding contact with affected animals and in keeping away from contaminated feed and water. Also, new animals should be isolated for at least 30 days. Once the disease makes its appearance, sick animals should be isolated and rigid sanitary measures should be initiated.

There is no known treatment, but antibiotics effectively combat the secondary bacterial invaders that accompany the disease.

Pink Eye (Keratitis)

This is a common name for various inflammatory conditions of the eyes of cattle. Sheep and goats may also be affected, but this should not be confused with the virus pink eye or influenza of horses. The general diseased-eye condition is also known under the medical terms ophthalmia, conjunctivitis, and keratitis. It attacks animals of any age, but does not usually occur in the winter months. It seems to become more virulent in certain years and in certain communities. The disease is wide-spread throughout the United States, especially among range and feed-lot cattle. Pink eye is encountered in nearly half of U.S. beef cattle herds and affects 3 per cent of all beef cattle.[1]

SYMPTOMS:

The first thing one may notice is the liberal flow of tears and the tendency to keep the eyes closed. There will be redness and swelling of the lining membrane of the eyelids and sometimes of the visible part of the eye. There may also be a discharge of pus. Ulcers may form on the cornea. If unchecked, they may cause blindness and even loss of the eye. The attack may also be marked by slight fever, reduction in milk flow, and slight digestive upset.

About one-half the animals in a herd become infected regardless of the treatment or control measures employed.

One record of steers on pasture showed that affected steers gained an average of 50 pounds less during the grazing season than those not affected.[2]

CAUSE, PREVENTION, AND TREATMENT:

The disease has a complicated and unsettled etiology. It seems that predisposing factors such as dust, vitamin A deficiency, strong sunlight, insects, and other conditions causing

---

[1]Ensminger, M. E., M. W. Galgan, and W. L. Slocum; Wash. Agri. Expt. Sta. Bul. 562, p. 12.

[2]Ibid. p. 15.

Fig. 211. Cow with pink eye. Note eye discharge and the cloudiness or milkiness of the cornea or covering of the eyeball. (Courtesy, Department of Veterinary Pathology and Hygiene, College of Veterinary Medicine, University of Illinois)

injury to the eye, usher in the disease. Various bacteria such as the pus-producing germs, the *staphylococcus* group; bacteria that usually are found in manure, the *colon* group; and *Corynebacterium* have been suggested as causative agents. An organism known as *Hemophilus bovis* usually is associated with the disease.

The prevention is quite unsatisfactory in view of the lack of knowledge as to the cause. Separation of affected animals is, of course, in order, as is changing quarters for the unaffected animals.

Good clean feed and water and confinement in a dark stall are always recommended for sick animals. There are now on the market various pink eye preparations whose basic active ingredients are one or more of the sulfonamide drugs. Their use has given variable results and the local veterinarian should be contacted for the best treatment.

Some veterinarians use crystal violet dye on the eye, and, if severe pain is in evidence, deaden the eye with a pain killer such as procaine. Other veterinarians are using foreign protein injections with some success.

Pneumonia

Pneumonia is an inflammation of the lungs in which the air sacs fill up with an inflammatory exudate or discharge. The disease is often secondary to many other conditions. It is difficult to describe and classify for the lung is subject to more forms of inflammation than any other organ in the body. It affects all animals. In cattle, it is seen most commonly as calf pneumonia, and frequently it accompanies shipping fever. If untreated, 50 to 75 per cent of affected animals die. Pneumonia causes one-fifth of all non-nutritional mortality in U.S. beef cattle.[1]

SYMPTOMS:

The disease is ushered in by a chill, followed by elevated temperature. There is quick, shallow respiration, with dis-

Fig. 212. Calf with pneumonia. Note characteristic spread of front legs in an effort to ease breathing. (Courtesy, Department of Veterinary Pathology and Hygiene, College of Veterinary Medicine, University of Illinois)

[1]Ensminger, M. E., M. W. Galgan, and W. L. Slocum. Wash. Agri. Expt. Sta. Bul. 562. p. 12.

charge from the nostrils and perhaps from the eyes. A cough may be present. The animal appears distressed, stands with legs wide apart, drops in milk production, shows no appetite, and is constipated. There may be crackling noises with breathing, and gasping for breath may be noted. If the disease terminates favorably, the cough loosens and the appetite picks up.

CAUSE, PREVENTION, AND TREATMENT:
The causes are numerous. Many microorganisms found in other acute and chronic diseases, such as mastitis and metritis, have been incriminated. Sometimes pneumonia is caused by a virus. One common cause that should be stressed is the inhalation of water or medicines that well-meaning but untrained persons give to animals in drenches. Also, it is generally recognized that changeable weather during the spring and fall, and damp barns, are conducive to pneumonia.

Prevention includes providing good hygienic surroundings and practicing good, sound husbandry.

Sick animals should be segregated and placed in quiet, clean quarters away from drafts.

Treatment, which should be by the veterinarian, may include (1) an antibiotic, or (2) a sulfa. Also, the sick animal should be given easily digested, nutritious feeds.

Rabies (Hydrophobia or Madness)

Rabies (hydrophobia or "madness") is an acute infectious disease of all warm-blooded animals and man. It is characterized by deranged consciousness and paralysis, and terminates fatally. This disease is one that is far too prevalent, and, if present knowledge were applied, it could be controlled and even eradicated.

When a human being is bitten by a dog that is suspected of being rabid, the first impulse is to kill the dog immediately. This is a mistake. Instead, it is important to confine the animal under the observation of a veterinarian until the disease, if it is present, has a chance to develop and run its course. If no recognizable symptoms appear in the animal within a period of two weeks after it inflicted the bite, it is safe to assume that there was no rabies at the time. Death occurs within a few days after the symptoms appear, and the dog's brain can be examined for specific evidence of rabies.

With this procedure, unless the bite is in the region of the neck or head, there will usually be ample time in which to administer the Pasteur treatment to exposed human beings. As the virus has been found in the saliva of a dog at least five days before the appearance of the clinically recognizable symptoms, the bite of a dog should always be considered potentially dangerous until proved otherwise. In any event, when a human being is bitten by a dog, it is recommended that a physician be consulted immediately. Each year about 30,000 persons in the United States undergo the Pasteur treatment.

SYMPTOMS:

Less than 10 per cent of the rabies cases appear in cattle, horses, swine, or sheep. The disease usually manifests itself in two forms: the furious, irritable, or violent form or the dumb or paralytic form. It is often difficult to distinguish between the two forms, however. The furious type usually merges into the dumb form because paralysis always occurs just before death.

The furious form is seen most often in cattle. In its early stages, the disease is marked by loss of appetite, cessation in milk

Fig. 213. Cow with rabies. Note the violent butting with the head; a characteristic of the furious form which is seen most often in cattle. At this stage, the animal is insane and is very dangerous, for it may attack and bite itself, other animals, or man. (Courtesy, Pitman-Moore, Indianapolis, Ind.)

secretion, anxiety, restlessness, and a change in disposition. This initial phase is followed by a stage of madness and extreme excitation indicated by a loud bellowing marked by a change in the voice, pawing of the ground, inability to swallow, and violent butting with the head. In all respects, the animal is insane and is very dangerous, for it may attack and bite itself or other animals and man. On the fourth or fifth day, the animal becomes quieter and unsteady. This indicates approach of posterior paralysis. Loss of flesh is already very evident. On the sixth day, the animal may go into a coma and die.

CAUSE, PREVENTION, AND TREATMENT:

Rabies is caused by a filtrable virus which is usually carried into a bite wound by the infected saliva of a rabid animal. The malady is generally transmitted to farm animals by dogs and certain wild animals, such as the fox and skunk.

Rabies can best be prevented by attacking it at its chief source, the dog. With the advent of an improved anti-rabies vaccine for the dog, it should be a requirement that all dogs be immunized. This should be supplemented by regulations governing the licensing, quarantine, and transportation of dogs. For understandable reasons, the control of rabies in wild animals is extremely difficult. In areas where rabies is present, all cattle should be vaccinated.

Once the disease has been introduced into a farm animal, little can be done. Theoretically, the Pasteur treatment could be administered immediately after the bite by a rabid animal; but this is not generally used in animals, perhaps because of a more variable (shorter) incubation period in animals and the expense involved. After the disease is fully developed, there is no known treatment.

Shipping Fever (Hemorrhagic Septicemia or Stockyard Fever)

This is a disease or group of infectious diseases often accompanied by high mortality, which affects cattle, horses, sheep and swine. It is named shipping fever because it is most frequently associated with animals whose resistance has been lowered due to travel.

Shipping fever occurs widely throughout the world, especially among thin and poorly nourished young animals that are subjected to shipment by rail or truck during periods of inclement weather, though it may occur in animals in good condition. The disease is, therefore, a serious problem to both shippers and receivers of cattle.

SYMPTOMS:

The disease develops rapidly and lasts for about a week or less. There is usually an elevation of the body temperature, discharge from the nose and eyes, a hacking cough, and difficulty in breathing and there may be a swelling in the region of the neck. There may be intestinal symptoms with diarrhea, but the disease usually manifests itself in the pulmonary form. In very acute

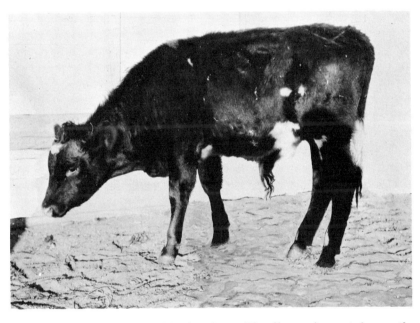

Fig. 214. A steer with shipping fever. The disease is most frequently associated with animals whose resistance has been lowered due to travel; hence the name shipping fever. (Courtesy, USDA)

forms, animals may die showing no symptoms. Death losses may be high in untreated cases.

CAUSE, PREVENTION, AND TREATMENT:

The cause of the disease is very uncertain. Some of the *Pasteurella* group of organisms are often recovered in an outbreak. It is suggested that a specific primary virus complicated by

Pasteurella or other members of the bronchial flora is the etiology of the disease. Predisposing factors, such as lowering the resistance of the host, seem necessary. Change in weather and feed, overcrowding, hard driving, lack of rest, and improper shelter all help usher in the disease.

As a preventive measure, one should eliminate as many as possible of the predisposing factors that lower the animal's vitality. The efficacy of biologics is questionable because of the variable results, but many cattlemen believe that vaccination with bacterins at least ten days before shipping reduces losses. The advisability of using biologics should be left to a competent veterinarian. Newly purchased animals should be isolated for two to three weeks before being placed with the herd.

Where cattle have been subjected to great stress—long shipment, extensive handling, and/or exposure to severe weather conditions—some are advocating the feeding of high levels of antibiotics for a time; one company recommends feeding 350 mg. of antibiotic per head per day for 30 days after arrival at the feedlot or farm. However, more research needs to be done on this preventive measure.

Treatment should be handled by a veterinarian. In the early stages, either (1) large doses of serum or (2) the sulfas or antibiotics may be used, with varying degrees of success expected. Good feeding and management will help.

Tetanus (Lockjaw)

Tetanus is chiefly a wound infection disease that attacks the nervous system of horses (and other equines) and man, although it does occur in cattle, swine, sheep and goats. In the Southwest, it is quite common in sheep after shearing, docking and castrating. In the central states, tetanus frequently affects calves, lambs, and pigs, following castration or other wounds. It is generally referred to as lockjaw.

In the United States, the disease occurs most frequently in the South, where precautions against tetanus are an essential part of the routine treatment of wounds. The disease is worldwide in distribution.

SYMPTOMS:

The incubation period of tetanus varies from one to two weeks but may be from one day to many months. It is usually as sociated with a wound but may not directly follow an injury. The first noticeable sign of the disease is a stiffness first observed about the head. The animal often chews slowly and weakly and swallows awkwardly. The third eyelid is seen protruding over the forward surface of the eyeball (called "haws"). The animal then shows violent spasm or contractions of groups of muscles brought on by the slightest movement or noise. The animal usually attempts to remain standing throughout the course of the disease until close to death. If recovery occurs, it will take a month or more. In over one-half the cases, however, death ensues, usually because of sheer exhaustion or paralysis of vital organs.

CAUSE, PREVENTION, AND TREATMENT:

The disease is caused by an exceedingly powerful toxin (more than one hundred times as toxic as strychnine) liberated by the tetanus organism (*Clostridium tetani*). This organism is an anaerobe (lives in absence of oxygen) which forms the most hardy spores known. It may be found in certain soils, horse dung, and sometimes in human excreta. The organism usually causes trouble when it gets into a wound that rapidly heals or closes over it. In the absence of oxygen, it then grows and liberates the toxin which follows up nerve trunks. Upon reaching the spinal cord, the toxin excites the symptoms noted above.

The disease can largely be prevented by reducing the probability of wounds, by general cleanliness, by proper wound treatment, and by vaccination with tetanus toxoid in the so-called "hot" areas. When an animal has received a wound from which tetanus may result, short term immunity can be conferred immediately by use of tetanus antitoxin, but is of little or no value after the symptoms have developed. All valuable animals should be protected with tetanus toxoid.

All perceptible wounds should be properly treated, and the animal should be kept quiet and preferably should be placed in a dark quiet corner free from flies. Supportive treatment is of great importance and will contribute towards a favorable course. This may entail artificial feeding. The animal should be placed under the care of a veterinarian.

Tuberculosis

Tuberculosis is a chronic infectious disease of man and animals, which occurs world-wide. It is characterized by the development of nodules (tubercules) that may calcify or turn into abscesses. The disease spreads very slowly, and affects mainly the lymph nodes. There are three kinds of tuberculosis bacilli— the human, the bovine, and the avian (bird) types. Practically every species of animal is subject to one or more of the three kinds, as shown in Table 41.

In general, the incidence of tuberculosis is steadily declining in the United States, both in animals and humans. In 1917, when a thorough nationwide eradication campaign was first initiated, 1 cow in 20 had the disease; whereas today the number is less than 1 in 400. Meanwhile, human mortality from tuberculosis has dropped from 150 per 100,000 in 1918 to well under 50 per 100,000. Some decline in the incidence of the disease in poultry and swine has also been noted, but the reduction among these species has been far less marked.

SYMPTOMS:

Tuberculosis may take one or more of several forms. Human beings get tuberculosis of the skin (lupus), of the lymph nodes (scrofula), of the bones and joints, of the lining of the brain (tuberculous meningitis), and of the lungs. For the most part, tuberculosis in animals involves the lungs and lymph nodes. In cows, the udder becomes infected in chronic cases.

Many times an infected animal will show no outward phys-

Fig. 215. Cow in the last stages of tuberculosis. Cattle are susceptible to all three kinds of tuberculosis. (Courtesy, Dr. B. T. Simms, USDA)

TABLE 41

RELATIVE SUSCEPTIBILITY OF MAN AND ANIMALS TO 3 DIFFERENT KINDS OF TUBERCULOSIS GERMS

Species	Susceptibility to Three Kinds of Tuberculosis Germs			Comments
	Human Type	Bovine Type	Avian (bird) Type	
Humans.............	Susceptible	Moderately susceptible	Questionable	Pathogenicity of avian type for humans is practically nil.
Cattle.............	Slightly susceptible	Susceptible	Slightly susceptible	
Swine.............	Moderately susceptible	Susceptible	Susceptible	Ninety per cent of all swine cases are due to the avian type.
Chickens.............	Resistant	Resistant	Very susceptible	Chickens only have the avian type.
Horses and mules ...	Relatively resistant	Moderately susceptible	Relatively resistant	Rarely seen in these animals in the U. S.
Sheep.............	Fairly resistant	Susceptible	Susceptible	Rarely seen in these animals.
Goats.............	Marked resistance	Highly susceptible	Susceptible	Rarely seen in these animals in the U. S.
Dogs.............	Susceptible	Susceptible	Resistant	Highly resistant.
Cats.............	Quite resistant	Susceptible	Quite resistant	Usually obtained from milk of tubercular cows.

ical signs of the disease. There may be a gradual loss of weight and condition and swelling of joints, especially in older animals. If the respiratory system is affected, there may be a chronic cough and labored breathing. Next to the lungs and lymph nodes, the udder is most frequently affected, showing increased size and swelling of the supra mammary lymph gland. Other seats of infection are genitals, central nervous system, and the digestive system.

CAUSE, PREVENTION, AND TREATMENT:

The causative agent is a rod-shaped organism belonging to the acid-fast group known as *Mycobacterium tuberculosis*. The disease is usually contracted by eating feed or drinking fluids contaminated by the discharges of infected animals. Hogs may also contract the disease by eating part of a tubercular chicken.

With cattle, periodic testing and removal of the reactors is the only effective method of control. It is well to abide by the old adage "once a reactor, always a reactor."

The test consists of the introduction of tuberculin—a standardized solution of the products of the tubercle bacillus—into an approved location on the animal.

There are three principal methods of tuberculin testing—the intradermic, subcutaneous, and ophthalmic. The first of these is the method now principally used. It consists of the injection of tuberculin into the dermis (the true skin).

Upon injection into an infected animal, tuberculin will set in the body a reaction characterized by a swelling at the site of injection. In human beings, the X-ray is usually used for purposes of detecting the presence of the disease.

As a part of the federal-state tuberculosis eradication campaign of 1917, provision was made for indemnity payments on animals slaughtered.

Preventive treatment for both humans and animals consists of pasteurization of milk and creamery by-products and the removal and supervised slaughter of reactor animals. Vaccination against human tuberculosis, using B.C.G., is now being generally practiced in some foreign countries and is being experimentally tried on some groups in this country. B.C.G. is the abbreviated designation of Bacille' Calmette-Guerin, which is named after two French scientists who first prepared the vaccine and who are its chief advocates.

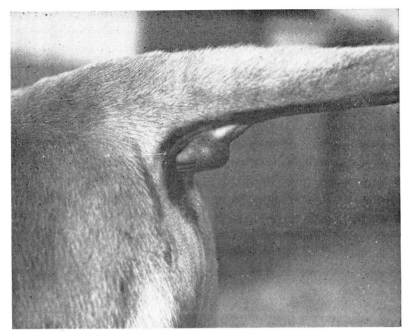

Fig. 216. A positive reaction (indicating the presence of tuberculosis) to the intradermic (into the true skin) tuberculin test in a cow. Reactors show a noticeable swelling, varying from the size of a pea to the size of a walnut, at the point of injection. The reading is made approximately 72 hours after injection. (Courtesy, Department of Veterinary Pathology and Hygiene, College of Veterinary Medicine, Universtiy of Illinois)

In human beings, tuberculosis can be arrested by hospitalization and complete rest, but in animals this method of treatment is neither effective nor practical. To date, medical treatment has been unsatisfactory, although beneficial results have been reported from giving streptomycin to affected humans.

All 48 states will accept for entry cattle meeting either of the following T.B. tests: (1) accredited herds tested within 12 months, or (2) individual negative test within 30 days.

Vaginitis

This is an infectious disease which localizes in the lining of the vagina, causing an inflammation of varying intensity. It occurs throughout the United States.

SYMPTOMS:

The tissue of the vagina is reddish, roughened, and granular in appearance. Infected animals are usually difficult breeders.

Economic losses are in terms of lower percentage calf crop and decreased milk production.

CAUSE, PREVENTION, AND TREATMENT:

The cause is unknown. It is believed that the infection is commonly transmitted by the bull at the time of service, but this is not the only means of transmission since virgin heifers may be infected.

Prevention consists in purchasing clean animals from clean herds and avoiding the use of bulls that have been exposed to the infection. Artificial insemination can be effectively employed in a control program.

No treatment is entirely satisfactory. Consult the local veterinarian.

Vibrionic Abortion (Vibriosis or Vibrio Fetus)

This is an infection of the reproductive organs of cattle, which causes infertility and abortion. For certain diagnosis, laboratory methods must be used.

SYMPTOMS:

Infected herds are characterized by more than normal (1) sterility, and (2) abortions between the fifth and seventh month of pregnancy (abortions rarely exceed 3 to 5 per cent). In total, vibrionic abortion costs U.S. cattlemen 140 million dollars annually.[1]

CAUSE, PREVENTION, AND TREATMENT:

The disease is caused by the microorganism *Vibrio fetus*, which is transmitted at the time of coitus.

Prevention consists in avoiding contact with diseased animals and contaminated feed, water and materials. Artificial insemination with antibiotic-treated semen is a rapid and practical method of stopping infection from cow to cow.

Aborting cows should be isolated, and aborted fetuses and membranes should be burned or buried. Contaminated quarters should be thoroughly cleaned and disinfected.

Infected cows are treated by injecting drugs into the uterus and/or by allowing sexual rest.

Warts

Warts, which are small tumors, are an infectious disease of

---

[1] USDA, The Yearbook of Agriculture 1956, *Animal Diseases*, p. 12.

cattle and other animals and man. Young animals, under two years of age, are most often affected.

SYMPTOMS:

Warts are protruding growths on the skin, varying from very small to quite large, pendulous growths weighing several pounds. They may appear anywhere on the body, but are especially common on the teats and/or around the head.

Fig. 217. An extreme case of warts. (Courtesy, Fort Dodge Laboratories, Inc., Fort Dodge, Iowa)

Although warts are a nuisance, their presence does not normally interfere with the animal's health. However, they damage the hide, making the leather derived therefrom weak in the affected area.

CAUSE, PREVENTION, AND TREATMENT:

Warts are caused by a virus. It appears that each class of animals is attacked by a specific virus.

The following preventive measures are recommended:

1. Segregate "warty" cattle.

2. Clean and disinfect all exposed pens, stables, chutes, and rubbing posts.

3. Milk "warty" cows last.

The most common treatment among cattlemen consists in softening the wart with oil for several days, and then tying off the growth with thread or a rubber band or snipping it off with sterile scissors. The stump should then be treated with tincture of iodine. Wart vaccines help in some cases. The veterinarian may resort to surgical removal of extremely large warts.

Winter Dysentery (Winter Scours)

This is an acute infectious disease of stabled cattle, both dairy and beef, most frequently occurring between the months of November and March.

SYMPTOMS:

It causes few death losses, but afflicted animals lose in condition; and, in lactating animals, there is a sharp reduction in milk flow.

The period of incubation is extremely short, varying from 3 to 5 days. A profuse watery diarrhea is the main symptom. Often the feces are dark brown in color, and tend to become darker when intestinal hemorrhages occur. Usually the temperature remains normal, and the appetite is unchanged. Calves and young animals are least susceptible, but animals of all ages are affected. The seasonal incidence of the disease, the age and number of animals affected, together with the suddenness of the onset, are helpful in arriving at a correct diagnosis.

CAUSE, PREVENTION, AND TREATMENT:

The disease is caused by an organism, *Vibrio jejuni,* and perhaps a virus.

Prevention consists in isolating new or replacement animals. Also, any animal suffering from an acute attack of dysentery should be separated from the herd. Where the disease is encountered, rigid sanitation should be practiced.

The veterinarian may administer antibiotics or an intestinal antiseptic. For relief of dehydration intravenous injections of physiological salt solution, accompanied by glucose, are useful.

X-Disease (Hyperkeratosis)

Since 1941, X-disease has been recognized in the majority of the states.

SYMPTOMS:

X-disease is characterized by a watering of the eyes, wrinkling of the thickened skin, loss of hair, diarrhea and emacia-

Fig. 218. Animal with X-disease. Note wrinkling of the thickened skin. (Courtesy, Dean Robert Graham, College of Veterinary Medicine, University of Illinois)

tion. All ages are affected, but animals under two years of age most susceptible. The death loss may be as high as 80 per cent in young calves.

CAUSE, PREVENTION, AND TREATMENT:

Chlorinated naphthalene compounds, such as are contained in certain oils and greases used on machinery, have been identified as one of the causes.

Prevention consists in keeping cattle away from tractors, combines, old oil drums, drainage from grease racks, and roofing asphalt; or other places where it may be possible for them to contact grease or oil. If pelleted feeds are used, make sure that the lubricant used in the pelleting machinery contains no highly chlorinated naphthalene compounds.

Present treatments are unsatisfactory.

SOME COMMON PARASITES AFFECTING BEEF CATTLE[1]

The parasites that affect cattle comprise more than one hundred species. Fortunately, not all of these are of importance in the United States.

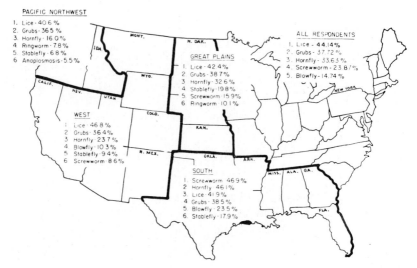

PACIFIC NORTHWEST
1. Lice - 40.6 %
2. Grubs - 36.5 %
3. Hornfly - 16.0 %
4. Ringworm - 7.8 %
5. Stablefly - 6.8 %
6. Anaplasmosis - 5.5 %

ALL RESPONDENTS
1. Lice - 44.14%
2. Grubs - 37.72 %
3. Hornfly - 33.63 %
4. Screwworm - 23.87 %
5. Blowfly - 14.74 %

GREAT PLAINS
1. Lice - 42.4 %
2. Grubs - 38.7 %
3. Hornfly - 32.6 %
4. Stablefly - 19.8 %
5. Screwworm - 15.9 %
6. Ringworm - 10.1 %

WEST
1. Lice - 46.8 %
2. Grubs - 36.4 %
3. Hornfly - 23.7 %
4. Blowfly - 10.3 %
5. Stablefly - 9.4 %
6. Screwworm - 8.6 %

SOUTH
1. Screwworm - 46.9 %
2. Hornfly - 46.1 %
3. Lice - 41.9 %
4. Grubs - 38.5 %
5. Blowfly - 23.5 %
6. Stablefly - 17.9 %

Fig. 219. Six most common beef cattle parasites, by areas. This figure is based on a survey (Wash, Agri. Expt. Sta. Bul. 562, p. 27) made by Washington State University, which covered a 24-state area and included more than a half million cattle. It is recognized that cattlemen may not always have been accurate in their diagnosis; nevertheless, this is the most complete record of its type available. (Print, courtesy Washington State University)

The prevention and control of parasites is one of the quickest, cheapest, and most dependable methods of increasing beef and milk production with no extra cattle, no additional feed, and little more labor. This is important, for, after all, the farmer or rancher bears the brunt of this reduced meat and milk production, wasted feed, and damaged hides. It is hoped that the discussion that follows may be helpful in (1) preventing the propagation of parasites and (2) causing the destruction of parasites through the use of the most effective vermifuge or insecticide.

---

[1]Several new and promising insecticides and vermifuges for controlling parasites are now on the market. However, further research is desirable in order to determine the value of many of these products. Where parasitism is encountered, therefore, it is suggested that the stockman obtain from local authorities the current recommendation relative to the choice and concentration of the insecticide and vermifuge to use.

Fig. 220. Calf with "bottle jaw." Generally this condition is indicative of a heavy infestation of several species of internal parasites. (Courtesy, Dean R. S. Sugg, School of Veterinary Medicine, Alabama Polytechnic Institute)

Anaplasmosis

Anaplasmosis is an infectious disease whose etiology and symptomatology are similar to cattle tick fever, except that more carriers are involved. It is caused by a minute parasite, *Anaplasma marginale*, which invades the red blood cells. The parasite is transmitted from infected to healthy animals by ticks, horseflies, and mosquitoes and probably by other biting insects.

DISTRIBUTION AND LOSSES CAUSED BY ANAPLASMOSIS:

The disease is widely distributed in warm climates throughout the world. In the United States, it has been prevalent throughout the southern states, but it is slowly spreading to the northern states.

Although there is a wide range in the death rate of stricken herds, the average mortality varies from 25 to 60 per cent of the infected animals. The most severe losses are found in older animals and in hot weather.

LIFE HISTORY AND HABITS:

The habitat of the causative parasite, *Anaplasma marginale*, outside the animal body is not entirely known. In infected animals, the protozoa live in the red blood cells. The parasite and, consequently, the disease may be transmitted from animal to animal by means of biting insects and by such mechanical agencies as needles, dehorning instruments, etc. Any animal that has once contracted the disease permanently retains the parasite in the blood, though no signs of ill health may be evident. Such animals are "carriers," and are potential sources of danger to others.

DAMAGE INFLICTED OR SYMPTOMS
OF AFFECTED ANIMALS:

The symptoms may be those of a mild, acute, or chronic condition. Calves usually have the mild type of infection, simply becoming "dumpy" for a few days and then apparently recovering, though their blood remains the permanent abode of the parasite.

The more characteristic symptoms in mature animals include rapid, pounding heart action, labored and difficult breathing, dry muzzle, marked depression, tremors of the muscles. loss

Fig. 221. Cow exhibiting typical symptoms of acute anaplasmosis. (Courtesy USDA)

of appetite, and a great reduction in the milk flow. Animals usually show yellowing of the eye and other mucus membranes and of the skin, as in jaundice. Depraved appetite, evidenced by the eating of bones or dirt, is not uncommon. Sick animals may also show brain symptoms and an inclination to fight. Unlike cattle tick fever, bloody urine is not common in anaplasmosis. In severe acute cases, death may follow in one to a few days. Recovery is usually very slow, and although no clinical symptoms remain, such animals continue as permanent carriers of the parasite.

PREVENTION, CONTROL, AND TREATMENT:

Prevention of anaplasmosis in an infected area is very difficult. The most effective control measures consist of: (1) Spraying approved insecticides in livestock buildings and on cattle to kill and ward off biting insects that spread the disease; and (2) preventing its spread through such mechanical means as surgical instruments, dehorners, needles, etc., by sterilizing them thoroughly before using on the next animal.

In those areas where the disease exists only in scattered herds, effective control includes the marketing of animals that have recovered from the disease. On the other hand, where anaplasmosis is widespread and results in extensive losses, consideration should be given to the lifetime protection afforded by inoculating newborn calves with some virulent blood. Although the inoculated calf is protected by the latter procedure, it must be remembered that a continuing source of infection is provided thereby.

Good care and good nursing are valuable. Affected animals under treatment should be kept quiet, because forced exertion may prove fatal. Blood transfusions are helpful. Limited experimental work indicates that certain antibiotics and/or antimalarial compounds may be effective as a treatment, and as a means of eliminating carriers, but further studies of this type are necessary.

Blowfly

The flies of the blowfly group include a number of species that find their principal breeding ground in dead and putrifying flesh, although they sometimes infest wounds or unhealthy tissues of live animals and fresh or cooked meat. All the im-

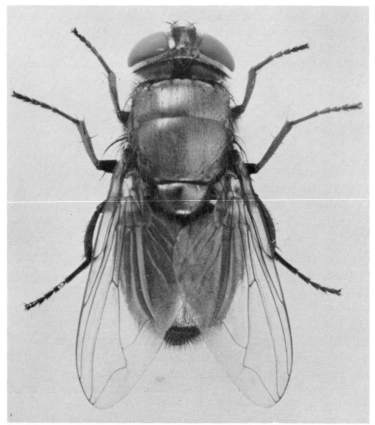

Fig. 222. The black blowfly (*Phormia regina.*) These flies are characterized by a metallic luster. (Courtesy, USDA)

portant species of blowflies except the flesh flies, which are grayish and have three dark stripes on their backs, have a more or less metallic luster.

DISTRIBUTION AND LOSSES CAUSED BY BLOWFLIES:

Although blowflies are widespread, they present the greatest problem in the Pacific Northwest and in the South and southwestern states. Death losses from blowflies are not excessive, but they cause much discomfort to affected animals and lower production.

LIFE HISTORY AND HABITS:

With the exception of the group known as gray flesh flies, which deposit tiny living maggots instead of eggs the blowflies have a similar life cycle to the screwworm, except that the cycle is completed in about one-half the time.

DAMAGE INFLICTED OR SYMPTOMS OF AFFECTED ANIMALS:

The blowfly causes its greatest damage by infesting wounds and the soiled hair or fleece of living animals. Such damage, which is largely limited to the black blowfly (or wool-maggot fly), is similar to that caused by screwworms. Sheep are especially susceptible to attacks of blowflies, because their wool frequently becomes soiled or moistened by rain and accumulations of feces and urine. The maggots spread over the body, feeding on the skin surface, where they produce a severe irritation and destroy the ability of the skin to function. Infested animals rapidly become weak and fevered; and, although they recover, they may remain in an unthrifty condition for a long period.

Because blowflies infest fresh or cooked meat, they are often a problem of major importance around packing houses or farm homes.

PREVENTION, CONTROL, AND TREATMENT:

Prevention of blowfly damage consists of eliminating the pest and decreasing the susceptibility of animals to infestation. The practices of docking lambs and tagging sheep at intervals will materially lessen blowfly damage in this class of animals.

As blowflies breed principally in dead carcasses, the most effective control is effected by promptly destroying all dead animals by burning or deep burial. The use of traps, poisoned baits, and electrified screens is also helpful in reducing trouble from blowflies. Suitable repellents, such as pine tar oil, help prevent the fly from depositing its eggs.

When animals become infested with blowfly maggots, their wounds should be treated twice weekly either with (1) Formula MS 62 or (2) EQ-335 Screwworm Remedy diluted one part to nine parts of water. These are the same treatments prescribed for screwworm maggots. Also chloroform is frequently used to kill the larvae.

Bovine Trichomoniasis

This is a protozoan venereal disease of cattle characterized by early abortions (usually between the second and fourth months of pregnancy) and temporary sterility. The protozoa that cause the disease, known as *Trichomonas foetus,* are one-celled, microscopic in size and capable of movement. They are found in aborted fetuses, fetal membranes and fluids, vaginal secretions of infected animals, and the sheaths of infected bulls. Diagnosis can be confirmed microscopically. The infected bull is the source of the infection. On the other hand, the disease appears to be self-limiting in the cow.

DISTRIBUTION AND LOSSES CAUSED BY BOVINE TRICHOMONIASIS:

This disease is being reported with increasing frequency throughout the United States and has become a serious problem in many herds. The economic loss is primarily due to the low percentage calf crops in infected herds.

LIFE HISTORY AND HABITS:

The protozoa that cause the disease are a one-celled microscopic organism with three threadlike whips (flagella) at the front and one at the rear. At the present time, the evidence indicates that the disease is spread from the infected to the clean cow by an infected bull at the time of service and that other types of contact infection do not occur. Following one or perhaps two abortions, cows appear to be immune to reinfection. Further than these facts, little is known of the life history and habits of *Trichomonas foetus.*

DAMAGE INFLICTED OR SYMPTOMS OF AFFECTED ANIMALS:

There is no systemic disturbance manifested by the infected bull. There may be some mucus discharged from the sheath, and the latter may be slightly inflamed. The only clinical evidence of infection is the transmission of the disease to the cattle serviced.

Infected cows frequently show a whitish vaginal discharge, and the following characteristic conditions usually exist when a herd is infected: (1) Animals may not conceive, or (2) animals may become pregnant but the ovum or embryo may be destroyed. If the latter condition occurs, pus may gather and be retained (designated as pyometra), or the embryo may be expelled in the first two to four months. Often this abortion is missed, and the animal is declared sterile. In still other cases, infected animals may have a normal birth.

Early abortions or erratic heat periods in individuals or

Fig. 223. Bull with trichomoniasis. This animal appeared normal, but spread the disease during the breeding act. (Courtesy, Department of Veterinary Pathology and Hygiene, College of Veterinary Medicine, University of Illinois)

herds that are known to be free of Bang's disease should lead one to suspect the presence of the Trichomonad infection. Definite diagnosis of infection in the bull is made by means of a microscopic examination of smears taken from the prepuce of the bull or the vagina of the cow.

PREVENTION, CONTROL, AND TREATMENT:

Prevention lies in the use of clean bulls. If practical, infected animals should be sold for slaughter or allowed 90 days of sexual rest. Otherwise, treatment should be attempted.

Effective control consists of exercising great precaution in introducing new animals into the herd, in breeding outside cows, and in taking cows outside the herd for breeding purposes.

In 1954, a University of California veterinary scientist announced a successful treatment for bulls infected with trichomoniasis. It consists in a veterinarian administering a two-way treatment of sodium iodide given intravenously and bovoflavin salves applied to the penis.

Infected cows should be tested for a minimum of three months, and then bred by artificial insemination to a known clean bull.

Cattle Tick Fever (Texas Fever, Splenetic Fever, Etc.)

This is an infectious protozoan disease of adult cattle caused by a protozoa called *Babesia bigemina,* which depends upon the tick, chiefly *Boophilus annulatus,* for its survival and transmission.

Fig. 224. An adult cattle tick (*Boophilus annulatus*), chief transmitter of cattle tick fever. (Courtesy, USDA)

CATTLE TICK FEVER:
DISTRIBUTION AND LOSSES CAUSED BY

Prior to 1906, at which time a concerted effort was initiated to eradicate the cattle fever tick, this infectious disease of cattle and the parasite which transmits it were the most serious obstacles faced by the cattle industry in the fifteen southern and southwestern states, representing a combined area of nearly one-fourth of the United States. At that time, conservative estimates placed the yearly losses at $40,000,000. Today, 99 per cent of the formerly infested area has been freed (it is confined to the Gulf Coast area only), and the once appalling losses have been practically eliminated.

In addition to the serious death losses encountered in infected herds, the loss of blood—the only food of the cattle fever tick—results in serious damage. Infected young animals are stunted, mature animals are emaciated, and the milk flow of infected dairy animals is greatly reduced. Death occurs in about 10 per cent of the chronic and 90 per cent of the acute cases.

LIFE HISTORY AND HABITS:

In 1889 and 1890, investigators of the USDA, Bureau of Animal Industry, established (1) that intracellular one-celled parasites, or protozoa, known as *Babesia* are the direct causative agents of the disease, and (2) that cattle tick infestation is necessary in the transmission of the disease. Thus, for the first time in either human or veterinary medicine, the discovery was made that an intermediate biological carrier may transmit a disease. It is noteworthy that this pioneer work opened up an entirely new field in medical science, pointing the way for studies that later solved the problems of the spread of such dreaded diseases as malaria, yellow fever, Rocky Mountain spotted fever, typhus, and others.

The life history and habits of the protozoa which causes cattle tick fever are as follows: Infected ticks, which have sucked blood from an infected cow, pass along the protozoa *Babesia* (*Piroplasma*) *bigemina* to their eggs. The female tick falls to the ground and deposits from two to four thousand eggs. In from two to three weeks, these eggs hatch into young ticks or larvae. The larvae climb on nearby vegetation to await the passing of cattle to which they attach themselves, biting and sucking blood from the host. In the latter process, the protozoa (*Piroplasma*) *is* passed into the blood of cattle—the protozoa of infected ticks having been passed into the eggs of the tick and through all stages of its growth.

DAMAGE INFLICTED OR SYMPTOMS OF
AFFECTED ANIMALS:

The incubation period of cattle tick fever is about ten days. The disease is characterized by high temperature, rapid breathing, enlarged spleen, engorged liver, pale and yellow membranes, and red to black urine. Sometimes the symptoms subside only to reoccur at another time. Although immune, the recovered animals are permanent carriers of the disease. In infected areas, native cattle are either immune or only slightly affected.

PREVENTION, CONTROL, AND TREATMENT:

Prevention of the disease consists of avoiding contact with the cattle fever tick, the only natural agent by which cattle tick fever is transmitted from animal to animal.

The most effective control measures are directed at the eradication of the fever ticks, either by killing them on the pastures or on the cattle. Pastures may be rendered tick-free by excluding all the host animals—cattle, horses, and mules—until all the ticks have died of starvation in eight to ten months.

For recommended insecticides and formula for cattle tick control, see Table 42, Handy Spray and Dip Guide for Control of External Parasites of Cattle, beginning on page 638.

Fig. 225. Cattle with cattle tick fever. The disease is characterized by high temperature, rapid breathing, enlarged spleen, engorged liver, pale and yellow membranes, and red to black urine. (Courtesy, Dr. B. T. Simms, USDA)

The treatment of sick animals, other than removal of all ticks and movement to clean pastures, is considered impractical. Although immune, recovered animals are permanent carriers of the disease.

Coccidiosis

Coccidiosis—a parasitic disease affecting cattle, sheep, goats, swine, pet stock, and poultry—is caused by microscopic protozoan organisms known as *Coccidia*, which live in the cells of the intestinal lining. Each class of domestic livestock harbors its own species of *Coccidia*, thus there is no cross-infection between animals.

DISTRIBUTION AND LOSSES CAUSED BY COCCIDIOSIS:

The distribution of the disease is world-wide. Except in very severe infections, or where a secondary bacterial invasion develops, infested farm animals usually recover. The chief economic loss, which is estimated at $10,000,000 annually for all U.S. cattle (both beef and dairy animals),[1] is in lowered gain and production. It is most severe in young dairy calves and feeder cattle.

LIFE HISTORY AND HABITS:

Infected animals may eliminate daily with their droppings thousands of coccidia organisms (in the resistant öocyst stage). Under favorable conditions of temperature and moisture, *Coccidia* sporulate to maturity in three to five days, and each öocyst contains eight infective sporozoites. The öocyst then gains entrance into an animal by being swallowed with contaminated feed or water. In the host's intestine, the outer membrane of the öocyst, acted on by the digestive juices, ruptures and liberates the eight sporozoites within. Each sporozoite then attacks and penetrates an epithelial cell, ultimately destroying it. While destroying the cell, however, the parasite undergoes sexual multiplication and fertilization with the formation of new öocysts. The parasite (öocyst) is then expelled with the feces and is again in a position to reinfest a new host.

The coccidia parasite abounds in wet, filthy surroundings; resists freezing and ordinary disinfectants; and can be carried long distances in streams.

DAMAGE INFLICTED OR SYMPTOMS OF AFFECTED ANIMALS:

A severe infection with *Coccidia* produces diarrhea, and the feces may be bloody. The bloody discharge is due to the destruction of the epithelial cells lining the intestines. Ensuing exposure

[1]Ensminger, M. E., M. W. Galgan, and W. L. Slocum, Wash. Agri. Expt. Sta. Bul. 562, p. 31.

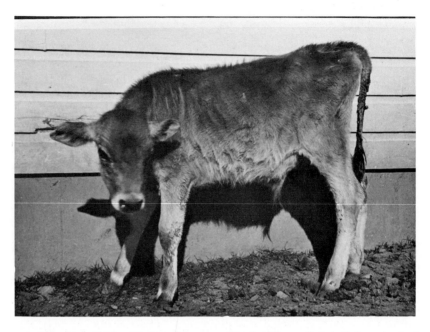

Fig. 226. Calf suffering from coccidiosis. The soiled tail is a typical symptom. (Courtesy, USDA, Regional Laboratory An. Dis. Res., Auburn, Alabama)

and rupture of the blood vessels then produces hemorrhage into the intestinal lumen.

In addition to a bloody diarrhea, affected animals usually show pronounced unthriftiness and weakness.

PREVENTION, CONTROL, AND TREATMENT:

Coccidiosis can be prevented by protecting animals from feed or water that is contaminated with the protozoa that causes the disease. Prompt segregation of affected animals is important and should be done if practical. Manure and contaminated bedding should be removed daily. Low, wet areas should be drained. If possible, segregation and isolation of animals by age should be used in controlling the disease. All precautions should be undertaken to keep droppings from contaminating the feed. Although the öocysts resist freezing and certain disinfectants and may remain viable outside the body for one or two years, they are readily destroyed by direct sunlight and complete drying.

Treatment should be undertaken mainly for the relief of symptoms. Some of the sulfonamides and nitrofurans may be employed as a drug treatment, but a veterinarian should be consulted. Also, blood transfusions may be necessary. Good nursing is essential.

Gastro-Intestinal Nematode Worms

Internal parasites of cattle include many species, which may be found in the stomach, small intestine, and/or large intestine; including the following: twisted stomach worm, medium stomach worm, minute stomach worm, nodular worm, hookworm, cooperids and lungworm.

DISTRIBUTION AND LOSSES CAUSED BY GASTRO-INTESTINAL NEMATODE WORMS:

One or more species of internal parasites of cattle are found throughout the U. S., but they may be especially severe in the South and on permanent pastures.

The losses, which are estimated at $12,000,000 to $15,000,000 annually for all U.S. cattle (both beef and dairy animals),[1] are in terms of lowered feed efficiency caused by disturbed digestion, lowered meat and milk production, and some death losses. Young animals are more severely affected than mature cattle.

LIFE HISTORY AND HABITS:

Most of the parasites listed above have similar life cycles, of which the common stomach worm is typical. Infested cattle carry the mature worms in the fourth stomach. Eggs from these worms are expelled with manure and develop on the pasture into infestive larvae. Then cattle become infested by eating grass infested with the larvae. The latter develop into mature worms in the stomach and these again produce eggs that recontaminate the pasture.

DAMAGE INFLICTED OR SYMPTOMS OF AFFECTED ANIMALS:

An animal with a light infestation rarely shows any outward symptoms, and the symptoms are not specific. But infested animals generally show loss of weight, retarded growth, anemia, diarrhea, and/or lowered resistance to other diseases. With a heavy infestation, there may be a swelling under the jaw (bottle jaw); and the parasites may even cause the death of the animals.

---

[1]Ensminger, M. E., M. W. Galgan, and W. L. Slocum, Wash. Agri. Expt. Sta. Bul. 562, p. 31.

Fig. 227. Calf with stomach worms. (Courtesy, Department of Veterinary Pathology and Hygiene, College of Veterinary Medicine, University of Illinois)

PREVENTION, CONTROL, AND TREATMENT:

Preventive and control measures include (1) rotating pastures, (2) segregating calves from mature animals, and (3) keeping feeders and waterers sanitary.

Cattle are generally treated with phenothiazine, the exact dosage depending on the size and condition of the animal and the species of worm predominating. The veterinarian should be consulted for more specific information.

Effective cattle parasite control can be obtained by feeding low levels of phenothiazine continuously, at the rate of 1.5 to 2.0 grams per day. Low-level phenothiazine has been successfully administered to cattle in the following ways:

1. **Phenothiazine-salt.**—A mixture of one part of phenothiazine and ten parts of salt, fed free-choice.

2. **Phenothiazine-mineral mixture.**—A mixture of one part of phenothiazine to nine parts of the normally used mineral. Thus, the following mixture has been used suc-

cessfully: three parts limestone, three parts bonemeal, three parts salt and one part phenothiazine. The generally recommended treatment for the removal of adult parasites of cattle, which should be administered in the spring and again in the fall following the pasture season, consists of the following: twenty grams (about two-thirds of an ounce) of phenothiazine for each 100 pounds of body weight, with an upper limit of 70 to 80 grams. The dose can be given in a number of ways; namely, as a drench, in a bolus or capsule, or mixed with the feed (in the latter case, mix the phenothiazine in the regular feed).

Grubs (Warbles or Heel Fly)

Cattle grubs are the maggot stage of insects known as heel flies, warble flies, or gadflies. In the United States, there are really two species with similar habits; namely, the common cattle grub, *Hypoderma lineatum*, and the northern cattle grub, *Hypo-*

Fig. 228. Adult female heel fly (*Hypoderma lineatum*) whose maggot stage is responsible for the common cattlegrub. (Courtesy, USDA)

derma bovis. The cattle grub or heel fly is probably the most destructive insect attacking beef and dairy animals.

DISTRIBUTION AND LOSSES CAUSED BY CATTLE GRUBS:

The species *Hypoderma lineatum* is widely distributed throughout the United States, whereas *Hypoderma bovis* is chiefly confined to the northern states.

The total annual economic loss from cattle grubs in the United States, including both beef and dairy animals, is estimated at $100,000,000,[1] and it may even exceed this figure when decreased gains and milk production are taken into consideration. The damage inflicted by cattle grubs affects cattlemen, packers, tanners, and, finally, consumers. The kinds of losses include the following:

1. **Decreased gains or milk production, mechanical injury, or even death.**—Though the fly does not bite or sting, when it lays its eggs on the lower leg, it usually terrifies the animal, causing

Fig. 229. Heifers running away from heel flies. Though the fly does not bite or sting, when it lays its eggs on the lower leg, it usually terrifies the animal, causing it to run with tail hoisted, seeking relief. (Courtesy, Livestock Conservation, Inc.)

it to run with tail hoisted, seeking relief. It may run through fences, over cliffs, or become hopelessly bogged down in a mudhole or swamp. Beef animals suffer weight losses, and milk production from dairy cows may be reduced from 10 to 25 per cent during the period heel flies are laying their eggs.

2. **Carcass damage.**—According to meat packers, about 35 per cent of all beef carcasses are damaged by grubs. The yellowish, watery patches caused by the migration of the larvae

[1]Ensminger, M. E., M. W. Galgan, and W. L. Slocum. Wash. Agri. Expt. Sta. Bul. 562, p. 31.

under the skin are referred to by butchers as "pilled" or "licked beef." Two to three pounds of "jellied" beef must be trimmed from the loins and ribs of each "grubby" animal, and the damaged cut of meat is devalued 2 cents per pound because of the ragged and unattractive appearance.

3. **Injury of hides.**—Approximately one-third of all cattle hides produced in the United States are damaged by grubs. This

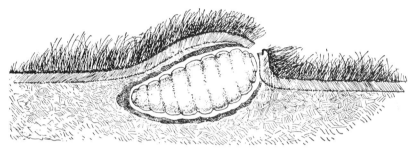

Fig 230. Hole in the hide on the back of an animal, with a grub inside. Note hide opening through which the grub obtains air and finally escapes. (Courtesy, USDA)

loss is caused by the migration of the grub through the back, which leaves a scar in the most valuable part of the hide. According to trade custom, if a hide has as many as five grub holes, it is classed as grade No. 2 and is subject to a discount of 1 cent per pound. Commonly as many as forty and occasionally one hundred or more grub holes are found in a single hide. Hides of the latter quality are not considered worth tanning and are sold for byproducts.

4. **Shock to animal.**—In certain older animals that have been previously sensitized, the breaking of a grub under its skin may cause a terrific reaction (anaphylaxis or allergic reaction). The area may be greatly swollen and form an abscess, and there may be such a general reaction that the animal may die from shock. At the first signs of shock, the local veterinarian should be summoned quickly, to administer appropriate stimulants.

LIFE HISTORY AND HABITS:

Heel flies develop from grubs that have dropped from the backs of cattle. The common heel fly is a large, dark, hairy, beelike fly which resembles a small bumble bee. Though the habits of the two species of heel flies differ slightly, especially in their

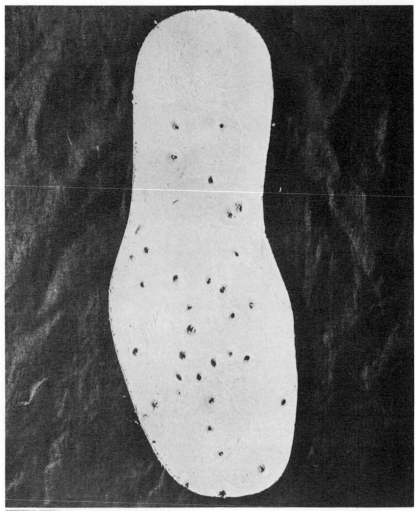

Fig. 231. Shoe sole damaged by cattle grubs. About one-third of all cattle hides produced in the U. S. are damaged by grubs. (Courtesy, Livestock Conservation, Inc.)

season of activity, their life cycles are essentially the same, and may be summarized as follows:

1. The heel fly attacks cattle in the warm days of spring or early summer, the female depositing about three hundred eggs, usually on the lower legs and particularly just above the hoof (hence the name "heel fly"). The heel fly is short lived, neither the male nor female surviving more than about a week.

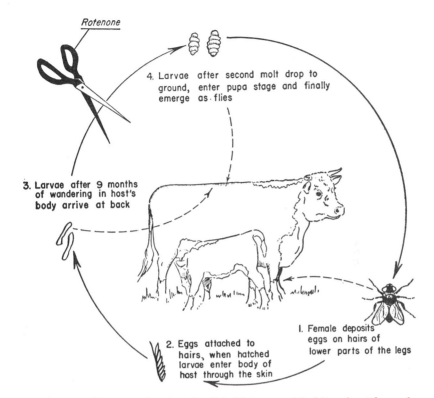

Fig. 232. Diagram showing the life history and habits of cattle grubs. As noted (see scissors) effective control and treatment (cutting the cycle of the parasite) may be obtained by the application of rotenone (spray, dip, or dust). The first application should be made 25 to 30 days after grubs first appear in the back, with subsequent treatments at 30-day intervals thereafter as long as grubs are present in the back. Control may also be secured by the use of a systemic insecticide. (Drawing by R. F. Johnson)

2. Within three to five days after their deposit, the eggs hatch and the tiny larvae force their way through the skin and into the animal body where they feed, grow, and migrate about in the host for the next nine months—especially in the connective tissue of the surface of organs in the abdomen, between the mucous and muscular layers of the gullet, and infrequently in the spinal canal.

3. After about nine months of wandering, the larvae arrive at the back of the animal where they remain for about five weeks, molting twice and growing before leaving the host.

4. The larvae then leave the animal's back, drop to the

ground, become pupae, and, finally, when temperature conditions are favorable (usually in six to ten weeks), emerge as flies.

DAMAGE INFLICTED OR SYMPTOMS OF AFFECTED ANIMALS:

The attack of the heel fly is unmistakable when, in the spring or early summer, cattle are seen madly running with their tails hoisted high over their backs in an attempt to escape. The presence of the grub (larva) in the back, usually from December to May, causes a characteristic swelling, which usually becomes conspicuous, so that a grubby back has a lumpy appearance.

PREVENTION, CONTROL, AND TREATMENT:

Complete prevention of cattle grub damage within any given herd cannot be obtained unless all cattle grubs throughout the country are exterminated. This means a nationwide campaign in which all cooperate to eradicate the menace, farm by farm, county by county, and state by state.

For recommended insecticides and formula for cattle grub control, see Table 42, Handy Spray and Dip Guide for Control of External Parasites of Cattle.

Horn Fly (Cattle Fly, Stock Fly, or Cow Fly)

This fly is one of the most numerous and worst annoyances of cattle. It is often found resting at the base of the horn, hence the name horn fly; but by no means does it confine itself to this location on the animal. Horn flies may congregate by the hundreds or even thousands on the backs, shoulders, and bellies of cattle.

DISTRIBUTION AND LOSSES CAUSED BY THE HORN FLY:

The horn fly is widely distributed throughout the United States. It is one of the most numerous and worst annoyances of cattle. The presence of this insect produces irritation and worry, loss of blood, reduced vitality, and, in the South, sores that may become infested with screwworms. From an economic standpoint, beef cattle gains are sharply reduced, and dairy cattle suffer lowered milk production. These losses, for both beef and dairy animals, are estimated at $150,000,000 annually.[1]

[1]Ensminger, M. E., M. W. Galgan, and W. L. Slocum, Wash. Agri. Expt. Sta. Bul. 562, p. 31.

Fig. 233. Cattle heavily infested with horn flies at the base of the horn, hence the name horn fly. (Courtesy, USDA)

LIFE HISTORY AND HABITS:

This fly, *Haematobia irritans,* is about one-half the size of an ordinary housefly or the stablefly and possesses a piercing beak. Unlike the house fly and stable fly, it remains on cattle throughout the day and night. Horn flies usually feed twice a day, sometimes more frequently.

The life cycle and habits of the horn fly are as follows:

1. The adult fly leaves the cow only for a brief five- to ten-minute period to lay eggs. The eggs are laid beneath the droppings, where they are protected from the sun and rain and hatch out into tiny white maggots in about sixteen hours. Each female fly is capable of laying 375 to 400 eggs during a lifetime.

2. The maggots crawl into the droppings where they feed and grow. They become full-grown in another four days; then they crawl down into the lower part of the droppings or into the soil to pupate and later emerge as a fly.

3. About an hour after the fly emerges from its pupal case, it seeks the nearest cow where it settles and starts feeding. The

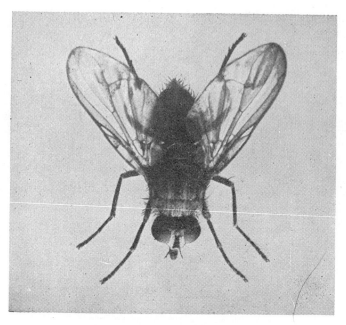

Fig. 234. Enlargement of an adult female horn fly. It is about one-half the size of an ordinary house fly. (Courtesy, USDA)

fly may mate as early as the second day after emergence and may deposit eggs on the third day.

The entire life cycle of the horn fly averages about nine to twelve days during the summer months, and the adult fly lives about seven weeks. Thus it is small wonder that such hordes of this insect exist.

DAMAGE INFLICTED OR SYMPTOMS OF AFFECTED ANIMALS:

The tormented cattle often refuse to graze during the day and seek protection by hiding in dark buildings, brush or tall grass. Heavily infested cattle may also have rough, sore skin, and they suffer an inevitable loss in condition.

PREVENTION, CONTROL, AND TREATMENT:

Prevention and control rest chiefly in disturbing the main breeding ground of the horn fly. This is best accomplished by spreading fresh droppings with a spring tooth harrow in order to hasten their drying. Running pigs with cattle will accomplish the same purpose. These methods of control are not practical on extensive grazing areas, but they may be used in small pastures. The accumulations of cattle manure around barns should be

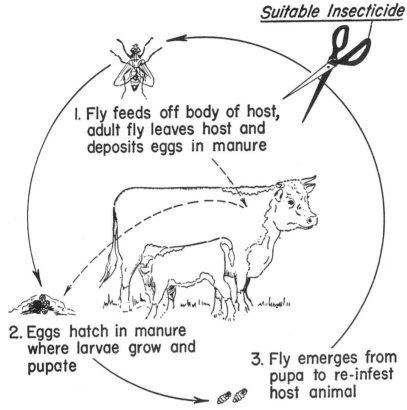

Suitable Insecticide

1. Fly feeds off body of host, adult fly leaves host and deposits eggs in manure

2. Eggs hatch in manure where larvae grow and pupate

3. Fly emerges from pupa to re-infest host animal

Fig. 235. Diagram showing the life history and habits of the horn fly. As noted (see scissors) effective control (cutting the life cycle of the parasite) consists of thorough spraying of animals with a suitable insecticide throughout the fly season. First and foremost, however, it is important that fresh droppings be spread with a spring tooth harrow to hasten their drying and that accumulations of cattle manure around barns be hauled out at frequent intervals and spread thinly on the land. (Drawing by R. F. Johnson)

hauled out at frequent intervals and spread thinly on the land, preferably with a manure spreader.

For recommended insecticides and formula for horn fly control, see Table 42, Handy Spray and Dip Guide for Control of External Parasites of Cattle.

Lice

The louse is a small, flattened, wingless insect parasite of which there are several species (hog lice, which are the largest species, may range up to one-fourth inch in length). The two main types are sucking lice and biting lice. Of the two groups, sucking lice are the most injurious.

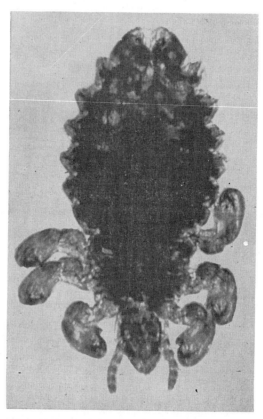

Fig. 236. The short-nosed suckling louse of cattle. (*Haematopinus eurysternus*). (Courtesy, Department of Veterinary Pathology and Hygiene, College of Veterinary Medicine, University of Illinois)

Most species of lice are specific for a particular class of animals. Thus cattle harbor a number of common species of lice—including the long-nosed and short-nosed sucking types of lice, and the little red biting lice—but cattle lice will not remain on the other farm animals, nor will lice from other animals infest cattle. Lice are always more abundant on weak, unthrifty animals and are more troublesome during the winter months than during the rest of the year.

DISTRIBUTION AND LOSSES CAUSED BY LICE:

The presence of lice upon animals is almost universal, but the degree of infestation depends largely upon the state of animal nutrition and the extent to which the owner will tolerate parasites. The irritation caused by the presence of lice retards growth, gains and/or production of milk. The combined losses from cattle lice, including both beef and dairy animals, are estimated at $20,000,000 annually.[1]

LIFE HISTORY AND HABITS:

Lice spend their entire life cycle on the host's body. They attach their eggs or nits to the hair near the skin where they hatch in about two weeks. Two weeks later the young females begin laying eggs, and after reproduction they die on the host. Lice do not survive more than a week when separated from the host, but, under favorable conditions, eggs clinging to detached hairs may continue to hatch for two or three weeks.

DAMAGE INFLICTED OR SYMPTOMS OF AFFECTED ANIMALS:

Infestation shows up most commonly in winter in ill-nourished and neglected animals. There is intense irritation, restlessness, and loss of condition. As many lice are blood suckers, they devitalize their host. There may be severe itching and the animal may be seen scratching, rubbing, and gnawing at the skin. The hair may be rough, thin, and lack luster; and scabs may be evident. In cattle, favorite locations for lice are the root of the tail, on the inside of the thighs, over the fetlock region, and along the neck and shoulders. In some cases, the symptoms may resemble that of mange and it must be kept in mind that the two may occur simultaneously.

With the coming of spring, when the hair sheds and the animals go to pasture, lousiness is greatly diminished.

PREVENTION, CONTROL, AND TREATMENT:

Because of the close contact of domesticated animals, especially during the winter months, it is practically impossible to

---

[1] Ensminger, M. E., M. W. Galgan, and W. L. Slocum, Wash. Agri. Expt. Sta. Bul. 562, p. 31.

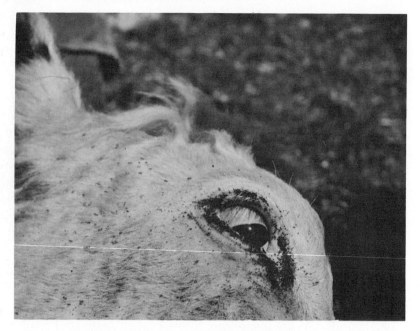

Fig. 237. Short-nosed cattle lice concentrated near the eye of a cow. (Courtesy, USDA)

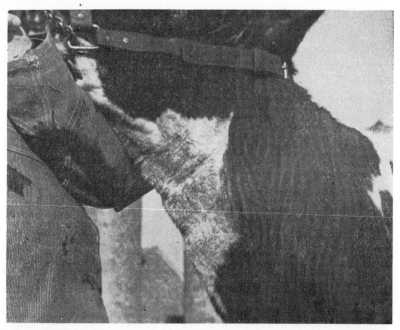

Fig. 238. Cow's neck heavily infested with short-nosed sucking lice. These pests seek the sheltered parts of the body on which to feed. (Courtesy, Department of Veterinary Pathology and Hygiene, College of Veterinary Medicine, University of Illinois)

Fig. 239. Spraying cattle with a power sprayer. Two- to four-hundred pounds pressure is adequate. (Courtesy, Food Machinery and Chemical Corporation)

prevent entirely herds and flocks from becoming slightly infested with the pests. Nevertheless, lice can be kept under control.

For effective control, all members of the herd must be treated simultaneously at intervals, and this is especially necessary during the fall months about the time they are placed in winter quarters. Spraying or dipping during freezing weather should be avoided, however. It is also desirable to treat the housing and bedding.

If a power sprayer is used, from 200 to 400 pounds pressure is adequate for spraying cattle.

Dipping vats have long been used successfully in treating cattle, hogs, and sheep, and sometimes horses. The chief virtue of dipping vats lies in the fact that animals so treated are thoroughly covered. On the other hand, a dipping vat is rather costly to construct, lacks motility and flexibility, and results in considerable left-over dip at the finish of the operation. Dipping vats are especially effective where large numbers of animals can be assembled together.

Dusting is less effective than spraying or dipping, but may be preferable when few animals are to be treated or during the winter months.

For recommended insecticides and formula for cattle lice control, see Table 42, Handy Spray and Dip Guide for Control of External Parasites of Cattle.

Liver Fluke

The liver fluke, *Fasciola hepatica*, is a flattened, leaf-like, brown worm, usually about an inch long. It affects cattle, sheep, goats and other animals.

DISTRIBUTION AND LOSSES CAUSED BY LIVER FLUKE:

The liver fluke is distributed throughout the world, wherever there are low-lying wet areas and suitable snails. In the United States, it is most common in some of the areas of the western and southwestern range country.

Lowered gains and milk production and feed inefficiency are the chief losses. In addition, vast quantities of liver are condemned each year at the time of slaughter—an estimated 1200 tons annually. In packing houses, such livers are referred to as "fluky livers" or "rotten livers." In total, the annual U.S. losses from liver fluke are estimated at $3,500,000 to $5,000,000, for beef and dairy animals combined.[1]

LIFE HISTORY AND HABITS:

Flukes reproduce by means of eggs which, after passing from the host, hatch into embryos equipped with cilia that enable

[1]Ensminger, M. E., M. W. Galgan, and W. L. Slocum, Wash. Agri. Expt. Sta. Bul. 562, p. 31.

them to move about. Upon encountering certain kinds of snails, they penetrate into the body of the intermediate host and develop into cercariae (flukes in the larval stage), which leave the snails and become encysted on the nearby vegetation. The encysted cercariae are then ingested by animals during grazing. The fluke is liberated from the cyst, penetrates the intestinal wall, migrates about the abdominal cavity, and finally reaches the liver where maturity is attained two or three months after infestation.

DAMAGE INFLICTED OR SYMPTOMS OF AFFECTED ANIMALS:

Infested cattle show anemia, as indicated by pale mucous membranes, digestive disturbances, loss of weight, and general

Fig. 240. Brahman bull dying from fluke infestation. (Courtesy, Pitman-Moore Co., Indianapolis, Ind.)

weakness. As with most parasites, positive diagnosis consists of finding eggs in the feces by microscopic examination.

PREVENTION, CONTROL, AND TREATMENT:

The following measures are recommended for the prevention and control of liver fluke:

1. Drainage or avoidance of wet pastures.

2. Where relatively small snail-infested areas are involved,

it may be practical to destroy the snail (carrier of liver fluke), preferably in the spring season, through—

(1) Applying 3 to 6 lbs. of copper sulfate (bluestone or blue vitrol) per acre of grassland, mixing and applying the small quantity of copper sulfate with a suitable carrier (such as a mixture of 1 part of the copper sulfate to 4 to 8 parts of either sand or lime), and

(2) Treating ponds or sloughs with 1 part of copper sulfate to 500,000 parts of water.

When copper sulfate is used in the dilutions indicated, it is not injurious to grasses and will not poison farm animals, but it may kill fish.

Snail-infested pastures should not be used for making hay.

The recommended treatment, which should be under the direction of a veterinarian, consists in drenching with hexachlorethane in a bentonite suspension. Good results may be expected from two treatments each year, preferably in the spring and fall.

Lungworm

The lungworm, *Dictyocaulus viviparous,* is a white, threadlike worm $1\frac{1}{2}$ to 3 inches long, found in the trachea and bronchi of cattle—especially calves.

DISTRIBUTION AND LOSSES CAUSED BY LUNGWORMS:

Lungworms are distributed throughout the United States, especially on wet pastures.

The losses are chiefly in lowered feed efficiency, milk, and meat production. With a heavy infestation, there may be death losses.

LIFE HISTORY AND HABITS:

In the bronchial tubes of the lungs, female lung worms produce large numbers of eggs. Usually, these hatch in the air passages and liberate larvae that are coughed up, swallowed, and eliminated in the feces. Sometimes the coughed-up eggs hatch in the stomach or intestines, but they may pass unhatched from the host, particularly when there is severe diarrhea.

Under favorable conditions, the larvae eliminated with the feces develop into the infestive stage in about a week. Then they crawl upon blades of grass, where they are ingested by grazing cattle. Thence they penetrate the intestinal wall and reach the lymph glands, from which they are eventually carried to the lungs.

Cattle lungworms mature in three to four weeks, at which time larvae appear in the feces. The worms live from two to four months in the host.

DAMAGE INFLICTED OR SYMPTOMS OF AFFECTED ANIMALS:

Typical symptoms include coughing, labored breathing, loss of appetite, unthriftiness, and intermittent diarrhea. Death may follow, probably from suffocation or pneumonia.

PREVENTION, CONTROL, AND TREATMENT:

Where lungworms are found, the following prevention and control measures are recommended:

1. Practice rigid sanitation.
2. Where practical, segregate calves from older animals.
3. Keep calves on a good ration.
4. Do not spread infested manure on pastures.
5. Utilize dry pasture if possible.

Medical treatments are of doubtful value. Good nursing—good feed and care—will help. The veterinarian should be consulted for supportive treatment.

Mites

Mites produce a specific contagious disease known as mange (or scabies, scab, or itch). These small insect-like parasites, which are almost invisible to the naked eye, constitute a very large group. They attack members of both the plant and animal kingdom.

Each species of domesticated animals has its own peculiar species of mange mites, and, with exception of the sarcoptic mites, the mites from one species of animals cannot live and propagate permanently on a different species. The sarcoptic mites are transmissible from one class of animals to another, and, in the case of the sarcoptic mite of the horse and cow, from animals to man. There are two chief forms of mange: sarcoptic mange, caused by burrowing mites, and psoroptic mange, caused by mites that bite the skin and suck blood but do not burrow. The sarcoptic form is most damaging for, in addition to their tunneling, the mites secrete an irritating poison. This combination results in severe itching.

Mites are responsible for the condition known as mange (scabies) in cattle, sheep, horses, and swine. The disease appears to spread most rapidly among young and poorly nourished animals.

DISTRIBUTION AND LOSSES CAUSED BY MITES:

Injury from mites is caused by blood sucking and the formation of scabs and other skin affections. In a severe attack, the skins may be much less valuable for leather. Growth is retarded, and production of meat and milk is lowered.

LIFE HISTORY AND HABITS:

The mites that attack cattle breed exclusively on the bodies of their hosts, and will live for only two or three weeks when removed therefrom. The female mite which produces sarcoptic mange—the most severe form of scabies—lays from ten to twenty-five eggs during the egg-laying period, which lasts about two weeks. At the end of another two weeks, the eggs have hatched and the mites have reached maturity. A new generation of mites may be produced every fifteen days.

The disease is more prevalent during the winter months, when animals are confined and in close contact with each other.

DAMAGE INFLICTED OR SYMPTOMS OF AFFECTED ANIMALS:

When the mite pierces the skin to feed on cells and lymph, there is marked irritation, itching, and scratching. Exudate forms on the surface, and this coagulates, crusting over the surface. The crusting is often accompanied or followed by the formation of a thick, tough, wrinkled skin. Often there are secondary skin infections. The only certain method of diagnosis is to demonstrate the presence of the mites.

PREVENTION, CONTROL, AND TREATMENT:

Prevention consists of avoiding contact with diseased animals or infested premises. In case of an outbreak, the local veterinarian or livestock sanitary officials should be contacted.

Mites can be controlled by spraying or dipping infested animals with suitable insecticidal solutions, and by quarantine of affected herds. For recommended insecticides and formula for cattle mite control, see Table 42, Handy Spray and Dip Guide for Control of External Parasites of Cattle.

Fig. 241. A severe case of mange on a cow, caused by sarcoptic mites. Note the rough and wrinkled condition of the skin, with crusting over the surface. (J. W. McManigal, Agricultural Photographer, Horton, Kansas)

Ringworm

Ringworm, or barn itch, is a contagious disease of the outer layers of skin. It is caused by certain microscopic molds or fungi (*Trichophyton, Achorion,* or *Microsporon*). All animals and man are susceptible.

DISTRIBUTION AND LOSSES CAUSED BY RINGWORM:

Ringworm is widespread throughout the United States. It is a contagious disease of the outer layer of skin caused by certain microscopic molds or fungi, which affects all animals and man. Though it may appear among animals on pasture, it is far more prevalent as a stable disease. It is unsightly, and affected animals may experience considerable discomfort; but the actual economic losses attributed to the disease are not too great.

LIFE HISTORY AND HABITS:

The period of incubation for this disease is about one week. The fungi form seed or spores that may live eighteen months or longer in barns or elsewhere.

Fig. 242. Dipping Cattle. The chief virtue of dipping vats lies in the fact that animals so treated are thoroughly covered. (Courtesy, Dave Brannon, Extension Entomologist, Washington State University)

Ringworm is usually a winter disease, with recovery the following summer.

DAMAGE INFLICTED OR SYMPTOMS OF AFFECTED ANIMALS:

Round, scaly areas almost devoid of hair appear mainly in the vicinity of the eyes, ears, side of the neck, or the root of the tail. Crusts may form, and the skin may have a gray, powdery, asbestos-like appearance. The infected patches, if not checked. gradually increase in size. Mild itching usually accompanies the disease.

Fig. 243. Heifer with ringworm. The fungi causing these raised circu lar areas may be transmitted to man. (Courtesy, Department of Veterinary Pathology and Hygiene, College of Veterinary Medicine, University of Illinois)

PREVENTION, CONTROL, AND TREATMENT:

The organisms are spread from animal to animal or through the medium of contaminated fence posts, curry combs, and brushes. Thus prevention and control consists of disinfecting everything that has been in contact with infected animals. The affected animals should also be isolated. Strict sanitation is an essential in the control of ringworm.

The hair should be clipped, the scabs removed, and the area sandpapered and washed with soap. The diseased parts should be painted with tincture of iodine or salicylic acid and alcohol (one part in ten) every three days, until cleared up. Certain proprietary remedies available only from veterinarians have proved very effective in treatment.

Screwworm

Among all the insect pests on this earth, those which raise their maggots in the living flesh of animals—such as the screwworm—are peculiarly loathsome. True screwworms seldom get through the unbroken skin, but will penetrate moist pockets like the prepuce of a gelding and the dimple in front of a cow's udder. They are not found in cold-blooded animals such as turtles, snakes, and lizards.

Man-made wounds resulting from branding, shearing, castrating, dehorning, and docking afford a breeding ground for this parasite. Add to this the wounds from some types of vegetation, from fighting, and from blood-sucking insects and ample places for propagation are provided.

DISTRIBUTION AND LOSSES CAUSED BY SCREWWORMS:
Normally, the primary screwworm fly is confined to the southern and southwestern states, including Arizona and the southern half of California. Occasionally, under exceptionally favorable weather conditions or through the shipping of infested animals from further south, destructive outbreaks of the pest have occurred in some of the Corn Belt states.

In infested areas, the screwworm is undoubtedly the greatest enemy of all the insect species with which the livestock owner must contend. For example, in the Southwest, where it inflicts the most injury, many ranchmen report that 50 per cent of their normal annual livestock losses are caused by this parasite. Screwworm losses are estimated at $15,000,000 annually for U.S. beef and dairy animals.[1]

LIFE HISTORY AND HABITS:
The primary screwworm fly is bluish green in color, with three dark stripes on its back and reddish or orange color below the eyes. The fly generally deposits its eggs in shingle-like masses

[1]Ensminger, M. E., M. W. Galgan, and W. L. Slocum, Wash. Agri. Expt. Sta. Bul. 562, p. 31.

on the edges or the dry portion of wounds. From 50 to 300 eggs are laid at one time, with a single female being capable of laying about 3,000 eggs in a lifetime. Hatching of the eggs occurs in eleven hours, and the young whitish worms (larvae or maggots) immediately burrow into the living flesh. There they feed and grow for a period of four to seven days, shedding their skin twice during this period.

When these worms have reached their full growth, they assume a pinkish color, leave the wound, and drop to the ground, where they dig beneath the surface of the soil and undergo a transformation to the hard-skinned, dark-brown, motionless pupa. It is during the pupa stage that the maggot changes to the adult fly.

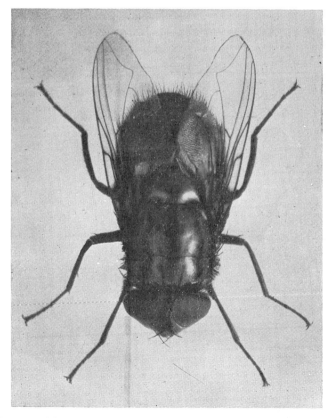

Fig. 244. The screwworm fly (*Cochliomyia americana*). This fly is bluish green in color, with three dark stripes on its back and reddish or orange color below the eyes. (Courtesy, USDA)

After the pupa has been in the soil from seven to sixty days, the fly emerges from it, works its way to the surface of the ground, and crawls up on some nearby object (bush, weed, etc.) to allow its wings to unfold and otherwise to mature. Under favorable conditions, the newly emerged female fly becomes sexually mature and will lay eggs five days later. During warm weather, the entire life cycle is usually completed in twenty-one days, but under cold, unfavorable conditions the cycle may take as many as eighty days or longer.

DAMAGE INFLICTED OR SYMPTOMS OF
AFFECTED ANIMALS:

The injury caused by this parasite is inflicted chiefly by the maggots. The early symptoms in affected animals are loss of appetite and condition, and listlessness. Unless proper treatment is administered, the great destruction of many tissues kills the host in a few days.

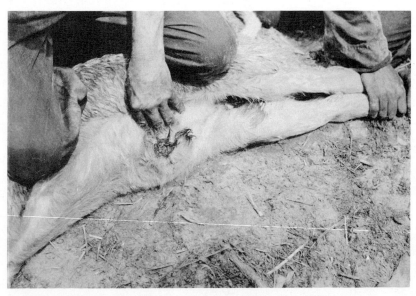

Fig. 245. Screwworm in navel of calf. (Courtesy, USDA)

PREVENTION, CONTROL, AND TREATMENT:

Prevention in infested areas consists mainly of keeping animal wounds to a minimum and of protecting those that do materialize.

As the primary screwworm must have living warm-blooded animals in which to breed and in order to survive, it must produce a new generation during each four-month period. It is evident, therefore, that the most effective control measures can be obtained during the winter months. During this season, the life cycle is slowed down, and it is difficult for the fly to live and breed. Thus, the most effective control consists of preventing infestation of wounds and of killing all possible maggots during the winter and spring months. Additional control is secured through timing as much as possible those farm and ranch operations that necessarily produce wounds during the winter season when the flies are least abundant and least active. The use of Burdizzo pincers in castration, the dehorning of animals at an early age and during the proper season, the eradication of plants that cause injuries, breeding so that young will arrive during the seasons of least fly activity, and avoidance of anything else that might produce wounds will all aid greatly in screwworm control. In brief, the elimination of wounds or injuries to the host constitutes effective control.

If possible, there should be facilities available for handling and treating infested animals. It is highly desirable to have a screened, fly-proof area available for wounded or infested animals.

Recommended treatment consists in applying with a paint brush to affected areas twice weekly until the wound is healed either (1) Formula MS 62 (Smear 62), or (2) EQ-335 Screwworm Remedy. These remedies both protect wounds against infestation and kill the larvae. Smear 62 has the following constituents:

	Parts by weight
Diphenylamine	3.5
Benzol	3.5
Turkey red oil	1.0
Lamp black	2.0

EQ-335 Screwworm Remedy, obtains its numerical designation from the proportions of the two main active ingredients, lindane (3%) and pine oil (35%). In addition, it contains mineral oil (42%), emulsifier (10%), and santocel (10%).

In comparison with Smear 62, EQ-335 is (1) more effective, (2) more expensive, (3) cleaner (alleviating the staining and messiness of Smear 62 due to the presence of lamp black), and (4) less volatile and less inflammable.

Both of these products may be homemade, but it is more convenient, and perhaps little or no more expensive, to purchase a commercially mixed product, which should be used according to directions.

In the absence of MS 62 or EQ-335, some stockmen apply heavy vaseline or pine tar oil to recent wounds and to the navels of newborn animals to repel the flies, and they apply benzene (not benzine) to infested wounds. Also, chloroform is freqently used to kill the larvae. (See Table 42, Handy Spray and Dip Guide for Control of External Parasites of Cattle.)

Stablefly (Stock Fly, Biting Housefly, or Dog Fly)

The stablefly, *Stomoxys calcitrans*, which is about the size of a housefly, is usually found in the vicinity of animals and derives its nourishment from sucking blood. It attacks all classes of farm amimals and man.

DISTRIBUTION AND LOSSES CAUSED BY THE STABLEFLY:

The stablefly is found in all the temperate regions of the world. Its chief economic loss to animals is in terms of lowered efficiency in work horses, decreased gains in beef cattle, and lowered milk production in dairy cattle, amounting to as much as 50 per cent in seasons when the numbers of flies become large. It is estimated that U.S. cattle losses, including both beef and dairy animals, due to the stablefly approach $20,000,000 annually.[1] In addition to causing such lowered production losses, the stablefly has been incriminated in the mechanical transmission of anthrax, swamp fever, surra, and even infantile paralysis of man. It is also known to be an intermediate host for the peritoneal roundworm of cattle and the small-mouth stomach worm of horses. Along certain beaches, the annoyance to man has been so great that resort interests have been affected and real estate values have been lowered.

LIFE HISTORY AND HABITS:

Like other true flies, the stablefly has four stages—egg, larva, pupa, and adult fly. Briefly, the life history and habits are as follows:

---

[1]Ensminger, M. E., M. W. Galgan, and W. L. Slocum, Wash. Agri. Expt. Sta. Bul. 562, p. 31.

1. The adult females lay the eggs on fermenting organic matter, such as straw or manure, where they hatch in one to three days, producing a tiny, creamy-white maggot or larva.

2. In from six to thirty days—the time depending upon the food, moisture, and warmth—the larvae grow and transform into the pupae stage.

3. In another five to twenty days—the time depending upon climatic conditions—the pupa is transformed into the adult fly.

4. Flies begin mating when two to three days old and lay eggs when five days old. An adult fly may live for six weeks, with each female laying up to six hundred eggs in a lifetime. The stablefly usually feeds on blood one to two times daily, generally

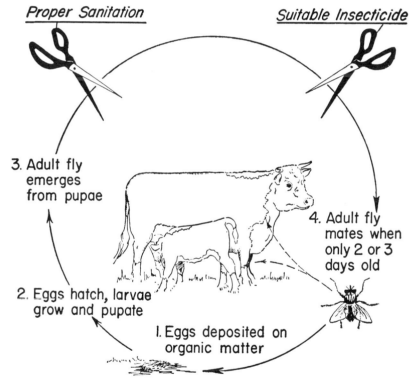

Fig. 246. Diagram showing the life history and habits of the stablefly. As noted (see scissors) effective control (cutting the life cycle of the parasite) consists of thorough spraying—especially the legs and lower part of the body—with a suitable insecticide throughout the fly season. First and foremost, however, it is important that there be proper disposal of manure and elimination of all fermenting or decaying organic material. (Drawing by R. F. Johnson)

TABLE 42

HANDY SPRAY AND DIP GUIDE FOR CONTROL OF EXTERNAL PARASITES OF CATTLE[1]

(Precautions.—In applying insecticides to livestock or around barns, do not contaminate feed, feed and water troughs, or allow runoff into streams. Observe all other precautions specified on the container and in the sections which follow this table, and avoid personal exposure.)

Animal and Insect	Insecticide	Tolerance (ppm)	Formulation and Strength (D=dust; EC=emulsifiable concentrate; S=spray; WP=wettable powder; B=bait)	Dosage (Dilute material per animal unless otherwise indicated)	Application	Minimum Days From Last Application to Slaughter	Other Restrictions and Comments
Beef or Dairy Cattle[3]							
Cattle grubs	Rotenone		5% D / 5% D (7½ lb./100 gal. water)	3 oz. / 2-4 qt.	Rub thoroughly on back. Wash or apply with power sprayer 1-3 times to backs every 30 days. Begin treatment 25 to 30 days after grubs appear in the backs.		
Horn flies	Methoxychlor	0 (in milk)	50% D (WP)	1 Tbsp.	Sprinkle on back and neck every 3 weeks.		Do not use as spray or dip.
	Pyrethrins + Synergist[3]		0.05% + 0.5% S	1-2 qt.	As wet spray every 3-7 days.		
			Oil Soln. or EC, 1% + 10% S	1-2 oz.	As mist spray daily, by hand or with treadle sprayer.		
	Lethane or Thanite		Oil Soln., 3-5%	1-2 oz.	do.		
Horse flies	Pyrethrins + Synergist[3]		0.05-0.1% + 0.5-1.0% S	1-2 qt.	As wet spray every 2-3 days.		
			Oil Soln. or EC, 1% + 10% S	1-2 oz.	As mist spray, same as for horn flies.		
Stable flies and Mosquitoes	Pyrethrins + Synergist[3]		0.05-0.1% + 0.5-1.0% S	1-2 qt.	As wet spray every 2-3 days.		
			Oil Soln. or EC, 1% + 10% S	1-2 oz.	As mist spray, same as for horn flies.		
	Lethane or Thanite		Oil Soln., 3-5%	1-2 oz.	do.		
Lice	Pyrethrins + Synergist[3]		0.025% + 0.25% S		Spray animals thoroughly, repeat after 2-3 weeks.		
	Rotenone		5% D (1-2 lb./100 gal. water) / 0.5-1% D		Dust animals thoroughly.		

Pest	Insecticide	Strength	Amount to use	Directions		Remarks
Mites	Lindane	0.03–0.05% S		Make 2 applications 7–10 days apart.		Discard milk for 48 hrs. after use of lindane, or feed to dairy calves, swine poultry.
Screwworms	Diphenylamine	35% (Smear 62)	Minimum amount necessary to treat wound. Do not use more than 3 tsp. on baby calves.	Brush or smear on wound and surrounding area, twice first week and weekly thereafter until healed.		
	Lindane	3% (EQ-335)				
Ticks	Arsenic (As$_2$O$_3$)	0.175–0.19% Soln.	Dosage of all these materials will vary with size of animals and amount of hair.	Immerse animals every 14 days.		
	Pyrethrins + Synergist[3]	0.1% + 1% S		As needed; immerse or spray animals thoroughly.		
	Rotenone	5% D (12 oz./gal. water)		As needed; spray animals thoroughly.		
Spinose ear tick	Lindane	0.75% in xylenepine oil	½ oz.	Inside ears with spring-bottom oiler.		
Beef Cattle Only[4] Cattle grubs	Co-Ral (Bayer 21/199)—a systemic insecticide	0.5% S (16 lbs. Co-Ral 25% WP/100 gals. water)	2–4 qts.	Spray before Oct. in South and before Nov. in North. Spray to wet skin of animal.	60	Do not repeat within less than 60 days. Animal should have access to feed and water before and after treatment. If administered properly, one treatment per season is adequate. Do not treat calves under 3 months of age. Grub kill of 75 to 95% can be expected.

[1] The authors are very grateful to the following eminent entomologists who very kindly reviewed this table and made many helpful suggestions for its improvement: Mr. David H. Brannon, Extension Entomology Specialist, Washington State University; Dr. A. M. Lnquist, Head Insects Affecting Man and Animals Section, Entomology Research Division, Agricultural Research Service, USDA, Beltsville, Maryland; Dr. Gaines W. Eddy, Entomologist in Charge, Entomology Research Division, Agricultural Research, USDA, Corvallis, Oregon; Mr. M. P. Jones, Extension Entomologist, USDA, Washington, D. C.; and Dr. Ernest W. Laake, City Entomologist, Public Health Department, Dallas, Texas.

[2] Certain insecticides that may be used for beef cattle only are so listed further along in this table. It is not considered practical to dip lactating dairy cows.

[3] The pyrethrins synergist should be piperonyl butoxide or MGK 264.

[4] The insecticides listed herein may be used for beef cattle in addition to those listed on the table for both beef and dairy animals.

TABLE 42—(Continued)

Animal and Insect	Insecticide	Tolerance (ppm)	Formulation and Strength (D=dust; EC=emulsifiable concentrate; S=spray; WP=wettable powder; B=bait)	Dosage (Dilute material per animal unless otherwise indicated)	Application	Minimum Days From Last Application to Slaughter	Other Restrictions and Comments
Beef Cattle only							
Cattle grubs (cont'd)	Trolene (Dow ET-57)—a systemic insecticide		40% in bolus, or pill.	One 37.5 gram bolus/300 lb. body wt.	Orally with balling gun or dissolved in water as oral drench. Treat before Oct. in South and before Nov. in North.	60	do.
Horn flies	Methoxychlor	3 (in fat)	EC or WP 0.5% S	2 qt.	To backs at intervals of 3 weeks or as needed.		
			50% WP	1 Tbsp.	do.		
			5% Oil S	1 gal./20 ft. cable.	Saturate back rubbers.		
	DDT	7 (in fat)	5% Oil	1 gal./20 ft. of cable.	Saturate back rubbers.	30	
	Toxaphene	7 (in fat)	5% Oil	1 gal./20 ft. cable	do.	28	
			EC or WP, 0.5% S	Amount will vary with size of animals.	To backs every 3 weeks or as needed.	28	
			50% D	1 Tbsp.	do.	28	
	Malathion	4	EC or WP, 0.5%	2 qts.	To backs every 2 or 3 weeks, or as needed.		Do not use on calves under one month of age.
Lice	Lindane		EC or WP, 0.03% S	Dosage of all these materials will vary with size of animals and amount of hair.	Spray animals thoroughly; repeat after 2-3 weeks if needed.	30	Do not exceed 0.03% on calves less than 6 months old.
	Methoxychlor	3 (in fat)	EC or WP, 0.5% (1-1.5% for tail louse) 10% D		do. Dust animals thoroughly.		
	Toxaphene	7	EC or WP, 0.5%		Immerse or spray thoroughly; repeat after 2-3 weeks if needed.	28	
	Malathion	4	EC or WP, 0.5%	2 qts.	Spray thoroughly; repeat after 2-3 weeks if needed.		Do not spray calves less than 1 month old.

Pest	Insecticide		Formulation	Dosage	Directions		Remarks
Mites	Lime sulfur (2% sulfide sulfur)		2% S or dip		Make 4 or more applications of lime-sulfur at intervals of 6 or 7 days.		
Ticks	Lindane		EC or WP, 0.025%	Dosage will vary with size of animals and amount of hair.	Immerse or spray animals thoroughly; repeat after 2 or 3 weeks or as needed.	30	For spinose ear tick apply sprays at low pressure so as not to injure inner ear.
	Toxaphene	7	EC or WP, 0.5%		Immerse or spray animals thoroughly; repeat after 2 or 3 weeks or as needed.	28	Do not overdose with any material, especially on calves.
	Malathion	4	EC or WP, 0.5%		Spray animals thoroughly; repeat after 2–3 weeks if needed.		

attacking the lower parts of the animal's body, particularly the outer sides of the front legs, where the animal's tail is less likely to dislodge them.

DAMAGE INFLICTED OR SYMPTOMS OF AFFECTED ANIMALS:

In addition to production losses, the continuous attack of these parasites causes constant fighting and restlessness among the animals. In seeking natural protection, animals frequently resort to mudholes, brush, etc.

PREVENTION, CONTROL, AND TREATMENT:

The destruction of natural breeding grounds of the stablefly is the first and primary means of prevention. This calls for the frequent spreading of manure and the elimination of all fermenting or decaying organic material—such as straw stacks, piles of waste roughages, etc.

Sprays are the best secondary means for controlling stableflies. For recommended insecticides and formula for stablefly control, see Table 42, Handy Spray and Dip Guide for Control of External Parasites of Cattle.

Handy Spray and Dip Guide for Control of External Parasites of Cattle

Table 42 contains recommendations for the control of external parasites of cattle.

Several new and promising insecticides are now on the market. However, further research is desirable in order to determine the value of many of these products. Where cattle parasites are encountered, therefore, it is suggested that the stockman obtain from local authorities the current recommendations relative to the choice and concentration of the insecticide to use.

HOW TO PREPARE SPRAYS OR DIPS:

In most cases several concentrations of both wettable powders and emulsions of each insecticide are on the market. Because of this, the recommended concentrations of sprays and dips in Table 42 are in terms of percentage concentration of the active ingredient in the finished spray or dip.

In preparing sprays and dips, most stockmen rely almost entirely on the directions found on the container. With products manufactured by reputable companies, this is probably satisfactory. However, any stockman can easily prepare an insecticide of any desired strength (1) by referring to Table 43, or (2) by following the simple mathematical formula below Table 43.

TABLE 43

HANDY GUIDE FOR MAKING DESIRED STRENGTH
OF INSECTICIDES[1]

Type and Percentage of Insecticide in Concentrate	Amount of Concentrate to Add to Water to Make Different Percentage Strengths in Finished Spray or Dip			
	For 5 gallons		For 100 gallons	
	0.5 per cent	2.5 per cent	0.5 per cent	2.5 per cent
Wettable Powder:				
25%	13 oz.	——	16 lbs.	——
40%	8 oz.	2.5 lbs.	10 lbs.	50 lbs.
50%	6½ oz.	2.0 lbs.	8 lbs.	40 lbs.
75%	4½ oz.	1½ lbs.	5½ lbs.	27 lbs.
Emulsion:				
25%	1½ cups	2 qts.	2 gals.	10 gals.
50%	¾ cups	1 qt.	1 gal.	5 gals.

[1]To make 0.25 per cent strengths, use half the amount given in Table 43 for the 0.5 per cent strength.
        To make 5 per cent strength, use two times the amount given in Table 43 for the 2.5 per cent strengths.
        Where Table 43 is not applicable, the number of pounds of any given insecticide wettable powder or emulsion—regardless of its concentration—to add in order to make a desired number of gallons of spray or dip of the desired strength may be computed readily and accurately as shown in the following example:

Example: How many pounds of 50 per cent wettable DDT powder are required in order to prepare 100 gallons of 0.5 per cent finished DDT spray for the control of flies?

Answer: (gallons of finished spray or dip desired) $\times$ $\dfrac{\text{(wt. of 1 gal.}}{\text{of water)}}$ $\times$ $\dfrac{\text{(percentage of active ingredient desired in finished spray or dip)}}{\text{(percentage active ingredient in insecticide)}}$

Or $\dfrac{100 \times 8^2 \times 0.5}{50}$ = 8 pounds

[2]To be more exact, this figure is 8.337, but 8.0 is close enough for all practical purposes.

CAUTIONS AND INSTRUCTIONS RELATIVE
TO SPECIFIC INSECTICIDES:

The following cautions and instructions relative to specific insecticides should be observed:

1. Always read and observe the precautions on the label.

2. Lindane, DDT, and toxaphene should not be used (1) on cows or goats being milked or in dairy barns, (2) on animals fattened for slaughter in 30 days, or (3) on young animals under 3 months of age.

3. Benzene hexachloride is no longer recommended.

4. The gamma isomer concentration of lindane should not exceed (1) 0.03 per cent for animals under one year of age, or (2) 0.05 per cent for animals over one year of age.

5. Where interstate shipment is involved, the USDA recognizes lime-sulfur and lindane treatments for mites.

6. Methoxychlor may be safely used on animals intended for early slaughter, but not on milk animals.

7. Pyrethrin can be obtained with synergists (or activators) other than piperonyl butoxide. Since they are ready-mixed anyway, the stockman should use them according to the directions found on the container.

GENERAL APPLICATION DIRECTIONS:

Some general application directions follow:

1. Insecticides are poisonous. Handle them with care. Follow the directions and heed all precautions on the container label.

2. When handling or mixing concentrated insecticides, avoid spilling them on your skin and keep them out of your eyes, nose, and mouth. If any is spilled on the skin or clothing, wash it off and change your clothing immediately. Wear a respirator and goggles when you are working with concentrated sprays or dusts.

3. Store insecticides in closed containers in a dry place where children, irresponsible persons, and animals cannot reach them. Be sure that insecticides are clearly labeled.

4. If you accidentally swallow an insecticide, induce vomiting by taking 1 tablespoonful of salt in a glass of water. Repeat if necessary. Call a doctor.

5. To protect fish and wildlife, be careful not to contaminate streams, lakes, or ponds with insecticides. Do not clean spraying equipment or dump excess spray material near such water. Avoid getting this material onto pasture grass or feed.

6. In using insecticides, avoid contamination of feeds, feed utensils and drinking vessels. See that the building is ventilated when spraying indoors. Wash yourself thoroughly and change your clothes after spraying.

7. Depending on the size of the herd and the available equipment, liquid insecticides may be applied with a power sprayer, a hand-sprayer, a sponge, or a brush. With power sprayer, it is desirable to operate at 100 to 200 pounds pressure and to use 2 to 4 gallons of spray material per animal; except in grub control where 400 pounds pressure should be used and about 1 gallon of spray material per animal applied.

8. In freezing weather, it is preferable to treat with dusts, applied with any available duster according to the directions found on the insecticide container; even though dusting is less effective than spraying or dipping.

9. Spray materials should be kept well agitated or mixed while being used.

DISINFECTANTS[1]

Under ordinary conditions, proper cleaning of barns removes most of the microorganisms, along with the filth, thus eliminating the necessity of disinfection. In case of a disease outbreak, however, the premises must be disinfected.

Effective disinfection depends on five things:

1. Thorough cleaning before application.

2. The phenol coefficient of the disinfectant, which indicates the killing strength of a disinfectant as compared to phenol (carbolic acid). It is determined by a standard laboratory test in which the typhoid fever germ often is used as the test organism.

3. The dilution at which the disinfectant is used.

4. The temperature; most disinfectants are much more effective if applied hot.

5. Thoroughness of application, and time of exposure.

Disinfection must in all cases be preceded by a very thorough cleaning, for organic matter serves to protect disease germs and otherwise interferes with the activity of the disinfecting agent.

Sunlight possesses disinfecting properties, but it is variable and superficial in its action. Heat and some of the chemical disinfectants are more effective.

The application of heat by steam, by hot water, by burning, or by boiling is an effective method of disinfection. In many cases, however, it may not be practical to use heat.

In choosing a chemical disinfectant, it should be realized that not all disease-producing bacteria are susceptible to the same chemical agents. Table 44 gives a summary of the limitations, usefulness, and strength of some common disinfectants.

---

[1]The authors had the benefit of the authoritative review and suggestions of Dr. W. H. Gillespie, Associate Professor of Veterinary Microbiology, Washington State University, Pullman, Washington, in the preparation of this section and Table 44.

TABLE 44

HANDY DISINFECTANT GUIDE[1]

Kind of Disinfectant	Usefulness	Strength	Limitations and Comments
Alcohol	Effective against the less resistant disease germs provided there is adequate exposure.	70 per cent alcohol—the content usually found in rubbing alcohol.	Limited application. Not recommended for general use. Often used as a local antiseptic in obtaining blood samples or making hypodermic injections. Not reliable for sterilization of instruments.
Bichloride of Mercury (mercuric chloride; corrosive sublimate)	Destroys less resistant bacteria under favorable conditions. Tends to prevent growth rather than actually destroying bacteria. Organic mercurials, sometimes used as local antiseptics, are less poisonous and more reliable.	Tablets used in a dilution of 1 to 1,000.	Unreliable as a germ killer in the presence of organic matter. Also cattle are especially susceptible to mercury poisoning. For farm disinfection, bichloride of mercury is inferior to iodine, lye, saponified cresols, and the new cationic bactericides.
Boric Acid	As a wash for eyes, and other sensitive parts of the body.	1 oz. in 1 pt. water (about 6% solution).	It is a weak antiseptic. It may cause harm to the nervous system if absorbed into the body in large amounts. For this and other reasons, antibiotic solutions and saline solutions are fast replacing it.
Cationic Bactericides (Many commercial products available, including QAC, i.e., quaternary ammonium compounds)	Primarily detergents but some are actively bactericidal. Often used in sanitizing dairy or other equipment and utensils. **Use only as recommended by competent sanitarian.**	Concentration varies with different products and under different conditions. Follow authoritative recommendations.	They have only a slight toxicity and are non-irritant and odorless. They are neutralized by soap, anionic detergents and even by mineral content of some waters. Superior to chlorine compounds in the presence of organic matter.
Cresols (Many commercial products available)	A generally reliable class of disinfectant. Effective against brucellosis, hog cholera, shipping fever, swine erysipelas and tuberculosis.	4 oz. per gal.; or according to the directions found on the container.	Cannot be used where odor may be absorbed, and therefore, not suited for use around milk and meat, (sodium orthophenylphenate is an exception, being free from objectional odor).
Heat (by steam, not water, burning, or boiling)	In the burning of rubbish or articles of little value, and in disposing of infected body discharges. The steam "Jenny" is very effective for sterilization (example: poultry equipment) **if properly employed.**	10 minutes exposure to boiling water is usually sufficient.	Exposure to boiling water will destroy all ordinary disease germs but sometimes fails to kill the spores of such diseases as anthrax and tetanus. Moist heat is preferred to dry heat, and steam under pressure is the most effective. Heat may be impractical or too expensive.

TABLE 44—(Continued)

Kind of Disinfectant	Usefulness	Strength	Limitations and Comments
Hypochlorites (chlorine compounds)	For deodorizing manure, sewers, drains, and for disinfecting milk cans and bottles and around dairy barns.	200 parts available chlorine per million of water. Unstable; replace solution frequently as recommended.	Excellent for disinfection, but with following limitations: Not effective against the T.B. organism and spores. Its effectiveness is greatly reduced in presence of organic matter, such as milk, even in small quantities. Hypochlorites deteriorate rapidly when exposed to air.
Iodine	Extensively used as skin disinfectant, for minor cuts and bruises.	Generally used as tincture of iodine 2%.	Never cover with a bandage. Clean skin before applying iodine.
Lime (Quicklime; burnt lime; calcium oxide)	As a deodorant when sprinkled on manure and animal discharges; or as a disinfectant when sprinkled on the floor or used as a newly-made "milk of lime" or as a whitewash.	Use as a dust; as "milk of lime"; or as a whitewash, but use fresh.	Not effective against organism of T. B. and the spore formers. Wear goggles, when adding water to quicklime.
Lye (Sodium hydroxide; caustic soda)	On concrete floors; in milk houses because there is no odor; against microorganisms of brucellosis and the viruses of foot-and-mouth disease, hog cholera and vesicular exanthema. In strong solution (5%), effective against anthrax and blackleg.	1 can (13 oz.) to 12 to 15 gal. water. To prepare a 5% solution, add 5 (13 oz.) cans to 10 gal. water.	Damages fabrics, aluminum, and painted surfaces. Be careful, for it will burn the hands and face. Not effective against organism of T. B., Johne's disease, or strangles or most spores. When used in hog houses, lye should be mixed with hot water, as the heat of the water will destroy the worm eggs. **Diluted vinegar can be used to neutralize lye.**
Sal Soda	It may be used in place of lye against foot-and-mouth disease and vesicular exanthema.	10½% solution (13½ oz. to 1 gal. water)	
Soap	Its power to kill germs is very limited. Greatest usefulness is in cleansing and dissolving coatings from various surfaces, including the skin, prior to application of a good disinfectant.	As commercially prepared.	Although indispensable for sanitizing surfaces, soaps should not be used as disinfectants. They are not regularly effective; staphylococci and the organisms which cause diarrheal diseases are resistant.
Soda ash (or sodium carbonate)	It may be used in place of lye against foot-and-mouth disease and vesicular exanthema.	4% solution (1 lb. to 3 gal. water). Most effective in hot solution.	Commonly used as a cleansing agent, but has disinfectant properties, especially when used as a hot solution.

¹The authors had the benefit of the authoritative review and suggestions of Dr. R. W. H. Gillespie, Associate Professor of Veterinary Microbiology, Washington State University in the preparation of this table.

POISONOUS PLANTS[1]

Poisonous plants have been known to man since time immemorial. Biblical literature alludes to the poisonous properties of certain plants, and history records that poison-hemlock (made from the plant from which it takes its name) was administered by the Greeks to Socrates and other state prisoners.

No section of the United States is entirely free of poisonous plants, for there are hundreds of them. Also, surprising as it may seem, plants do not readily fall into poisonous and non-poisonous groups. Some are poisonous only at certain seasons of the year and under other specific conditions. Others are even excellent and nutritious forages providing they do not constitute the sole diet.

The heaviest livestock losses from poisonous plants occur on the western ranges because (1) there has been less cultivation and destruction of poisonous plants in range areas, and (2) the frequent overgrazing on some of the western ranges has resulted in the elimination of some of the more nutritious and desirable plants, and these have been replaced by increased numbers of the less desirable and poisonous species. It is estimated that poisonous plants account for three to five per cent of all range animal losses each year; and in some areas more. For the nation as a whole, and with both beef and dairy animals combined, losses from poisonous plants total $350,000 annually.[2]

The list of poisonous plants is so extensive that no attempt is made herein to discuss them. Instead, those who are interested in pursuing further the subject are referred to specific books and bulletins relative to poisonous plants. Both the stockman and the veterinarian should have a working knowledge of the principal poisonous species in the area in which they operate.

Conditions That Indicate Plant Poisoning

Since plants contain many different poisons, there are no general symptoms by which to recognize plant poisoning in animals. It may be suspected, however, if the following conditions prevail:

---

[1] The author had the benefit of the authoritative review and suggestions of Dr. L. W. Rasmussen, Weed Specialist, Washington State University, Pullman, Washington, in the preparation of this section.

[2] Ensminger, M. E., M. W. Galgan, and W. L. Slocum; Wash. Agri. Expt. Sta. Bul. 562, p. 26.

1. If there is sudden onset of obscure illness without visible cause;

2. If a number of animals in a herd show acute disorders of the central nervous system or of the digestive tract without fever, but with prostration or rapid loss of weight;

3. If there is rapid heart action, stomach and intestinal irritation, general distress, and repeated attempts to void feces; and/or

4. If the above symptoms are followed by extreme weakness, coma, and collapse, and accompanied by difficult breathing.

Fig. 247. Cow with snakeroot poisoning. Marked weakness results in the "tremble" characteristic of this condition. (Courtesy, Dept. of Veterinary Pathology and Hygiene, College of Veterinary Medicine, University of Illinois)

It should be recognized, however, that plant poisoning may differ considerably in intensity, depending on (1) the kind and amount of plant eaten, (2) the stage of plant growth, (3) the kind and amount of other feed eaten simultaneously, and (4) the tolerance of the individual animal to the poison.

In addition to the above facts, diagnosis is made more complicated because it is difficult to differentiate certain types of plant poisoning from sickness due to chemicals or to certain infectious diseases. Thus, diagnosis had best be left to the skill of a trained veterinarian.

Preventing Losses from Poisonous Plants

With poisonous plants, the emphasis should be on prevention of losses rather than on treatment, no matter how successful the latter. The following are effective preventive measures:

1. **Follow good pasture or range management** in order to improve the quality of the pasture or range. Plant poisoning is nature's sign of a "sick" pasture or range, usually resulting from misuse. When a sufficient supply of desirable forage is available, poisonous plants are not often eaten, for they are less palatable. On the other hand, when overgrazing reduces the available supply of the more palatable and safe vegetation, animals may, through sheer hunger, consume the toxic plants.

2. **Know the poisonous plants common to the area.** This can usually be accomplished through (1) studying drawings, photographs, and/or descriptions, (2) checking with local authorities, or (3) sending two or three fresh whole plants (if possible, include the roots, stems, leaves, and flowers) to the state agricultural college—first wrapping the plants in several thicknesses of moist paper.

By knowing the poisonous plants common to the area, it will be possible—

(1) To avoid areas heavily infested with poisonous plants which, due to animal concentration and overgrazing, usually include waterholes, salt grounds, bed grounds, and trails.

(2) To control and eradicate the poisonous plants effectively, by mechanical or chemical means (as recommended by local authorities) or by fencing off.

(3) To recognize more surely and readily the particular kind of plant poisoning when it strikes, for time is important.

(4) To know what first aid, if any, to apply, especially when death is imminent or where a veterinarian is not readily available.

(5) To graze with a class of livestock not harmed by the particular poisonous plant or plants, where this is possible. Many plants seriously poisonous to one kind of livestock are not poisonous to another, at least under practical conditions.

(6) To shift the grazing season to a time when the plant is not dangerous, where this is possible. That is, some plants are poisonous at certain seasons of the year, but comparatively harmless at other seasons.

(7) To avoid cutting poison-infested meadows for hay when it is known that the dried cured plant is poisonous. Some plants are poisonous in either green or dry form, whereas others are harmless when dry. When poisonous plants (or seeds) become mixed with hay (or grain), it is difficult for animals to separate the safe from the toxic material.

3. **Know the symptoms that generally indicate plant poisoning,** thus making for early action.

4. **Avoid turning to pasture in very early spring.** Nature has ordained most poisonous plants as early growers—earlier than the desirable forage. For this reason, as well as from the standpoint of desirable pasture management, animals should not be turned to pasture in the early spring before the usual forage has become plentiful.

5. **Provide supplemental feed during droughts or after early frost.** Otherwise, hungry animals may eat poisonous plants in an effort to survive.

6. **Avoid turning very hungry animals where there are poisonous plants,** especially those that have been in corrals for branding, etc., that have been recently shipped or trailed long distances, or that have been wintered on dry forage. First feed the animals to satisfy their hunger or allow a fill on an area known to be free from poisonous plants.

7. **Avoid driving animals too fast when trailing.** On long drives, either allow them to graze along the way or stop frequently and provide supplemental feed.

8. **Remove promptly all animals from infested areas when plant poisoning strikes.**

9. **Treat promptly,** preferably by a veterinarian.

Treatment

Unfortunately, plant-poisoned animals are not generally discovered in sufficient time to prevent loss. Thus prevention is decidedly superior to treatment.

When trouble is encountered, the owner or caretaker should *promptly* call a veterinarian. In the meantime, the animal should be (1) placed where adequate care and treatment can be given, (2) protected from excessive heat and cold, and (3) allowed to eat only feeds known to be safe.

The veterinarian may determine the kind of poisonous plant involved (1) by observing the symptoms, and/or (2) by finding out exactly what poisonous plant was eaten through looking over the pasture and/or hay and identifying leaves or other plant parts found in the animal's digestive tract at the time of autopsy.

It is to be emphasized, however, that many poisoned animals that would have recovered had they been left undisturbed, have been killed by attempts to administer home remedies by well meaning but untrained persons.

STATE INDEMNITY PAYMENTS

Although subject to change as the laws of the respective states change, Table 45 summarizes the information relative to state indemnity payments as it existed in 1957. It is suggested that each stockman secure the regulations applicable to the state in which he resides by writing to his State Department of Agriculture.

TABLE 45

SUMMARY OF STATE INDEMNITY PAYMENTS

Disease	States That Pay No Indemnity		States That Pay More Than Federal Maximum		States That Pay Less Than Federal Maximum		States That Pay Amounts Equaling Federal Indemnity	
Brucellosis	Ala.	Miss.	Conn.	N. J.	Fla.	Neb.	Alaska	Mo.
	Ark.	Mont.	Del.	Pa.	Ga.	N. C.	Ariz.	P. Rico
	Calif.	Nev.	N. H.	R. I.	Idaho	N. M.	Iowa	S. C.
	Colo.	N. Y.			La.	Ore.	Md.	Wash.
	Hawaii	N. D.			Minn.	S. D.	Mass.	Wisc.
	Illinois	Ohio			Mo.	W. Va.	Mich.	
	Ind.	Okla.						
	Kan.	Tenn.						
	Ky.	Tex.						
		Utah						
		Va.						
		Wyo.						
Tuberculosis	All states pay		Calif.	N. J.			Ala.	N. M.
	Tuberculosis		Conn.	N. Y.			Ariz.	N. C.
	Indemnity		Del.	N. D.			Colo.	Ore.
			Illinois	Ohio			Fla.	S. C.
			Ind.	Okla.			Ga.	S. D.
			Iowa	Pa.			Idaho	Tex.
			Me.	R. I.			Kan.	Utah
			Mass.	Tenn.			Ky.	Va.
			Mont.	Vt.			La.	Wash.
			Nev.	Hawaii			Md.	Wisc.
			N. H.	P. Rico			Mich.	
							Minn.	
							Miss.	
							Mo.	
							Neb.	

Foot-and-mouth disease and other animal diseases which threaten the livestock industry, as covered in CFR, Title 9, Subchapter B, Part 53.

Most states have provision for the expenditure of emergency funds in the event of an outbreak of such a foreign animal disease, and other funds would be forthcoming through special action of their respective state legislatures.

QUESTIONS FOR STUDY AND DISCUSSION

1. Why are such publications as (1) The 1942 Yearbook of Agriculture entitled *Keeping Livestock Healthy*, and (2) the 1956 Yearbook of Agriculture entitled *Animal Diseases* of value to livestock producers?

2. What is normal temperature, pulse rate, and breathing rate of beef cattle, and how would you determine each?

3. Select a specific farm or ranch (either your own or one with which you are familiar) and outline (in 1, 2, 3, order) a program of beef cattle health, disease prevention, and parasite control.

4. Obtain the following publications from the Animal Disease Eradication Division, Agricultural Research Service, USDA, Washington, D.C.: Subchapter B. Title 9, of the Code of Federal Regulations, parts 51 and 53. Also, write to your State Department of Agriculture for information about indemnity payments. Then determine the indemnity payments that you could expect were you to encounter an outbreak of (1) brucellosis or (2) foot-and-mouth disease.

5. Assume that a specific contagious disease (you name it) has broken out in your herd. What steps would you take to meet the situation (list in 1, 2, 3, order; be specific)?

6. Assume that a specific parasite (you name it) has become troublesome in your herd. What steps would you take to meet the situation (list in 1, 2, 3, order; be specific)?

7. Assume that you have, during a period of a year, encountered cattle death losses from three different diseases. What kind of disinfectant would you use in each case?

8. Assume that you have encountered death losses from a certain poisonous plant (you name it). What steps would you take to meet the situation (list in 1, 2, 3, order; be specific)?

SELECTED REFERENCES

Title of Publication	Author(s)	Publisher
Animal Diseases	Yearbook of Agriculture, 1956	U. S. Department of Agriculture, Washington 25, D. C.
Animal Sanitation and Disease Control	R. R. Dykstra	Interstate Printers & Publishers, Danville, Illinois, 1949.
Brucellosis	A symposium— 1949	American Assn. for the Advancement of Science, 1515 Massachusetts Ave., N. W., Washington, D. C.
Diseases of Cattle	1942	U. S. Department of Agriculture, Washington, D. C.
Farmer's Veterinary Handbook, The	J. J. Haberman	Prentice-Hall, New York, 1953.
Home Veterinarian's Handbook, The	E. T. Baker	MacMillan Co., New York, 1949.
Infectious Diseases of Domestic Animals, The	W. A. Hagan D. W. Bruner	Comstock Publishing Associates, Ithaca, New York, 1957.
Insecticide Recommendations	Agricultural Handbook No. 120	U. S. Department of Agriculture, Washington, D. C.
Keeping Livestock Healthy	Yearbook of Agriculture, 1942	U. S. Department of Agriculture, Washington, D. C.
Livestock Health Encyclopedia	Rudolph Seiden	Springer Publishing Co., New York, 1951.
Merck Veterinary Manual, The		Merck & Co., Rahway, New Jersey, 1955.
Principles of Veterinary Science	F. B. Hadley	W. B. Saunders Co., Philadelphia, 1949.
Stockman's Handbook, The	M. E. Ensminger	Interstate Printers & Publishers, Danville, Illinois, 1959.
Veterinary Guide for Farmers	G. W. Stamm	Windsor Press, Chicago, 1950.
Veterinary Handbook for Cattlemen	J. W. Bailey	Springer Publishing Co., New York, 1958.

In addition to the above selected references, valuable publications on different subjects pertaining to beef cattle diseases, parasites, disinfectants, and poisonous plants can be obtained from the following sources:

Division of Publications
Office of Information
U. S. Department of Agriculture
Washington 25, D. C.

Your state agricultural college

Several biological, pharmaceutical, and chemical companies.

CHAPTER XIV

MARKETING AND SLAUGHTERING CATTLE AND CALVES[1]

Contents   Page

[1]In the preparation of Chapter XIV, invaluable criticisms and suggestions as to organization and content were received from the following reviewers: Mr. C. T. "Tad" Sanders, Executive Secretary, American National ivestock Auction Assn., Kansas City, Mo.; Mr. H. R. Merman, formerly Head Buyer, Armour and Co., Ogden, Utah; Mr. Howard White, Director, Livestock Procurement, Argobast & Bastian Co., Allentown, Penn.; and Dr. Fred J. Beard, Chief Meat Grading Branch, Livestock Division, Agricultural Marketing Service, USDA, Washington, D.C.

655

Livestock marketing—along with breeding, feeding, and management—is an integral part of the modern livestock production process. It is the end of the line; that part which gives point and purpose to all that has gone before. The importance of cattle marketing is further attested by the following facts:

Fig. 248. Two Egyptian cattlemen taking an ox to market; from Bas Relief found in Sakara in the tomb of King Ephto Stoptep. At first, meat animals were bartered for articles made by craftsmen. Eventually, bartering gave way to cash sales as coined money began to circulate. (Courtesy, The Bettmann Archive)

1. In 1957, 27,059,000 cattle and 12,324,000 calves were slaughtered in the U.S.[1]

2. In 1957, U.S. farmers and ranchers received 19.3 per cent of their cash income from marketing cattle and calves.[2]

3. Livestock markets establish values of all animals, including those down on the farm or ranch. On January 1, 1958, there were 93,967,000 head of cattle in the U.S., with an aggregate value of $11,234,712,000, or $120.00 per head.[3]

It is important, therefore, that the cattleman know and follow good marketing practices.

---

[1]Data provided by Harold Breimyer, Head, Livestock, Fats and Oils Section; Agricultural Marketing Service, USDA.

[2]*The Livestock and Meat Situation*, Agricultural Marketing Service, USDA, July, 1958.

[3]*Livestock and Poultry Inventory*, January 1, Agricultural Marketing Service, USDA, Feb. 14, 1958.

METHODS OF MARKETING CATTLE

The cattleman is confronted with the perplexing problem of determining where and how to market his animals. Usually there is a choice of market outlets, and the one selected often varies between classes and grades of cattle and among sections of the country. Thus, the method of marketing usually differs between slaughter and feeder cattle, and both of these differ from the marketing of purebreds.

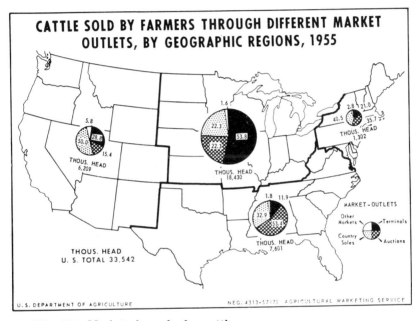

CATTLE SOLD BY FARMERS THROUGH DIFFERENT MARKET OUTLETS, BY GEOGRAPHIC REGIONS, 1955

Fig. 249. Market channels for cattle.

Most market cattle are sold through the following channels: (1) terminal public markets, (2) livestock auction markets, or (3) country selling—including sales direct to packers, local dealers, and farmers.

In a study[1] made by the U.S. Department of Agriculture in 1955, it was found that farmers sold cattle and calves through different market outlets in about the following proportions:

[1]*Market Outlets for Livestock Producers*, March, 1958, Agricultural Marketing Service, USDA, Marketing Research Report No. 216, p. 11.

| | Term-inal Markets | Auc-tions | Country Sales | | | | All Others |
			Direct to Packers	Local Deal-ers	Farm-ers	Total Country Sales	
	(%)	(%)	(%)	(%)	(%)	(%)	(%)
Cattle............	38.4	28.6	11.8	9.3	9.5	30.6	2.4
Calves, un-der 1 year of age.	21.6	43.0	7.5	14.3	10.2	32.0	3.4

More cattle (38.4%) were sold through terminal markets; more calves (43.0%) were sold through auctions.

Terminal Public Markets

Terminal public markets (also referred to as terminal markets, central markets, public stockyards, and public markets) are livestock trading centers, where livestock are assembled at a single geographic location in large numbers to be sold on a "private treaty basis," and which possesses complete facilities for receiving, caring for, handling, and selling livestock. About 60 U.S. markets are so classified. Various numbers of commission firms, depending on the size of the market, sell livestock at these markets; and all buyers and sellers of livestock are privileged to use these facilities.

The first of the present terminal public markets was established at Chicago in 1865. Most of the larger terminal markets operating today were established in the latter half of the 19th century.

Up through World War I, the majority of slaughter livestock in the United States was sold through terminal public markets directly by farmers or by local buyers shipping to them. Since then, the importance of these markets has declined in relation to other outlets (See Fig. 250). In 1923, federally inspected slaughterers purchased 90 per cent of their cattle in central markets; in 1951, 73 per cent. During this same period, the percentage of federally inspected slaughter of calves sold through terminal markets declined from 86 per cent to 56 per cent. By 1956, it appears that the percentage of federally inspected slaughter cattle bought at terminal markets may have dropped to about 70

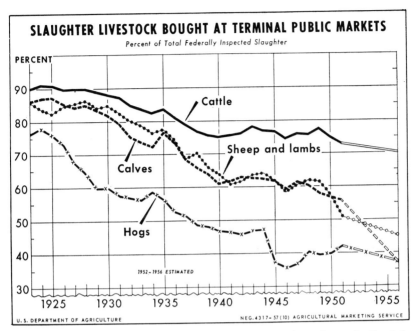

Fig. 250. This shows that terminal public markets have declined in relative importance.

per cent, and calves to 37 per cent.[1] But these figures do not tell the whole story; when the total slaughter at all commercial slaughtering establishments is considered, the percentage bought at terminal markets is somewhat less. The latter situation is so because nonfederally inspected slaughterers tend to buy larger proportions of their livestock at markets other than terminal markets.

Most of the large public markets are located in or adjacent to the Corn Belt. However, several large markets for calves are in Texas and Oklahoma.

LEADING TERMINAL CATTLE MARKETS:

With the development of the Corn Belt and western range cattle industry, the markets established at various points on the Great Lakes and along the Mississippi and Missouri rivers became important. It is logical that these should have remained leading cattle markets because of their proximity to both producers and

[1] Phillips, Victor B. and Gerald Engleman, *Market Outlets for Livestock Producers*, USDA, Marketing Research Report No. 216, p. 5.

consumers. About 70 per cent of the cattle and calves is raised west of the Mississippi, while about 70 per cent of the beef is consumed east of this geographical location.

Fig. 251. Cattle buying scene on the Chicago market. (Courtesy, Swift and Co.)

Although the central markets vary from year to year in their total receipts, Table 46 shows the largest terminal cattle markets and their receipts of cattle.

LEADING TERMINAL CALF MARKETS:

Upon the central markets, cattle under approximately four hundred pounds in weight are designated as calves. As would be expected, many of these animals are of dairy breeding, especially

TABLE 46
CATTLE RECEIPTS (EXCLUDING CALVES) OF TEN LEADING
TERMINAL CATTLE MARKETS, BY RANK, 1957[1]

Market	1957
Chicago, Illinois	2,548,294
Omaha, Neb.	1,997,628
Sioux City, Iowa	1,408,399
Kansas City, Mo.	1,387,818
South St. Paul, Minn.	1,219,431
St. Louis National Stock Yards, Illinois	1,093,541
Denver, Colo.	867,743
St. Joseph, Mo.	725,631
Oklahoma City, Okla.	654,476
Fort Worth, Texas	610,908
Total of 60 public markets	21,085,391

[1] *Livestock Receipts and Disposition of Livestock at Public Markets*—February, 1958, Agricultural Marketing Service, USDA, p. 3.

the surplus bull calves that are not needed for breeding purposes. Of the remainder, a considerable number are culled out from beef herds because of undesirable type or breeding from the standpoint of future development. It can be expected, therefore, that the leading calf markets would not coincide with the leading cattle markets.

Table 47 shows the ten leading terminal calf markets in the United States. Milwaukee and South St. Paul, the two largest calf markets, are primarily outlets for veal calves from neighboring dairy areas.

TABLE 47
CALF RECEIPTS OF TEN LEADING TERMINAL CALF
MARKETS, BY RANK, 1957[1]

Market	1957
Milwaukee, Wis.	564,073
South St. Paul, Minn.	520,053
Kansas City, Mo.	294,921
Houston, Texas	280,530
St. Louis National Stock Yards, Illinois	258,510
Fort Worth, Texas	187,370
San Antonio, Texas	158,666
Springfield, Mo.	158,205
Sioux City, Iowa	133,856
Louisville, Ky.	120,156
Total of 60 public markets	4,481,873

[1] *Livestock receipts and disposition at Public Markets*, February, 1958, Agricultural Marketing Service, USDA, p. 4

LEADING TERMINAL FEEDER CATTLE MARKETS:

Cattle feeding often involves a two-phase type of operation. Thus the western range area is well adapted to a cow-and-calf proposition, and because of the abundance of relatively cheap forage many of the steers are grown out and marketed as yearlings or two-year-olds. On the other hand, the Corn Belt produces a great surplus of grain and is noted as a cattle feeding center. It is but natural, therefore, that the leading feeder cattle markets should be conveniently located between the range producing area and the Corn Belt feeding area. Table 48 gives the ten leading terminal feeder cattle markets by rank, whereas Table 49 shows the state destination of feeder cattle.

Thus the first table shows the central markets upon which most feeder cattle are handled, whereas the second table indicates the states which acquire the greatest numbers of market feeder cattle from outside sources for fattening purposes.

In recent years, there has been an increasing tendency to market feeder cattle direct, without passing them through the central market. A considerable and increasing number of western producers also are arranging to have their feeders fed out on contract. Despite these other methods of handling, over four million head of cattle pass through United States central markets each year.

Fig. 252. Portion of the cattle pens of the Kansas City market. Kansas City has long been the greatest feeder cattle market in the U. S. (Courtesy, Kansas City Stock Yard Co.)

TABLE 48

FEEDER CATTLE RECEIPTS OF TEN LEADING TERMINAL
MARKETS, BY RANK, 1957[1]

Market	1957
Kansas City, Mo.	669,537
Sioux City, Iowa	448,339
Omaha, Neb.	406,734
Oklahoma City, Okla.	270,019
Amarillo, Texas	256,047
Denver, Colo.	222,939
Forth Worth, Texas	168,679
West Fargo, N. Dak.	157,074
So. St. Paul, Minn.	154,515
St. Louis, Illinois	116,472
Total feeder cattle received at United States public markets	4,450,592

[1] *Livestock Receipts and Disposition at Public Markets*—February, 1958, Agricultural Marketing Service, USDA, p. 3.

TABLE 49

TEN LEADING STATE-DESTINATIONS OF MARKET FEEDER
CATTLE (NOT INCLUDING "DIRECT" SHIPMENTS), BY RANK, 1957[1]

State	No. Shipped into
Iowa	873,881
Illinois	408,262
Texas	390,722
Nebraska	383,055
Kansas	362,088
Missouri	309,764
California	250,702
Oklahoma	189,586
Colorado	167,090
Minnesota	153,778
Total to 48 states	4,711,564

[1] *Market News*, Agricultural Marketing Service, USDA, January 28, 1958, p. 82.

CHARGES AT TERMINAL PUBLIC MARKETS:

Cattlemen need to be acquainted with livestock marketing costs. Although commission and yardage rates vary slightly (1) according to size of consignment and (2) between markets, Table 50 summarizes the typical charges at a terminal market for trucked-in cattle shipments.

According to a special tabulation[1] of packer and stockyards records covering the year 1954, average marketing charges per

[1] *Livestock Terminal Markets in the United States*, January, 1959, Agricultural Marketing Service, USDA, Marketing Research Report No. 299, p. 31.

TABLE 50[1]
TYPICAL TERMINAL MARKETING CHARGES FOR TRUCKED-IN
CATTLE SHIPMENTS

	Cattle
	(25 steers average 1,100 lbs.)
Commission[2]	$28.50
Yardage[2]	22.50
Hay	2.15
Fire Insurance	.07
Nat'l Livestock and Meat Bd.	.50
Total Marketing Cost	$53.72
Marketing Cost per Head	2.14
Marketing Cost per Cwt.	.19

[1] From the *Chicago Daily Drovers Journal*, through the courtesy of the Editor. But with the National Livestock and Meat Board computed on the basis of the current 50¢/single deck rate, instead of the former 25¢ rate.
[2] Rates vary slightly according to the size of consignment and also between markets.

head paid by producers on cattle and calves marketed through terminals were $2.33 for cattle and $1.25 for calves.

Livestock Auction Markets

Livestock auctions (also referred to as sales barns, livestock auction agencies, community sales, and community auctions) are trading centers where animals are sold by public bidding to the buyer who offers the highest price per hundredweight or per head.

This method of selling livestock in this country is very old, apparently being copied from Great Britain where auction sales date back many centuries.

Apparently the auction method of selling was used in many of the colonies as a means of disposing of property, imported goods, secondhand household furnishings, farm utensils and animals.

According to available records, the first public livestock auction sale was held in Ohio in 1836 by the Ohio Company, whose business was importing English cattle. This event also marked the first sale of purebred cattle ever held in America.

Although there are some records of occasional livestock auction sales during the 19th century, there is no indication of any auction market that continued operation throughout the period of the greatest development of terminal public stockyards markets. It is within the current century that present auction development had its beginnings. In fact, livestock auction markets have had their greatest growth since 1930, both in numbers established and the extensiveness of the area over which they operate.

Fig. 253 shows the growth in numbers of livestock auctions from 1900 to 1955. About 200 auctions were operating by 1930;

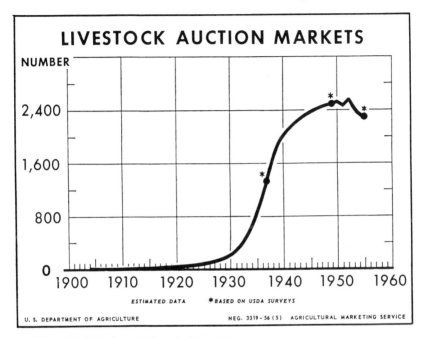

Fig. 253. Number of livestock auctions.

by 1937, this number had increased to 1,345. The peak in numbers was reached in 1952, when over 2,500 different livestock auctions were holding sales; but, by 1958, the total number had declined to 2,350.

Several factors contributed to the phenomenal growth in auction markets during the thirties, chief of which were the following:

1. The decentralization of markets. Associated with this was the improvement and extension of hard surfaced roads accompanied by the increased use of trucks as a means of transporting livestock to and from the market place. Use of trucks increased flexibility in the handling of various sized lots of livestock and in the direction of movement; and, with the advent of better roads, trucks could be used for transporting livestock moderate distances

both quickly and economically. Also, growing numbers of small packers, located at distant points from terminal markets, were able to procure livestock more efficiently at auction markets.

2. The development of more uniform class and grade classifications for livestock.

3. Improvements made by the federal government in providing more extensive collection and dissemination of market news.

4. The greater convenience afforded in disposing of small lots of livestock and in purchasing stockers, feeders, and breeding animals.

5. The recognized educational value of these nearby markets, which enabled producers to keep currently informed of local market conditions and livestock prices.

6. The depression of 1930-33. When livestock prices are low—such as was true during the depression years—transportation and other marketing expenses compose a greater part of the total gross value received from the sale of livestock. Since, at this time the commission charges at most auctions were based on a percentage of the gross sale value of the animal, marketing expenses at auctions tended to be low when prices were low. Also, with the proximity of auctions to producing areas, out-of-pocket transportation expenses were less for livestock sent to local auction than for shipments to more distant market outlets.

7. The abnormal feed distribution caused by the droughts of 1934 and 1936 in the western Corn Belt and range states created conditions favoring increased sales at auctions. Some immature and unfinished stock in these areas were sold at nearby auctions to farmers having a plentiful supply of feed on hand. Also, stocker and feeder cattle were shipped out of the drought sections to auctions located in areas where feed supplies were more abundant.

8. The desire to sell near home. By contrast to large public terminal markets which receive some livestock from considerable distances, auction markets draw their supplies largely from the communities in which they are located.

Prior to the advent of community livestock auctions, the small livestock operator had two main market outlets for his animals—(1) shipping them to the nearest terminal public market, or (2) selling them to buyers who came to his farm or ranch. Generally, the first method was too expensive because of the transportation distance involved and the greater expense in shipping small lots. The second method pretty much put the producer at the mercy of the buyer, because he had no good alternative to taking the price he was offered, and often he did not know the value of his animals. By contrast, the big operator is not particularly concerned about these things. Because of his large scale, usually he can take advantage of any of several terminal markets, and he knows enough about values that he can deal satisfactorily with buyers who come to his farm or ranch. Thus, the community livestock auctions are really of greatest importance to the small operator.

In 1955, Iowa was the leading state in number of auctions, with 185 in operation. Texas was second with 151. The nation's largest livestock auction market, in total animals sold and gross dollar volume, is the Norfolk Live Stock Sales Co., Norfolk, Nebraska; whereas the world's largest cattle auction market is the Amarillo Livestock Auction, Amarillo, Texas.

FEEDER CALF AUCTIONS:

Feeder calves are sold through the following market channels: auctions, direct, terminal public markets, and dealers. In recent years, feeder calf sales, held auction style, have been especially popular in many states. Generally such sales are organized on a state-wide or area basis, with the state agricultural extension service cooperating.

In advance of the auction, all entries are usually "sifted" by a committee, whose duty it is to assure the desired quality. The calves that pass the initial inspection are then delivered to the auction market a day ahead of the sale, at which time they are (1) tagged, (2) weighed, and (3) graded. Following this, each calf is penned with other calves of similar breed, sex, grade, and weight; thereby providing uniform lots for buyers. Usually, the pens are marked, giving the grade, sex, breed, and average weight of each lot of calves. The buyers are then given an opportunity to inspect the pens of calves prior to the sale. At the appointed time, each uniform lot of calves is offered for sale by the auction method.

For successful feeder calf auctions, it is necessary that there be both volume and quality. Large numbers attract more buyers and make it possible to sell calves in larger and more uniform lots; and buyers want to buy the highest quality possible for a given price.

The better managed feeder calf sales serve as an excellent educational medium. Producers observe the grading demonstration, see how the weights of their calves compare with those of the neighbors, and realize the price spread between grades.

Two of the most important advantages to accrue from feeder calf sales are: (1) producers with a few head are provided market advantages comparable to large operators, and, (2) cattle feeders are given an opportunity to purchase feeder calves of specified quality and in small or large lots, without the time and expense of shopping around.

CHARGES AT AUCTIONS:

Rates charged for marketing livestock vary at different auctions. Services for which charges are levied may include selling, yardage, weighing, insurance, brand inspection, and health inspection. Many auctions do not provide all these services. A commission or selling fee, however, is charged at all markets and is the primary source of income to auction operators. At some auctions, the commission covers yardage and weighing in addition to the selling service. Some operators levy a separate charge for each service provided, while others charge a single rate to cover all services.

Auction operators levy their charge, on a per head basis, on a percentage of gross value, or by a combination of the two methods.

Straight per head charges on cattle and calves vary considerably. However, the most usual charges for cattle range from $1.50 to $2.00 per head. Charges on calves are less than on cattle, usually ranging from $1.00 to $1.50 per head.

For auctions reporting straight percentage charges, the most usual charge on cattle and calves is 3 per cent.

Country Selling

Country selling refers to producers' sales of livestock direct to packers, local dealers, or farmers without the support of commission men, selling agents, buying agents, or brokers.

Prior to the advent of terminal public markets in 1865, country selling accounted for virtually all sales of livestock. Sales of livestock in the country declined with the growth of terminal markets until the latter method reached its peak of selling at the time of World War I. But country selling was accelerated by the large nation-wide packers following World War I in order to meet the increased buying competition of the small interior packers. The decline in the proportion of all livestock moving through terminal public markets was largely accounted for by the growth in country selling until the late 1930's and by the growth in auctions since.

Like auction selling, direct selling has a certain appeal, inasmuch as it permits producers to observe and exercise some control over selling while it takes place; whereas consignment to distant terminal public markets at times represents an irreversible commitment to sell. Larger and more specialized livestock farmers feel competent to sell their livestock direct.

Improved highways and trucking facilitated the growth of country selling. Farmers were no longer tied to outlets located at important railroad terminals or river crossings. Livestock could move in any direction. Improved communications, such as the radio and telephone, and an expanded market information service, also aided in the development of country selling of livestock, especially in sales direct to packers.

Direct selling to meat packers is an important outlet for slaughter cattle in many areas, especially in the Pacific coast states. Some packers buy cattle direct from producers at the plant; others send their buyers into the country, from farm to farm or feedlot to feedlot, where they make bids on the livestock that they inspect.

Local dealers operate in all parts of the country. These include country buying operations by local buyers, by contract buyers for later delivery, by buyers purchasing on orders for others, and by a variety of speculative buyers. Speculative buyers are known by a variety of names in different parts of the country; they are sometimes called livestock buyers, traders, scalpers, truck buyers, stock buyers, pin-hookers, and scavengers. Some of these country buyers purchase livestock at fixed establishments similar to packer-owned country buying points.

Choice of Market Outlets

Marketing is dynamic; thus changes are inevitable in types of market outlets, market structures, and market services. Some outlets have gained in importance; others have declined.

The choice of a market outlet represents the seller's evaluation of the most favorable market among the number of alternatives available to him. No simple and brief statement of criteria can be given as a guide to the choice of the most favorable market channel. Rather, an evaluation is required of the contributions made by alternative markets in terms of available services offered, selling costs, the competitive nature of the pricing process, and ultimately the producer's net return. Thus, an accurate appraisal is not simple.

From time to time, producers can be expected to shift from one type of market outlet to another. Because price changes at different market outlets do not take place simultaneously, nor in the same amount, nor even in the same direction, one market may be the most advantageous outlet for a particular class and grade of cattle at one time, but another may be more advantageous at some other time. The situation may differ for different classes and kinds of livestock and may vary from one area to another.

Regardless of the channel through which the producer markets his livestock, in one way or another, he pays or bears, either in the price received from the livestock or otherwise, the entire cost of marketing. Because of this, he should never choose a market because of convenience of habit, or because of personal acquaintance with the market and its operator. Rather, the choice should be determined strictly by the net returns from the sale of his livestock; effective selling and net returns are more important than selling costs.

In a survey, made in 1955 and covering 1,558 cattlemen and 502,616 head of cattle, the author obtained data on the question of preference of market outlets of American cattlemen.[1] Information was secured relative to the choice of market outlets for feeder cattle and for fat cattle. Tables 51 and 52 show the channels used for feeder cattle, and Tables 53 and 54 show the channels for fat cattle. In each case, the first table shows the percentage of cattlemen using each outlet, whereas the second table shows the percentage of cattle disposed of through each outlet.

The two feeder cattle tables do not parallel each other in terms of the most-used market outlets; neither do the fat cattle tables. This is so because some very large operators patronized certain market channels. For example, less than one-fifth of the cattlemen were responsible for marketing nearly one-half of all feeder cattle through local buyers, and 4.5 per cent of the cattlemen were responsible for marketing one-third of all fat cattle direct to packers.

---

[1]Ensminger, M. E., M. W. Galgan, and W. L. Slocum, Wash. Agri. Expt. Sta. Bul. 562, pp. 70-73.

TABLE 51

MARKET AVENUES FOR FEEDER CATTLE, IN NUMBER OF CATTLEMEN

Cattlemen Following the Practice:

Market Avenues for Feeder Cattle	In West	In South	In Great Plains	In Pacific Northwest	All Respondents	
	(%)	(%)	(%)	(%)	(no.)	(%)
Local Buyers	26.5	11.2	14.6	21.0	295	18.6
Community Livestock Auctions	11.9	14.0	25.3	15.5	246	15.5
Central Markets	9.6	8.6	11.9	7.3	153	9.6
Direct to Packers	2.2	3.9	0.9	4.1	40	2.5
Through Own Auctions	2.1	0.9	1.5	2.7	24	1.5
Coop. Shipping Association	0.9	0.9	1.2	0.5	15	0.9
Other Methods	4.3	2.8	4.6	5.0	61	3.8

TABLE 52

MARKET AVENUES FOR FEEDER CATTLE, IN PERCENTAGE OF CATTLE MARKETED

Cattle Marketed:

Market Avenues for Feeder Cattle	In West	In South	In Great Plains	In Pacific Northwest	All Respondents
	(%)	(%)	(%)	(%)	(%)
Local Buyers	64.0	33.8	31.7	46.7	47.6
Community Livestock Auctions	7.0	13.2	28.1	15.6	13.3
Central Markets	13.4	34.9	22.4	8.2	21.8
Direct to Packers	2.7	4.4	0.6	8.2	2.8
Through Own Auctions	3.0	1.3	3.5	10.6	2.5
Coop. Shipping Association	3.2	7.8	0.9	0.2	4.1
Other Methods	6.8	4.7	12.8	10.5	7.8

TABLE 53

MARKET AVENUES USED FOR FAT CATTLE, IN NUMBER OF CATTLEMEN

Market Avenues for Fat Cattle	Cattlemen Following the Practice:					
	In West	In South	In Great Plains	In Pacific Northwest	All Respondents	
	(%)	(%)	(%)	(%)	(no.)	(%)
Central Markets	8.7	8.2	14.9	11.9	155	9.8
Community Livestock Auctions	8.3	12.4	7.0	13.2	155	9.8
Local Buyers	5.2	4.9	3.0	5.5	74	4.7
Direct to Packers	6.2	4.0	2.1	9.1	72	4.5
Through Own Auctions	1.6	1.2	0.3	1.8	19	1.2
Other Methods	1.3	1.1	0.9	2.7	18	1.1
Coop. Shipping Association	0.4	0.7	0.3	0.9	9	0.6

TABLE 54

MARKET AVENUES USED FOR FAT CATTLE, IN PERCENTAGE OF CATTLE MARKETED

Market Avenues for Fat Cattle	Cattle Marketed:				
	In West	In South	In Great Plains	In Pacific Northwest	All Respondents
	(%)	(%)	(%)	(%)	(%)
Direct to Packers	54.0	21.6	3.2	25.1	33.6
Central Markets	14.5	28.7	77.8	38.4	29.3
Local Buyers	21.7	22.1	9.5	5.5	20.2
Community Livestock Auctions	7.1	20.0	7.8	23.7	12.5
Through Own Auctions	1.4	3.2	0.8	2.8	2.0
Coop. Shipping Association	0.6	2.8	0.3	2.3	1.4
Other Methods	0.7	1.7	0.5	2.2	1.1

A comparison of Figs. 254 and 255 shows the greater importance of local buyers and cooperative shipping associations in the marketing of feeder cattle than in marketing slaughter cattle. The study revealed that most feeder cattle are marketed, in order of importance, through the following three channels: local buyers, central markets, and livestock auctions. Most fat cattle are marketed through the following four channels: direct to packers, central markets, local buyers, and livestock auctions.

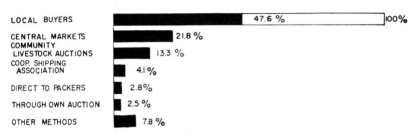

LOCAL BUYERS   47.6 %   100%

CENTRAL MARKETS   21.8 %
COMMUNITY
LIVESTOCK AUCTIONS   13.3 %
COOP. SHIPPING
ASSOCIATION   4.1 %

DIRECT TO PACKERS   2.8%

THROUGH OWN AUCTION   2.5 %

OTHER METHODS   7.8 %

Fig. 254. Market avenues for feeder cattle. (Print, courtesy Washington State University)

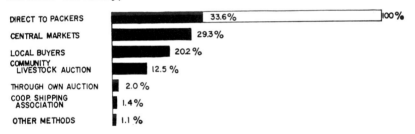

DIRECT TO PACKERS   33.6%   100%

CENTRAL MARKETS   29.3%

LOCAL BUYERS   20.2%

COMMUNITY
LIVESTOCK AUCTION   12.5 %

THROUGH OWN AUCTION   2.0 %

COOP. SHIPPING
ASSOCIATION   1.4%

OTHER METHODS   1.1 %

Fig. 255. Market avenues for fat cattle. (Print, courtesy Washington State University)

PREPARING AND SHIPPING CATTLE[1]

Improper handling of cattle immediately prior to and during shipment may result in excess shrinkage; high death, bruise, and crippling losses; disappointing sales; and dissatisfied buyers. Unfortunately, many stockmen who do a superb job of producing cattle, dissipate all the good things that have gone before by doing a poor job of preparing and shipping. Generally speaking, such omissions are due to lack of know-how, rather than any deliberate attempt to take advantage of anyone. Even if the sale is consummated prior to delivery, negligence at shipping time

[1]This section was authoritatively reviewed by the following two competent cattlemen, both of whom ship a great many cattle: Mr. Gene Brown, Sinton and Brown, Betteravia, Calif.; and Mr. Walter Davis, Fresno, Calif.

will make for a dissatisfied customer. Buyers soon learn what to expect from various producers and place their bids accordingly.

In addition to the important specific considerations covered in the four sections which follow, the following general considerations should be accorded in preparing cattle for shipment and in transporting them to market:

1. **Select the best suited method of transportation.**—The cattleman should decide between truck and rail transportation on the basis of which method best suits his particular situation. Most generally, hauls under 500 miles distance are made by truck and greater distances by rail, but modern trucks and improved highways are extending the distance of truck shipments.

If transportation is to be made by rail, about three days in advance of shipment, the agent of the station from which the cattle are to be loaded should be requested to get the car or cars spotted. The size and type (single or double deck) car should be specified; also, any special equipment—such as partitions and linings—should be requested at that time. The agent should be advised as to the desired time of loading and the destination of the shipment. All major railroads clean, disinfect, and bed stock cars prior to spotting them for loading, but it is always well that the shipper inspect cars to make sure that these matters have been handled to his satisfaction. Generally they bed cattle cars with about one inch of sand, and in the winter time they add straw on top of the sand for calves. If the shipper desires a type of bedding other than supplied by the carrier, he may provide it at his own expense. To avoid any misunderstanding, it is recommended that requests for rail cars either be requested or confirmed in writing.

2. **Vaccinate feeder calves against shipping fever.**—Where young animals, long shipments, inclement weather, and/or not too thrifty animals are involved—conditions predisposing shipping fever—feeder cattle should be vaccinated with bacterins at least 10 days before shipping.

3. **Feed properly prior to loading out.**—Never ship cattle on an excess fill. Instead, withhold grain feeding 12 hours before loading (omit one feed), and do not allow access to water within 2 to 3 hours of shipment. Cattle may be allowed free access to dry, well-cured grass hay up to loading time, but more laxative-type hays, such as alfalfa or clover, should not be fed within 12 hours of shipment even if the animals were accustomed to them

previously. Likewise, cattle on green or succulent feed should be conditioned to dry feeds prior to shipment.

Cattle that are too full of concentrated or succulent feeds or full of water at the time of loading will scour and urinate excessively. As a result, the floors become dirty and slippery and the animals befoul themselves. Such cattle undergo a heavy shrink and present an unattractive appearance when unloaded.

Abrupt ration changes of any kind prior to shipment should be avoided. Occasionally, a misinformed cattleman withholds water, but gives a liberal feeding of salt prior to shipment; to obtain maximum water consumption and fill on the market. This "sharp" practice cannot be condemned too strongly; it is cruel to animals, and experienced buyers are never deceived.

4. **Keep cattle quiet.**—Prior to and during shipment, cattle should be handled carefully. Hot, excited animals are subject to more shrinkage, more disease and injury, and more dark cutting[1] if slaughtered following shipment.

If the animals are trailed on-foot to the shipping point, they should be moved slowly and allowed to rest and to drink moderately prior to loading. Although loading may be exasperating at times, take it easy; never lose your temper. Avoid hurrying, loud hollering, and striking. Never beat an animal with such objects as pipes, sticks, canes, or forks; instead, use either (1) a flat, wide canvas slapper with a handle, or (2) an electric prod (the latter judiciously).

5. **Consider health certificates, permits, and brand inspection in interstate shipments.**—When cattle are to be shipped into another state, the shipper should check into and comply with the state regulations relative to health certificates, permits, and brand inspection. Usually, the local veterinarian or railroad agent will have this information. Should there be any question about the health regulations, however, the state livestock sanitary board (usually located at the state capital) of the state of destination should be consulted. Knowledge of and compliance with such regulations well in advance of shipment will avoid frustrations and costly delays.

6. **Comply with the 28-hour law in rail shipments.**[2]—Ac-

[1]Brady, D. E. and H. B. Hedrick, *Journal of Animal Science*, Nov. 1956, Vol. 15, No. 4, p. 1290; and
    Hedrick, H. B., D. E. Brady, and C. W. Turner, *Proceedings of the Ninth Research Conference*, Sponsored by the Council on Research, American Meat Institute, at the Univ. of Chicago, March 22-23, 1957.
[2]No such law applies to truck transportation of animals.

tually, the shipper has no alternative to taking advantage of feed and rest stops during long hauls by rail; by federal law, passed in 1873, livestock cannot be transported by rail for a longer period than twenty-eight consecutive hours without unloading for the purpose of giving feed, water, and rest for a period of at least five consecutive hours before resuming transportation. The period may be extended to thirty-six hours upon written request from the owner of the animals; and most experienced cattle shippers routinely so request. With less than carload lots (LCL shipments), the owner may provide feed and water in the car with instructions that the animals be fed and watered enroute.

The shipper may instruct the railway company on the kind and amount of feed to be given in transit, with these instructions written on the waybill or on the livestock contract which each shipper signs. If no such instructions are given by the owner of the cattle, the amount of feed prescribed by the U.S.D.A. is given at the livestock feeding yards; namely, per carload of beef cattle or range calves (1) 200 pounds of hay at the first feeding station, and (2) 300 pounds of hay at the second and subsequent feed stations. Usually grass hay of good quality is fed. The feeding is done by the railway company crew, and charge is made to the shipper for the amount of feed consumed.

Where two or more cars of cattle are shipped, the railroad will provide a free ticket for a caretaker, including return to the point of origin. When shipping by rail and where possible, it is recommended that the shipper take advantage of this arrangement. When this is done, the caretaker can make certain that the animals are properly fed and given access to clean water at the stops enroute; also, under certain circumstances, it may be wise to allow cattle to make as much as a 12-hour rest stop and to feed twice before reloading.

7. **Feed or graze in transit if advantageous.**—In some cases, where cattlemen graze or fatten animals at distant points from their base of operations, privileges are granted so that animals may be grazed or fed in transit from one day to 12 months. For example, through this arrangement, a Montana rancher might bill his livestock to the Chicago stockyards, but with the privilege of stopping in Minnesota (or some other intermediate point) to fatten them out over a period up to one year, before finally putting them on the Chicago market. Under these circumstances, the shipper would pay one rate with the stopover charge instead of paying a rate from his shipping point in Montana to the point in

Minnesota, and another from the intermediate point in Minnesota to Chicago. These regulations apply only to certain specified conditions, which can be determined by making inquiry of the local railroad agent.

8. **Use partitions when necessary.**—When mixed loads (consisting of cattle, sheep, and/or hogs) are placed in the same truck or car, partition each class off separately. Also, partition calves from cattle, and separate out cripples and stags; tie bulls.

9. **Avoid shipping during extremes in weather.**—Whenever possible, avoid shipping when the weather is either very hot or very cold. During such times, shrinkage and death losses are higher than normal. During warm weather, avoid transporting animals during the heat of the day; travel at night or in the evening or early morning.

Additional points pertinent to proper preparing and shipping cattle are covered in the four sections which follow.

How to Prevent Bruises, Crippling, and Death Losses

Losses from bruising, crippling, and death that occur during the marketing process represent a part of the cost of marketing livestock; and, indirectly, the producer foots most of the bill.

The following precautions are suggested as a means of reducing cattle market losses from bruises, crippling, and death:

1. Dehorn cattle, preferably when young.

2. Remove projecting nails, splinters, and broken boards in feed racks and fences.

3. Keep feed lots free from old machinery, trash, and any obstacle that may bruise.

4. Do not feed grain heavily just prior to loading.

5. Use good loading chutes; not too steep.

6. Bed with sand free from stones, to prevent slipping.

7. For calves, cover sand with straw in cold weather.

8. Provide covers for trucks to protect from sun in summer and cold in winter.

9. Always partition mixed loads into separate classes, and partition calves from cattle.

10. Have upper deck of truck high enough to prevent back bruises on calves below.

11. Remove protruding nails, bolts, or any sharp objects in truck or car.

12. Load slowly to prevent crowding against sharp corners and to avoid excitement. Do not overload.

13. Use canvas slappers instead of clubs or canes.

14. Tie all bulls in truck or car, and partition stags and cripples.

15. Place "bull board" in position and secure before car door is closed on loaded cattle.

16. Drive trucks carefully; slow down on sharp turns and avoid sudden stops.

17. Inspect load enroute to prevent trampling of animals that may be down.

18. Back truck slowly and squarely against unloading dock.

19. Unload slowly. Do not drop animals from upper to lower deck; use cleated inclines.

All these precautions are simple to apply; yet all are violated every day of the year.

Number of Cattle in a Railroad Car and in a Truck

Overcrowding of market animals causes heavy losses. Sometimes a railroad car or a truck is overloaded in an attempt to effect a saving in hauling charges. More frequently, however, it is simply the result of not knowing space requirements.

The suggested number of animals, Tables 55 and 56, should be tempered by such factors as distance of haul, class of cattle, weather, and road conditions.

1. **By Rail.**—Normally, railroad cars are either 36 or 40 feet

TABLE 55

CATTLE PER RAILROAD CAR[1]

Car Size	Cattle, wt. 1,000 Pounds
36 foot car	26
40 foot car	28

[1] Recommendations of Western Weighing and Inspection Bureau, Room 460, Union Station, Chicago, Ill.

in length. The size of the car and the class and size of animals determine the number of head that can be loaded in a given car. For comfort in shipping, the car should be loaded heavily enough so that the animals stand close together, but overcrowding is to be avoided. Table 55 gives some indication as to the number of cattle that may be loaded in a railroad car.

2. **By Truck.**—Table 56 shows the number of cattle for safe trucking.

TABLE 56

NUMBER OF CATTLE FOR SAFE LOADING IN A TRUCK[1]

Floor Length	Average Weight of Cattle, Lbs.					
	450	600	800	1000	1200	1400
(ft.)	(no.)	(no.)	(no.)	(no.)	(no.)	(no.)
8	8	7	5	4	4	3
10	10	8	7	6	5	4
12	13	10	8	7	6	5
15	16	13	10	9	8	7
18	20	16	13	11	9	8
20	22	18	14	12	10	9
24	27	22	17	15	13	11
28	31	25	20	17	15	13
30	34	27	22	19	16	14
32	36	29	23	20	17	15
36	41	33	26	22	19	17
42	48	39	31	28	22	20

[1] Table 56 is taken from the authoritative recommendations of Livestock Conservation, Inc., Union Stock Yards, Chicago, Ill.

Kind of Bedding to Use for Cattle in Transit

Among the several factors affecting livestock losses, perhaps none is more important than proper bedding and footing in

TABLE 57

HANDY GUIDE RELATIVE TO BEDDING AND FOOTING MATERIAL
WHEN TRANSPORTING LIVESTOCK[1]

Class of Livestock	Kind of Bedding for Moderate or Warm Weather; above 50° F.	Kind of Bedding for Cool or Cold Weather Below 50° F.
Cattle	Sand, 2 inches	Sand; for calves use sand covered with straw
Sheep and Goats	Sand	Sand covered with straw
Swine	Sand, ½ inch to 2 inches	Sand covered with straw
Horses and Mules	Sand	Sand

[1] Straw or other suitable bedding (covered over sand) should be used for protecting and for cushioning breeding stock that are loaded lightly enough to permit their lying down in the car or truck.
Sand should be clean and medium-fine, and free from brick, stones, coarse gravel, dirt, or dust. *Fine* cinders may be used as footing for cattle, horses and mules, but not for sheep or hogs. They are picked up by and damage the wool of sheep, and they damage hog casings.
In hot weather, wet sand down before loading.

transit. This applies to both rail and truck shipments, and to all classes of animals.

Footing, such as sand, is required at all times of the year, to prevent the car or truck floor from becoming wet and slick, thus predisposing to injury of animals by slipping or falling. Bedding, such as straw, is recommended for warmth in the shipment of calves during extremely cold weather, and as cushioning for dairy cows, breeding stock, or other animals loaded lightly enough to permit their lying down. Recommended kinds and amounts of bedding and footing materials are given in Table 57. (Because many loads are mixed, information relative to each class of animals is provided in Table 57.)

Shrinkage in Marketing Cattle

The shrinkage (or drift) refers to the weight loss encountered from the time animals leave the feed lot until they are weighed over the scales at the market. Thus, if a steer weighed 1,000 pounds at the feed lot and had a market weight of 970 pounds, the shrinkage would be 30 pounds or 3.0 per cent. Shrink is usually expressed in terms of percentage. Most of this weight loss is due to excretion, in the form of feces and urine and the moisture in the expired air. On the other hand, there is some tissue shrinkage, which results from metabolic or break-down changes.

The most important factors affecting shrinkage are:

1. **The Fill.**—Naturally, the larger the fill animals take upon their arrival at the market, the smaller the shrinkage.

2. **Time in Transit.**—The longer the animals are in transit and the greater the distance, the higher the total shrinkage.

3. **Truck Vs. Rail Transportation.**—Based on practical experience and observation, most stockmen are of the opinion (1) that truck shipments result in less shrinkage than rail shipments for short hauls, and (2) that rail shipments result in less shrinkage than truck shipments for long hauls. This may be due to the fact that cattle hauled by rail have a feed and rest stop while those moved by truck usually do not.

4. **Season.**—Extremes in temperature, either very hot or very cold weather, result in higher shrinkage.

5. **Age and Weight.**—Young animals of all species shrink proportionally more than older animals.

6. **Overloading.**—Overloading always results in abnormally high shrinkage.

7. **Rough Ride, Abnormal Feeding and Mixed Loads.**—Each of these factors will increase shrinkage.

On the average, market cattle shrink from 3 to 6 per cent, with younger animals shrinking more than older and fatter animals. Experienced cattle feeders report that it takes an average of seven days after arrival at the feedyard to regain a shrink of 10 per cent on feeder cattle.

SHRINKAGE TABLES:

Both cattle sellers and buyers must give consideration to shrinkage. For example, if a buyer offers $19.00 per hundred with a 4 per cent shrink allowance, the producer will want to know how much he will receive. The answer can be quickly and easily obtained from Table 58 as follows: Look at $19.00 under column 1, headed "Offer." Go across to column headed "4%." As shown, the producer will receive $18.24 for his cattle.

TABLE 58

PRICES IN $ PER 100 POUNDS WITH SHRINKAGE DEDUCTED

Offer	2%	3%	4%	6%	8%
$35.00	$34.30	$33.95	$33.60	$32.90	$32.20
34.00	33.32	32.98	32.64	31.96	31.28
33.00	32.34	32.01	31.68	31.02	30.36
32.00	31.36	31.04	30.72	30.08	29.44
31.00	30.38	30.07	29.76	29.14	28.52
30.00	29.40	29.10	28.80	28.20	27.60
29.00	28.42	28.13	27.84	27.26	26.68
28.00	27.44	27.16	26.88	26.32	25.76
27.00	26.46	26.19	25.92	25.38	24.84
26.00	25.48	25.22	24.96	24.44	23.92
25.00	24.50	24.25	24.00	23.50	23.00
24.00	23.52	23.28	23.04	22.56	22.08
23.00	22.54	22.31	22.08	21.62	21.16
22.00	21.56	21.34	21.12	20.68	20.24
21.00	20.58	20.37	20.16	19.74	19.32
20.00	19.60	19.40	19.20	18.80	18.40
19.00	18.62	18.43	18.24	17.86	17.48
18.00	17.64	17.46	17.28	16.92	16.56
17.00	16.66	16.49	16.32	15.98	15.64
16.00	15.68	15.52	15.36	15.04	14.72
15.00	14.70	14.55	14.40	14.10	13.80
14.00	13.72	13.58	13.44	13.16	12.88
13.00	12.74	12.61	12.48	12.22	11.96
12.00	11.76	11.64	11.52	11.28	11.04
11.00	10.78	10.67	10.56	10.34	10.12
10.00	9.80	9.70	9.60	9.40	9.20

If the producer has decided that $19.00 is his minimum asking price, he may refuse the offer and ship his cattle to market. Then, he will wish to know how much he will have to receive in order to compensate for shrinkage. The answer can be obtained from Table 59, as follows: Look at $19.00 under column 1, headed "Asking;" then read under the proper column to the right. Thus, if the animals shrink 4 per cent during marketing, the price will have to be $19.79 in order to compensate for shrinkage.

TABLE 59

PRICES IN $ PER 100 POUNDS TO COMPENSATE FOR SHRINKAGE

Asking	2%	3%	4%	6%	8%
$35.00	$35.71	$36.08	$36.46	$37.23	$38.64
34.00	34.69	35.05	35.42	36.17	36.96
33.00	33.67	34.02	34.37	35.11	35.87
32.00	32.66	32.99	33.33	34.04	34.78
31.00	31.63	31.96	32.29	32.98	33.70
30.00	30.61	30.93	31.25	31.91	32.61
29.00	29.59	29.88	30.21	30.85	31.52
28.00	28.57	28.87	29.17	29.79	30.43
27.00	27.55	27.84	28.12	28.72	29.35
26.00	26.53	26.80	27.08	27.66	28.26
25.00	25.51	25.77	26.04	26.59	27.17
24.00	24.49	24.74	25.00	25.59	26.08
23.00	23.47	23.71	23.96	24.46	25.00
22.00	22.45	22.68	22.92	23.40	23.91
21.00	21.43	21.65	21.88	22.34	22.83
20.00	20.41	20.62	20.83	21.28	21.74
19.00	19.39	19.58	19.79	20.21	20.65
18.00	18.37	18.56	18.75	19.50	19.57
17.00	17.35	17.53	17.71	18.09	18.48
16.00	16.33	16.49	16.67	17.02	17.39
15.00	15.31	15.46	15.63	15.96	16.30
14.00	14.29	14.43	14.58	14.98	15.22
13.00	13.27	13.40	13.54	13.83	14.13
12.00	12.24	12.37	12.50	12.77	13.04
11.00	11.22	11.34	11.46	11.70	11.96
10.00	10.20	10.31	10.42	10.64	10.87

MARKET CLASSES AND GRADES OF CATTLE

The generally accepted market classes and grades of live cattle are summarized in Table 60. The first five divisions and subdivisions include those factors that determine the class of the animal or the use to which it will be put. The grades indicate how well the cattle fulfill the requirements to which they are put.

Factors Determining Market Classes of Cattle

The market class of cattle is determined by (1) use selection, (2) sex, (3) age, and (4) weight.

TABLE 60
THE MARKET CLASSES AND GRADES OF CATTLE

Cattle or Calves	Use Selection	Sex Classes	Age	Weight Divisions Wt. (Group)	(lbs.)	Commonly Used Grades
Cattle	Slaughter Cattle	Steers	Yearlings	Light Medium Heavy	750 down 750–950 950–up	Prime, Choice, Good, Standard, Commercial, Utility, Cutter, Canner
			2-year-old and over	Light Medium Heavy	1100 down 1100–1300 1300-up	Prime, Choice, Good, Standard, Commercial, Utility, Cutter, Canner
		Heifers	Yearlings	Light Medium Heavy	750 down 750–900 900 up	Prime, Choice, Good, Standard, Commercial, Utility, Cutter, Canner
			2-year-old and over	Light Medium Heavy	900 down 900–1050 1050 up	Prime, Choice, Good, Standard, Commercial, Utility, Cutter, Canner
		Cows	All ages	All Weights		Choice, Good, Standard, Commercial, Utility, Cutter, Canner
		Bulls (choice & good grade bulls often called "beef" or "butcher" bulls, & lower grades bologna bulls)	Yearlings	All Weights		Choice, Good, Commercial, Utility, Cutter, Canner
			2-year-old and over	Light Medium Heavy	1300 down 1300–1500 1500 up	Choice, Good, Commercial, Utility, Cutter, Canner
		Stags	All ages	All Weights		Choice, Good, Commercial, Utility, Cutter, Canner
	Stocker & Feeder Cattle	Steers	Yearlings	Light Medium Heavy Mixed		Fancy, Choice, Good, Medium, Common, Inferior
			2-year-old and over	Light Medium Heavy Mixed		Fancy, Choice, Good, Medium, Common, Inferior
		Heifers	Yearlings	Light Medium Heavy Mixed		Fancy, Choice, Good, Medium, Common, Inferior
			2-year-old and over	Light Medium Heavy Mixed		Fancy, Choice, Good, Medium, Common, Inferior
		Cows	All ages	All Weights		Choice, Good, Medium, Common, Inferior
		Bulls	All ages	All Weights		Choice, Good, Medium, Common, Inferior
		Stags	All ages	All Weights		Choice, Good, Medium, Common, Inferior
	Milkers & Springers	Cows (milkers or springers)	All ages	All Weights		None
Calves	Vealers	No Sex Class (Sex characteristics of no importance at this age)	Under 3 months	Light Medium Heavy	110 down 110–180 180 up	Prime, Choice, Good, Standard, Utility, Cull
	Slaughter Calves	Steers Heifers Bulls	3 months to 1 year	Light Medium Heavy	200 down 200–300 300 up	Prime, Choice, Good, Standard, Utility, Cull
	Stocker & Feeder Calves	Steers Heifers Bulls	Usually 6 mo. to 1 year	Light Medium Heavy Mixed		Fancy, Choice, Good, Medium, Common, Inferior

CATTLE AND CALVES:

All members of the bovine family are designated as calves until they are one year of age, after which they are known as cattle. On the average, about 21 per cent are calves and 79 per cent cattle.

USE SELECTION OF CATTLE AND CALVES:

The cattle group is further divided into three use divisions, each indicating something of the purpose to which the animals will be put. These divisions are: (1) slaughter cattle, (2) stocker and feeder cattle, and (3) milkers and springers. Slaughter cattle include those which are considered suitable for immediate slaughter; stockers and feeders include those which are to be taken back to the country and grown for a time or fattened; and milkers and springers include those cows recently freshened or soon due to calve and which are sold for milk purposes.

The calf group is also subdivided into three classes: (1) vealers, including milk-fat animals under three months of age which are sold for immediate slaughter; (2) slaughter calves that are between the ages of three months and one year, which have usually received grain in addition to milk, and which are fat enough for slaughter; and (3) stocker and feeder calves which are of weaning age and are sold to go back into the country for further growing or fattening.

In the selection of stocker and feeder cattle or calves, the sex, age, weight, and grade are of importance. In addition, consideration should be given to the following factors: (1) constitution and thrift, (2) natural fleshing, (3) breeding, (4) uniformity, (5) absence of horns, and (6) temperament and disposition.

As can be readily understood, the use to which animals are put is not always clear-cut and definite. Thus, when feed is abundant and factors are favorable for cattle fattening, feeders may outbid packer buyers for some of the animals that would normally go for slaughter purposes. On the other hand, slaughterers frequently outbid feeders for some of those animals that would normally go the stocker and feeder route.

THE SEX CLASSES:

Cattle are divided into five sex classes: steers, heifers, cows, bulls and stags. Each of these five groups has rather definite and easily distinguishable characteristics that are related to the commercial value of the carcass—especially in the cattle group—and which are important in determining the suitability of animals as stockers and feeders. In older cattle, sex is an important factor affecting carcass quality, finish, and conformation. The definition of each sex class follows:

Steer.—A steer is a male bovine animal that was castrated at an early age, before reaching sexual maturity and before developing the physical characteristics peculiar to bulls.

Heifer.—A heifer is a female bovine animal that has not had a calf or has not reached the stage of advanced pregnancy or has not developed the mature form of a cow.

Cow.—A cow is a female bovine animal that has had one or more calves or that has reached the stage of advanced pregnancy. Barren female bovine animals that have reached maturity and have developed the predominating physical characteristics peculiar to cows also are so classified.

Bull.—A bull is an uncastrated male bovine animal of any age.

Stag.—A stag, as applied to cattle, is a male bovine animal that was castrated after it had developed the physical characteristics of a mature bull.

Calves are merely divided into three sex classes: steers, heifers, or bulls. Because the secondary sex characteristics are not very pronounced in this group, the sex classes are of less importance for slaughter purposes than in older cattle. On the other hand, bull calves are not preferred as feeders because castration involves extra trouble and risk of loss.

AGE GROUPS:

Because the age of cattle does affect certain carcass characteristics, it is logical that age groups should exist in market classifications. The terms used to indicate approximate age ranges for cattle are: vealers, calves, yearlings, two-year-old and older cattle. As previously indicated, vealers are under three months of age,[1] whereas calves are young cattle between the vealer and yearling stage. Yearlings range from twelve to twenty-four months in age, and two-year-olds from twenty-four to thirty-six months. Older cattle are usually grouped along with the two-year-olds as "two-year-old and over."

---

[1]Vealers must also be over twenty-one days of age for slaughter. Under age veal calves are called "deacons" or "bob veal."

WEIGHT DIVISIONS:

It is common to have three weight divisions: light, medium, and heavy. When several weight divisions are included together, they are referred to as "mixed weight." The usual practice is to group animals by rather narrow weight divisions because purchasers are frequently rather "choosey" about weights and market values often vary quite sharply with variations in weights.

The Market Grades of Cattle

While no official grading of live animals is done by the U. S. Department of Agriculture, marked grades do form a basis for uniform reporting of livestock marketing. The grade is the final step in classifying any kind of market livestock. It indicates the relative degree of excellence of an animal or group of animals. The three factors of primary importance in determining cattle grades are conformation, finish, and quality.

Table 60 lists the commonly used grades of cattle by classes. As noted, the number of grades varies somewhat between classes chiefly because certain groups of animals present a wider range of variations in conformation, finish, and quality than do other groups. Slaughter steers and heifers are divided into eight grades: Prime, Choice, Good, Standard, Commercial, Utility, Cutter, and Canner. However, only seven grades apply to slaughter cows, and six grades to slaughter bulls, and stags. The Prime grade is not applied to cows, bulls, and stags, chiefly because of deficient conformation, finish, and quality in these classes; and no Standard grade is applied to bulls and stags because this term implies younger cattle than is usually found in these two classes. Further, as in carcasses, bulls and stags on foot are always designated as "slaughter bulls" and "slaughter stags," since meat obtained from these respective classes is never interchanged (1) with each other, or (2) with meat carrying the same grade name from steers, heifers, and cows.

The terms Cutter or Canner are applied to the two lowest grades of slaughter cattle. Cutter cattle are so poor in form and lacking in muscle and fat covering that only such wholesale cuts as the loin and round are cut out and sold over the block. The balance of the carcass is boned out and used in sausage and canned-meat products. Canners are almost entirely processed as ground and canned meats.

The grades of vealers and slaughter calves are: Prime, Choice, Good, Standard, Utility and Cull.

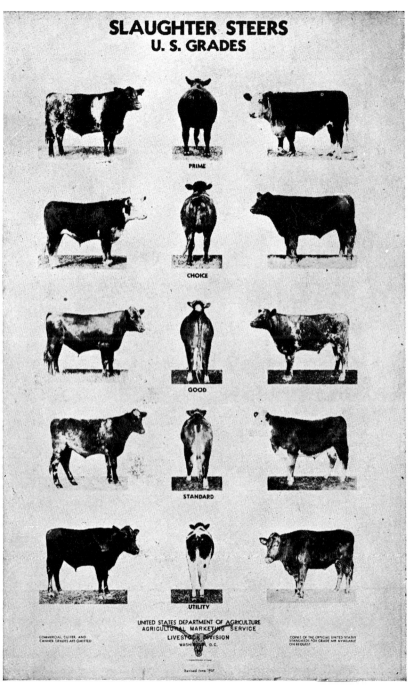

Fig. 256. The market grades of slaughter steers. (Courtesy, USDA, Agricultural Marketing Service)

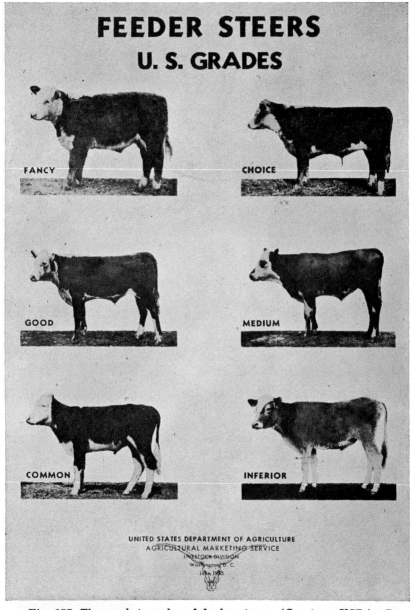

Fig. 257. The market grades of feeder steers. (Courtesy, USDA—Production and Marketing Administration)

Stocker and feeder steers and heifers, and stocker and feeder calves are divided into six grades: Fancy, Choice, Good, Medium, Common, and Inferior. The highest grade is called "Fancy" or "Fancy selected" instead of "Prime," and the term "Inferior" is used for the lowest grade. The grade "Prime" is not applied to stocker and feeder cattle or calves because it signifies a high degree of finish that such animals do not possess. The term "Inferior" is used in grading stocker and feeder cattle in order to denote poor breeding and conformation as well as poor condition. Only five grades apply to stocker and feeder cows, bulls, and stags—the grade Fancy being deleted because of insufficient quality.

High grade feeder animals normally produce high grade slaughter animals, but no amount of care and management can transform low grade feeder animals into high grade slaughter animals. On the other hand, with proper finish, many feeders

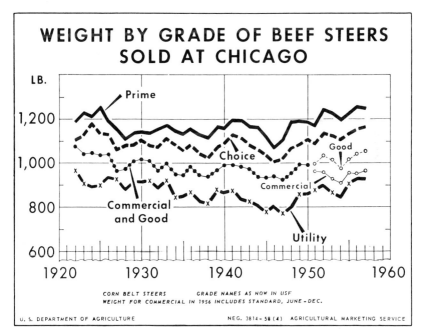

Fig. 258. This shows that the higher grades of fat cattle usually carry more weight, and the lower grades are lighter and usually underfinished. Note that Good and Commercial cattle were carried as one line until 1951 and that from thence forward they were split into the Good and Commercial grades; this procedure was followed because the new federal grades went into effect at that time.

regularly plan to up the projected slaughter grades of lower quality feeder cattle by at least one grade.

As would be expected, the higher grades of fat cattle usually carry more weight, and the lower grades are lighter and usually underfinished. Fig. 258 shows the relationship of the weight of beef steers to the grade.

Because the production of the better grades of cattle usually involves more expenditure in the breeding operations (due to the need for superior animals) and feeding to a higher degree of finish; there must be a spread in market grades in order to make the production of the top grades profitable. Fig. 259 shows the ten-year average price per hundredweight of beef steers, by grades, on the Chicago market from 1948 to 1957.

Prices of Beef Steers Sold Out of First Hands, By Grades, Chicago, 1948-1957

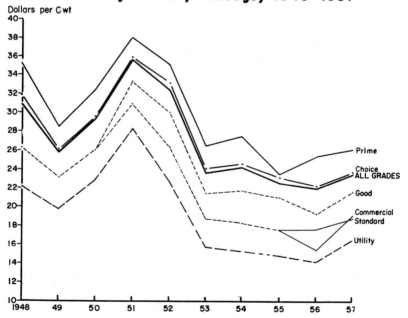

Fig. 259. This shows that there is a rather uniform difference in the selling price of the different grades of cattle, with a slightly greater spread between the lower grades. Note that Good and Commercial cattle were carried as one line until 1951 and that from thence forward they were split into the Good and Commercial grades and that in 1955 Commercial became Standard and Commercial. This procedure was followed because the new federal grades went into effect at that time. (Data from Mr. Harold F. Breimyer, Head, Livestock, Fats and Oils Section, Agricultural Marketing Service, USDA, Washington, D. C. Drawing by Steve Allured)

OTHER CATTLE MARKET TERMS AND FACTORS

In addition to the more or less general terminology used in cattle dealing and reporting, the following terms and factors are significant:

Native and Western Cattle

"Native cattle" are those coming from the farms of the Corn Belt, East, and South; whereas "western cattle" are the branded cattle coming from the western ranges. Not so long ago, western cattle lacked the breeding and quality of native cattle. But this condition no longer prevails. Today, many of the champion steers at the major shows throughout the country come from range herds, and, in general, range shipments possess far more uniformity than native cattle.

Grassers and Fed Cattle

The term "grassers" designates animals that have not been grain fed and which come direct from the pasture or range. Fed cattle are those that have been fed grain. "Short-fed" cattle are those which have been grain fed for 60 to 120 days, whereas "long-fed" cattle have been grain fed for more than 120 days.

Baby Beef

The term "baby beef" is frequently applied to Prime or Choice animals (either steers or heifers) from twelve to eighteen months of age and weighing 700 to 1,200 pounds on foot. For the most part these animals have never been allowed to lose their milk fat.

Butcher Stock

On many markets the term "butcher stock" is used to designate heifers, cows, bulls, and stags marketed for slaughter and suitable to be sold in the carcass as block beef. These carcasses are largely sold to city and country retail dealers or butchers; hence the term "butcher stock" is applied to this class of market cattle.

Bologna Bulls

Bologna bulls are bulls that are muscular but not sufficiently fat for block beef purposes. The meat from such carcasses is usually used in the manufacture of bologna sausage.

SOME CATTLE MARKETING CONSIDERATIONS

Enlightened and shrewd marketing practices generally characterize the successful cattle enterprise. Among the considerations of importance in marketing cattle, are those which follow.

Cyclical Trends in Market Cattle

The price cycle as it applies to livestock may be defined as that period of time during which the price for a certain kind of livestock advances from a low point to a high point and then declines to a low point again. In reality, it is a change in animal numbers that represents the stockman's response to prices. Although there is considerable variation in the length of the cycle within any given class of stock, in recent years it has been observed that the price cycle of the different classes of animals is about as follows: Hogs, 3 to 5 years; sheep, 9 to 10 years; and cattle, 10 to 12 years (see Fig. 260).

The specie cycles are a direct reflection of the rapidity with which the numbers of each class of farm animals can be shifted under practical conditions to meet consumer meat demands. Thus, litter-bearing and early-producing swine can be increased in numbers much more rapidly than either cattle or sheep.

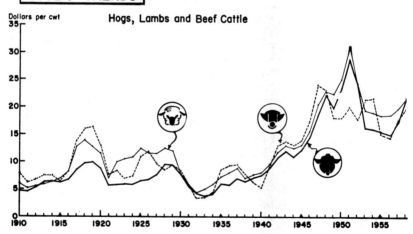

Fig. 260. Average price received by U. S. farmers for each class of livestock, 1910-1958. In general, this shows that the price cycle of each animal is approximately as follows: hogs, 3 to 5 years; sheep, 9 to 10 years; and cattle, 10 to 12 years. (Based on data obtained from USDA, *Statistical Bulletin No. 180*, Agricultural Marketing Service, p. 30-33; and *Livestock Market News Statistics and Related Data*, 1956, June 1957, Agricultural Marketing Service, p. 51.)

When market cattle prices are favorable, established cattle enterprises are expanded, and new herds are founded, so that about every 10 to 12 years, on the average, the market is glutted and prices fall, only to rise again because too few cattle are being produced to take care of the demand for beef. Normal cycles are disturbed by droughts, wars, general periods of depression or inflation, and Federal controls.

Seasonal Changes in Market Cattle

Cattle prices vary by seasons, by classes, and by grades; as

TABLE 61

WHEN TO BUY AND SELL CATTLE[1]

Kind and Class of Cattle	Lowest Prices (When to Buy)	Highest Prices (When to Sell)
Fat Steers:		
Prime	Feb. to July	Sept. thru Jan.
Choice	Feb. to July	Sept. to Nov.
Good, Standard, and Commercial	Feb. and Dec.	May to Sept.
Utility	Aug. to Feb.	April to June
Fat Heifers (top grades)	Feb. to May	Sept. to Nov.
Cows	Nov.	May
Stocker and Feeder Cattle	June to Jan.	Feb. thru May

[1] Based on averages.

shown in Table 61, and in Figs. 261, 262, 263, and 264. Consideration is given herein to fat steers, fat heifers, cows, and stocker and feeder cattle.

1. **Fat steers.**—Fig. 261 shows the seasonal variation in fat steer prices, by grades. From this and other market information, the following conclusions are drawn:

(1) The feeder who has cattle that will grade Prime will usually hit the highest market in September through January, with the peak being in January. On the average, however, the peak price on Choice cattle is of shorter duration; the highest price being in September and October, followed by a price decline in November and December.

The lowest market for both Prime and Choice grades, from February to July, coincides with the season of heaviest receipts. This situation is due to the fact that most Corn Belt feeders winter-feed and market in the spring.

The feeder who has slaughter cattle that will grade Good, Standard, and Commercial should sell from May to September, whereas the feeder who has Utility grade slaughter steers should sell from April to June; ahead of grass-fat cattle.

(2) The higher and the lower grades of fat steers follow somewhat different trends.

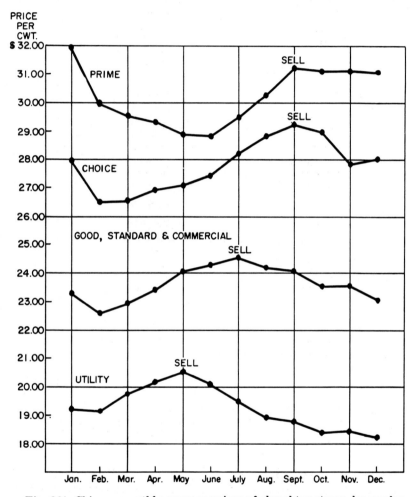

Fig. 261. Chicago monthly average prices of slaughter steers, by grades, for the 10-year period 1948 to 1957. (Based on data obtained from *Livestock and Meat Statistics*, 1957. Statistical Bull. No. 230, July 1958, USDA, p. 214-218.

(3) The price spread between the grades is narrowest in the spring, when marketings of grain-fed cattle are heaviest.

(4) The heavy run of grass cattle in the fall causes lower

prices for Good, Standard, Commercial and Utility grade fat steers.

2. **Fat heifers.**—Fig. 262 shows the seasonal variation in fat heifer prices (top grades). From this and other market information, the following conclusions are drawn:

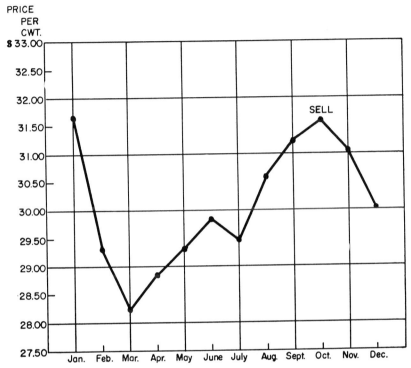

Fig. 262. Chicago *top* price of heifers for the 10-year period, 1948 to 1957. This shows the seasonal variation in fat heifer prices. (Based on data obtained from *Yearbook of Figures*, published by Chicago Daily Drovers Journal, 1957, p. 37)

(1) The seasonal changes in the price of fat heifers coincide rather closely with those of Choice fat steers, the highest market for the top grades usually being in September to November and the lowest from February to May.

(2) It is more difficult for the producer to take advantage of high market seasons with heifers than with steers, because the former are usually discounted in price after they pass the 750 to 800 pound mark and, therefore, must be sold.

3. **Cows.**—Fig. 263 shows the seasonal variation in cow

prices for the four bottom grades. From this and other market information, the following conclusions are drawn:

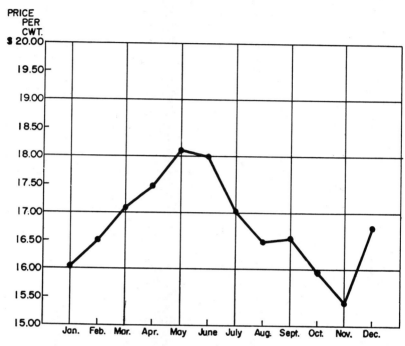

Fig. 263. Chicago monthly average prices of cows for the 10-year period, 1948 to 1957. This shows the seasonal variation in cow prices. (Based on data obtained from *Yearbook of Figures, 1957*)

(1) Usually, dry cows and cows that are to be culled from the herd for one reason or another had best be marketed in the spring, from April to June.

(2) The heavy run of grass cattle in the late fall causes lower prices for cows from October to December.

(3) The lower prices in the fall will likely nullify the value of any increased weight put on cows during the summer and fall. Thus, unless there is an overabundance of grass or unless the cows can be raised a grade through increased weight gains, it is usually best to market the stock in the spring.

(4) The different grades follow similar trends.

4. **Stocker and Feeder cattle.**—Fig. 264 shows the seasonal variation in stocker and feeder steer prices. To cattle feeders, this graph is a buying guide; to cattle producers, it is a selling guide.

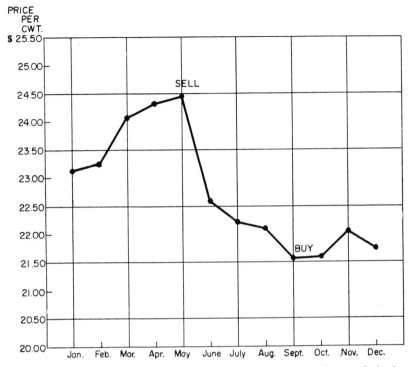

Fig. 264. Kansas City monthly average prices of stocker and feeder steers (of all weights and grades) for the 10-year period, 1948-1957. This shows the seasonal variation in stocker and feeder steer prices.

From this figure and other market information, the following conclusions are drawn:

(1) Stocker and feeder cattle prices are usually lowest from June to January and highest from February through May; the prices reflect the seasons of highest and lowest receipts, respectively.

(2) Stocker and feeder cattle receipts are greatest in the fall and early winter because this is the season when farmers and ranchers sell their surplus and grass-fat cattle in preparation for winter, and when Corn Belt feeders want to fill their feed lots in order to utilize the new crop and available labor.

(3) It is difficult for the producer of stocker and feeder cattle to take advantage of seasonal trends because pasture and range conditions often determine or actually dictate the time of sale from the range.

Dockage

The value of some market animals is low because dressing losses are high, or because part of the product is of low quality. Cattle with lumpy jaw are usually bought subject to the amount of wastage.

PACKER SLAUGHTERING AND DRESSING OF CATTLE

Table 62 shows the proportion of cattle and calves slaughtered commercially (meaning that they were slaughtered in

TABLE 62

PROPORTION OF CATTLE AND CALVES SLAUGHTERED
COMMERCIALLY, 1953 to 1957[1]

Year	Cattle			Calves		
	Total Number Slaughtered (Commercially and Non-commercially)	Number Slaughtered Commercially	Per cent Slaughtered Commercially	Total Number Slaughtered (Commercially and Non-commercially)	Number Slaughtered Commercially	Per cent Slaughtered Commercially
	(1,000 head)	(1,000 head)	(%)	(1,000 head)	(1,000 head)	(%)
1953	24,465	23,605	96.48	12,200	11,668	95.64
1954	25,889	25,017	96.63	13,270	12,746	96.05
1955	26,587	25,722	96.75	12,864	12,377	96.21
1956	27,754	26,862	96.79	12,997	12,512	96.27
1957	27,059	26,184	96.77	12,324	11,859	96.23

[1] Data provided by Mr. Harold Breimyer, Head, Livestock, Fats and Oils Section, Agricultura Marketing Service, USDA, Washington, D. C.

federally inspected and other wholesale and retail establishments), and the proportion slaughtered on farms. The total figure refers to the number dressed in all establishments and on farms. Although farm slaughter procedure may differ somewhat, the ultimate objective is always the same. Because of the greater total numbers of cattle involved in this system of handling, only packer slaughtering and dressing—the kind that is done commercially—will be discussed.

Cattle intended for slaughter purposes are bought primarily on the basis of projected quality of carcass and dressing percentage. Upon reaching the packing house, they rapidly pass through the operations of killing and dressing. Unlike most manufacturing, meat packing is primarily a disassembly process wherein the manufacturing operation starts with a complete unit that is progressively broken down into its component parts. The various parts then are subjected to divergent processing operations. Because of their size and other physical characteristics, cattle cannot be processed with the endless chain method of dressing that is used in the dressing of hogs, calves, and sheep.

Steps in Slaughtering and Dressing Cattle

The slaughtering and dressing procedure differs somewhat between plants, but in general the process consists of the following steps:

1. **Rendering insensible.**—The cattle are rendered insensible[1].

2. **Shackling, hoisting, sticking, and bleeding.**—The animal is next shackled, hoisted by the hind legs, stuck, and bled. The head is then skinned and removed.

3. **Lowering to floor and partial skinning.**—The carcass is next lowered to the floor; the shanks are skinned and removed at the knees and hocks; the hide is opened along the median line on the belly and is removed from the belly and sides; and the breast and aitch (rump) bones are split by sawing.

4. **Raising to "half-hoist" position and further skinning.**— Beef hooks are inserted on the gam cord and the carcass is partially raised to a position known as "half-hoist." In this position, the skinning of the shanks is completed and the round and rump are skinned out.

5. **Hoisting carcass to overhead track, completing skinning, removing viscera.**—All internal organs are removed except the kidneys. If the plant is under federal inspection, the carcass and viscera are examined at this stage in the slaughtering process.

6. **Splitting carcass and removing tail.**—The carcass is then split through the center of the backbone and the tail is removed.

7. **Washing and drying.**—The split carcasses or sides are washed with warm water under pressure.

8. **Shrouding.**—The better carcasses are shrouded tightly with cloth so that they may have a smoother appearance following chilling.

---

[1]By federal law, passed in 1958 and effective June 30, 1960, unless a packer uses humane slaughter methods, he forfeits the right to sell meat to the government. The law lists the following two methods as humane:

1. By rendering insensible to pain by a single blow or gunshot or an electrical, chemical, or other means that is rapid and effective, before being shackled, hoisted, thrown, cast or cut.

2. By slaughtering in accordance with the ritual requirements of the Jewish faith or any other religious faith.

9. **Sending to coolers.**—Following slaughtering, the sides are sent to the coolers where they are kept at a temperature of about 34° F. for a minimum period of twenty-four hours before ribbing.

How Slaughter of Veal Calves Differs

Because of their smaller size, calves may be dressed by the "endless-chain" method. A wheel hoist is used in lifting the shackled calves to the rail. They are then stuck, bled, dressed, and washed. Because of the high moisture content of veal, the hide is usually left on for the purpose of reducing evaporation. This also produces a more desirable carcass color. When the hide is left on, it is thoroughly washed before the carcass is sent to the cooler.

Kosher Slaughter

Meat for the Jewish trade must come from animals slaughtered according to the rules of *Shehitah* (the ancient dietary rules). Although we usually think in terms of cattle when kosher slaughtering is mentioned, calves, sheep, lambs, goats, and poultry are slaughtered in a similar manner.

The killing is performed by a rabbi of the Jewish church or a specially trained representative; a person called the *shohet* or *shochet,* meaning slaughterer. In kosher slaughter, the animal is hoisted without stunning and is cut across the throat with a special razor-sharp knife, known as a *chalaf.* With one quick, clean stroke the throat is cut; through the jugular vein and other large vessels, together with the gullet and windpipe. Two reasons are given for using this method of killing instead of the more conventional method of stunning and sticking; namely (1) it produces more instant death with less pain, and (2) it results in more rapid and complete bleeding, which Orthodox Hebrews consider essential for sanitary reasons.

The shohet also makes an inspection of the lungs, stomach and other organs while dressing. If the carcass is acceptable, it is marked on the brisket with a cross inside a circle. The mark also gives the date of slaughter and the name of the inspector.

Since neither packers nor meat retailers can hold kosher meat longer than 216 hours (and even then it must be washed at seventy-two hour intervals), rapid handling is imperative. This fact, plus the heavy concentration of Jewish folks in the eastern cities results in large numbers of live cattle being shipped from the markets farther west to be slaughtered in or near the eastern consuming areas.

The Dressing Percentage

Dressing percentage may be defined as the percentage yield of chilled carcass in relation to the weight of the animal on foot. For example, a steer which weighed 1,200 pounds on foot and yielded a carcass weighing 720 pounds may be said to have a dressing percentage of 60. The offal—so-called because formerly (with the exception of the hide, tallow, and tongue) the offal (waste) was thrown away—consists of the blood, head, shanks, tail, hide, viscera, and loose fat.

A high carcass yield is desirable because the carcass is much more valuable than the by-products. Although the packers have done a marvelous job in utilizing by-products, about 91.5 per cent of the income from steers is derived from the sale of the carcass and only 8.5 per cent from the by-products. Thus the estimated dressing percentage of slaughter cattle is justifiably a major factor in determining the price or value of the live animal.

The chief factors determining the dressing percentage of cattle are: (1) the amount of fill, (2) the finish or degree of fatness, (3) the general quality and refinement (refinement of head, bone, hide, etc.) and (4) the size of udder. The better grades of steers have the highest dressing percentage, with thin canner cows showing the lowest yield. Tables 63 and 64 give the dress-

TABLE 63

AVERAGE AND NORMAL RANGE IN DRESSING
PERCENTAGE OF CATTLE, BY GRADES[1]

Grade	Dressing Percentage	
	Average	Normal Range
	(%)	(%)
Prime	63	60–67
Choice	59	57–64
Good	57	55–61
Standard	55	53–58
Commercial	54	52–59
Utility	49	45–53
Cutter	45	41–47
Canner	42	37–44

[1] Dressing percentages provided by Dr. Fred J. Beard, Chief, Meat Grading Branch, USDA, Washington, D. C.

TABLE 64
AVERAGE AND NORMAL RANGE IN DRESSING
PERCENTAGE OF SLAUGHTER CALVES AND
VEALERS, BY GRADES[1]

Grade	Dressing Percentages	
	Average	Normal Range
	(%)	(%)
Prime...	62	60–66
Choice..	58	56–62
Good...	56	54–58
Standard..	53	50–55
Utility..	49	46–52
Cull..	44	40–46

[1] Dressing percentages provided by Dr. Fred J. Beard, Chief, Meat Grading Branch, USDA, Washington, D. C.

ing percentages that may be expected for different grades of cattle and calves.

The highest dressing percentage on record was a yield of 76¾ per cent made by a spayed Angus heifer at the Smithfield Fat Stock Show in England. It is estimated that market cattle in the United States dress about 53.3 per cent and veal calves about 56 per cent. The higher dressing percentage for veal calves is due to the fact that they are dressed with the hide on.

The average live weights of cattle and calves dressed by federally inspected meat packing plants, and their percentage yields in meats, for the year 1957 is given in Table 65.

TABLE 65
AVERAGE LIVE WEIGHT, CARCASS YIELD AND DRESSING
PERCENTAGES OF ALL CATTLE AND CALVES COMMERCIALLY
SLAUGHTERED IN THE U. S. IN 1957[1]

	Average Live Weight	Average Yield in Meats	Dressing Percentage
	(pounds)	(pounds)	(%)
Cattle...............................	958	529.6	55.3
Calves................................	217	121.5	56.0

Data provided by Mr. Harold F. Breimyer, Head, Livestock, Fats and Oils Section, Agricultural Marketing Service, USDA, Washington, D. C.

SELLING PUREBRED CATTLE

Selling purebred animals is highly specialized and scientific business. Purebred animals are usually sold at private treaty directly to other purebred breeders or commercial producers or through auctions which may either be sponsored by one or a few breeders (joint sales or consignment sales).

In general, the vast majority of bulls saved for breeding purposes go into commercial herds. Only the elite sires are retained with the hope of affecting further breed improvement in purebred herds. On the other hand, the sale of purebred females is fairly well restricted to meeting the requirements for replacement purposes in existing purebred herds or for establishing new purebred herds.

Most consignment sales are sponsored by a breed association, either local, state-wide, or national in character. Such auctions, therefore, are usually limited to one breed. Purebred auction sales are conducted by highly specialized auctioneers. In addition to being good salesmen, such auctioneers must have a keen knowledge of values and be familiar with the blood lines of the breeding stock.

QUESTIONS FOR STUDY AND DISCUSSION

1. Why is cattle marketing important?
2. In recent years, many top authorities have said that cattle marketing is the cattleman's number one problem. Why do they feel this way?
3. Since World War I, terminal public markets have declined in importance while livestock auction markets and country selling have increased. Why has this happened?
4. What method of marketing (what market channel) do you consider most advantageous for the cattle sold off your home farm or ranch, and why?
5. Does each market channel give adequate assurance of honesty, of sanitation, and of humane treatment of animals?
6. Why is it important that a cattleman know the leading markets for each class of cattle?
7. How do you account for the fact that the leading terminal public markets for fat cattle, for calves, and for feeder cattle do not coincide?
8. Which is the more important to the livestock seller: (1) low marketing costs, or (2) effective selling and net returns?
9. Outline, step by step, how you would prepare and ship cattle.

10. Define on-foot market (1) classes and (2) grades of cattle and tell of their value.
11. Why is it important that a cattleman know the market classes and grades of cattle and what each implies?
12. Why are grade names and specifications changed from time to time?
13. Since there is a rather uniform difference in the selling price of the different grades of cattle, with the top grades bringing the higher prices, why do not more cattlemen produce the top grades?
14. How may a cattleman take advantage of cyclical trends and seasonal changes?
15. Discuss the importance of each: (1) proper bedding for cattle in transit and (2) shrinkage.
16. Do packers control market cattle prices?
17. In what ways does the selling of purebred cattle differ from the selling of commercial cattle?

SELECTED REFERENCES

Title of Publication	Author(s)	Publisher
Animal Science	M. E. Ensminger	Interstate Printers & Publishers, Danville, Ill., 1960
American Live Stock Market, The—How It Functions	A. C. Davenport	Drovers Journal Print, Chicago, Ill., 1922.
Beef Marketing Margins and Costs	Misc. Bul. No. 710	U. S. Department of Agricultur Washington 25, D. C.
Beef on the Farm— Slaughtering, Cutting, and Curing	Farmers' Bul. No. 1415	U. S. Department of Agriculture, Washington 25, D. C.
Charting the Seasonal Market for Meat Animals	H. F. Breimyer C. A. Kause	Agri. Handbook No. 83, U. S. Department of Agriculture, Washington, D. C., 1955.
Competition in the Meat Packing Business	Bert Horan	Swift & Co., Chicago 9, Ill.
Economic Effects of U. S. Grades for Beef	Marketing Research Report No. 298	U. S. Department of Agriculture, Washington 25, D. C.
Essentials of Marketing Livestock	R. C. Ashby	The National Live Stock Exchange, 1953.
Hired Truck Transportation in Marketing Livestock	Marketing Research Report No. 297	U. S. Department of Agriculture Washington 25, D. C.

Title of Publication	Author(s)	Publisher
Improving Livestock Marketing Efficiency	I. M. Stevens R. L. Fox	General Report 39, Farmer Cooperative Service, U. S. Department of Agriculture, Washington 25, D. C.
Livestock Auction Markets in the Southeast	G. E. Turner C. F. Brasington	Marketing Research Report No. 141, U. S. Department of Agriculture, Washington D. C., 1956.
Livestock Auction Markets in the United States	Gerald Engelman B. S. Pence	Marketing Research Report No. 223, U. S. Department of Agriculture, Washington 25, D. C.
Livestock Marketing	A. A. Dowell Knute Bjorka	McGraw-Hill Book Co., New York, N. Y., 1941.
Livestock Marketing in the United States	H. H. Smith	Bul. 442-A, Agricultural Extension Service, Colorado State University, Fort Collins, Colo.
Livestock Shrinkage		Western Livestock Marketing Research Committee, Denver, Colo.
Livestock Terminal Markets in the United States	Marketing Research Report. No. 299	U. S. Department of Agriculture, Washington 25, D. C.
Losses of Livestock in Transit in Midwestern and Western States	J. E. Rickenbacker	Marketing Research Report 247, Farmer Cooperative Service, Washington 25, D. C.
Market Outlets for Livestock Producers	Marketing Research Report No. 216	U. S. Department of Agriculture, Washington 25, D. C.
Marketing Cattle and Calves Through Southern Auctions	R. G. Stout	Southern Cooperative Series, Bul. 48, Agri. Expt. Sta. of Ala., Ark., Ga., Ky., La., Miss., N. C., Okla., S. C., Tenn., Va., and W. Va.
Marketing Feeder Cattle and Sheep— In North Central Region	V. J. Brensike	North Central Regional Publication 25, Univ. of Nebraska, College of Agriculture, Lincoln, Neb., 1952.
Marketing Livestock in the Corn Belt Region	Knute Bjorka Corn Belt Livestock Marketing Research Committee	Agri. Expt. Sta. Bul. 365, South Dakota State College, Brookings, S. D., 1942.
Marketing of Livestock and Meat, The	S. H. Fowler	Interstate Printers & Publishers, Danville, Ill., 1957.
Marketing Slaughter Cattle by Carcass Weight and Grade	A. A. Dowell G. Engelman E. F. Ferrin P. A. Anderson	Agri. Expt. Sta. Tech. Bul. 181, University of Minnesota, St. Paul, Minn., 1949.
Marketing Western Feeder Cattle	I. M. Stevens, et. al.	Agri. Expt. Sta. Bul. 317, University of Wyoming, Laramie, Wyo., 1952.
Market Outlets for Livestock Producers	Marketing Research Report No. 216	Agricultural Marketing Service, U. S. Department of Agriculture, Washington 25, D. C.

Title of Publication	Author(s)	Publisher
Problems and Practices of American Cattlemen	M. E. Ensminger M. W. Galgan W. L. Slocum	Wash. Agri. Expt. Sta. Bul. 562, Washington State University, Pullman, Wash., 1955.
Stockman's Handbook, The	M. E. Ensminger	Interstate Printers & Publishers, Danville, Ill., 1959.
Trade in Western Livestock at Auctions; 1, Development Relative Importance Operations	Harold Abel D. A. Broadbent	Utah Agri. Expt. Sta. Bul. 352, University of Utah, Logan, Utah, 1952.
Trade in Western Livestock at Auctions: 2, Analysis of Livestock Marketings	C. R. Harston D. C. Voorhies	Wash. Agri. Expt. Sta. Bul. 537, A Western Regional Research Pub., Washington State University, Pullman, Wash., 1952.
Trends in Prices of Purebred Cattle	A. A. Dowell Arnold Brekke	Agri. Expt. Sta. Bul. 398, University of Minnesota, St. Paul, Minn., 1948.
What Governs Livestock Prices	F. A. Kutish	Swift & Co., Agricultural Research Dept., Chicago, Ill.

CHAPTER XV

BEEF AND VEAL, AND BY-PRODUCTS FROM CATTLE SLAUGHTER

Contents   Page

Beef over the block is the ultimate objective in producing cattle; it is the end product of all breeding, feeding, care and management, marketing, and processing. It is imperative, therefore, that the progressive cattleman, the student, and the beef cattle scientist have a reasonable working knowledge of beef and veal and of the by-products from cattle slaughter. Such knowledge will be of value in selecting animals and in determining policies relative to their handling. To this end, this chapter is presented.

Of course, the type of animals best adapted to the production of meat over the block has changed in a changing world. Thus, in the early history of this country, the very survival of animals was often dependent upon their speed, hardiness, and ability to fight. Moreover, long legs and plenty of bone were

707

Fig. 265. A modern meat market. Meat over the block is the ultimate objective in producing cattle, sheep, and swine. Providing America's meat requires 216,000 retail meat dealers. (Courtesy, Meat Merchandising)

important attributes when it came time for animals to trail hundreds of miles as drovers took them to market. The Texas Longhorn was adapted to these conditions.

With the advent of rail transportation and improved care and feeding methods, the ability of animals to travel and fight diminished in importance. It was then possible, through selection and breeding, to produce meat animals better suited to the needs of more critical consumers. With the development of large cities, artisans and craftsmen and their successors in industry required fewer calories than those who were engaged in the more arduous tasks of logging, building railroads, etc. Simultaneously, the American family decreased in size. The demand shifted, therefore, to smaller and less fatty cuts of meats; and, with greater prosperity high quality steaks and roasts were in demand. To meet the needs of the consumer, the producer gradually shifted to the breeding and marketing of younger animals with maximum cut-out value of the primal cuts. The need was for a blocky conformation with short legs and a short neck. Instead of marketing large, ponderous, fat, three-to-five-year-old steers, baby beef came into prominence (see Fig. 41, p. 95).

This change in market demand is reflected in the progressively lighter weights of the grand champion steers exhibited at the International Livestock Show. For example, in the first five years of the show, beginning in 1900, the winning steers averaged 1,693 pounds in weight; whereas for the 10-year period (1948-1957) the Grand Champion Steers averaged 1,090 pounds. Thus, through the years, consumer demand has exerted a powerful influence upon the type of cattle produced. To be sure, it is necessary that such production factors as prolificacy, economy of feed utilization, rapidity of gains, size, longevity, etc., receive due consideration along with consumer demands. But once these production factors have received due weight, cattle producers—whether they be purebred or commercial operators—must remember that meat over the block is the ultimate objective.

Now, and in the future, beef producers need to select and feed so as to obtain increased marbling and tenderness, without excess fat. Already, Production Testing programs and livestock shows are being reoriented to give greater emphasis to these consumer demands.

WORLD BEEF CONSUMPTION

In general, consumption of meat is higher in new or frontier-type countries that are sparsely populated than in the older and

TABLE 66

MEAT PRODUCTION AND PER CAPITA CONSUMPTION
IN SPECIFIED COUNTRIES

Country (leading countries, by rank, of all meats, 1957)	Total Meat Production, 1957[1]	Beef and Veal Production, 1957[2]	Per Cent Beef and Veal of All Meats Consumed, 1957	Per Capita Consumption of All Meats, 1956[3]
	(million lbs.)	(million lbs.)	(%)	(lbs.)
1. United States	26,930	15,720	58.4	167
2. U. S. S. R.	10,840	4,400	40.6	—
3. *Argentina	6,380	5,545	86.9	255
4. Germany (West)	5,706	2,045	35.8	105
5. France	5,508	2,778	50.4	128
6. United Kingdom	3,752	1,826	48.7	132
7. Brazil	3,230	2,588	80.1	52
8. Australia	2,852	1,773	62.2	218
9. Canada	2,318	1,438	62.0	148
10. *Italy	2,072	962	46.4	45
11. Denmark	1,551	426	27.5	128
12. New Zealand	1,429	595	41.6	224
Total in 43 countries	95,190	49,130	51.6	

[1] *Foreign Agriculture Circular*, USDA, FAS, July 29, 1958, p. 7.
[2] *Ibid*, p. 3.
[3] *Foreign Crops and Markets*, USDA, FAS, August, 1957, p. 9.
* 1956 data; no 1957 figures available.

more densely populated regions of the world. In many of the latter areas, insufficient grain is produced to support the human population when consumed directly. This eliminates any possibility of keeping animals, except as scavengers. Certainly, when it is a choice between the luxury of meat and animal by-products or starvation, people will elect to accept a lower standard of living and go on a grain diet. In addition to the available meat supply, food habits and religious restrictions affect the amount of meat consumed.

Table 67 gives a summary of per capita meat consumption in the leading meat-eating countries of the world and shows the favored position of beef.

TABLE 67

PER CAPITA MEAT CONSUMPTION IN SPECIFIED COUNTRIES, 1957[1]

Country (leading countries by rank of all meats)	All Meats[2] (excluding lard)	Beef and Veal	Per Cent Beef and Veal of All Meats
	(lbs.)	(lbs.)	(%)
1. Argentina	242	210	87
2. New Zealand	229	113	49
3. Australia	221	127	57
4. Uruguay	168	130[3]	77
5. United States	159	93	58
6. Denmark	142	54	38
7. Canada	137	84[3]	61
8. United Kingdom	134	55[3]	41
9. France	122	64	52
10. West Germany	107	39	36

[1] *Foreign Agricultural Service*, USDA, by Mr. M. A. Drisko, Director.
[2] Beef, veal, pork, lamb, mutton, goat and horsemeat on a carcass weight basis.
[3] Excludes canned beef and veal.

UNITED STATES BEEF CONSUMPTION

Although comprising less than six per cent of the world's population and having only a tenth of its cattle, the people of the United States eat about one-fourth of the total world production of beef. This nation is the world's largest consumer of beef and veal; in 1957, we ate 16.1 billion pounds, or an average of 93.3 pounds per person.

The story of U.S. beef consumption is further presented in Table 68 and Figs. 266 and 267. From these, the following conclusions may be drawn:

TABLE 68

U. S. PER CAPITA MEAT CONSUMPTION

Year	All Meats[1]	Beef	Veal	Per Cent Beef and Veal of All Meats
	(lbs.)	(lbs.)	(lbs.)	(%)
1953[2]	155.3	77.6	9.5	56.08
1954[2]	154.7	80.1	10.0	58.24
1955[3]	162.8	82.0	9.4	56.14
1956[3]	166.7	85.4	9.5	56.93
1957[3]	159.0	84.5	8.8	58.68
5-yr. ave.	159.7	81.9	9.4	57.21

[1] Includes all red meat (beef, veal, pork, lamb, and mutton) and excludes poultry and lard.
[2] *The Livestock and Meat Situation*, March 1958, USDA, Agricultural Marketing Service, Table 4, p. 12.
[3] *The Livestock and Meat Situation*, May 1958, USDA, Agricultural Marketing Service, Table 11, p. 25.

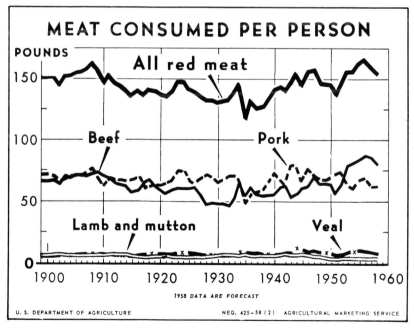

Fig. 266. Per capita meat consumption in the United States, by kind of meat, 1899-1958. As noted, the amount of meat consumed in this country varies from year to year. In recent years, the average American has consumed more beef than any other kind of meat. (Courtesy, USDA, Agricultural Marketing Service)

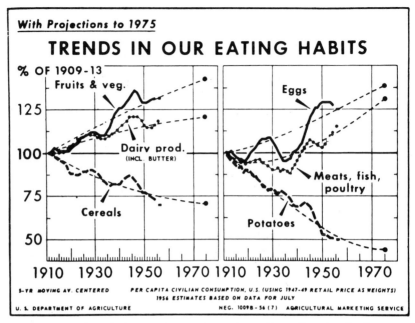

Fig. 267. Trends in our per capita consumption of major food groups, with projections to 1975. Until 1937, the long-time trend in meat consumption was downward; since then it has been upward. (Print, courtesy Washington State University)

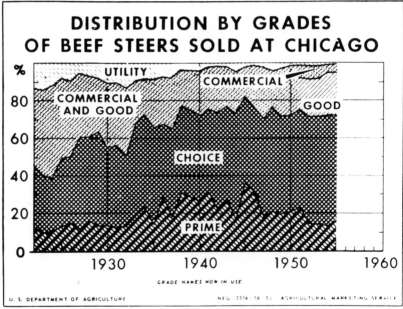

Fig. 268. The trend is for fewer very highly finished animals; less Prime and more Choice and Good. (Print, courtesy Washington State University)

1. Beef is the preferred red meat in the United States, having replaced pork in this position in the early 1950's.
2. Until 1937, the long-time trend in meat consumption was downward; since then it has been upward.
3. Meat—along with fruit and vegetables, dairy products, and eggs—continues to be the preferred food. By contrast, the consumption of cereals and potatoes has declined.

Figure 268 reveals that, over a period of years, the trend has been for fewer very highly finished cattle; that is, less Prime and more Choice and Good grades. This shift, of course, has come about by producers responding to consumer demands.

BEEF IMPORTS AND EXPORTS

Cattlemen are prone to ask why the United States, with a cattle population second only to India, buys cattle, and beef and veal, abroad. Conversely, consumers sometimes wonder why we export beef and veal. Occasionally there is justification for such fears, on a temporary basis and in certain areas, but as shown in Tables 69 and 70, this nation neither imports nor exports large quantities of cattle, beef and veal.

Table 69 reveals that the United States imports more beef than it exports. But, as shown in Table 70, total beef imports actually constitute a very small percentage of the available U. S. beef and veal.

The amount of beef imported from abroad depends to a substantial degree on (1) the level of U. S. meat production, (2) consumer buying power, (3) cattle prices, and (4) quotas and tariffs. When cattle prices are high, more meat is imported. (See

TABLE 69

U. S. IMPORTS AND EXPORTS OF BEEF AND OTHER MEATS

Year	Imports			Export		
	Beef and Veal	All Meats	Per Cent of Beef and Veal of All Meats	Beef and Veal	All Meats	Per Cent of Beef and Veal of All Meats
	(1,000 lbs.)	(1,000 lbs.)	(%)	(1,000 lbs.)	(1,000 lbs.)	(%)
1953[1]	160,099	312,467	51.31	38,731	126,960	30.51
1954[1]	125,692	302,697	41.52	33,824	99,895	33.86
1955[1]	118,514	288,303	41.11	40,664	117,918	34.48
1956[2]	111,860	258,159	43.33	89,291	175,539	50.87
1957[2]	232,461[3]	384,214[3]	60.51	88,561[3]	183,930	48.15
5-year average	149,725	309,168	47.55	58,214	140,808	39.57

[1] *Foreign Agriculture Circular*, USDA, FAS, Washington, D. C., March 16, 1956, pp. 18 & 19.
[2] *Foreign Agriculture Circular*, FLM 4–58, USDA, FAS, Washington, D. C., June 3, 1958, pp. 12 and 18.
[3] Preliminary.

TABLE 70

IMPORTS OF CATTLE, BEEF, AND VEAL COMPARED WITH U. S. PRODUCTION[1]

Year	Cattle and Beef Imports[2]	Beef and Veal Production	Beef Imports As a Percentage of Production
	(million lbs.)	(million lbs.)	(%)
Av. 1949–53	459	11,241	4.2
Annual:			
1954	261	14,610	1.8
1955	315	15,147	2.1
1956	247	16,094	1.5
1957	597	15,739	3.8

[1] *Foreign Agriculture*, USDA, FAS, August 1958, pp. 6 and 18.
[2] Including animals imported on foot converted to a dressed-weight basis.

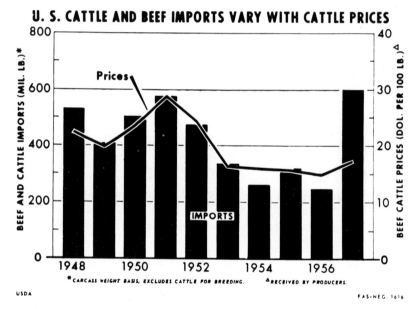

Foreign Agriculture

Fig. 269. U. S. cattle prices and beef imports go up and down together. (Print, courtesy Washington State University)

Fig. 269.) Actually, there may be some virtue in judiciously increasing imports of beef and cattle during times of scarcity and high prices, as an alternative to pricing beef out of the market. The position of butter versus oleomargarine is proof enough of this assertion, for butter was priced out of the market.

The amount of beef exported from this country is dependent upon: (1) the volume of meat produced in the United States, (2) the volume of meat produced abroad, and (3) the relative vigor of international trade, especially as affected by buying power and trade restrictions.

Our beef and veal imports come from many countries—chiefly Argentina, Uruguay, Paraguay, Brazil, New Zealand, Canada, Ireland, Australia, Mexico, Costa Rica, and the Dominican Republic. Because of restrictions designed to prevent the introduction of foot-and-mouth disease, neither fresh nor salted refrigerated beef can be imported to the United States from South America; beef importations from these countries is canned or fully cured (i.e. corned beef). Most live cattle are imported for feeding and breeding purposes and relatively few are destined for immediate slaughter. The majority of feeders come from Mexico and Canada, but some breeding cattle enter the United States from a number of countries.

The United States sends fresh and frozen beef and veal to Canada, and frozen beef to Spain, Turkey, and Israel. Canned and cured beef is exported to British Guiana, Jamaica, Surinam, the Philippines, and other countries. Also, the U. S. cattle industry depends on foreign markets to take significant quantities of such by-products as tallow and hides.

QUALITIES IN BEEF DESIRED BY THE CONSUMER

Because consumer preference is such an important item in the production of beef, it is well that the farmer and rancher, the packer, and the meat retailer be familiar with these qualities, which are summarized as follows:

1. **Palatability.**—First and foremost, people eat meat because they like it. Palatability is influenced by the tenderness, juiciness, and flavor of the fat and lean.

2. **Attractiveness.**—The general attractiveness is an important factor in selling meats to the housewife. The color of the lean, the degree of fatness, and the marbling are leading factors in determining buyer appeal. Most consumers prefer a white fat and a light or medium red color in the lean.

3. **Moderate amount of fat.**—Middle- and low-income groups discriminate against too much fat, especially when it must be trimmed heavily.

4. **Small cuts.**—Most purchasers prefer to buy cuts of meat

that are of a proper size to meet the needs of their respective families. Because the American family has decreased in size, this has meant smaller cuts. This, in turn, has had a profound influence on the type of animals and on market age and weight.

5. **Ease of preparation.**—In general, the housewife prefers to select those cuts of beef that will give her the greatest amount of leisure time. Steaks of beef can be prepared with greater ease and in less time than can roasts or stews. Hamburger and sausage are also easy to prepare.

THE FEDERAL GRADES OF BEEF

The grade of meat may be defined as a measure of its degree of excellence based on conformation, finish, and quality; factors which determine selling and eating qualities. It is intended that the specifications for each grade shall be sufficiently definite to make for uniform grades throughout the country and from season to season, and that on-hook grades shall be correlated with on-foot grades.

Both producers and consumers should know the federal grades of meats and have a reasonably clear understanding of the specifications of each grade. From the standpoint of producers—including both purebred and commercial operators—this is important, for, after all, meat over the block is the ultimate objective. From the standpoint of consumers, especially the housewife who buys most of the meat, this is important, because (1) in these days of self-service prepackaged meats there is less opportunity to secure the counsel and advice of the meat cutter when making purchases, and (2) the average consumer is not the best judge of the quality of the various kinds of meats on display in the meat counter.

The following are definitions of the grade factors as they apply to beef, both carcasses and wholesale cuts:

1. **Conformation.**—*Conformation refers to the general build, form, shape, contour or outline of the carcass, side, or cut.* Superior conformation implies a plump, stocky, or blocky carcass, with short neck and shanks, full loins, deep, plump rounds, well-fleshed ribs, and smooth shoulders. This is in contrast to ranginess and angularity. Such conformation assures retail cuts that will be shapely and have full muscles and a large percentage of edible meat to bone and that will make for the maximum cut-out value of primal cuts.

2. **Finish.**—*Finish refers to the amount, quality, and distribution of fat.* Superior finish implies a smooth, even covering of fat over most of the exterior surface of the carcass, a much thinner covering over the interior surface of the ribs, and a liberal intermixture of fat with lean, called marbling. In grading, it is recognized that the degree of finish and marbling is related to some extent to the age of the animal from which it is produced. Thus less finish and marbling is required for top-grade meats obtained from younger animals, but it is necessary that the character of the fat and the conformation and quality meet the degree of perfection required for the grade.

3. **Quality.**—*Quality refers to the eating quality of the meat and is indicated by certain characteristics of the fat and lean tissue, the bone, and the marbling.* Superior quality implies well marbled lean that is firm and fine in texture, a minimum of connective tissue, and a desirable color of lean typical of the species. The finish is also firm (not soft or oily) and the meat is produced from young animals as indicated by the bones. Quality is considered the most important of the three grade factors because it furnishes for consumers the most dependable criterion of the merit of meat.

Federally graded meats are so stamped (with an edible vegetable dye) that the grade will appear on the retail cuts as well as on the carcass and wholesale cuts. These are summarized in Table 71, for beef and veal.

Unlike meat inspection, government grading is purely voluntary, on a charge basis. In 1957, 48.76 per cent of the total

TABLE 71

FEDERAL GRADES OF BEEF AND VEAL[1]

Beef	Calf and Veal
1. Prime[2]	1. Prime
2. Choice	2. Choice
3. Good	3. Good
4. Standard	4. Standard
5. Commercial	5. Utility
6. Utility	6. Cull
7. Cutter	
8. Canner	

[1] In rolling meat, the letters "U.S." precede each federal grade name. This is important, as only government-graded meat can be so marked. For convenience, however, the letters "U.S." are not to be used in this table or in the discussion which follows.

[2] Cow beef is not eligible for the prime grade.

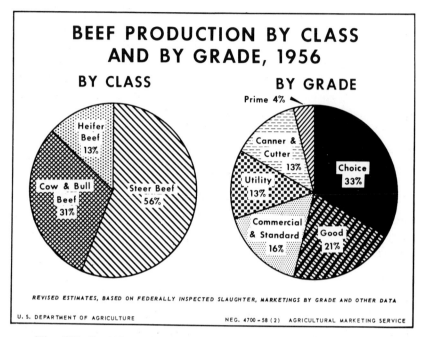

BEEF PRODUCTION BY CLASS AND BY GRADE, 1956

BY CLASS

BY GRADE

Prime 4%

Heifer Beef 13%

Cow & Bull Beef 31%

Steer Beef 56%

Canner & Cutter 13%

Utility 13%

Commercial & Standard 16%

Choice 33%

Good 21%

REVISED ESTIMATES, BASED ON FEDERALLY INSPECTED SLAUGHTER, MARKETINGS BY GRADE AND OTHER DATA

U. S. DEPARTMENT OF AGRICULTURE   NEG. 4700–58 (2)   AGRICULTURAL MARKETING SERVICE

Fig. 270. In 1956, a little more than two-thirds of all beef produced was steer and heifer beef; most of the rest was cow beef.

Because the largest part of steer and heifer beef is the equivalent of Good grade or better, close to 60 per cent of the total beef production in that year was of the three top grades. (Picture from *The Livestock and Meat Situation*, USDA, Agricultural Marketing Service, March, 1958)

U. S. production of beef was federally graded, and 17.21 per cent of the veal.

Figure 270 shows the percentage distribution of beef by classes and grades,[1] in 1956. American consumers are eating better grade beef than ever before. As shown, about 58 per cent of all beef eaten is in the three top grades—Prime, Choice, and Good—whereas, earlier, only about 50 per cent of the beef consumed was in these grades. This up-grading, of course, was brought about by producers responding to consumer demands.

Some additional and pertinent facts relative to federal grades of beef are:

1. **There is no sex differentiation between steer, heifer and cow beef.**—Federal grades make no distinction between steer,

[1]Fig. 270 does not infer that all beef was federally graded. Rather, estimates of the proportion of each grade of the total beef produced in the U. S. in 1956 were arrived at from federally inspected slaughter, marketings by grade, and other data.

heifer and cow beef. It is not intended that this should be construed to imply that there is no carcass difference between these sex classes. As a matter of fact, it is generally recognized that there is a pronounced difference between the sex classes of cattle, with a lesser difference between the sex classes of sheep and hogs. This step in simplification was taken so that it might be easier for the buyer or consumer to purchase meat on the basis of quality, without the added confusion of a more complicated system.

2. **Bull and stag beef is identified.**—Bull and stag beef is identified by class as "bull" beef and "stag" beef, respectively. Within each of these classes, there are the following six grades: (1) Choice, (2) Good, (3) Commercial, (4) Utility, (5) Cutter, and (6) Canner. However, no designated grade of bull beef or of stag beef is comparable in quality to a similarly designated grade of beef obtained from steers, heifers or cows. Neither is the quality in a designated grade of bull beef comparable to a similarly designated grade of stag beef.

3. **Lower grades seldom sold as retail cuts.**—It is seldom that the lower grades—Cutter and Canner beef, and Cull veal—are sold as retail cuts. The consumer, therefore, only needs to become familiar with the upper grades of each kind of meat.

As would be expected, in order to make the top grade in the respective classes, the carcass or cut must possess a very high degree of conformation and quality, and adequate finish. The lower grades of meats are deficient in one or more of these factors determining grade. Because each grade is determined on the basis of a composite evaluation of all three factors (conformation, finish, and quality), a carcass or cut may possess some characteristics that are common to another grade. It must also be recognized that all of the wholesale cuts produced from a carcass are not necessarily of the same grade as the carcass from which they are secured.

AGING BEEF

Except for veal, fresh beef is not at optimum tenderness immediately after slaughter. It must undergo an aging or ripening process before it really becomes tender. This process consists of the dissolution of the connective tissue (collagen) by the action of enzymes. Beef should be aged from two to six weeks at temperatures ranging from 34° to 38° F., but only the better grades can be aged for the longer periods. Beef must have a fat covering to protect the meat from bacterial action by sealing it from the air. With well-finished beef, some trimming is necessary anyway and the removal of the mold does not constitute any additional loss. The aging process may be hastened by the use of

Fig. 271. Aging beef in cooler. It should be aged from 2 to 6 weeks at temperatures ranging from 34° to 38° F. (Courtesy, American Meat Institute)

ultra-violet lights in high temperature coolers with controlled humidity.

DISPOSITION OF THE BEEF CARCASS

Beef carcasses are of two types, namely those suitable for (1) block beef and (2) processed meats.

1. **Block beef.**—Block beef refers to beef that is suitable for sale over the block. Such beef is purchased by the retailer in sides, quarters, or wholesale cuts. Block beef may enter regular channels of trade either as "fresh chilled" or "fresh frozen." Fresh chilled beef is chilled at temperatures ranging from 34° to 38° F. for a minimum of twenty-four hours before moving out to the retail trade, or it may be held longer if aging is desired. Frozen beef is subjected to temperatures of 0° F. or below and is frozen solid, in which form it can be kept for a period of several months. United States consumers prefer "fresh chilled" beef. It is estimated that 97 per cent of the block beef is so handled. On the other hand, the bulk of the export beef is frozen.

2. **Processed meats.**—Beef that is not suitable for sale over the block is (1) boned out and disposed of as boneless cuts, (2) canned, (3) made into sausage, or (4) cured by drying and smoking. It is estimated that about one-fifth of all slaughter cattle are disposed of as processed meats.

THE BEEF CARCASS AND ITS WHOLESALE CUTS

The methods of cutting beef are more varied than are found in the cutting of veal, lamb, or pork. Each area has its traditional cuts of beef. In the Midwest and West, most cutting is according to the Chicago style in which the wholesale cut known as the rib has the seven last ribs on the front quarter, thus leaving five ribs on the chuck. On the other hand, the eastern seaboard states adhere mostly to the New York style in which the rib cut includes eight ribs, and the short chuck four ribs.

In quartering beef, all thirteen ribs are left on the forequarter for the Brooklyn and Philadelphia markets; whereas three ribs are included on the hindquarter for the Boston market. Most other markets cut one rib on the hindquarter. Naturally, the number of ribs left on the hindquarter affects the percentage weight of fores and hinds. Thus, a three-rib hindquarter represents about 50 per cent of the side; one-rib hinds represent about 48 per cent of the side; whereas a hind without any ribs represents only 46 to 47 per cent of the side.

Although considerable beef is shipped to retail shops as sides and quarters, most retailers like to handle a considerable quantity of wholesale cuts because of the flexibility afforded. If steaks are in greater demand, therefore, steak-yielding cuts

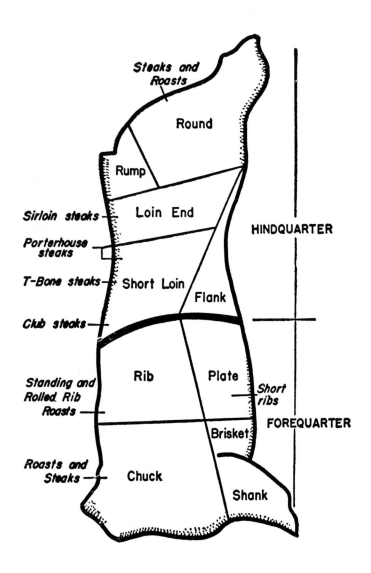

BEEF

Fig. 272. Wholesale cuts of beef and some of the common retail cuts, when cut Chicago style. (Drawing by R. F. Johnson; photo courtesy Washington State University)

may be obtained without getting an oversupply of cuts better adapted for other purposes (roasts, stews, etc.).

When cut Chicago style, the forequarter yields five wholesale cuts: chuck, rib, plate, brisket, and shank. The hindquarter is divided into five wholesale cuts: round, rump, loin end, short loin, and flank. Fig. 272 shows the wholesale cuts of a side of beef when cut according to the Chicago style.

THE VEAL CARCASS AND ITS WHOLESALE CUTS

Because veal has very little protective fat covering and is high in moisture, it does not lend itself to aging or ripening. It is therefore necessary that veal be moved into retail channels fairly rapidly.

The size of the veal carcass will determine the method of cutting. The larger carcasses (calf rather than veal carcasses) are generally halved and then quartered much like beef car-

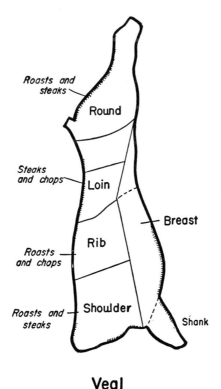

Veal

Fig. 273. Wholesale cuts of veal and some of the common retail cuts. (Drawing by R. F. Johnson)

casses, whereas practically all of the younger veal carcasses are cut into fore and hind saddles.

The fore saddle consists of that part of the carcass anterior to the twelfth rib or the two unsplit forequarters. The hind saddle consists of the two unsplit hindquarters posterior to the twelfth rib.

When the veal carcass is further divided, the common wholesale cuts from the hindquarter are the leg and loin; and from the forequarter, the rib, shoulder, breast, and shank. Figure 273 shows the common wholesale cuts of veal. The veal carcass is generally sold with the liver and sweetbread attached.

BEEF AND VEAL RETAIL CUTS AND HOW TO COOK THEM

Whether a beef carcass is cut up in the home or by an expert, it should always be cut across the grain of the muscle tissue and the thick cuts should be separated from the thin cuts and the tender cuts from the less tender cuts.

Figure 274 illustrates the wholesale and retail cuts of beef cut Chicago or Western style, the most widely used method of cutting, and gives the recommended method or methods of cooking each. Figure 275 presents similar information for veal.

In order to buy and/or process beef and veal wisely, and to make the best use of each part of the carcass, the consumer should be familiar with the types of cuts and how each should be processed.

Every grade and cut of meat can be made tender and palatable provided it is cooked by the proper method. Also, it is important that meat be cooked at low temperature, usually between 300° and 325° F. At this temperature, it cooks slowly, and as a result is juicier, shrinks less, and has a better flavor than when cooked at high temperatures.

THE NUTRITIVE QUALITIES OF BEEF

Perhaps most people eat beef simply because they like it. They derive a rich enjoyment and satisfaction therefrom.

But beef is far more than just a very tempting and delicious food. From a nutritional standpoint, it contains certain essentials of an adequate diet; high quality proteins, calories, minerals, and vitamins. This is important, for how we live and how long we live are determined in large part by our diet.

the Identification of Beef Cuts

Meat Cuts and How to Cook Them
BEEF CHART

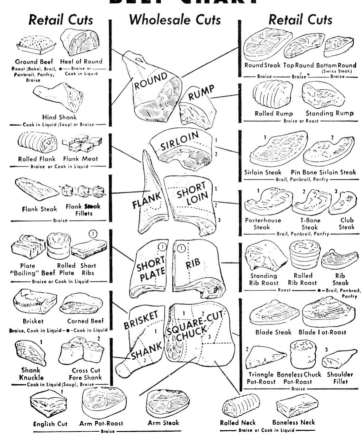

Retail Cuts | Wholesale Cuts | Retail Cuts

Ground Beef Heel of Round
Roast (Bake), Broil, ● — Braise or —
Panbroil, Panfry, Cook in Liquid
Braise

ROUND

RUMP

Hind Shank
— Cook in Liquid (Soup) or Braise —

Rolled Flank Flank Meat
— Braise or Cook in Liquid —

SIRLOIN

Flank Steak Flank Steak
Fillets
— Braise —

FLANK SHORT LOIN

Plate Rolled Short
"Boiling" Beef Plate Ribs
— Braise or Cook in Liquid —

SHORT PLATE RIB

Brisket Corned Beef
Braise, Cook in Liquid — ● — Cook in Liquid

BRISKET SQUARE-CUT CHUCK

SHANK

Shank Cross Cut
Knuckle Fore Shank
— Cook in Liquid (Soup), Braise —

English Cut Arm Pot-Roast Arm Steak
— Braise —

Round Steak Top Round Bottom Round
(Swiss Steak)
— Braise — — Braise* — — Braise —

Rolled Rump Standing Rump
— Braise or Roast —

Sirloin Steak Pin Bone Sirloin Steak
— Broil, Panbroil, Panfry —

Porterhouse T-Bone Club
Steak Steak Steak
— Broil, Panbroil, Panfry —

Standing Rolled Rib
Rib Roast Rib Roast Steak
— Roast — ● — Broil, Panbroil, Panfry

Blade Steak Blade Pot-Roast

Triangle Boneless Chuck Shoulder
Pot-Roast Pot-Roast Fillet
— Braise —

Rolled Neck Boneless Neck
— Braise or Cook in Liquid —

● Prime and choice grades may be broiled, panbroiled or panfried.

Fig. 274. The wholesale and retail cuts of beef, cut Chicago or Western style—the most widely used method of cutting—and the recommended method or methods of cooking each. (Courtesy, National Livestock and Meat Board)

the Identification of Veal Cuts

Meat Cuts and How to Cook Them
VEAL CHART

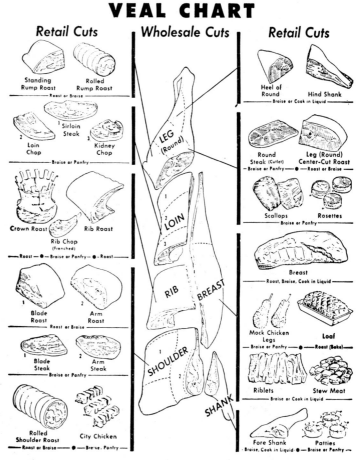

Fig. 275. The wholesale and retail cuts of veal, and the recommended method or methods of cooking each. (Courtesy, National Livestock and Meat Board)

It is estimated that the average American gets the following percentages of his food nutrients from meat:[1]

63% of his protein   42% of his vitamin B_1 (thiamine)

47% of his iron   24% of his vitamin B_2 (riboflavin)

28% of his phosphorous   79% of his niacin

(Plus generous amounts of other B vitamins—including the important B_{12})

Effective beef promotion necessitates full knowledge of the nutritive qualities of meats, the pertinent facts of which follow:

1. **Proteins.**—The word protein is derived from the Greek word "proteous," meaning "in first place." Protein is recognized as a most important body builder. Fortunately, meat contains the proper quantity and quality of protein for the building and repair of body tissues. On a fresh basis, meat contains 15 to 20 per cent protein. Also, it contains all of the amino acids, or building stones, which are necessary for the making of new tissue; and the

Fig. 276. Rib roast of beef, prepared by roasting. (Courtesy, American Meat Institute)

[1]From a study conducted by the U.S.D.A. The percentages of daily dietary allowance are based on recommendations of the National Research Council for an average 154-lb. sedentary man.

proportion of amino acids in meat almost exactly parallels that in human protein.

2. **Calories.**—Meat is a rich source of energy, the energy value being dependent largely upon the amount of fat it contains. A pound of moderately fat beef provides about 1,350 calories, or nearly half the daily energy requirement of the average adult.

3. **Minerals.**—Minerals are necessary in order to build and maintain the body skeleton and tissues and to regulate body functions. Meat is a rich source of several minerals, but is especially good as a source of phosphorus and iron. Phosphorus combines with calcium in building the bones and teeth. Phosphorus also enters into the structure of every body cell, helps to maintain the alkalinity of the blood, is involved in the output of nervous energy, and has other important duties.

Iron is necessary for the building of blood, and its presence protects against nutritional anemia. It is a constituent of the hemoglobin or red pigment of the 25 trillion or more body corpuscles. Thus, it helps to carry the life-giving oxygen to every part of the body. The average adult would be assured an adequate supply of iron if two servings of meat were taken daily along with one serving of liver each week.

4. **Vitamins.**—Thousands of years ago, people knew that certain foods possessed unique nutritive properties. For example, as early as 1500 B. C., the Egyptians and Chinese hit upon the discovery that eating livers would improve one's vision in dim light. We now know that livers furnish vitamin A, a very important factor for night vision. In fact, medical authorities recognize that night blindness, glare blindness, and poor vision in dim light are all common signs pointing to the fact that the person so affected is not getting enough vitamin A in his diet.

Meat is one of the richest sources of the important B group

TABLE 72

VITAMIN CONTENT OF FRESH BEEF[1]

Meat Product	Thiamine	Riboflavin	Niacin	Vitamin B$_{12}$
	(mg./100 grams)	(mg./100 grams)	(mg./100 grams)	(micrograms/ 100 grams)
Beef liver	0.23	3.39	13.5	51
Beef round	0.17	0.16	5.7	1.8

[1] *Nutritional Observatory*, Heinz Nutritional Research Division, Mellon Institute of Industrial Research, Vol. 14, No. 2, April, 1953.

of vitamins, especially thiamine, riboflavin, niacin, and vitamin B_{12} (See Table 72).

These B vitamins are now being used to reinforce certain foods and are indispensable in our daily diet. Thiamine stimulates appetite, prevents beriberi, aids in the utilization of carbohydrates, and promotes the health of the body cells. Riboflavin is necessary for cell oxidation and protects against nervous disorders and also liver disturbances. Niacin prevents and cures pellagra, a diet deficiency disease which formerly afflicted hundreds of thousands of persons in this country, especially in the South. Vitamin B_{12} stimulates the appetite, increases the rate of growth and the efficiency of food utilization, and is necessary for normal reproduction. Indeed, one of the reasons for the rapid decline in B vitamin deficiencies in America may well be the increased amount of meat and other B vitamin-containing foods in the daily diet.

5. **Digestibility.**—Finally in considering the nutritive qualities of meats, it should be noted that this food is highly digestible. About 97 per cent of meat proteins and 95 per cent of meat fats are digested.

We come to realize, therefore, the important part that beef is playing in the nutrition of the nation.

BEEF PRICES AND SPREAD

Some folks are prone to compare what the packer is paying for cattle on-the-hoof to what they are paying for a pound of steak over the meat counter. Vent to such feelings is sometimes manifested in political campaign propaganda, consumer boycotts, sensational news stories, and the chain-type telephone meat strike.

Is there any real justification for this often-vicious criticism? Who or what is to blame for high meat prices and for the spread?

If good public relations are to be maintained, it is imperative that each member of the beef team—the cattleman, the packer, and the retailer—be fully armed with documented facts and figures with which to answer such questions and to refute such criticisms. Also, the consumer should know the truth of the situation.

Who Controls Beef Prices; Are Profits Excessive?

On the surface, the above heading appears to pose a very controversial subject. Actually, much of it is due to misunderstanding; most folks know too little about the other fellow's business. When meat prices are high, there is a tendency on the part of the consumer to blame any or all of the following: (1) the farmer or rancher, (2) the meat packer, or (3) the meat retailer. Also, these three may blame each other. The following sections are designed to ferret out the facts relative to beef prices and profits.

BEEF PRICES AND CATTLEMEN'S PROFITS:

It is preposterous to think that nearly four million U.S. cattle producers could control prices, for cattlemen are well-known individualists and the competition between them is too great. However, some consumers feel that cattlemen, as a group, make excess profits—that they are responsible for the high price of beef. They hear that ranchers are getting 30¢ a pound for feeder calves weighing 500 pounds at weaning time, and that a cattle feeder can buy a 500-pound calf for $150.00 and sell it eight months later as a 1,000-pound steer at $250.00; so they decide that it is, indeed, a lucrative business.

Unfortunately, all too many meat consumers fail to realize that a heifer cannot be bred until she is about 1½ years of age, that the pregnancy period requires another nine months, and, finally, that the young are usually grown six to twelve months before being sold to cattle feeders, who fatten them from four months to a year. Thus, under the most favorable conditions, this manufacturing process, which is under biological control and cannot be speeded up, requires about 4 years in which to produce a new generation of market cattle. Most of these critics also fail to realize that, for various reasons, only an average of 63 out of each 100 cows bred in the U.S. wean off young; that in addition to cattle and feed costs, there are shipping charges, interest on borrowed money, death losses, marketing charges, taxes and numerous other costs, before the steer finally reaches the packer.

For the cattle, and all the expenses and services that go into their production, the cattleman gets from 19 to 38 cents of the consumer's beef dollar.[1] But these figures do not tell the whole story! They do not relate the "bedeviling" effect of well-meant imposed or threatened legislation, the shivering hours spent in the barn or shed as numb fingers attempt to bring life into a new-

---

[1]*Beef Marketing Margins and Costs*, USDA, Agricultural Marketing Service, Misc. Pub. 710, pp. 21-33.

born calf; they do not tell of droughts or of the sweat of a long work week which begins at 40 hours.

Thus, it is perfectly clear that the farmer or rancher is not receiving excessive profits in meat production. With knowledge of the above facts, and considering the long-time risks involved, it is doubtful if very many people will object to the occasional good years when the cattleman has a chance to recoup the losses he suffers during the lean years.

BEEF PRICES AND MEAT PACKERS' PROFITS:

Of course, meat packing companies, like other businesses, are owned and operated by people; and all people want to be paid for their work. Therefore, they are entitled to a fair and reasonable profit; otherwise, they would not stay in business. The only question is—do they control prices and are they making too lush profits? Here are the pertinent facts on which to base an answer to this question:

1. Packers do not and cannot control prices because there is too intensive competition between them; there are more than 4,000 meat packers in the United States.

2. From 1947-1957, meat packers' net earnings amounted to 8/10 cent per dollar of sales; for 1957, it was 7/10 cent per dollar of sales; which is not enough. By comparison, it is noteworthy that the net earnings per dollar of sales of 25 individual companies[1] in the United States averages 9.4 cents.[2]

3. From 1947-1957, the net profit of packing companies per 100 pounds of live animal averaged 24 cents; and for 100 pounds of dressed meat, it averaged 39 cents.[2] Thus, on the average, for each 1,000-pound steer purchased, the packer netted about $2.40 in profit. Certainly this is a reasonable and legitimate earning. Of course, the volume of sales (the number of animals processed in a year), the efficiency of operations, and the utilization of by-products makes it possible for the industry to operate on these comparatively small margins.

Actually, the packers' profits are so small that, were they eliminated entirely, they would have practically no effect on the

---

[1]In 1957, each of 25 individual companies in the United States made more money than the entire meat packing industry. As a whole, the net earnings of these 25 companies amounted to $7,012,900,000—or 88 times the net earnings of $79,000,000 made by all the meat packers. However, the total sales of these 25 companies, which were $74,719,400,000, were only 6.1 times the $12,075,000,000 sales of the meat packing industry.

[2]*Financial Facts About the Meat Packing Industry 1957*, published by the American Meat Institute, Chicago, Ill.

FINANCIAL FACTS ABOUT THE MEAT PACKING INDUSTRY 1956

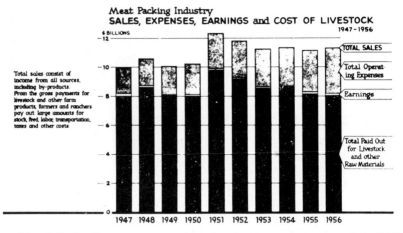

Fig. 277. On the average, meat packers' net earnings amount to 8/10 cent per dollar of sales. In 1957, 140 food processors (excluding meat) averaged 3.6 cents per dollar of sales. (Courtesy, American Meat Institute)

ultimate selling price of the retail cuts. The truth of the matter is that the meat packer is in the middle of an impossible situation; on the one hand, the nation's five million livestock producers want high prices for all the animals that they can sell, while, on the other, more than 170 million consumers desire to buy as much meat as they wish at low prices.

BEEF PRICES AND MEAT RETAILERS' PROFITS:

Finally, let us consider the meat retailer. Like the cattleman and the packer, he, too, is in business to make money; thus, he buys carcass beef at as low a price as possible and he sells the retail cuts at as high a price as consumers will pay. But does he control meat prices, and is he making excessive profits? Here are the facts:

1. In 1948, there were 251,149 retail meat outlets in the United States; by January, 1957, this number had decreased to 216,125; 35,000 meat retailers went out of business in this 10-year period. This would indicate that the meat retailer is having his problems, too.

2. On the average, year after year, the meat retailer nets less than 2 cents on each $1.00 of sales.

3. There is much competition between the 216,000 U.S. retail outlets that sell meat. As a result, no meat retailer can keep

his prices out of line for very long; otherwise, consumers will just quit patronizing his market.

4. There is an old axiom in the meat business which says "you sell it or you smell it." This simply refers to the fact that the vast majority of meats (about 75 per cent) are sold in fresh form, and that, as a perishable product, it must be moved promptly into consumption channels and sold for whatever it will bring. If the retailer attempted to get a higher price than the market afforded, the amount of the product demanded would diminish, the meat would not be sold, and it would soon spoil.

THE HOUSEWIFE CONTROLS MEAT PRICES:

From the above it should be obvious that neither the cattleman, the packer, nor the meat retailer controls meat prices. Unknowingly, the person who really dictates the price of cattle on-foot, the price of dressed beef, and the price of retail cuts is the little wife. She actually puts the price tag on the retail cuts. For purposes of illustrating her impact on meat and cattle prices, let us assume the following vital statistics: That the cattleman sells the packer a Choice grade steer at 25¢ per pound, that the packer sells the retailer the on-the-hook carcass at 40¢ per pound, and that the retailer prices porterhouse steaks at $1.10 per pound.

Mrs. Homemaker casts her "vote" at the meat counter.

Fig. 278. The housewife determines meat prices. (Photo courtesy, Swift & Co.: print courtesy Washington State University)

When the housewife walks along the counter, she, and she alone, determines what she will buy. If she feels that $1.10 a pound is too much to pay for the porterhouse steak, she simply does not buy porterhouse steak. She may buy sirloin steak or chuck pot-roast or perhaps move down the counter a few feet and buy some pork chops, or a little further down the counter she will find some broilers or perhaps some fish. She does not say anything to the retailer about his price of $1.10 being too high for the porterhouse steak. There is no organized boycott on the part of the housewives, but it does not take the retailer long to discover that his price on porterhouse steak is out of line.

If porterhouse steak will not sell at $1.10, the retailer will lower the price to $1.05 or to 99¢ a pound. He probably will try to raise the prices on some other beef cuts to take care of the loss on porterhouse steak. If he is unable to make up the deficit, there is only one thing to do and that is to tell the packer that he cannot afford to pay 40¢ a pound for carcass beef. He may tell the packer that he will pay 37¢ a pound, and in all probability the packer will refuse this offer; so the retailer will buy one side of beef instead of two; he will buy 400 pounds of pork loins instead of 300 pounds, and he may double his order for poultry. Then, in two or three days, as beef begins to back up in his coolers, the packer will probably call the retailer and make a deal with him. They may compromise on 38½¢ a pound instead of 37¢ or 40¢, and the retailer starts buying his normal quantity of beef.

If the packer cannot get 40¢ a pound for carcass beef, it does not take him very long to tell his livestock buyers that he cannot afford to pay 25¢ a pound for live steers and that they will have to cut the price to 24¢. If the run is heavy, the packer may be able to buy all the cattle he needs at 24¢, but if the run is light, he may be forced to pay 25¢, realizing that he will lose less money by paying 25¢ for steers than he will lose by not having enough work to keep his employees busy. The packer faces a dilemma; he must keep enough livestock coming into the plant to keep it in operation, but he must also buy livestock at low enough prices so that the dressed meat can be sold at a profit.

From the above, it is apparent that, as in the case of all other commodities on a free market, meat prices are determined by the laws of supply and demand; by what the consumers as a group are able and willing to pay for the available supply. In plain simple terms, this means that what you and your neighbor and all America eat tonight will determine tomorrow's beef prices.

What Determines the Spread Between On-Foot Cattle Prices and Retail Beef Prices?

When a cattleman receives a check for $250.00 for a 1,000 pound steer—25¢ a pound—and on the way home stops at a retail meat market and buys a steak at $1.00 per pound, he is prone to think that he is on the wrong side of the counter; that he ought to be a meat packer or meat retailer.

Why is there so much spread between the price of a steer on-foot and the price of a pound of steak? This is a straight-forward question which deserves a straight-forward answer. Here are the facts.

A STEER IS NOT ALL STEAK:

Cattle are not all beef, and beef is not all steak. It is important, therefore, that those who produce and slaughter animals and those who purchase wholesale and/or retail cuts know the approximate (1) percentage yield of chilled carcass in relation to the weight of the animal on foot, and (2) yield of different retail

STORY OF THE STEER

Cattle are not all beef		*Beef is not all steak*			
1000 lbs STEER	**590 lbs BEEF**	**465 lbs RETAIL CUTS**			
			lbs	Price	Total
		Porterhouse, T-Bone & Club steak	35	$1.19	$41.65
		Sirloin steak	40	1.09	43.60
		Round steak	65	.89	57.85
		Rib roast	45	.79	35.55
		Boneless rump roast	25	.99	24.75
		Chuck roast	100	.59	59.00
		Hamburger	45	.55	24.75
		Stew meat & misc. cuts	110	.65	71.50
at 29½¢ per lb...	at 45¢ per lb...	Bones, Fat, Waste & Shrink	125		1.50
Packer pays $295	**Retailer pays $265**	**Consumer pays $360**			
	Value of by-products, such as hides, fats, hair, animal feeds, fertilizer, etc., in part offsets packers' dressing, handling and selling expenses, so that the beef from a steer generally sells at wholesale for less than the live animal cost.	Retailer mark-up must cover such costs as rent, labor, depreciation on equipment and fixtures, etc., as well as trimming loss and natural shrinkage in weight of beef carcass when converted into retail cuts.			

Based on average market prices prevailing in Chicago for April, 1958

DEPARTMENT OF MARKETING
AMERICAN MEAT INSTITUTE

Chart No. 685-R1
April, 1958

Fig. 279. This shows that an average 1,000 pound steer will yield about 590 pounds of carcass or 465 pounds of retail cuts. (Courtesy, American Meat Institute)

cuts. For example, the average steer weighing 1,000 pounds on foot and grading Good will only yield 465 pounds of retail cuts (the balance consists of hide, internal organs, etc.). Thus, a little less than half of a live beef animal can be sold as retail cuts of beef. In other words, the price of beef at retail would have to be more than double the live cost even if there were no processing and marketing charges at all. Secondly, the higher priced cuts make up only a small part of the carcass. Thus, this 465 pounds will cut out only about 35 pounds of porterhouse, T-bone, and club steak. The other cuts retail at lower prices than do these choice cuts; also, there are bones, fat and cutting losses which must be considered.

INCREASED SERVICES AND ATTRACTIVENESS:

Since about 60 per cent of the nation's working women are married and the other 40 per cent are spending more time at the club, it is understandable why they want more convenience. They desire that food purchases be largely prepared for immediate cooking, for their kitchen time is limited. Thus, when the housewife buys meat, she also buys many unseen services such as trimming, boning, packaging, tenderizing and freezing. All of these services have increased the farm-to-consumer spread.

The trend toward "convenience foods" is increasing fast.

Fig. 280. Convenience foods make for higher prices. (Photo courtesy Swift & Co.; print, courtesy Washington State University)

MARKETING AND PROCESSING CHARGES
AND PROFITS:

Everyone and everything connected with the meat industry influences the spread between on-foot and retail prices. Investment capital is not free; it must yield returns comparable with other industries which compete for the use of capital. In addition, there are costs for labor, rent, supplies, transportation, and equipment. Over and above these costs, there should be a reasonable and fair profit.

What about decreasing margins by reducing the profits of the marketing agencies? The two major organizations involved are the meat packing industry and the retail stores. As previously stated, the average net profit of each—the meat packer and the meat retailer—amounting to less than one and two per cent, respectively, on each $1.00 of sales—is very small. Were profits from both businesses eliminated entirely—and if producers received all of this additional amount—cattle prices would be raised about ½-cent a pound.

Cattlemen and consumers also need to recognize that when the demand or the supply changes for beef, there is of necessity much more change in the price of live cattle than there is in the price of beef over the counter. This is so because of the tendency for marketing margins to be more fixed—that is, the costs of labor, rent, supplies, transportation and equipment do not fluctuate rapidly.

Other Factors Affecting Beef Prices and Spread

This includes those forces other than supply and demand, per se, which affect beef prices and help to explain why a steak may cost four times the price of cattle on foot.

CONSUMERS WITH HIGH INCOMES
DEMAND CHOICE CUTS AND TOP GRADES:

In periods of prosperity—when incomes are rising—consumers place a premium on the preferred kind, cut, and quality of meat, rather than any marked increase in total meat consumption. Also, people on higher incomes eat more beef, veal and lamb and less pork (Fig. 281), and they eat more of the expensive cuts of beef, such as steaks and roasts, and less stewing beef and sausage.

Also, due to the increased money available and shorter working hours, there is a desire for more leisure time, which, in turn, increases the demand for those meat cuts or products which require the minimum time in preparation. In many respects these two factors operate together; in other words, with high buying power, people hunt the choicer and easier prepared cuts of meat—

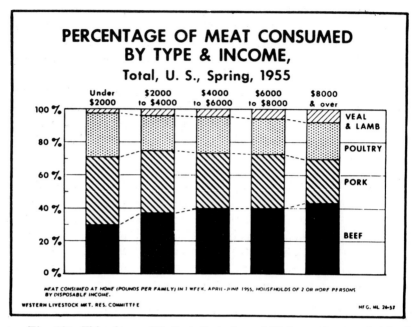

Fig. 281. This shows (1) that there is a shift in preference for beef as compared to pork, and (2) that folks in the higher income brackets prefer beef to pork. (Print, courtesy Washington State University)

porterhouse and T-bone steaks, and hamburger (the latter because of the ease of preparation).

All this suggests that producers of meat animals and processors and distributors have much to gain in periods of good times by taking steps to provide the desired kind and quality of products; by breeding for increased carcass quality, by feeding cattle to enhance grade, and by processing and preparing a higher quality and more attractive product.

NATURE MAKES FEW CHOICE CUTS AND TOP GRADES:

But the novice may wonder why these choice cuts are so scarce; even though people are able and willing to pay a premium for them. The answer is simple; nature does not make many choice cuts or top grades, regardless of price. Cattle are born with only two loins, a right and left one. The balance of the cuts are equally wholesome and nutritious, and, though there are other steaks, many of the cuts are better adapted for use as roasts, stews, and soup bones. To make bad matters worse, not all cattle are of a quality suitable for the production of steaks—for example, the meat from most "worn-out" dairy animals and thin cattle of beef breeding is not sold over the block. To be sure, the lower grades are equally wholesome and nutritious; they are simply graded down because the carcass is somewhat less desirable in conformation, finish, and quality.

Thus, when the national income is exceedingly high, there is a demand for the choicest but limited cuts from the very top but limited grades of meats. This is bound to make for extremely high prices for such grades—for the supply is limited, but the demand is great.

CONSUMER TREND TO MORE BEEF AND LESS PORK:

Another underlying trend which accentuates the price of beef is the shift in consumer preference from pork to beef. Expenditures for pork dropped from around $3\frac{1}{4}$ per cent of the consumer income in the early 1930's to about 2 per cent in 1957; whereas, during this same period, consumer expenditures for beef increased from $2\frac{1}{3}$ per cent to $2\frac{2}{3}$ per cent.[1]

Competition with Other Food Products and Services

Meat must compete with other products for the consumer's dollar. Thus, in addition to preference, relative price is an important factor.

Also, meat must compete with certain non-food items, for there are people who would go hungry in order to be able to spend their money for other purposes. On the average, consumers spend 5 to 6 per cent of their disposable income, or about 25 per cent of their food budget, for meat.

Finally, sometimes the consumer is prone to blame his budget troubles on food, and meat in particular, simply because he forgets that he is spending part of his income on things which he did not have before—including such things as TV sets, automatic dryers, and two automobiles.

Packing House By-Products from Cattle Slaughter

The meat or flesh of animals is the primary object of slaughtering. The numerous other products are obtained incidentally. Thus, all products other than the carcass meat are designated as by-products, even though many of them are wholesome and highly nutritious articles of the human diet. Yet it must be real-

[1]Engelman, Gerald and R. L. Gaarder, *Marketing Meat-Type Hogs*, USDA, Agricultural Marketing Service, Marketing Research Report 227.

ized that upon slaughter cattle, sheep, and hogs produced in the
United States yield an average of 47, 53, and 30 per cent, respectively, of products other than carcass meat. When a meat packer
buys a steer, lamb, or hog, he buys far more than the cuts of
meat that will eventually be obtained from the carcass; that is,
only about 50 per cent of a meat animal is meat.

In the early days of the meat packing industry, the only
salvaged by-products were hides, wool, tallow, and tongue. The
remainder of the offal was usually carted away and dumped into
the river or burned or buried. In some instances, packers even
paid for having the offal taken away. In due time, factories for
the manufacture of glue, fertilizer, soap, buttons, and numerous
other by-products sprang up in the vicinity of the packing plants.
Some factories were company-owned; others were independent
industries. Soon much of the former waste material was being
converted into materials of value.

Naturally, the relative value of carcass meat and by-products
varies both according to the class of livestock and from year to
year. It is estimated that packers retrieve the following percentages of the live cost of different classes of slaughter animals
from the value of the by-products: steer, 8.51 per cent; calf, 15.1
per cent; sheep, 8.15 per cent; and hog, 9.57 per cent. Sheep pelts
and cattle hides account for 3.92 and 2.61 per cent, respectively,
of the total income from these classes of animals; hog and calf
hides are sold with the carcass.[1] In recent years, tallow and hides
—two important by-products of cattle slaughter—have decreased
in value; and this in turn has been reflected in cattle prices.

In contrast to the four early-day by-products—hide, wool,
tallow, and tongue—modern cattle slaughter alone produces approximately eighty by-products which have a great variety of
uses. Although many of the by-products from cattle, sheep and
hogs are utilized in a like manner, there are a few special products which are peculiar to the class of animals (e.g., wool and
"catgut" from sheep).

The complete utilization of by-products is one of the chief
reasons why large packers are able to compete so successfully
with local butchers. Were it not for this conversion of waste material into salable form, the price of meat would be much higher

---

[1]Except for calves, figures from *Armour's Analysis*, published by Armour's Livestock Bureau, Chicago, Ill., April-August, 1958. Figure for
calves provided by Wilson & Co., in a personal communication from Vice
President G. B. Thorne to the author.

than under existing conditions. In fact, under normal conditions, the wholesale value of the carcass is about the same as the cost of the animal on foot. The returns from the sale of by-products cover all operating costs and return a reasonable profit.

It is not intended that this book should describe all of the by-products obtained from cattle slaughter. Rather, only a few of the more important ones will be listed and discussed briefly (see Figure 282).

Fig. 282. It is not within the scope of this book to picture and describe all of the products which are manufactured from by-products obtained from slaughter. Instead, Fig. 282 is presented in order to show some of the more important items for which by-products are used; items which contribute to the convenience, enjoyment and health of people in all walks of life. (Courtesy, American Meat Institute)

1. Bone for bone china.
2. Horn and bone handles for carving sets.
3. Hides and skins for leather goods.
4. Rennet for cheese making.
5. Gelatin for marshmallows, photographic film, printers' rollers.
6. Stearin for making chewing gum and candies.
7. Glycerin for explosives used in mining and blasting.
8. Lanolin for cosmetics.
9. Chemicals for tires that run cooler.
10. Binders for asphalt paving.
11. Medicines such as various hormones and glandular extracts, insulin, pepsin, epinephrine, ACTH, cortisone; and surgical sutures.
12. Drumheads and violin strings.
13. Animal fats for soap.
14. Wool for clothing.
15. Camel's hair (actually from cattle ears) for artists' brushes.
16. Cutting oils and other special industrial lubricants.
17. Bone charcoal for high-grade steel, such as ball bearings.
18. Special glues for marine plywoods, paper, matches, window shades.
19. Curled hair for upholstery. Leather for covering fine furniture.
20. High-protein livestock feeds.

1. **Hides.**—Hides are particularly valuable as a by-product of cattle slaughter. Thus most of the discussion in this section will be especially applicable to cattle hides.

Cattle hides have been used by man since the dawn of time; and leather, particularly cowhide, has held an important place in commerce throughout recorded history. It was an important part of the clothing and armour of ancient and medieval times, and today it has hundreds of industrial uses.

On the average, the hide represents 2.61 per cent of the total on-foot value of steers. There are two great classes of cattle hides, based on their place of origin; packer hides and country hides. Packer hides are the most valuable of the two because they are more uniform in shape, cure, and handling; much freer from cuts and gashes; and uniformly graded and available in larger lots.   .

The presence of needlessly large brands lowers the value of the hide. Cattle grubs (ox-warbles) also damage hides. It is estimated that one-third of all cattle hides produced in the United States are damaged by grubs. If there are five or more grub holes in the hide, it is classed as No. 2 and is discounted 1 cent per pound. Because of the larger throat cut, hides from kosher-killed cattle are less valuable.

The leather from animal hides is used for shoes, harness and saddles, belting, traveling bags, razor strops, footballs, baseball mitts, "sheepskins" for diplomas, sweat bands for hats, gloves, and numerous other leather goods.

2. **The fats.**—Next to hides and pelts, the fats (not including lard) are the most valuable by-product derived from slaughtering. Products rendered from them are used in the manufacture of oleomargarine, soaps, animal feeds, lubricants, leather dressing, candles, fertilizer, etc.

Oleomargarine, which is perhaps the best known of the products in which rendered animal fat is incorporated, is usually a mixture of vegetable oils and select animal fat.[1] Oleo oil, one

---

[1]Oleomargarine is of two kinds: (1) a mixture of 50 to 80 per cent animal fat and 20 to 50 per cent vegetable oil, churned with pasteurized skimmed milk, or (2) 100 per cent vegetable oil, churned with pasteurized skimmed milk. Oleomargarine was first perfected in 1869 by the Frenchman, Mege, who won a prize offered by Napoleon III for a palatable table fat which would be cheaper than butter, keep better, and be less subject to rancidity.

of the chief animal fats of this product, is obtained from beef and mutton or lamb.

3. **Variety meats.**—The heart, liver, brains, kidneys, tongue, cheek meat, tail, feet, sweetbreads (thymus and pancreatic glands), and tripe (pickled rumen of cattle and sheep) are sold over the counter as variety meats or fancy meats.

4. **Hair.**—Artist and camel-hair brushes are made from the fine hair on the inside of the ears of cattle. Other hair from cattle and hogs is used in tooth brushes; paint brushes; mattresses; upholstery for furniture, automobiles, and passenger planes; air filters; baseball mitts; parachute seat pads, etc.

5. **The horns and hoofs.**—At one time considered a nuisance, horns and hoofs are now converted into napkin rings, goblets, tobacco boxes, knife and umbrella handles, combs, buttons, etc.

6. **Blood.**—The blood is used in the refining of sugar, in making blood sausage and stock feeds; in making buttons, and in making shoe polish, etc.

7. **Meat scraps and muscle tissue.**—After the grease is removed from meat scraps and muscle tissue, they are made into meat-meal or tankage.

8. **Bones.**—The bones and cartilage are converted into stock feed, fertilizer, glue, crochet needles, dice, knife handles, buttons, teething rings, toothbrush handles, and numerous other articles.

9. **Intestines and bladders.**—Intestines and bladders are used as sausage, lard, cheese, snuff, and putty containers. Lamb casings are used in making surgical sutures, strings for various musical instruments, and strings for tennis rackets.

10. **Glands.**—Various glands of the body are used in the manufacture of numerous pharmaceutical preparations (see Figure 283).

Proper preparation of glands requires quick chilling and skillful handling. Moreover, a very large number of glands must be collected in order to obtain any appreciable amount of most of these pharmaceutical products. For example, the glands from more than 100,000 lambs are necessary to produce one pound of adrenalin, a powerful heart stimulant; and it takes pancreas glands from 1,500 cattle or 7,500 hogs to produce one precious ounce of insulin, and this is the only source. But, fortunately,

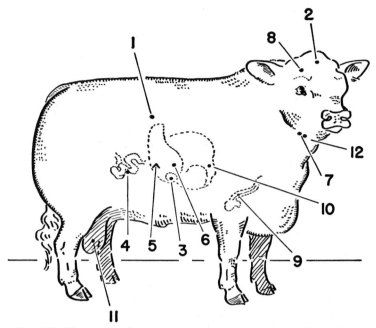

Fig. 283. Meat animals are the source of more than 100 medicines and medical products, which doctors and veterinarians administer daily to millions of people and animals to save lives, battle disease, relieve pain, and restore health. This figure shows the approximate location of a few of the glands and other tissues used in the manufacture of some of the pharmaceutical products of human and veterinary medicine. (Drawing by R. F. Johnson. Also, the author gratefully acknowledges the helpful suggestions of the following authorities who reviewed this figure and caption: P. A. Klavano, D.V.M. and Pharmacologist, and W. M. Dickson, Physiologist; both are staff members of the College of Veterinary Medicine, Washington State University)

1. **Adrenal (suprarenals).**—Source of (1) epinephrine (used for asthma, hay fever, allergies and shock), and (2) adrenal cortex extract (used for Addison's Disease, and in post surgical and burn shock).

2. **Brain.**—Source of kephalin (or cephalin), used on oozing surfaces to check bleeding.

3. **Gall Bladder.**—Source of (1) bile salts and (2) dehydrocholic acid—used for gall bladder disturbances and abnormalities of fat digestion, and (3) cortisone (used for rheumatic fever, arthritis, various allergies, inflammatory eye diseases, etc.).

4. **Intestines.**—Lamb intestines are used for surgical sutures.

5. **Liver.**—Source of (1) liver extract (used for pernicious anemia), and (2) heparin (used to delay clotting of shed blood of ulcers and following surgery).

6. **Pancreas.**—Source of (1) insulin (the only substance known to medical science which can control diabetes), (2) trypsin (the protein-digesting enzyme), (3) amalase (the starch-splitting enzyme), and (4) lipase (the fat-splitting enzyme). Each enzyme is used for digestion of these respective nutrients; and trypsin is also used to soften scar tissue or digest necrotic tissue in wounds and ulcers.

7. **Parathyroid.**—Parathyroid extract is used for tetany, which follow~ removal of these glands.

8. **Pituitary.**—Source of (1) posterior pituitary extract (used to increase blood pressure during shock, to promote uterine contraction during and after childbirth, and to control excessive urination of diabetes insipidus), and (2) ACTH (used for rheumatic fever, arthritis, acute inflammation of eyes and skin, acute alcoholism, severe asthma, and hay fever and other allergy conditions).

9. **Red Bone Marrow.**—Bone marrow concentrates used in treatment of various blood disorders.

10. **Stomach.**—Source of rennin, used to aid milk digestion.

11. **Testes.**—Source of the enzyme hyaluronidase.

12. **Thyroid.**—Thyroid extract is used for mal-functions of the thyroid gland (some goiters, cretinism and myxedemal).

13. **Blood.**—Source of thrombin, applied locally to wounds to stop bleeding.

14. **Bones and Hides.**—Source of gelatin, used as a plasma extender.

15. **Lard.**—With 1% benzoin added, it produces Benzoinated Lard, which is used as a medical ointment base.

only minute amounts of insulin are required—the insulin from two hogs per day, or from seven hundred and fifty hogs per year, will suffice for each diabetic.

11. Collagen.—The collagen of the connective tissues—sinews, lips, head, knuckles, feet, and bones—is made into glue and gelatin. The most important use for glue is in the woodworking industry. Gelatin is used in baking, ice cream making, capsules for medicine, coating for pills, photography, culture media for bacteria, etc. About 50 per cent of the United States production of gelatin comes from veal.

12. Contents of the stomach.—Contents of the stomach are used in making fertilizer.

Thus, in a modern packing plant, there is no waste; literally speaking, "everything but the squeal" is saved. These by-products benefit the human race in many ways. Moreover, their utilization makes it possible to slaughter and process beef at a much lower cost. But this is not the end of accomplishment! Scientists are continually striving to find new and better uses for packing house by-products in an effort to increase their value.

QUESTIONS FOR STUDY AND DISCUSSION

1. Why should the cattleman have a reasonable working knowledge of the end products, beef and veal?

2. Consumer studies indicate the following transition in preferences relative to beef:

   (1) Preference for more red meat and less fat.

   (2) Preference for more highly processed meat; that is, meat that is boned-out, trimmed, etc., prior to purchase.

   (3) Preference for more frozen meat.

   Discuss the impact of each of these trends from the standpoint of the producer, the processor, and the consumer.

3. What factors account for the favored position of beef in world meat consumption?

4. What factors contributed to beef taking the lead over pork in U.S. per capita consumption?

5. Should the U.S. import beef? Should we have cattle and beef quotas and tariffs?

6. Should the U.S. export beef?

7. What qualities do you desire in beef? Are these qualities reflected adequately in the top federal grades of beef?

8. Do you approve of federal grading of beef? Justify your answer.

9. Why do most consumers prefer beef that has been properly aged?

10. Discuss the relationship of choice of retail beef cuts and method of cookery.

11. What facts relative to the nutritive qualities of beef are important in effective beef promotion?

12. Choose and debate either the affirmative or negative to each of the following questions:

    (1) Beef prices are controlled by (a) the cattleman, (b) the packer, or (c) the retailer.

    (2) Excessive profits are made by (a) the cattleman, (b) the packer, or (c) the retailer.

13. Discuss the factors that determine the spread between on-foot cattle prices and retail beef prices.

14. How can small local slaughterers without the benefit of modern by-product processing facilities compete with larger packers?

SELECTED REFERENCES

Title of Publication	Author(s)	Publisher
Animal Science	M. E. Ensminger	Interstate Printers & Publishers, Danville, Ill. 1960
Adventures in Diet	Vilhjalmur Stefanson	Reprinted from Harper's Magazine by the Institute of American Meat Packers, (Now American Meat Institute) 59 Van Buren St., Chicago, Ill.
Beef and Veal Grading in Canada	H. J. Maybee	Canada Department of Agriculture, Ottawa, Canada.
Beef Marketing Margins and Costs	Misc. Pub. 710	U. S. Department of Agriculture, Washington, D. C., 1956.
By-Products in the Packing Industry	R. A. Clemen	University of Chicago Press, Chicago, Ill., 1927.
Federal Beef Grading	Misc. Pub. 391	U. S. Department of Agriculture, Washington, D. C.
Financial Facts About the Meat Packing Industry		American Meat Institute, 59 East Van Buren St., Chicago 5, Ill.
Inspection Stamp as A Guide to Wholesome Meat, The	Ag. Information Bul. 92	U. S. Department of Agriculture, Washington, D. C.
Meat Inspection, Regulations Governing the, of the United States	U. S. D. A.	U. S. Government Printing Office, Washington, D. C.
Meat for the Family	J. J. Wanderstock J. I. Miller	Cornell Extension Bul. 732, 1947, Cornell Univ., Ithaca, N. Y.
Meat for the Table	Sleeter Bull	McGraw-Hill Book Co., New York, 1951.
Meat Reference Book		American Meat Institute, 59 East Van Buren St., Chicago 5, Ill.
Meat We Eat, The	P. Thos. Ziegler	Interstate Printers & Publishers, Danville, Ill., 1958.
Official United States Standards for Grades of Carcass Beef		U. S. Department of Agriculture, Washington, D. C.
Stockman's Handbook, The	M. E. Ensminger	Interstate Printers & Publishers, Danville, Ill., 1959.
Ten Lessons on Meat for Use in Schools	Department of Home Economics	National Live Stock and Meat Board, 407 South Dearborn St. Chicago, Ill.
Spread Between Prices of Livestock and Meat, The	J. C. Bottum	Swift & Co., Agri. Research Dept., Chicago, Ill.
U. S. Grades for Beef	Leaflet 310	U. S. Department of Agriculture, Washington, D. C.

Also, literature on meats may be secured by writing to meat packers and processors and trade organizations; in particular, the following two trade organizations:

American Meat Institute
59 E. Van Buren Street
Chicago 5, Illinois

National Live Stock and Meat Board
407 South Dearborn Street
Chicago, Illinois

CHAPTER XVI

SELECTING, FITTING, AND SHOWING BEEF CATTLE[1]

Contents

Just as every good salesman advertises his wares, the producer of beef cattle may find it advantageous to exhibit his best animals where they may be seen and admired by potential buyers. The great livestock shows throughout the land have exerted a profound influence in breed improvement. Here the exhibitor is afforded an opportunity to compare his cattle with those of his fellow breeders and to exchange ideas. There is no higher achievement than that of breeding and fitting a champion—an animal representing an ideal, which has been produced through intelligent breeding and then fitted to the height of perfection.

[1]Acknowledgement, with sincere thanks is given to the following competent cattle showmen who reviewed Chapter XVI: Mr. Joshua Briglands, Herdsman, Marellbar Farm, Libertyville, Ill.; Mr. Wm. Bennett, Jr., Herdsman, Washington State University, Pullman, Wash.; Mr. Dave Foster, Seretary, Washington Cattlemen's Assn., Ellensburg, Wash.; and Mr. Henry Fisher, Jr., Belmont, Wash.

The beginner may well start with the showing of one or more baby beef calves and then gradually expand as his experience justifies. Boys and girls 4-H Club work and boys FFA projects have afforded an unusual opportunity for such training. It is primarily with the hope of furthering the interest and training of the amateur that this chapter is presented.

ADVANTAGES OF SHOWING

Human nature being what it is, not all exhibitors share equally in the many advantages that may accrue from showing livestock. In general, however, the following reasons may be advanced for exhibiting animals:

1. It affords the best medium yet discovered for molding breed type. For this reason, it behooves the breed registry associations and the purebred breeders alike to accept their rightful responsibility in seeing that the animals winning top honors are those which most nearly meet the efficiency of production requirements of the producer and the meat quality demands of the consumer.

2. It provides an incentive to breed better animals, for the breeder can determine how well he is keeping pace with his competitors only after securing an impartial appraisal of his entries in comparison with others.

3. It offers an opportunity to study the progress being made within other breeds and classes of livestock.

4. It serves as one of the very best advertising or promotional mediums for both the breed and the breeder.

5. It gives breeders an opportunity to exchange ideas, thus serving as an educational event.

6. It offers an opportunity to sell a limited number of breeding animals.

7. It sets sale values for the animals back home, for such values are based on the sale of show animals.

SELECTING SHOW CATTLE

The success or failure attained in the show-ring depends to a great extent upon the animals selected. Inasmuch as several months are required to bring an animal into the peak of show condition, the selection of animals for the show should be made as early in the season as possible. The essential points to be considered are type, age, and breeding.

Type

Requiring as it does a projection into the future, no judging assignment is quite so difficult as that of selecting an animal for

Fig. 284. No judging assignment is quite so difficult as that of selecting show animals for further development, for it requires a projection into the future. (Drawing by R. F. Johnson)

further development. In general, the animal selected should be close to the ground; should be wide, deep, and compact of body; should have good lines and plenty of smoothness; and should stand on straight legs which are placed at each corner. The head should be wide, short, and broad muzzled—an indication of a good feeder. In addition, there should be a proper balance and blending of all parts, and the animal should be stylish and showy.

Age and Show Classification

It is desirable to select a calf as old as possible within the respective age classifications so that the animal may show to the best possible advantage.

Distinct and separate show classifications are provided for breeding animals and for fat steers.

1. **Breeding Beef Cattle.**—Practically all the major cattle shows throughout the country now have breeding classifications with January 1, May 1, and September 1 as the base dates. Thus the premium list of most major shows held in the fall of 1958 provided the individual classes indicated in Table 73.

In addition to providing for individual classifications for each sex as shown in Table 73, the major shows also make provision for championships and for various group classes. Since these differ somewhat between both shows and breeds, no attempt will be made to list them herein. Instead, the showman is admonished to study the premium list of the show or shows in which he plans

TABLE 73

HANDY SHOW CLASSIFICATION FOR BREEDING ANIMALS
OF BEEF BREEDS

Class (with similar but separate classes for bulls and heifers)	Age as Specified for Major Shows in 1958		
	Herefords	Shorthorns	Aberdeen-Angus
Two-year-olds	May 1 to Aug. 31, 1956 (applies to bulls only; no 2-year-old heifer class)	May 1, 1955 to April 30, 1956	Jan. 1 to April 30, 1956 (applies to bulls only; 2-year-old heifers calved between May 1 and Aug. 31, 1956)
Summer-senior yearlings			May 1 to Aug. 31, 1956 (applies to bulls only)
Senior yearlings	Sept. 1 to Dec. 31, 1956	May 1, to Dec. 31, 1956	Sept. 1 to Dec. 31, 1956 (applies to bulls only; sr. yearling heifers calved between Sept. 1 and Dec. 31, 1956)
Junior yearlings	Jan. 1 to April 30, 1957	Jan. 1 to April 30, 1957	Jan. 1 to April 30, 1957
Summer yearlings	May 1 to Aug. 31, 1957	May 1 to Aug. 31, 1957	May 1 to June 30, 1957
Summer yearlings			July 1 to Aug. 31, 1957
Senior calves	Sept. 1 to Oct. 31, 1957	Sept. 1 to Dec. 31, 1957	Sept. 1 to Oct. 31, 1957
Senior or winter calves	Nov. 1 to Dec. 31, 1957		Nov. 1 to Dec. 31, 1957
Junior calves	Jan. 1 to Feb. 28, 1958	After Jan. 1, 1958	After Jan. 1, 1958
Spring calves	After Mar. 1, 1958		

to exhibit. Entries must be made for both individual and group classifications, but no entries for championship classes are required.

2. **Fat Steers.**—The fat steer classification varies considerably, with some shows following weight divisions and others age divisions. Each system has its advocates. The 1957 Chicago International, America's premier fat stock show, used the following fat steer age divisions, with dental requirements for each class as specified[1]:

(1) Junior Yearling; calved between Jan. 1, and Apr. 30, 1956. A junior yearling may have the two center temporary incisor teeth replaced by permanent incisors. The

---

[1] With similar classifications for (1) each of the three leading beef breeds, and (2) interbreed competition. All steers are mouthed by a veterinarian and must meet the dental requirements indicated.

Fig. 285. Grand Champion carload (15 head) fat cattle at the Chicago International. Bred by T. O. Ranch, Raton, New Mexico, and fitted and shown by Karl Hoffman, Ida Grove, Iowa. (Courtesy, American Hereford Association)

remaining six temporary incisors must be in place and there may be no evidence of eruption of any permanent incisors other than the centers.

(2) Summer Yearling; calved between May 1, and Aug. 31, 1956. A summer yearling must have all eight temporary incisor teeth in place. There may be no evidence of eruption of any permanent incisors.

(3) Senior Calf; calved between Sept. 1, and Dec. 31, 1956. A senior calf must have all eight temporary incisor teeth firmly in place. There may be no evidence of eruption of any permanent incisors.

(4) Carloads; in most shows carloads of fat cattle consist of fifteen head of animals of either sex. At the Chicago International, the following weight divisions were used in the carloads:

    a. Under 1,050 pounds

    b. 1,050 and under 1,150 pounds

    c. 1,150 pounds and over

Breeding

Animals selected for show should always be from good ancestry, for this is added assurance of satisfactory future development.

FEEDING FOR THE SHOW

All animals intended for show purposes must be placed in a high state of condition. With breeding animals, this may be detrimental; nevertheless, custom decrees that a premium be placed on condition in the show-ring. Above all, steers must be fat. The essentials in feeding cattle for the show might be described as similar to those in feeding steers for market, except that more attention must be given to the smallest details. A suitable ration must be selected and the animal or animals must be fed with care over a sufficiently long period.

Rules of Feeding Show Cattle

Some general rules of feeding may be given, but it must be remembered that *the eye of the master fattens his cattle*. The most successful cattle fitters have worked out systems of their own through years of practical experience and close observation and do not follow certain set rules. Nevertheless, the beginner may well profit by the experience of successful fitters, and it is with this hope that the following general rules of feeding show cattle are presented.

1. **Practice economy, but avoid false economy.**—Although the ration should be as economical as possible, it must be remembered that condition is the primary objective, even at somewhat additional expense. In the first place, young animals either should be allowed to nurse as long as possible or fed a milk replacer,[1] perhaps to 15 months of age, because nothing seems to produce quite the bloom that milk does. Nurse cows are costly, but they are used by most successful herdsmen in fitting young animals. Moreover, the feeding of a good grain ration should begin as early as possible. Before weaning, a ration of equal parts of ground corn, ground oats, and wheat bran will be found satisfactory. Under some conditions, a reliable commercial feed may be economical, but roughages should usually be home grown.

2. **Use care in getting animals on feed.**—In starting animals

---

[1]For instructions relative to feeding milk replacer, see the section on this subject in Chapter IX of this book.

on feed, use extreme caution to see that they do not get digestive disturbances. Animals that are not accustomed to grain or other concentrates must be started on feed gradually, or serious digestive trouble may result. Until the animal gets on full feed, at no time should it be given more grain than can be cleaned up in about thirty to sixty minutes' time. In starting, a safe plan is to feed not more than *1 pound of grain at the first feed, or 2 pounds for the day. This may be increased approximately by ¼ to ½ pound daily until the animal is on full feed 2 to 4 weeks later.* From the beginning, it is safe to full-feed grass hay or the hay to which the animal is accustomed. Oats is the best concentrate for the beginning ration. As the grain feed is increased according to the directions given, gradually (1) replace the oats with the mixed ration selected, and (2) decrease the hay. Whenever the calf does not seem to have a good appetite and does not clean up the grain within an hour's time, the allowance should be reduced for the next few days and then gradually worked up to a full feed again. With careful observation and good judgment, it is possible to have an animal on practically full feed in two or three weeks' time. After full feeding is reached, the animal may be fed according to either of two plans: (1) by governing the allowance by the amount of feed that the animal will clean up in about thirty to sixty minutes' time,[1] or (2) by more or less self-feeding, with some feed being kept before the animal most of the time. Perhaps, in the final analysis, the method of feeding decided upon should vary according to the individual feeder.

Ordinarily it is best to start the animal on feed with grass hays and then gradually change to legumes, if legumes are to be included in the ration. By this method, the animal may be allowed a full feed of hay at the beginning of the feeding period with no danger of scouring. When forced feeding is being sought, it is usually preferable to use a grass hay or a mixed hay with a limited amount of legume in it because of the laxative effect of a legume under heavy feeding and possible bloat trouble.

3. **Provide a variety of feeds.**—A good variety of feeds increases the palatability of the ration and makes it easier to supply the proper balance of nutrients. Futhermore, a fattening ration consisting of only one or two feeds may lose its palatability during a long feeding period.

---

[1]One of the nation's most successful fitters feeds his show steers three times daily in amounts that will be cleaned up in twenty minutes time at each feeding.

4. **Feed a balanced ration.**—A balanced ration will be more economical and will result in better gains. That is to say, the ration should contain the proper balance of proteins, fats, and carbohydrates. It must also be remembered that a growing animal requires more grain than a mature one. Then, too, because of their high cost, it is not economical under most conditions to feed more proteins than are required.

5. **Do not overfeed.**—Feed plenty but do not overfeed. Overfeeding is usually caused by the desire of the inexperienced caretaker to push the animal too rapidly. After the calf has reached full feed, he may be given all the grain that he will clean up, provided that the appetite and well-being of the animal seem to so warrant and that the droppings are of the proper consistency.

6. **Do not underfeed.**—It never pays to starve a calf. Gains and profits result from feeds consumed in excess of the maintenance requirement. A common expression among cattle feeders is: "Get every bit of feed under their hides that you can." When animals are consuming too little grain to fatten, the feeder may look for several causes, such as the consumption of too much roughage, unpalatability of the ration, or discontentment on the part of the animal—that is, if the caretaker is not deliberately withholding grain (false economy).

7. **Full feed for economical fattening.**—When on full feed, the average animal will eat from 1½ to 2½ pounds of grain for each 100 pounds of live weight. The exact amount will depend primarily upon the age, size, and individuality of the animal; the bulkiness and palatability of the ration; and the amount of fat that the animal is carrying. A full feed of grain is the amount that an animal will clean up nicely in ½ to 1 hour's time at each feeding period.

8. **Supply palatable feeds.**—In order to consume the maximum amount, the animal must relish the feed. Unpalatable feeds may be fed in limited quantities, provided that they are mixed with more palatable ingredients. Blackstrap molasses is relished by animals and is excellent for increasing the palatability of the ration (although blackstrap molasses is preferable, beet molasses is satisfactory). Usually the molasses is added by diluting with water and mixing it with the grain ration just before feeding. One half to one pint of molasses diluted with an equal volume of water will be entirely satisfactory for this purpose. Most com-

mercial feeds contain some molasses in the mixture. Cooking certain feeds, especially barley, also makes for increased palatability.

9. **Provide succulent feeds.**—Succulence is provided in such feeds as silage, root crops, and grasses. These feeds have a beneficial effect in the ration. They increase the palatability and produce a laxative and cooling effect on the animal's digestive system. When no provision for succulent feed is made, the animal is likely to become dry of hair and hide, constipated, and unthrifty in appearance.

10. **The ration must not be too bulky.**—The beef animal is a ruminant, and, therefore, requires considerable bulk in order to distend the digestive tract. Mature animals can handle more roughage than calves. Furthermore, more bulk may be fed at the beginning of the fattening period than at the end. As the grain ration is increased, the animal will consume less roughage. When on full feed, 3 to 6 pounds of hay daily is ample. Consumption of too much bulk will cause the animal to become paunchy and will lower the dressing percentage.

11. **Do not feed damaged feeds.**—Moldy, musty, or spoiled feeds may cause serious digestive disturbances and should not be fed to animals being fitted for show or sale.

12. **Prepare grains.**—The grain ration of cattle intended for show purposes is almost always coarsely ground or crushed. Most herdsmen prefer steamed rolled grains. The preparation of hay is neither necessary nor advisable.

13. **Feed regularly.**—Animals intended for show should be fed with exacting regularity. In the earlier part of the feeding period, two feedings per day may be adequate. Later the animals may be fed three or even four times a day, particularly if they are rather thin and rapid improvement in condition is desired.

14. **Avoid sudden changes.**—Sudden changes in either the kind or amount of feed are apt to cause digestive disturbances. Any necessary changes should be gradual.

15. **Provide minerals.**—All animals should be given free access to salt at all times. For feeding where the salt is not exposed to the weather, loose salt, rock salt, and block salt are all satisfactory. Loose salt, however, is probably preferred if kept under shelter. Stabilized iodized salt should be used in iodine-deficient areas.

When a non-legume roughage is provided, it is especially likely that there will be a deficiency of calcium and phosphorus. Under these conditions and even when a legume roughage is used, the addition of calcium and phosphorus gives protection at very little cost. Probably as satisfactory and inexpensive a mineral as can be provided for cattle is feeding steamed bone meal. It may be placed in a mineral box to which the animals have free access. The best arrangement is to provide a double-compartment mineral box with salt in one side and steamed bone meal (or preferably a mixture of $\frac{1}{3}$ salt and $\frac{2}{3}$ bone meal) in the other.

16. **Keep the animal quiet and contented.**—Quiet and contentment are necessary for profit in the feed lot. The restless animal rarely makes good gains, whereas the quiet animal that will "eat and lie down" will show superior gains. This is not due to differences in digestive or assimilative powers, but rather to the fact that the quiet animal is putting on fat while the wild, nervous animal is using surplus energy for nonproductive purposes. Uncomfortable quarters, isolation from other animals, annoyance by parasites, sudden changes in quarters or feeds, improper handling, and unnecessary noise, are the most common causes of discontentment.

17. **Provide exercise.**—A certain amount of exercise is necessary in order to promote good circulation and to increase the thrift and vigor of the animal. Exercise also tends to stimulate the appetite and makes for greater feed consumption. Animals can usually be kept in condition by turning them in a paddock at night.

18. **Avoid scouring.**—If the droppings are too thin or there is scouring, (1) decrease the grain allowance, and (2) clean up the quarters. If trouble still persists, decrease the legume roughage and the protein supplement (especially linseed oil meal).

19. **Avoid sudden water changes.**—Frequently show cattle fail to drink enough water while at the fair. As a result, they become gaunt and show at a disadvantage. Usually this situation is caused by (1) the sudden change in drinking from a trough or tank at home to drinking out of a bucket at the show, and (2) the different taste of the water. This problem can be alleviated by (1) getting the animal accustomed to drinking from the same bucket that will be used at the fair, beginning 7 to 12 days before leaving home, and (2) adding a tiny bit of molasses

to each bucket of water, from the time bucket watering is started until the show is over, thus avoiding any flavor or taste change in the water.

Some Suggested Rations

Variations can and should be made in the rations, depending upon the individual animal, the relative prices of feeds, and the supply of home-grown feeds. To secure a high state of condition, a suitable ration must be selected and the animal or animals must be fed with care over a sufficiently long period. The rations listed are ones that have been used by successful showmen. They are higher in protein content than rations used in commercial fattening operations, but most experienced herdsmen feel that by such means they get more bloom. In general, when show animals are being forced fed on any one of these concentrate mixtures, experienced herdsmen prefer to feed a grass hay or a grass-legume mixed hay to a straight legume, because of the laxative effect and possible bloat hazard of the latter.

Rations 1 to 5 are bulky. They are recommended for use in starting prospective show animals on feed. Rations 6 to 11 are less bulky and more fattening. They are recommended for use

Ration No. 1

Ground barley	50 lbs.
Crushed oats	20 lbs.
Wheat bran	20 lbs.
Protein supplement[1]	10 lbs.

Ration No. 2

Ground corn	20 lbs.
Ground barley	30 lbs.
Crushed oats	20 lbs.
Wheat bran	20 lbs.
Protein supplement[1]	10 lbs.

Ration No. 3

Crushed oats	30 lbs.
Ground barley	30 lbs.
Ground corn	10 lbs.
Wheat bran	20 lbs.
Protein supplement[1]	10 lbs.

Ration No. 4

Crushed oats	30 lbs.
Ground corn	60 lbs.
Protein supplement[1]	10 lbs.

Ration No. 5

Ground corn	40 lbs.
Crushed oats	30 lbs.
Wheat bran	20 lbs.
Protein supplement[1]	10 lbs.

Ration No. 6

Ground corn or sorghum chop	50 lbs.
Ground barley	40 lbs.
Protein supplement[1]	10 lbs.

Ration No. 7

Ground corn	60 lbs.
Crushed oats	20 lbs.
Dry beet pulp	10 lbs.
Protein supplement[1]	10 lbs.

Ration No. 8

Ground corn	40 lbs.
Ground barley	20 lbs.
Crushed oats	10 lbs.
Dry beet pulp	10 lbs.
Wheat bran	10 lbs.
Protein supplement[1]	10 lbs.

---

[1]See footnote next page

Ration No. 9
Crushed oats _____ 25 lbs.
Ground barley _____ 20 lbs.
Ground wheat _____ 20 lbs.
Ground corn _____ 20 lbs.
Wheat bran _____ 10 lbs.
Protein supplement[1] ____ 5 lbs.

Ration No. 10
Ground barley _____ 35 lbs.
Crushed oats _____ 20 lbs.
Ground wheat _____ 20 lbs.
Dry beet pulp _____ 15 lbs.
Protein supplement[1] _____ 10 lbs.

Ration No. 11
Rolled barley _____ 20 lbs.
Rolled corn _____ 20 lbs.
Rolled oats _____ 20 lbs.
Whole barley (dry wt.
  basis, but cooked before
  feeding) _____ 13 lbs.
Beet pulp, dried molasses _ 4 lbs.
Wheat bran _____ 6 lbs.
Commercial Supplement __ 8 lbs.
Linseed oil meal (pellets) _ 8 lbs.
Salt _____ 1 lb.

[1]The protein supplement may consist of linseed, cottonseed, peanut, or soybean cake—with pea-size cake preferred to meal—or a commercial supplement may be used. With most herdsmen, linseed oil meal is the preferred protein supplement. It gives the animal a sleek hair coat and a pliable hide. However, it is a laxative feed. Caution should be exercised in feeding it.

Although it is true that an animal getting good clover or alfalfa hay needs less protein supplement than does one eating non-leguminous roughage, it is not possible to supply all the needed protein with hay and still get enough grain into young animals to fatten them quickly.

during the latter part of the fitting period.

Ration 11 is used in fitting show steers at Washington State University. The cooked barley is prepared by (1) adding water in the proportion of 2 to 2½ gallons to each gallon of dry barley, and (2) cooking until the kernels are thoroughly swelled and can be easily crushed between the thumb and forefinger. Each steer also receives 4 pounds daily of a nurse cow replacer (or milk replacer). As the animal approaches show finish, the ration is changed by decreasing the rolled barely by 7 pounds and increasing the rolled oats by 5 pounds and the wheat bran by two pounds.

EQUIPMENT FOR FITTING AND SHOWING CATTLE

Every showman should have a durable and attractive box in which to keep the necessary equipment. The attractiveness of the exhibit can be enhanced by the presence of a nicely painted box on which the name of the exhibitor is neatly printed.

The equipment for the show may include the following: brushes, liners or currycombs, Scotch-combs, material and cloth for polishing horns and hoofs, soap, bluing, rasp, knife, blankets, rope halters, neat russet leather halters, show sticks, a small can of oil, clippers, water buckets, feed boxes, and articles for the personal use of the caretaker. It may also be well to include a small amount of epsom salts, raw linseed oil, mineral oil, and iodine. The size of the box and the amount of equipment one carries will depend upon the number of cattle being shown and the length of the show circuit.

A Rope Halter and How to Make It[1]

Attractive leather halters with lead straps and chains are ideal for showing cattle, but they are rather expensive. Rope halters are much more practical for everyday use and, if neatly made, are quite attractive in the show-ring.

MATERIALS NEEDED:

The following materials are needed for making a rope halter:

1. **Rope.**—Thirteen feet (15 ft. when making halters to use in breaking cattle to lead, thereby having a longer lead) of 3-strand manila rope. Use ½-inch rope for cattle over 6 months of age and ⅜-inch rope for calves under 6 months.

2. **Marlinspike.**—This is needed for opening up the strands of rope. It may be made by taking a piece of ¾-inch round, hardwood stick 6 inches long, and tapering it to a point on one end; or a small pointed piece of iron may be used.

3. **Measure and pencil.**—A rule or tape and a pencil.

DIRECTIONS FOR MAKING:

Here are the directions for making an Eye-Loop Rope Halter (See Fig. 286), which is adjustable in every respect except for the nose band. This type of halter keeps its adjustments; by contrast, the Double-Loop Rope Halter is objectionable for use in tying because it adjusts too easily with the result that many tied calves free themselves.

The steps in making an Eye-Loop Rope Halter are:

1. **Whip-splice one end.**—The end which is whip-sliced, to prevent its unraveling, will be known as the short end. For this purpose, use a waxed cord, fish line, or strong piece of string about 40″ long.

Double the whipping cord from one end to form a loop approximately 6 inches long. Lay this loop on top of the rope (Fig. 287A), which is held in the left hand, with the end of the loop about 2 inches from the end of the rope. Now with the thumb holding the cord about ½ inch from the end of the rope (Fig.

---

[1]In the preparation of this section, the author had the able assistance of Mr. Wm. Bennett, Jr., Beef Cattle Herdsman, and Mr. Steve Allured, Artist; both of Washington State University. Mr. Allured also made the drawings.

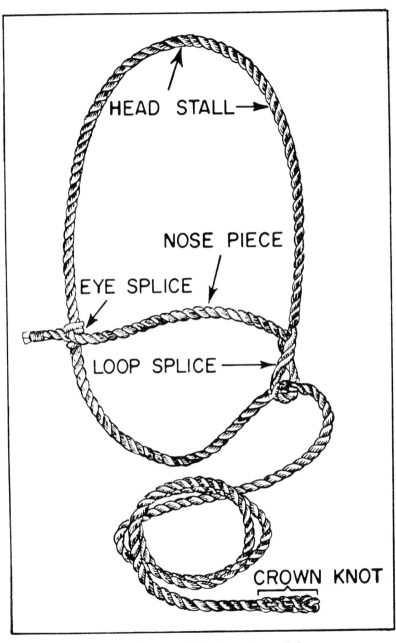

HEAD STALL→

NOSE PIECE

EYE SPLICE

LOOP SPLICE→

CROWN KNOT

Fig. 286. Completed Eye-Loop Rope Halter.

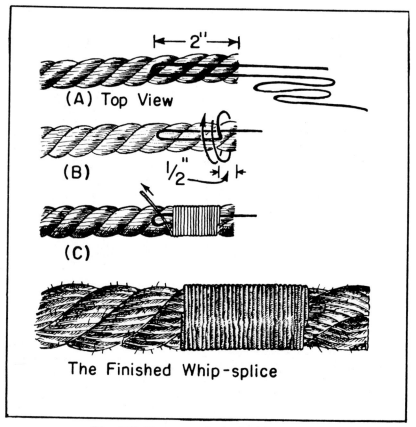

Fig. 287. Proper method of whip-splicing.

287B), make the first turn from front to back or clockwise around the rope, and be sure that this first turn locks the first wind in place.

Continue to wind tightly and neatly for a length of 1 inch. Then run the last wind up through the loop (Fig. 287C) and draw up tightly against the last turn and hold in place. Next grasp the cord out over the end of the rope and pull the loop under the windings for about ½ inch or half the length of the windings. These will now stay in place. With a knife, cut the remaining cord off even with the first and last windings. Soaking the whipping in water-proof cement makes the job more secure.

2. **Make the loop splice.**—The loop splice is made as follows (See Fig. 288) :

The short end of the rope will form the nose piece of the

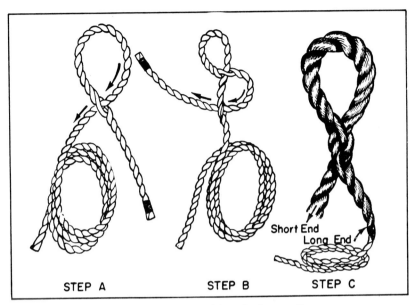

STEP A   STEP B   STEP C

Short End
Long End

Fig. 288. Steps in making the loop splice.

halter and will be its only permanent dimension. For average size cattle, use 15 to 16 inches for the short end (the future nose piece) ; for large bulls use 18 to 20 inches. Measure off this amount (the 15 to 16 inches, or up to 18 to 20 inches—as decided upon) from the whipping on the short end that you have just completed whip-splicing and pencil-mark the two strands to be raised. Lay the rope in front of you, short end to the right. Bend the long end up or away from you clockwise. With the aid of the marlinspike, raise the two strands on the top of the short end at the 15- to 16-inch mark and pull the long end down toward you and under the strands. Draw this long end through until the loop is about 1½ to 2 inches (make a 2-inch loop where the halter may get wet) inside diameter (See Fig. 288, Step A). A rule of thumb is that the inside diameter of the loop should be at least twice the thickness of the rope; a loop that is too small will close too tightly when the halter becomes wet and shrinks.

Next, take the short end and, with the help of the marlinspike, pass it under a top strand on the long rope as close to the loop as possible (See Fig. 288, Step B).

Pull the lead end snug, and the loop splice is complete as shown in Fig. 288, Step C. This makes for a loop with an equal number of strands on each side of the splice and leaves the inside of the splice fairly smooth where it bears against the jaw.

3. **Make the eye splice.**—Grasp the whip-spliced end in your left hand with the left thumb a couple of inches from the end and on top of the rope. Grasp the nose piece (short end) with your right hand thumb on the bottom of the rope, a couple of inches from the left hand. Twist your right hand away from you (Fig. 289A), pushing while you twist, so that the strands separate and finally kink (Fig. 289B). Take each kink and twist it so that it is completely turned, and arrange each kink on the same side of the rope and in line. Place the marlinspike through the 3 kinks (as shown in Fig. 289C or 289D—either of which is correct), and then follow with the long rope through all three (Fig. 289E). Draw the long rope through the eye splice until it is free of kinks and then

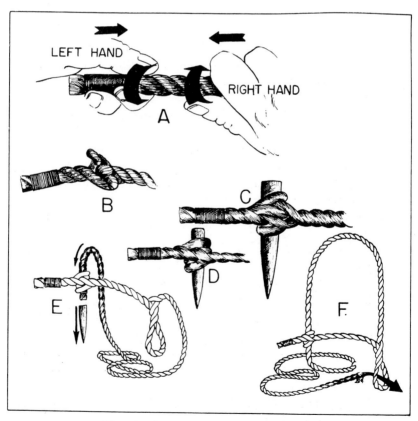

Fig. 289. Steps in making the eye splice.

adjust it back until it is approximately the size of the head piece. Arrange the kinks neatly on the rope.

Pass the long rope through the loop splice (Fig. 289F) and the halter is complete except for preparing the end of the lead rope. The halter is placed on the animal so that the loop splice is at the left of the jaw. Needed adjustments may be readily made after fitting it on the animal (when properly fitted on the animal, the nose piece should fall about $2/3$ the distance from the muzzle to the eyes).

4. **Prepare the end of the rope.**—The end of the lead rope may be prepared in either of three ways: (1) by whipping, (2) by making a crown knot, or (3) by making a wall knot.

Whipping leaves the end of the lead sufficiently small that it can be passed easily through tie rings. On the other hand, both the crown knot and the wall knot make it easier to hold on to an animal that is trying to get away. The procedure for preparing the end of the rope by each of these methods follows:

(1) **Whipping the end of the rope.**—If the lead end of the rope is to be whipped, this step is generally done at the very beginning as already directed for the short end of the rope (See Fig. 287).

(2) **Make the crown knot.**—Make the crown knot as follows (See Fig. 290):

a. Unlay the rope for 5 to 7 turns, depending upon the length of finish desired (Fig. 290, Step A) and throw up a bight in z between x and y and lock with the forefinger (See Fig. 290, Step A).

b. Pull x over z and lock with the thumb (See Fig. 290, Step B).

c. Pass y over x and linewards through bight z (See Fig. 290, Step C).

d. Hold the formation in the tips of the fingers and set by pulling on x, y, and z in turn until they are uniformly snug (See Fig. 290, Step D).

e. Tuck by passing each strand over one strand and under one strand, straight down the line, removing one or more yarns of the strand at each tuck after the first, according to the taper desired (See Fig. 290, Step E).

f. Moisten (barely) the completed crown knot and roll the splice under the foot.

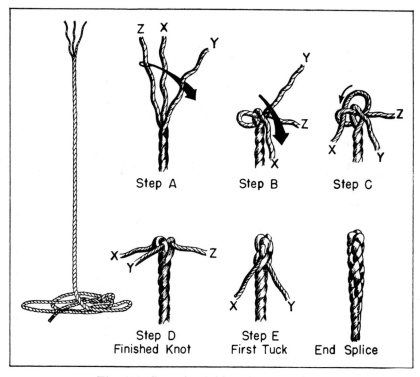

Fig. 290. Steps in making the crown knot.

(3) **Make the wall knot.**—If desired, a wall knot may be made as follows (See Fig. 291):

   a. Unlay the rope from 5 to 7 turns (Fig. 291, Step A) and throw down a bight in z and lock with the thumb (See Fig. 291, Step B).

   b. Throw a bight in y around z and lock under the first finger (See Fig. 291, Step B).

   c. Throw a bight in x around y, extending the end through the bight in z (See Fig. 291, Steps C and D).

   d. Hold in the tips of the fingers and set by pulling alternately on each strand until they are uniformly snug (See Fig. 291, Step E).

TRAINING AND GROOMING FOR THE SHOW

Assuming that the animal has been carefully selected and properly fed, there yet remains the assignment of parading be-

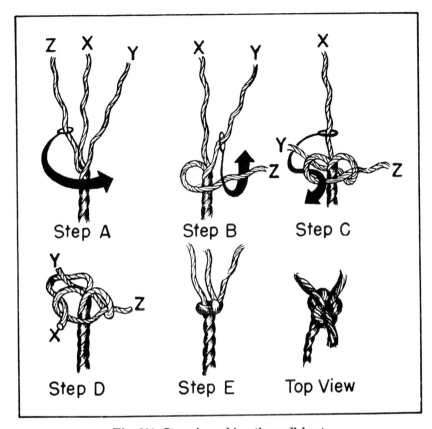

Fig. 291. Steps in making the wall knot.

fore the judge. In order to present a pleasing appearance in the show-ring, the animal must be well trained and thoroughly groomed. Competition is keen, and often the winner will be selected by a very narrow margin. Close attention to details may, therefore, be a determining factor in the decisions.

Gentling and Posing

Proper training of the animal requires time, and one must be patient, firm, and persistent. Such schooling makes it possible for the judge to see the animal at its best. First, the animal should be gentled by petting and brushing, and then it may be haltered. After the animal has become accustomed to the halter, it should be taught to lead. This should be correctly done from the left side and with the halter strap or rope neatly coiled in

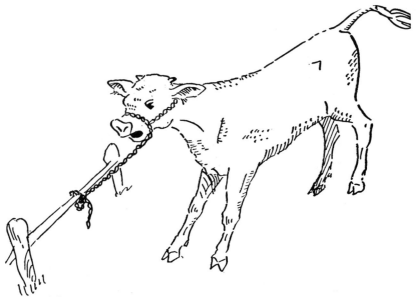

Fig. 292. Gentling and posing. (Drawing by R. F. Johnson)

the right hand. Although most dairy showmen prefer to walk backward, beef showmen usually follow the custom of walking forward, glancing back over the right shoulder at frequent intervals. The rope halter is preferable when starting the training program, but it is very important that the animal become accustomed to being led with the show halter well in advance of the show. The latter precaution is important because the animal reacts differently when led with the show halter than when led with the rope halter.

The next step is that of teaching the animal to stand or or "pose" properly, so that the judge may have an opportunity to examine it carefully. For correct posing the animal must stand squarely on all four feet (preferably with the fore feet on higher ground than the rear feet). The back should be held perfectly straight and the head held on a level with the top of the back. At first, this position may be quite strained and unnatural for the calf. For this reason, it should not be required to hold this position too long. Later, it should be possible to "pose" the calf for fifteen or twenty minutes at a time. In "posing," the showman should hold the strap in the left hand and face toward the animal. A long walking stick or "pointer" (about four feet in length) is usually used in placing the hind feet but the show-man's foot is best used in obtaining correct placement of the front feet. The show stick will be more useful in getting the hind feet placed properly and with ease, provided that a brad or nail is driven through the stick at a distance of about one inch from the end. The point of the brad or nail should protrude about one-third of an inch.

Trimming, Cleaning and Oiling the Feet

So that the animal will stand squarely and walk properly, the feet should be trimmed regularly. Long toes or unevenly

Fig. 293. Trimming the feet. (Drawing by R. F. Johnson)

worn hoofs are unsightly in appearance. Trimming can best be done with the animal in a set of stocks. With this method, it is possible to square up the sole and the sides of the feet as well as to cut back the ends of the toes. The practice of merely short-ening the toes by standing the animal on a hard surface and cutting off the ends with a hammer and chisel gives only tem-porary relief, very often not really correcting the difficulty. If a set of stocks cannot be made available, it may be advisable to throw the animal or to strap him along a wall or strong fence, thus making it possible to work on the bottoms of the feet.

The feet of some animals should be trimmed regularly as often as every two months. Too much trimming at any one time,

Fig. 294. Where cattle stocks are not available, this illustrates an easy method of throwing an animal to trim or treat the feet. (Drawing by R. F. Johnson)

however, may result in lameness. For this reason, it is not advisable to work on the feet immediately before the show.

Among the tools that may be used for trimming are the chisel, nippers, farrier's knife, and rasp. However, not all these need be available.

Quite often, when cattle are kept constantly in stables, the feet may become dry and brittle. This condition can usually be corrected by turning the animals out in a pasture paddock at night when there is dew on the grass. Packing the hoofs with wet clay, or applying Neat's foot oil will also be helpful in such cases. If the animal gets sore feet from standing in a filthy stable, the soreness should first be corrected. Following this, the feet should be washed and disinfected.

Before the animal enters the show-ring, its hoofs and dew claws should be thoroughly cleaned and then oiled. Application of almost any oil followed by a brisk rubbing with a woolen rag will give the desired results.

Training and Polishing the Horns

Often the horns will grow in an improper shape unless they are weighted or scraped to correct the faults. A well-curved set of horns will command the admiration of the judge, but poorly shaped horns will give the head a coarse, unattractive appearance. It must also be remembered that there is a difference in the desired shape with different breeds. The horns of the Hereford should curve downward, whereas the horns of the Shorthorn should curve slightly forward and inward.

Fig. 295. Note the properly (left) and improperly shaped horns (right). (Courtesy, USDA)

As soon as the horns are long enough (3 to 4 inches long) and sufficiently strong to bear the weight, it is time to begin training. For this purpose one-half pound weights (the correct size can be best determined by study and experience) are usually used. Care should be taken to prevent making a sharp turn in the horn by using a weight that is too heavy or by allowing the weights to remain on for too long a time. If the horns yield too readily, it is best to remove the weights and give the horns a rest of from ten days to a month, the length of time depending upon their condition. Then replace the weights until the desired effect is obtained. If the screw type of fastener is used, one should be careful not to force the screw into the horn so deeply that the depression cannot be removed. Horn weight losses may be reduced by tying strong twine around the screws on the two weights; then if one weight is knocked off, it will not be lost.

Fig. 296. Horn weights may be used in order to obtain symmetrical, properly curved and attractive horns. As soon as the horns are long enough and sufficiently strong, it is time to begin with a light weight. There is a variation in the degree of training that is desired in the different breeds. (Courtesy, USDA)

Horns may be pulled forward when they are 3 to 4 inches long by using a suitable spring or strap device for the purpose.

Extremely long horns may appear out of proportion and unsightly. In such cases, they can often be cut back as much as 2 or 3 inches, provided that not more than half an inch is removed at any one time and at no more frequent intervals than a month or six weeks. As a rule, most of the black tip can be removed without harming the sensitive part.

After the horns have been properly shaped, the next job is that of trimming and polishing. Usually it is best to smooth them down a week or two before the show. The rough surface may be smoothed with a sharp knife, a rasp, or a steel scraper; always scrape from the base toward the top. The final smoothing or finishing touches may then be given by using sand paper, fine emery cloth, steel wool, or a flannel cloth and emery dust.

Horns are usually polished just before the show. An excellent polish that will not collect dust can be obtained as follows: Apply a paste which is made by mixing olive oil or sweet oil with pumice stone or tripoli. Polish by rubbing briskly with a flannel cloth. A quick and more simple polish can be obtained by the use of glycerine, linseed oil, or mineral oil. However, a polish obtained in this manner is rather temporary, and the oil will collect dust quickly.

Grooming

Animals intended for show should be brushed daily. Vigorous brushing stimulates the circulation in the hide and keeps it in a loose, pliable condition. It also brings out the natural oil in the hair and removes dandruff, dirt, and dead hair. Short-haired animals (Red Poll and Devon breeds) should be brushed downward and to the rear with the lay of the hair; whereas animals of the long-haired breeds should first be brushed downward and then upward in the opposite direction of the lay of the hair in order to make it loose and fluffy. A woolen cloth may also be used to

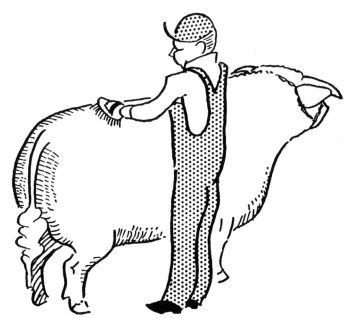

Fig. 297. Grooming. (Drawing by R. F. Johnson)

advantage for removal of dirt. Hold the brush in one hand and the cloth in the other.

It is well to use the curry comb sparingly at all times, especially in sensitive regions where the bone is near the surface. The primary purpose of the curry comb is to remove clinging particles that cannot be taken out with the brush. Furthermore, the curry comb should never be used on the tail switch, for it will pull out too many hairs and leave the switch light and skimpy.

Blanketing

Blanketing helps to keep the animal clean, alleviates annoyance from flies, gives the hair a more glossy appearance, and helps

Fig. 298. Blanketing. (Drawing by R. F. Johnson)

to keep the hide mellow and pliable. However, the use of a blanket may cause excessive sweating and loss of hair. Because of the latter hazard, most beef cattle showmen limit blanketing to those animals on which the hide needs softening.

If needed, an attractive blanket may be purchased from a stockman's supply house, or a cheap but satisfactory blanket may be made of burlap.

Clipping

Clipping is best done with electric clippers, although hand-clippers may be used. It should be done about six or seven days before the show so that the clipped hair will lose its stubby appearance.

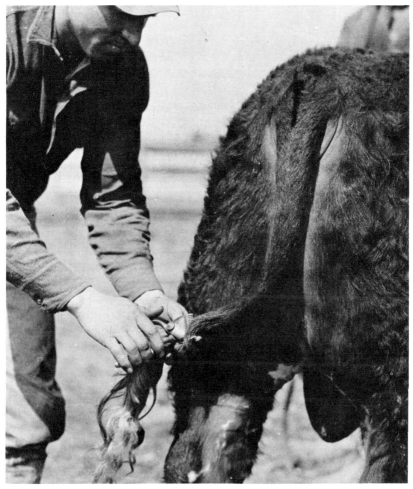

Fig. 299. Clipping the hair from the tail. One of the main objects in clipping the tail is to show the fullness of the twist and the thickness or beefiness of the hind quarters. Clipping should begin above the switch of the tail even with the point where the fullness of the twist begins to fail; and extend to the tailhead where it gradually tapers off, giving a blended effect with the rump. (Courtesy, USDA)

One of the main objects in clipping the tail is to show the fullness of the twist and the thickness or beefiness of the hind quarters. In order to do this to best advantage with each individual, good judgment should be exercised in determining the extreme points of clipping that will show these characteristics to advantage. In general, clipping should begin above the switch of the tail even with the point where the fullness of the twist begins to fail. Clipping should extend to the tail head, and the hair should be gradually tapered off near the body so that the tail blends nicely with the rump. To avoid leaving ridges of long hair extending down the center of the tail, the clippers should be run across the tail after they have been run upward to the tail head.

Sometimes the head is clipped so that it will appear cleaner cut, more shapely, and the poll more clearly defined. Such heads are clipped from a point just back of the jawbone and ½ inch behind the ears; leaving the eye-lashes and the hair on the nose.

Generally speaking, custom decrees that clipping shall be as follows:

Steers:
1. All tails clipped.
2. Heads clipped if naturally polled, or dehorned (clip the outside of the ears, but leave the insides untrimmed).
3. Horned heads not clipped.

Breeding Cattle:
1. Aberdeen-Angus.—Heads (but do not clip either the inside or the outside of the ears) and tails clipped.
2. Shorthorns (both horned and polled).—Neither tails nor heads clipped.
3. Herefords (both horned and polled).—Tails clipped; heads not clipped.

Washing

Frequent washing keeps the animal clean; stimulates a heavy growth of loose, fluffy hair; and keeps the skin smooth and mellow. Beginning about a month or six weeks before the show, the animal should be washed regularly once each week. In preparation for washing, place a chain about the neck. Never use a rope about the animal's neck when washing, for a wet rope cannot be easily loosened should the animal fall or otherwise get into trouble. Immediately prior to washing, vigorously brush the entire body with a stiff brush, removing all possible dirt and dandruff before wetting the animal.

An excellent cleaner and hair conditioner for washing may be prepared as follows: Mix one to two cups of good concentrated liquid cocoanut oil shampoo in one and one-half gallons of lukewarm water (or high-grade castile soap may be used). With a bristle wash brush, thoroughly wet the dry animal with the soap solution. Work the soap into a good lather, making sure that all parts of the body are well scrubbed and clean. Some parts of the animal that are frequently neglected in washing are the head, tail, legs, brisket, and belly.

In washing the head, avoid getting soap or water in the eyes, ears, nostrils, and mouth. Cattle do not like to have their heads washed. A precaution commonly used in washing the head safely is to wash one side at a time while firmly holding the ear on the side being washed. Death of the animal may result from getting water into the lungs through the nostrils or mouth.

Following washing, the animal should be rinsed off very thoroughly in order to remove all traces of soap and dirt from the hair and skin. For animals with light parts, a little bluing added to the last rinse water will improve the results. After re-

Fig. 300. Washing. (Drawing by R. E. Johnson)

moving surplus water by scraper,[1] the hair is curled, and the animal is walked or allowed to stand where the sun may aid in drying. Avoid standing the wet animal in a draft.

Washing usually causes an animal to appear gaunt. For this reason, it is usually best not to wash within ten or twelve hours of the show. In no sense should washing be considered as an excuse for allowing the stable to go without proper attention.

Curling

Cattle with long, fluffy hair are usually curled in order to emphasize great width and beefiness as well as to soften and minimize any undue roughness or weakness in conformation.

Experienced showmen vary the method or type of curling according to the individuality of the animal; giving consideration to the length of hair and to whether it is straight or naturally curly, and to the conformation and condition of the animal. Also, there are some differences between breeds; for example, in Aberdeen-Angus breeding classes it is common practice to curl the hair in the regions of the neck, the forepart of the shoulders and on the rear part of the thighs—leaving the hair on the other parts of the body uncurled. The most skillful showmen are able to produce a more natural effect rather than something that is quite artificial in appearance.

Regardless of the type of curl desired, in preparation therefor, the animal is always either (1) washed, rinsed, and scraped free of surplus water—as described under washing, or (2) dry-brushed, wetted down all over (preferably by means of a hand sprayer, although satisfactory wetting down may be accomplished by dipping a stiff brush into the water or creosote solution and by brushing the hair smoothly against the animal) with water alone or a solution made by adding one tablespoonful of creosote to each gallon of water, and scraped free of any surplus water. Naturally, the latter procedure is followed when a complete washing is not necessary or desired, as is frequently the case when animals are curled daily or twice daily when on the show circuit or when curled 1 to 2 hours before showing. Also, animals are frequently wetted down without washing when they

---

[1]At this stage (after scraping off the surplus water), some showmen spray the animal lightly with a solution made by adding one tablespoon creosote dip to one gallon of water; because the dip will help the curl. However, others eliminate this step; they do not use dip because they think it causes dandruff.

are being curled 1 to 2 times daily, as is customary 7 to 10 days prior to the first show.

In general, the following distinct types of curls are used:

1. **The Fluffy Curl.**—This is really a misnomer, for it is not a curl in the true sense of the word. Instead, the object is to produce a hair effect very much like that of a fluffy teddy bear or a fluffy ball of fur. When the art is plied by a master showman to a beast which possesses a long dense coat of hair, but which does

Fig. 301. The Fluffy Curl, on Clarissa Coronita 7th, Grand Champion Polled Shorthorn female at the Chicago International. This heifer was bred by Henry Fisher, Garfield, Wash., and shown by Lewis Thieman, Concordia, Mo.

not possess a tight natural curl (for example, most Shorthorns are straight-haired), the fluffy curl produces the most natural effect of all methods. Step by step, the fluffy curl is produced as follows:

(1) Either wash or wet down the hair of the animal as previously described.

(2) Part the hair (with a Scotch comb) from back of the poll to a point just back of the withers, and comb (with a Scotch comb) the moist hair in the direction of its

natural lay (from back of the withers toward the tail head along the top line; downward on the rest of the body) on all body parts except the head and rear end.

(3) Beginning along the top of the animal, make waves ½ inch to 1 inch apart (and about 2 inches wide) by drawing the back tip of a round curry comb in the direction of the natural lay of the hair in a short, wavy manner. Make waves on all body parts except the head, rear end, and legs. Proceed to step No. 4, thus allowing the necessary 2 to 3 minutes for the curl to set before applying step No. 5.

(4) Comb (with a Scotch comb) and/or brush the hair on the head forward and toward the muzzle on horned animals (generally the head of a polled animal is clipped), outward from the median line at the top of the neck and withers, and outward from the median line of the rear end; thus accentuating the width in these regions. Brush the hair on the ears toward the head.

(5) In order to tip back the ends of the hairs, while the coat is drying, brush it lightly (with a dry rice brush) opposite the direction of its natural lay (upward on all body parts except the top line; forward on the top line from the tail head to a point just back of the withers). Such brushing should begin at the tops of the hoofs and extend to the top of the animal; except in steers, where fineness of bone is desired, it is usually best not to fluff out the hair below the knees and hocks.

As the hair becomes fairly dry (the drying time varying with the weather and density of hair), discontinue brushing and draw (with a Sotch comb) it opposite the direction of its natural lay.

After the hair of straight-haired animals is well trained, one may start this step (step No. 5) with the Scotch comb, without first brushing as indicated above. But the procedure as indicated should always be followed with animals that are naturally curly haired.

(6) Continue to comb the dry hair outward and upward (with a large, coarse, hard rubber comb).

2. **The Wave Curl.**—This is sometimes referred to as the Hereford curl, because it is especially popular with Hereford

Fig. 302. The wave-curl. The round comb may be used in curling the hair of the Hereford to produce a wave-curl. This may be made by drawing the back side of a round curry comb downward in a short, wavy manner. The hair is then brushed or combed upward. Likewise, a wave-curl may be made by catching the tips of the hair and combing upward with the back side of the round curry comb, followed by brushing. (Courtesy, USDA)

showmen. This type of curl may be produced on any animal which possesses a rather tight natural curl, such as characterizes most Herefords, whereas the fluffy curl is produced on straight-haired animals. Step by step, the wave curl is produced in exactly the same manner as previously outlined for the fluffy curl. Thus, the reader is referred to the previous section. The chief difference is the end result obtained from applying step No. 5; namely in brushing and combing the hair in the opposite direction of its natural lay. In straight haired animals (such as most Shorthorns), the application of this step results in tipping the hair back—thus producing the fluffy curl; whereas in naturally curly haired animals (such as most Herefords), the application of this step results in denser, tighter curls—thus producing the wave curl.

In producing the fluffy curl and the wave curl, one further difference may be observed. In the wave curl, step No. 6 may either be omitted or applied lightly, depending on how tight a curl is desired.

3. **The Parallel Curl.**—In this type of curl, parallel lines spaced about one inch apart are marked along the body.

Step by step, the parallel curl is produced as follows:

(1) Either wash or wet down the hair of the animal as previously described.

(2) Part the hair (with a Scotch comb) along the center top line from back of the poll to the tail, and comb (with a Scotch comb) the moist hair downward on all parts except the head and rear end.

Fig. 303. The parallel curl on a Shorthorn.

(3) Mark off (with a "liner") parallel lines about one inch apart along the sides of the body, from in front of the shoulders to the rear edge of the thigh and from the point where the back and the sides blend to the knees and hocks. Either line both sides from rear to front or vice versa.

(4) From the tops of the hoofs to the point where the back and the sides blend, draw (with a Scotch comb) the hair upward, and then in order to curl the ends of the hairs, brush upward with a dry brush while it is drying. With steers, where fineness of bone is desired, it is usually best to comb the hair downward below the knees and hocks.

(5) Comb (with a Scotch comb) the hair on the head forward and toward the muzzle on horned animals, from the median line across the withers, from the center top line to where the back and sides blend, and from the median line of the rear end; thus accentuating the width in these regions.

4. **Diamond Curl.**—In this the animal is first lined (with a liner) in the shape of diamonds.

Like the parallel curl, this method is easily mastered by the amateur and is valuable in training the hair in early stages. However, like the parallel curl, it leaves marks that still show on the animal after further brushing, combing, and drying, and produces a distinctly artificial effect instead of the much sought natural effect.

Experienced herdsmen often accentuate the bone of breeding animals by soaping the hair on the legs and combing it outward and upward. For this purpose, a bar of mild soap is first soaked in water until it is soft. The legs are then moistened, following which the bar of soap is rubbed thoroughly over them. The hair is then combed or brushed outward and upward. After drying, any visible soap is removed by further combing or brushing. This treatment is usually applied about an hour before show time. Also the hair on the legs may be trained by using the soap treatment at intervals before show day.

Oiling

An animal in full "bloom" doesn't necessarily need artificial oil on its hair. However, if the hair seems unusually dry and

Fig. 304. Oiling. (Drawing by R. F. Johnson)

lifeless, it may be desirable to apply oil, provided it is limited to a light application properly applied.

Either a commercial oil or a home-made mixture of equal parts of glycerine, sweet oil and rubbing alcohol may be used. After curling, apply lightly and evenly with a small hand sprayer or woolen cloth, and then brush the animal.

It is to be remembered, however, that an animal should not be shown when the hair is either shiny or gummy from too much oil. Likewise, an animal should not be shown when the hair is wet.

Cleaning and Fluffing the Switch

The switch can usually be made most attractive by the fol-

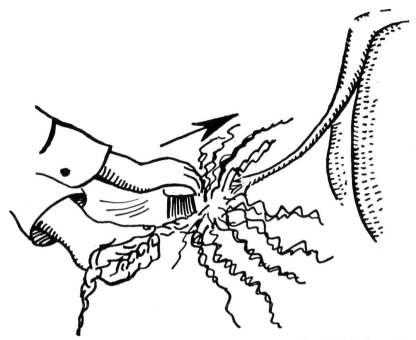

Fig. 305. Cleaning and fluffing the switch. (Drawing by R. F. Johnson)

lowing procedure: The evening before the show, wash the switch thoroughly with soap and warm water. If it is white, it may be made brighter by adding a little bluing to the water. Rinse it in water to which a small amount of alum has been added (the alum will make the switch more fluffy when combed out). Then while the hair is still damp, prepare about six three-strand braids and tie all of them together at the bottom. Leave the switch in this manner over night and until an hour or two before the show, then unbraid, and fluff by brushing the hair upward a few strands at a time.

MAKING FAIR ENTRIES

Well in advance of the show, the exhibitor should request that the show manager or secretary provide him with a premium list and entry blanks. All rules and regulations of the show should be studied carefully and followed to the letter—including requirements relative to entrance, registration certificates, vaccination, health certificates, stall fees, exhibitor's and helper's tickets, and other matters pertaining to the show.

Generally, entries must be filed with the show about thirty days in advance of the opening date. Most shows specify that entries be made out on printed forms and in accordance with instructions thereon. The class, age, breed, registry number, and usually the name and registry number of the sire and dam must be given. Entries must be made in all individual and group classes in which it is intended to show, but no entries are made in the championship classes, the first place winners being eligible for the latter.

PROVIDING HEALTH CERTIFICATES

Health certificates are always required for show animals involved in interstate shipment. The health certificate, which must accompany the bill of lading, must be signed by a licensed veterinarian. For cattle, most shows specify that this certificate indicate that within thirty days prior to entry and within ninety days prior to the date of exhibiting the veterinarian has examined each animal offered for entry and has found it free of tuberculosis, brucellosis, and other infectious or contagious diseases. This provides reasonable assurance that diseases are not being spread. In addition, some states require that a special permit issued by the state veterinarian must accompany cattle on their trip home from the show.

SHIPPING TO THE FAIR

Show animals may be shipped via either truck or rail. Most generally, hauls under five hundred miles distance are made by truck and greater distances by rail (usually in a box car rather than a stock car). Regardless of the method of shipping, it is important that the following details receive consideration:

1. Schedule the transportation so that the cattle will arrive within the limitations imposed by the show and at least two to three days in advance of the date that the animals vie for awards.

2. Before using, thoroughly clean and disinfect all public conveyances.

3. Use long, clean, bright straw for bedding in order not to soil the hair or introduce foreign matter into it. It is also a good plan to first sand the floor so that cattle will not slip.

4. In transporting by truck, cattle are generally stood crosswise of the truck, with the largest animal near the cab and tied facing to one side. The direction of facing the remaining animals

is alternated; the second animal is faced in the opposite direction from the first, and so on. In trucking, it is also best to tie animals fairly short and near enough together so that they will not lie down.

5. In rail shipments, the cattle are all tied to one side of the car and are not staggered as when transported by truck. Usually, fasteners are properly spaced on a 2- by 4-inch piece of lumber that is nailed securely along the side of the car 1½ to 2 inches from the floor. In rail shipment, adequate space should be left between animals so that they can lie down to rest whenever they desire. Greater cleanliness is secured if the droppings are removed at the time they are voided.

6. If space is at a premium, place the feed supply, bedding, and show equipment on a deck or platform in the railroad car or truck, preferably at least 5½ feet above the floor. Allow for air circulation and tying of smaller animals under the deck.

7. When mixed feeds are used, as is usually the case in fitting rations, a supply adequate for the entire trip should be taken along in the car. This will reduce the hazard of animals going off feed because of feed changes.

8. Limit show cattle to a half feed at the last feeding before loading out and while in transit.

9. In transit, the animals should be handled quietly and should not be allowed to become hot nor to be in a draft.

10. If the show car is to be reused, it should be locked, unless all materials and equipment are removed.

Show animals can usually be transported at one-half fare provided that the regulations are adhered to. When only one show is made, this consideration usually consists of paying full fare in going to the show and none for the return trip. Although the regulations are a bit more complicated, a half-fare may also be obtained when a carload is taken on the show circuit. It must be remembered, however, that show cattle may be transported by rail at less than full tariff rates only when the carriers' liability is limited to $75 for each bull or steer, $50 for each cow, and $20 for each calf six months old or under.

STALL SPACE, FEEDING, AND MANAGEMENT AT THE FAIR

As soon as the show is reached, the animals should be unloaded and placed in clean stalls that are freshly bedded with clean straw. The cattle should be arranged in order of size so as to make the exhibit as attractive as possible.

While at the show, it is preferable that the cattle receive the same ration to which they were accustomed at home. Usually only a half ration is allowed for the first twenty-four hours after arrival at the show, and a normal ration is provided thereafter. So that the animals will maintain their appetite, however, it is necessary that they receive exercise while at the show. It is usually best to exercise the animals one-half hour or more in the cool of the morning. This also is a convenient time to clean out the pens, while the animals are out for exercise.

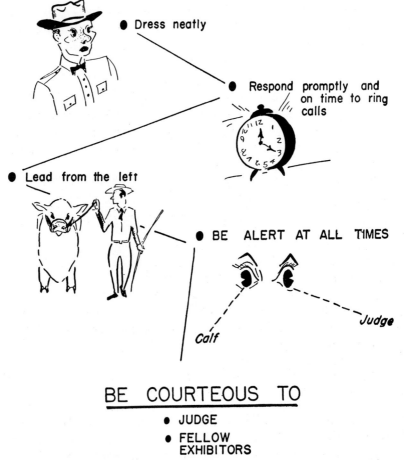

Fig. 306. Some of the guiding principles observed by the most successful showmen. (Drawings by R. F. Johnson)

It is customary for each exhibitor to identify his exhibit by means of a neat and attractive sign, the size of which must be within the limitations imposed by the show. This sign usually gives the name of the breed of cattle and the name and address of the exhibitor.

SHOWING THE ANIMAL

Expert showmanship cannot be achieved through reading any set of instructions. Each show and each ring will be found to present unusual circumstances. However, there are certain guiding principles which are always adhered to by the most successful showmen. Some of these are:

1. Train the animal long before entering the ring.

2. Have the animal carefully groomed and ready for the parade before the judge.

3. Dress neatly for the occasion.

4. Enter the ring promptly when the class is called.

5. Lead the animal from the left side (walking near the left shoulder), with the halter strap neatly coiled in the right hand.

6. Pose the animal correctly so that it stands on all four feet with the back held perfectly straight and the head on a level with the top of the back.

7. Keep one eye on the judge and the other on the animal. Center your attention entirely on showing the animal. The animal may be under the observation of the judge at a time when you least suspect it.

8. Keep calm and collected. Remember that the nervous showman creates an unfavorable impression.

9. Work in close partnership with the animal.

10. Be courteous and respect the rights of other exhibitors.

11. Be a good sport. *Win without bragging and lose without squealing.*

AFTER THE FAIR IS OVER

Most shows have regulations requiring that all exhibits remain on the grounds until a specified time, after which signed releases must be secured from the superintendent of the show. Because most exhibitors are anxious to travel when the show is over and there is considerable confusion at this time, it is usually advisable to load all equipment, left-over feed, and other articles before the release of animals is secured. Then all that remains to be done is to load out the animals.

Upon returning to the farm or ranch, it is usually good policy to isolate the show herd for a period of three weeks. This procedure reduces the possibility of spreading diseases or parasites to the balance of the herd.

The final assignment after the show is over consists of gradually reducing the condition of heavily fitted breeding animals. Experienced herdsmen accomplish this difficult task and yet retain strong vigorous animals. They do this successfully by (1) providing plenty of exercise, (2) increasing the amount of bulky feeds, such as oats, in the ration, (3) cutting down gradually on the grain allowance, and (4) retaining the succulent feeds and increasing the pasture or hay.

It is important that young stock to be developed for show purposes the following year continue to receive an adequate though lighter grain ration.

Where the herd is being exhibited on a circuit, the herdsman must use great care in keeping the animals in show condition at all times. The peak condition should be reached at the strongest show. In order to be successful, showing on the circuit requires great skill on the part of the caretaker, especially from the standpoint of feeding and exercising the cattle.

QUESTIONS FOR STUDY AND DISCUSSION

1. Under what circumstances would you recommend that each a purebred, a commercial, and a 4-H club member (1) should show, and (2) should not show beef cattle?

2. Take and defend either the affirmative or the negative position of each of the following statements:

   (1) Fitting and showing does not harm animals.

   (2) Livestock shows have been a powerful force in livestock improvement.

   (3) Too much money is spent on livestock shows.

   (4) Unless all animals are fitted, groomed, and shown to the same degree of perfection, show-ring winnings are not indicative of the comparative quality of animals.

SELECTED REFERENCES

Title of Publication	Author(s)	Publisher
Beef Production	R. V. Diggins C. E. Bundy	Prentice-Hall, Inc., Englewood Cliffs, N. J., 1956.
Selecting, Fitting, Showing Beef Cattle	J. E. Nordby H. E. Lattig	Interstate Printers & Publishers, Danville, Ill., 1956.
Stockman's Handbook, The	M. E. Ensminger	Interstate Printers & Publishers, Danville, Ill., 1959.

APPENDIX

SECTION I.—AVERAGE COMPOSITION AND DIGESTIBLE NUTRIENTS OF SOME COMMON FEEDS

Table I is a compilation of the nutrient composition of some common feedstuffs utilized by beef cattle. Such information is necessary for intelligent ration preparation, animal health, and efficiency. In using this table, however, it should be borne in mind that individual lots of any particular feeding stuff may differ in composition from the average. Such variations are apt to be especially large in the content of calcium and phosphorus of roughages. Thus, the figures for calcium and phosphorus should be accepted as approximate percentages present in different feeds produced on soil reasonably well supplied with these minerals

TABLE I

Average Composition and Digestible Nutrients of Some Common Feeds[1]

Feedstuff	Total Dry Matter	Protein	Dig. Protein	TDN[2]	DE[3]	Calcium	Phosphorus	Carotene
	%	%	%	%	Therms /lb.	%	%	mg/lb.
Dry Roughages[4]								
Alfalfa hay, all analyses....	90.5	15.3	10.9	50.7	1.02	1.47	0.24	8.2
Alfalfa hay, 1/10 to 1/2 bloom....	90.5	15.4	11.2	51.4	1.04	1.47	0.24	20.3
Alfalfa hay, 3/4 to full bloom....	90.5	14.1	10.2	50.3	1.02	1.22	0.22	8.5
Alfalfa hay, past bloom....	90.5	12.9	9.3	47.7	0.96	1.10	0.20	3.3
Alfalfa meal, dehydrated....	92.7	17.7	12.4	54.4	1.10	1.60	0.26	42.4
Alfalfa leaf meal, dehydrated....	92.7	21.1	16.0	57.2	1.16	1.69	0.25	62.9
Barley hay....	90.8	7.3	4.0	51.9	1.05	0.26	0.23	—
Barley straw....	90.0	3.7	0.7	42.2	0.85	0.33	0.10	—
Birdsfoot trefoil hay....	91.2	14.2	9.8	55.0	1.11	1.60	0.20	19.7
Bromegrass hay, all analyses....	88.8	10.4	5.3	49.3	1.00	0.42	0.19	—
Clover hay, alsike, all analyses....	88.9	12.1	8.1	53.2	1.07	1.15	0.23	—
Clover hay, crimson....	89.5	14.2	9.8	48.9	0.99	1.23	0.24	—

[1]From bulletin No. IV, *Nutrient Requirements of Beef Cattle,* revised 1958, with the permission of the National Research Council.

[2]In calculating the values for total digestible nutrients no digestion coefficients for a few feedstuffs were available, or the data were inadequate. In those instances the digestion coefficients for comparable feedstuffs were used.

[3]The values for digestible energy may be converted to metabolizable energy by multiplying by 82 per cent.

[4]The Committee on Animal Nutrition is indebted to Professor F. B. Morrison for the use of data from the 22nd Edition of *Feeds and Feeding* on the composition of roughages, silages and cereals presented in this table. The data on the composition of by-product feeds were supplied by the Committee of Feed Composition of the National Research Council (NRC Pub. No. 449, 1956). The digestion coefficients used in calculating the digestible protein and T.D.N. were also taken with Professor Morrison's permission from the 22nd Edition of *Feeds and Feeding.* These are based in part on the extensive compilation of digestion coefficients in *Feeds of the World* (W. Va. Agr. Exp. Sta., 1947), which was prepared by Dr. B. H. Schneider at the request of the Committee on Animal Nutrition.

TABLE I (Continued)

Feedstuff	Total Dry Matter	Pro-tein	Dig. Pro-tein	TDN[2]	DE[3]	Cal-cium-	Phos-phorus	Caro-tene
	%	%	%	%	Therms /lb.	%	%	mg/lb.

Dry Roughages—Continued

Feedstuff	Total Dry Matter	Pro-tein	Dig. Pro-tein	TDN[2]	DE[3]	Cal-cium-	Phos-phorus	Caro-tene
Clover hay, Ladino	89.5	18.5	14.2	59.5	1.20	1.53	0.29	—
Clover hay, red, all analyses	88.3	12.0	7.2	51.8	1.05	1.28	0.20	7.3
Clover and mixed grass hay, high in clover	89.6	9.6	5.5	51.8	1.05	0.88	0.21	6.1
Clover and timothy hay, 30 to 50% clover	88.1	8.6	4.7	51.0	1.03	0.69	0.16	—
Corn cobs, ground	90.4	2.3	0.0	45.7	0.92	0.11	0.04	—
Corn fodder, medium in water	82.6	6.8	3.3	53.9	1.09	0.25	0.14	1.8
Corn stover, medium in water	80.3	5.8	2.0	45.5	0.92	0.48	0.08	—
Cowpea hay, all analyses	90.4	18.6	12.3	51.4	1.04	1.37	0.30	—
Kafir fodder, very dry	90.0	8.7	4.5	53.6	1.08	0.35	0.18	2.0
Kafir stover, very dry	90.0	5.5	1.9	51.3	1.04	0.54	0.09	1.1
Lespedeza hay, annual, before bloom	89.1	14.3	7.2	49.2	0.99	1.03	0.20	20.4
Lespedeza hay, annual, in bloom	89.1	13.0	6.4	46.4	0.94	1.00	0.19	—
Lespedeza hay, annual, after bloom	89.1	11.5	3.6	39.6	0.80	0.90	0.15	—
Mixed hay, good, less than 30% legumes	89.2	8.8	4.8	48.8	0.99	0.90	0.19	6.4
Oat hay	88.1	8.2	4.9	47.3	0.96	0.21	0.19	—
Oat straw	89.8	4.1	0.7	44.8	0.90	0.24	0.09	—
Orchard grass hay, good	88.7	8.1	4.2	49.7	1.00	0.27	0.18	—
Pea hay, field	89.3	14.9	10.6	55.1	1.11	1.22	0.25	—
Peanut hay, mowed	91.4	10.6	6.9	58.4	1.18	—	—	8.0
Prairie hay, western, cut in midseason	91.3	6.0	2.0	45.1	0.91	0.33	0.12	9.1
Prairie hay, western, mature	91.9	4.4	0.9	43.7	0.88	0.36	0.08	3.6
Quack grass hay	89.0	6.9	2.5	40.3	0.81	—	—	—
Reed canary grass hay	91.1	7.7	4.9	45.1	0.91	0.33	0.16	—
Rye hay	91.3	6.7	2.4	42.5	0.86	—	0.18	—
Rye straw	92.8	3.5	0.0	42.2	0.85	0.26	0.09	—
Sorghum fodder, sweet, dry	88.9	6.2	3.3	52.4	1.06	0.34	0.14	1.1
Soybean hay, good all analyses	88.1	14.6	9.8	48.2	0.98	1.10	0.22	13.6
Soybean hay, in bloom or before	88.0	16.7	12.0	52.4	1.06	1.29	0.34	—
Soybean hay, seed developing	88.0	14.6	9.8	48.2	0.97	1.24	0.25	13.6
Soybean hay, seed nearly ripe	88.0	15.2	10.8	54.9	1.11	0.96	0.31	3.0
Soybean straw	88.9	3.9	1.1	38.6	0.78	—	0.05	—
Sudan grass hay, all analyses	89.4	8.8	4.3	48.6	0.98	0.36	0.27	—
Timothy hay, all analyses	89.0	6.6	3.0	49.1	0.99	0.35	0.14	4.4
Timothy hay, before bloom	89.0	9.7	6.1	56.6	1.14	—	—	9.2
Timothy hay, full bloom	89.0	6.4	3.2	51.1	1.03	—	0.20	4.2
Timothy hay, late seed	89.0	5.3	1.9	41.9	0.85	0.14	0.15	2.5
Timothy and clover hay, ¼ clover	88.8	7.9	4.0	49.8	1.01	0.58	0.15	—
Vetch and oat hay, over half vetch	87.6	11.9	8.4	50.7	1.02	0.76	0.27	—
Wheat hay	90.4	6.1	3.3	46.7	0.94	0.14	0.18	—
Wheat straw	92.6	3.9	0.3	40.6	0.82	0.15	0.07	—

Silages, Roots and Tubers

Feedstuff	Total Dry Matter	Pro-tein	Dig. Pro-tein	TDN[2]	DE[3]	Cal-cium-	Phos-phorus	Caro-tene
Alfalfa, not wilted, no preservative	24.7	4.1	2.6	13.5	0.27	0.35	0.08	15.1
Alfalfa, wilted	36.2	6.3	4.3	21.5	0.43	0.51	0.12	11.4
Alfalfa-molasses, not wilted	26.8	4.1	2.7	15.4	0.31	0.41	0.08	14.5
Beet top, sugar	31.6	3.8	2.5	14.9	0.30	0.31	0.07	5.1
Cabbage, entire	9.4	2.2	1.9	8.1	0.16	0.06	0.03	—
Carrots, roots	11.9	1.2	0.9	10.3	0.21	0.05	0.04	—
Clover, Ladino, and timothy	29.9	5.4	3.9	21.4	0.43	0.31	0.07	15.6
Corn, canning factory waste	22.4	2.0	1.1	16.1	0.33	—	—	—
Corn, dent, well-matured, all analyses	27.6	2.3	1.2	18.3	0.37	0.10	0.07	5.8
Corn, dent, well-matured, well-eared	28.5	2.3	1.3	19.8	0.40	0.09	0.07	—
Corn, dent, well-matured, fair in ears	26.3	2.1	1.1	17.2	0.35	0.09	0.06	—
Corn, dent, immature, before dough stage	20.3	1.8	0.9	12.9	0.26	0.11	0.07	—
Corn stover, mature ears removed	23.7	1.6	0.6	14.0	0.28	0.08	0.10	—
Corn and soybeans, well-matured, 30% or more soybeans	28.3	3.2	2.0	19.7	0.40	0.20	0.08	—
Grass silage, considerable legumes	25.6	3.6	2.0	15.5	0.31	—	—	17.1
Grass silage, some legumes	27.6	3.2	1.9	15.6	0.32	—	—	20.7
Grass silage, some legumes, molasses added	25.8	3.2	1.9	15.1	0.31	0.32	0.12	—
Grass silage wilted, molasses added	33.6	4.5	2.6	19.1	0.39	—	—	6.2
Mangels, roots	9.2	1.3	0.9	7.1	0.14	0.02	0.02	—
Oats, molasses added	32.0	2.7	1.4	16.9	0.34	0.10	0.09	17.7
Pea vine	24.5	3.2	1.9	14.0	0.30	0.32	0.06	21.0
Potatoes, tubers	21.2	2.2	1.3	17.4	0.35	0.01	0.05	—
Potato-alfalfa hay	35.9	5.3	3.3	21.1	0.43	—	—	—
Potato-mixed hay	33.7	3.8	2.2	21.6	0.44	—	—	—

TABLE I (Continued)

Feedstuff	Total Dry Matter	Protein	Dig. Protein	TDN[2]	DE[3]	Calcium-	Phosphorus	Carotene
	%	%	%	%	Therms /lb.	%	%	mg/lb.

			Silages, Roots and Tubers—Continued					
Potato-corn meal	31.7	2.0	1.0	27.0	0.55	—	—	—
Rutabagas, roots	11.1	1.3	1.0	9.5	0.19	0.05	0.03	—
Sorghum, sweet	25.4	1.6	0.8	15.2	0.31	0.08	0.05	2.7
Soybean, not wilted	24.8	4.2	2.9	14.6	0.29	0.35	0.09	14.6
Sudan grass	25.7	2.2	1.5	14.4	0.29	0.11	0.04	—
Timothy, not wilted, no preservative	30.9	3.3	1.8	18.4	0.37	0.18	0.09	14.1
Timothy, not wilted, molasses added	30.0	3.1	1.6	17.1	0.35	0.16	0.08	—
Turnips	9.3	1.3	0.9	7.8	0.16	0.06	0.02	—

			Concentrates					
Barley, excluding Pacific Coast	89.4	12.7	10.0	77.7	1.57	0.06	0.40	—
Barley, Pacific Coast	89.9	8.7	6.9	78.8	1.59	0.06	0.33	—
Beans, field or navy	90.0	22.9	20.2	78.7	1.59	0.15	0.57	—
Beet pulp, dried	90.8	9.1	4.3	68.2	1.38	0.68	0.10	—
Beet pulp, molasses, dried	92.0	9.1	6.0	72.3	1.46	0.56	0.08	—
Beet pulp, wet	11.6	1.5	0.8	8.8	0.18	0.09	0.01	—
Blood meal	90.5	79.9	56.7	58.9	1.19	0.28	0.22	—
Blood flour	90.8	82.2	78.9	81.2	1.64	0.45	0.37	—
Bone meal, raw	93.2	26.2	18.1	18.1	0.37	22.14	10.35	—
Bone meal, steamed	95.2	12.1	—	—	—	28.98	13.59	—
Brewers dried grains	92.4	25.9	20.7	66.0	1.33	0.27	0.50	—
Buttermilk, dried	92.5	32.0	28.8	83.0	1.68	1.34	0.94	—
Citrus pulp, dried	90.1	6.6	5.2	78.2	1.58	1.96	0.12	—
Cocoanut oil meal, expeller	92.8	20.4	17.3	76.3	1.54	0.21	0.61	—
Cocoanut oil meal, solvent	91.7	21.3	18.1	68.3	1.38	0.17	0.61	—
Corn and cob meal	86.1	7.4	5.4	73.2	1.48	0.04	0.22	—
Corn, yellow dent, #2	85.0	8.7	6.7	80.1	1.62	0.02	0.27	1.3
Corn, flint	88.5	9.8	7.5	83.4	1.68	—	0.33	—
Corn distillers dried grains	92.3	27.1	19.8	82.7	1.67	0.09	0.37	1.4
Corn distillers dried grains with solubles	91.9	27.2	19.9	81.0	1.64	0.17	0.68	1.7
Corn distillers dried solubles	93.1	26.9	21.3	80.2	1.62	0.35	1.37	0.3
Corn gluten feed	90.4	25.3	21.8	75.4	1.52	0.46	0.77	3.8
Corn gluten meal	90.7	42.9	36.5	79.9	1.61	0.16	0.40	7.4
Cottonseed, whole, pressed	92.4	28.0	20.2	58.6	1.18	0.17	0.64	—
Cottonseed feed	90.8	39.2	30.6	65.4	1.32	0.15	0.64	—
Cottonseed oil meal, expeller	92.7	41.4	34.4	73.4	1.48	0.18	1.15	—
Cottonseed oil meal, solvent	91.4	41.6	34.5	66.1	1.34	0.15	1.10	—
Fish meal, menhaden	92.2	61.3	49.7	67.0	1.35	5.49	2.81	—
Flaxseed screenings	91.4	15.8	8.8	58.5	1.18	0.37	0.43	—
Flaxseed screenings oil feed	91.3	24.1	13.5	54.6	1.10	0.44	0.63	—
Hominy feed, white	89.8	11.1	7.9	82.9	1.67	0.02	0.58	—
Hominy feed, yellow	90.7	11.1	7.9	83.7	1.69	0.05	0.52	3.1
Linseed feed	90.5	33.8	28.4	74.2	1.50	0.43	0.65	—
Linseed oil meal, expeller	90.9	35.3	30.7	76.3	1.54	0.44	0.89	—
Linseed oil meal, solvent	90.9	35.1	29.5	71.0	1.43	0.40	0.83	—
Meat scrap	93.5	53.4	43.8	65.4	1.32	7.90	4.03	—
Meat scrap, 50% protein	94.0	50.6	41.5	62.2	1.26	10.57	5.07	—
Milk, cow's	12.8	3.5	3.3	16.3	0.33	0.12	0.10	—
Milk, ewe's	19.2	6.5	6.2	26.2	0.53	0.21	0.12	—
Molasses, beet	76.0	6.7	3.5	59.6	1.20	0.16	0.03	—
Molasses, cane	74.5	3.2	0	54.9	1.11	0.89	0.08	—
Molasses, cane, dried	96.1	10.3	0	62.6	1.26	—	—	—
Oats, excluding Pacific Coast	90.2	12.0	9.4	70.1	1.42	0.09	0.33	—
Oats, Pacific Coast	91.2	9.0	7.0	72.2	1.46	—	—	—
Oats, rolled (oatmeal)	90.8	16.1	14.5	91.4	1.85	0.07	0.46	—
Oat groats (hulled)	90.4	16.2	14.6	91.9	1.86	0.08	0.46	—
Orange pulp, dried	89.3	7.0	5.5	78.8	1.59	0.63	0.10	—
Oyster shell, ground	99.6	1.0			—	38.05	0.07	—
Peanut oil meal, expeller	92.0	45.8	41.7	80.2	1.62	0.17	0.57	—
Peanut oil meal, solvent	91.5	47.4	43.1	74.3	1.50	0.20	0.65	—
Potato meal, dried	90.3	5.9	2.1	65.1	1.32	—	—	—
Rape seed	90.5	20.4	17.3	117.1	2.37	—	—	—
Rice bran	90.6	13.5	9.2	71.0	1.43	0.06	1.82	—
Rice polishings	89.9	11.8	9.0	83.0	1.68	0.04	1.42	—
Rye grain	89.5	12.6	10.0	76.5	1.55	0.10	0.33	—
Rye distillers dried grains	93.0	22.4	13.4	60.2	1.22	0.13	0.41	—

TABLE I (Continued)

Feedstuff	Total Dry Matter	Pro- tein	Dig. Pro- tein	TDN[2]	DE[2]	Cal- cium-	Phos- phorus	Caro- tene
	%	%	%	%	Therms /lb.	%	%	mg/ b.
Concentrates—Continued								
Rye middlings	89.8	17.1	13.0	71.4	1.44	0.06	0.63	—
Safflower oil meal expeller	90.6	19.7	15.8	48.4	0.98	0.23	0.71	—
Safflower oil meal, with hulls	93.2	23.7	19.0	51.5	1.04	—	—	—
Safflower oil meal, without hulls	91.1	38.4	33.8	64.4	1.30	0.31	0.58	—
Safflower seed	93.1	16.3	13.0	82.4	1.66	—	—	—
Skim milk, dried	93.9	33.5	30.2	80.3	1.62	1.26	1.03	—
Sorghum, Kafir	89.8	11.0	8.9	81.6	1.65	0.03	0.31	—
Sorghum, milo	89.0	10.9	8.5	79.4	1.60	0.03	0.28	—
Sorghum, milo, head chops	89.6	9.2	7.0	74.3	1.50	0.14	0.26	—
Soybeans	90.0	37.9	33.7	87.6	1.77	0.25	0.59	—
Soybean oil meal, expeller	89.7	43.8	36.8	77.0	1.56	0.27	0.63	—
Soybean oil meal, solvent	89.3	45.8	42.1	77.2	1.56	0.32	0.67	—
Sweet potato meal	90.2	4.9	0.7	72.7	1.47	0.15	0.14	32.2
Tankage, digester	92.1	59.8	50.8	66.1	1.34	5.94	3.17	—
Tankage, dige ter with bone	94.1	49.6	42.2	64.7	1.31	10.97	5.14	—
Wheat, hard, winter	89.4	13.5	11.3	79.6	1.61	0.05	0.42	—
Wheat, hard, spring	90.1	15.8	13.3	80.7	1.63	0.04	0.40	—
Wheat, soft, winter	89.2	10.2	8.6	80.1	1.62	—	0.29	—
Wheat, soft, Pacific Coast	89.1	9.9	8.3	79.9	1.61	—	—	—
Wheat bran	89.1	16.0	13.0	65.9	1.33	0.14	1.17	1.2
Wheat flour middlings	89.8	18.4	16.2	78.2	1.58	0.11	0.76	—
Wheat germ oil meal	89.7	27.3	22.9	84.1	1.70	0.07	1.06	3.0
Wheat screenings, good grade	90.4	13.9	10.0	68.7	1.39	0.44	0.39	—
Wheat standard middlings	89.7	17.2	14.3	76.9	1.55	0.15	0.91	1.4
Whey, dried	93.5	13.1	11.8	78.4	1.58	0.87	0.79	—
Yeast, brewers dried	93.4	44.6	38.4	72.4	1.46	0.13	1.43	—
Yeast, torula, dried	93.3	48.3	41.5	69.9	1.41	0.57	1.68	—

SECTION II. — ANIMAL UNITS

An animal unit is a common animal denominator, based on feed consumption. It is assumed that one mature cow or one mature horse represents an animal unit. The comparative (to a mature cow or a mature horse) feed consumption of other age groups or classes of animals determines the proportion of an animal unit which they represent. For example, it is generally estimated that the ration of one mature cow or one mature horse will feed five hogs raised to 200 pounds. For this reason, the animal units/head on this class and age of animals is 0.2. The following table gives the animal units for different classes and ages of livestock:

TABLE II
ANIMAL UNITS

Type of Livestock	Animal Unit per Head
Horse	1
Cow	1
Bull	1
Young cattle over 1 year old	0.5
Calf	0.25
Colt	0.5
Brood sow or boar	0.4
Hog raised to 200 pounds	0.2
Ewe or ram	0.14
Lamb	0.07
Poultry (per 100)	1
Chickens raised (per 200)	1

SECTION III. — WEIGHTS AND MEASURES OF COMMON FEEDS

In calculating rations and mixing concentrates, it is usually necessary to use weights rather than measures. However, in practical feeding operations it is often more convenient for the farmer or rancher to measure the concentrates. The following tabulation will serve as a guide in feeding by measure:

TABLE III

WEIGHTS AND MEASURES OF COMMON FEEDS

Feed:	Approximate weight	
	Lbs. per quart	Lbs. per bushel
Alfalfa meal	0.6	19
Barley	1.5	48
Beet pulp (dried)	0.6	19
Brewers' grain (dried)	0.6	19
Buckwheat	1.6	50
Buckwheat bran	1.0	29
Corn, husked ear	—	70
Corn, cracked	1.6	50
Corn, shelled	1.8	56
Corn meal	1.6	50
Corn-and-cob meal	1.4	45
Cottonseed meal	1.5	48
Cowpeas	1.9	60
Distillers' grain (dried)	0.6	19
Fish meal	1.0	35
Gluten feed	1.3	42
Linseed-oil meal (old process)	1.1	35
Linseed-oil meal (new process)	0.9	29
Meat scrap	1.3	42
Molasses feed	0.8	26
Oats	1.0	32
Oats, ground	0.7	22
Oat middlings	1.5	48
Peanut meal	1.0	32
Rice bran	0.8	26
Rye	1.7	56
Soybeans	1.8	60
Tankage	1.6	51
Velvetbeans, shelled	1.8	60
Wheat	1.9	60
Wheat bran	0.5	16
Wheat middlings, standard	0.8	26
Wheat screenings	1.0	32

SECTION IV. — ESTIMATING STEER WEIGHTS FROM HEART GIRTH MEASUREMENTS[1]

It is highly desirable to know the weight of steers at various stages during the fattening process so that (1) rations can be evaluated, (2) rate of gain can be calculated, and (3) show-ring classification can be determined.

Frequently suitable scales on which to weigh animals are not available. Under such conditions, a simple but reasonably accurate method of estimating body weight is very useful.

Based on heart girth measurements made on a number of steers exhibited at the Ogden and Salt Lake Junior Livestock shows, Professor James A. Bennett, Head, Department of Animal Husbandry, Utah State Agricultural College, developed the following ingenious formula for estimating steer weights:

Live Wt.=1.04 [27.5758 (heart girth in inches)—1049.67].

Based on this formula, the calculated live weight values for steers grading Prime and Choice and with heart girth measurements within the range of 63 to 80 inches is as shown in Table IV.

TABLE IV

ESTIMATING STEER WEIGHTS
FROM HEART GIRTH MEASUREMENTS

Heart Girth	Calculated Live Weight	Heart Girth	Calculated Live Weight
(inches)	(pounds)	(inches)	(pounds)
63	715	72	973
64	744	73	1002
65	773	74	1031
66	801	75	1060
67	830	76	1088
68	859	77	1117
69	887	78	1145
70	916	79	1174
71	945	80	1203

Thus, if a steer (grading Prime or Choice) has a heart girth measurement of 63 inches, his calculated weight may be determined by (1) multiplying 27.5758 by 63, (2) subtracting 1049.67 from the product, and (3) multiplying the remainder by 1.04; or read directly from Table IV.

In taking heart girth measurement, it is important (1) that the steer be kept off feed and water for a minimum of 12 hours (an overnight shrink will be satisfactory and will avoid throwing the animal off feed), (2) that the animal stand with all four legs squarely under the body and with the head up in a normal position, and (3) that the tape be passed around the body just back of the shoulders at the smallest circumference and pulled up snugly.

[1] Formulae used in estimating weights of dairy cattle from heart girth measurements are not applicable to fat steers; beef animals being lighter than dairy animals of the same heart girth measurement.

SECTION V. — GESTATION TABLE

The cattleman who has information relative to breeding dates can easily estimate parturition dates from Table V:

TABLE V

GESTATION TABLE FOR COWS

Date Bred	Date due, 283 days	Date Bred	Date due, 283 days
Jan. 1	Oct. 11	July 5	Apr. 14
Jan. 6	Oct. 16	July 10	Apr. 19
Jan. 11	Oct. 21	July 15	Apr. 24
Jan. 16	Oct. 26	July 20	Apr. 29
Jan. 21	Oct. 31	July 25	May 4
Jan. 26	Nov. 5	July 30	May 9
Jan. 31	Nov. 10	Aug. 4	May 14
Feb. 5	Nov. 15	Aug. 9	May 19
Feb. 10	Nov. 20	Aug. 14	May 24
Feb. 15	Nov. 25	Aug. 19	May 29
Feb. 20	Nov. 30	Aug. 24	June 3
Feb. 25	Dec. 5	Aug. 29	June 8
Mar. 2	Dec. 10	Sept. 3	June 13
Mar. 7	Dec. 15	Sept. 8	June 18
Mar. 12	Dec. 20	Sept. 13	June 23
Mar. 17	Dec. 25	Sept. 18	June 28
Mar. 22	Dec. 30	Sept. 23	July 3
Mar. 27	Jan. 4	Sept. 28	July 8
Apr. 1	Jan. 9	Oct. 3	July 13
Apr. 6	Jan. 14	Oct. 8	July 18
Apr. 11	Jan. 19	Oct. 13	July 23
Apr. 16	Jan. 24	Oct. 18	July 28
Apr. 21	Jan. 29	Oct. 23	Aug. 2
Apr. 26	Feb. 3	Oct. 28	Aug. 7
May 1	Feb. 8	Nov. 2	Aug. 12
May 6	Feb. 13	Nov. 7	Aug. 17
May 11	Feb. 18	Nov. 12	Aug. 22
May 16	Feb. 23	Nov. 17	Aug. 27
May 21	Feb. 28	Nov. 22	Sept. 1
May 26	Mar. 5	Nov. 27	Sept. 6
May 31	Mar. 10	Dec. 2	Sept. 11
June 5	Mar. 15	Dec. 7	Sept. 16
June 10	Mar. 20	Dec. 12	Sept. 21
June 15	Mar. 25	Dec. 17	Sept. 26
June 20	Mar. 30	Dec. 22	Oct. 1
June 25	Apr. 4	Dec. 27	Oct. 6
June 30	Apr. 9		

SECTION VI. — ALL-TIME TOP SALES

Cattlemen and students frequently like to refer to the great sales in the history of the many breeds. Presented herewith is a summary of some of the record beef cattle sales, both for individual animals and consignments or herds.

TABLE VI
ALL-TIME TOP INDIVIDUAL SALES[1]

Breed	Year of Sale	Identity of Animal	Sex	Price	Private Treaty or Auction	Seller	Purchaser
				Dollars			
Aberdeen-Angus	1946	Erianna B 6th	Female	25,000	Auction	J. G. Tolan, Pleasant Plains, Ill.	Vaughn Bros., Albion, Mich.
"	1948	Prince Sunbeam 249	Bull	60,000	Private Treaty	Sunbeam Farms, Miami, Okla.	Ellerslie Farm, Charlottesville, Va.
"	1950	Prince Eric of Sunbeam	Bull	100,000	Private Treaty	L. L. O'Bryan, Lakewood Farms, Mukwonago, Wis.	Shadow Isle Farm, Red Bank, N. J.
"	1951	Prince Ferndale WWF 1026750	Bull	40,000	Auction	Tim J. Pierce. Creston, Ill.	A. C. Luthor and Luther McClung, Ft. Worth, Texas
	1951	Eulimamere T-1245955	Female	25,500	Auction	J. G. Tolan, Pleasant Plains, Ill.	Kinloch Farm, Supply, Va.
	1951	Eileenmere 1201st, 1389035	Bull	40,000	Auction	J. G. Tolan, Pleasant Plains, Ill.	Mahrapo Farms, Mahwah, N. J.
	1951	Tolanis Bandolier 1389022	Bull	55,000	Auction	J. G. Tolan, Pleasant Plains, Ill.	Highland Farm, Round Hill, Va.
	1951	Shadow Isle Prince 1259470	Bull	57,000	Auction	Shadow Isle Farm, Red Bank, N. J.	R. L. Smith Farms, Chillicothe, Mo.
"	1952	Blackcap Bessie 6 of Sunbeam 1409243	Female	35,100	Auction	Sunbeam Farms, Miami, Okla.	R. L. Smith Farms, Chillicothe, Mo.
"	1952	Black Peer 79" of Angus Valley 1243485	Bull	60,000	Auction	Angus Valley Farms, Tulsa, Okla.	R. L. Smith Farms, Chillicothe, Mo.
"	1952	Homeplace Eileenmere 115" 1175460	Bull	70,000	Auction	Penney and James, Hamilton, Mo.	R. T. Davis, Wheatridge, Colo.
"	1952	Homeplace Gumer 5" 1340482	Female	38,000	Auction	Penney and James, Hamilton, Mo.	Taylor Bros., Essex, Mo.
"	1952	Ankonian 3501	Bull	58,000	Auction	Ankony Farm	Panther Ledge Farm, Allamochy, N. J.
"	1952	Prince Sunbeam 249th	Bull	100,000 (½ int.)	Private Treaty	Dr. Armand Hammer Shadow Isle Farm, Red Bank. N. J.	T. F. Murchison and Wm. A. Ljungdahl, San Antonio, Texas
	1952	Miss Blackcap of R.L.S. 8th 991133	Female	20,000	Auction	Shadow Isle Farm, Red Bank, N. J.	R. L. Smith Farms, Chillicothe, Mo.
"	1952	Evermere 40 of Shadow Isle	Female	29,500	Auction	R. L. Smith, Chillicothe, Mo.	Frank W. Cooper, Madison, Conn.
"	1952	Prince Sunbeam 328	Bull	60,000 (½ int.)	Private Treaty	Shadow Isle Farm, Red Bank, N. J.	Tom Slick, Essar Ranch, San Antonio Texas
"	1952	Eileenmere 1156th	Bull	50,000	Auction	J. G. Tolan, Pleasant Plains, Ill.	Bilbobern Farms, Elwood City, Pa.
"	1952	Blackcap Tolan Missie 9th	Fema	18,000	Auction	J. G. Tolan, Pleasant Plains, Ill.	McCormick's Ranch, Scottsdale, Ariz.

[1]Where a part interest is specified, the price listed represents the sale price for the part interest only.

TABLE VI (Continued)

Breed	Year of Sale	Identity of Animal	Sex	Price	Private Treaty or Auction	Seller	Purchaser
				Dollars			
Aberdeen-Angus	1953	Prince Esquire 2nd of Sunbeam	Bull	60,000	Auction	Sunbeam Farms, Miami, Okla.	F. W. Defoe, Mt. Pleasant Plantation, Andrews, S. C.
"	1953	Black Knight 98th of A. V.	Bull	50,000	Auction	Angus Valley Farms, Inc., Tulsa, Okla.	Kinloch Farm, Supply, Va.
"	1953	Mahrapo Black Jestress	Cow & calf	32,500	Auction	Shadow Isle Farm, Red Bank, N. J.	R. L. Smith Farms, Chillicothe, Mo.
"	1953	Angus Valley Blackcap Bessie 2 1214295	Female	13,000	Auction	Simon Angus Farm, Madison, Kan.	4-Winds, Dallas, Texas
"	1953	Barbarosa B. 1402575	Female	11,000	Auction	Simon Angus Farm, Madison, Kan.	Carlo Paterno, North Salem, N. Y.
"	1953	Bessie 5th of Shadow Isle	Female	16,200	Auction	Shadow Isle Farm, Red Bank, N. J.	White Gates Farm, Flanders, N. J.
"	1953	Runacres Evermere	Female	11,300	Auction	Runacres-Whitetail, joint sale Madison, Conn.	Lee Hill Farms, Fredericksburg, Va.
"	1953	Cherry Blossom 9th of Peebles	Female	15,000	Auction	Ridglea Farm, Dixon, Tenn.	R. L. Smith Farms Chillicothe, Mo.
"	1953	Bessie 5th of Shadow Isle	Female	16,200	Auction	Shadow Isle Farm, Red Bank, N. J.	White Gates Farm, Flanders, N. J.
	1953	Ellunamere 25th	Female	12,000	Auction	J. G. Tolan, Pleasant Plains, Ill.	R. E. Green, Oaktown, Ind.
'	1954	Prince 105th of TT.	Bull	115,000 (½ int.)	Private Treaty	Simon Angus Farms, Madison, Kan.	Byars Royal Oaks Farm, Tyler, and Four Wynnes Angus Farm, Kaufman, Texas
"	1954	Barbarosa Essar 13th	Female	38,500	Auction	M. & L. Ranch, Burnet, Texas	Hidewaway Farm, Chester, N. J., and H. &. L Farms, Marlboro, N. J.
"	1954	Angus Valley Evermere 7th	Female	13,100	Auction	Angus Valley Farm, Tulsa, Okla.	Hays Ranch, Kerrville, Texas
"	1954	Blackcap Bessie 40th of Wilton	Female	13,500	Auction	Wilton Farms, Davenport, Iowa	H. & L. Farm, Eatontown, N. J. and Hideaway Farm, Chester, N. J.
"	1954	Eisa of R.L.S.	Female	26,000	Auction	Greenmere Angus Oaktown, Ind.	Jefferson Farms, Butler, Pa.
"	1955	Homeplace Eileenmere 375th	Bull	87,000	Auction	Penney & James, Hamilton, Mo.	Thomas Staley, K. C., Mo., and C. A. Neilson, Hemet, Calif.
"	1955	Homeplace Enquiry Dell 3rd.	Female	16,000	Auction	Penney & James, Hamilton, Mo.	Panther Ledge Farm Allamuchy, N. J.
"	1956	Black Baron of Barnoldby	Bull	48,000	Auction	Osmond & Sons, Barnoldby-le-Beck, Grimsby, Scotland	L. L. O'Bryan, Muckwonago, Wis.
"	1956	Eileen of Shadow Isle	Female	22,100	Auction	Haystack Angus Ranch, Longmont. Colo.	Leo Rubin, Hillsdale, N. Y.

TABLE VI (Continued)

Breed	Year of Sale	Identity of Animal	Sex	Price	Private Treaty or Auction	Seller	Purchaser
				Dollars			
Aberdeen-Angus	1958	Ankony Bombardier	Bull	100,000 (½ int.)	Private Treaty	Ankony Farm, Rhinebeck, N. Y.	Haystack Ranch, Longmont, Colo.
"	1959	Elevate of Eastfield	Bull	75,000	Auction	T. H. Brewis, Eastfield of Lempitlaw, Kelso, Scotland	Lester Leachman, Claverack, N. Y.
Brahma	1950	Emperor Jr., 4th	Bull	10,000	Private Treaty	H. O. Partin & Sons, Kissimmee, Fla.	J. P. James, Bartow, Fla.
"	1956	King	Bull	10,000	Private Treaty	Lamar Beauchamp, Winter Haven, Fla.	E. E. O'Reilly, New Smyrna Beach Fla.
Brangus	1952	Clear Creek Duke 28th	Bull	10,000	Auction	Clear Creek Ranch, 2909 First Nat'l. Bldg., Oklahoma City, Okla.	F. B. Daniel, Orange, Va.
Charolais	1956		Female	5,400	Auction	A. M. Askew, Houston, Texas	4T Ranches, Weslaco, Texas
Hereford	1946	Real Silver Domino 44 3317191	Bull	52,000	Auction	Jack Turner, Fort Worth, Texas	Hills and Dales, La Grange, Ga.
"	1947	WHR Helmsman 89th 4635085	Bull	61,000	Auction	Wyoming Hereford Ranch, Cheyenne, Wyo.	Hi-Wan Ranch, Evergreen, Colo.
"	1947	T. T Zato Heiress	Female	35,000	Auction	Thornton Hereford Ranch, Gunnison, Colo.	Gerald Montgomery Madera, Calif.
"	1949	Baca Duke 2nd	Bull	65,000	Auction	Albert Noe Farms, Pulaski, Tenn.	A. H. Karpe, Greenfield Hereford Ranch, Bakersfield, Calif.
"	1950	Hillcrest Larry 4th 6,000,000	Bull	70,500	Auction	Hillcrest Farm, Chester, W. Va.	Chino Farms, Church Hill, Md.
"	1951	Baca Princess 63rd	Female	15,000	Auction	Freeman and Graves, Pulaski, Tenn.	E. S. Culver, Richland Farms, Pulaski, Tenn.
"	1951	M. W. Prince Larry 62nd	Bull	50,000	Private Treaty	Milky Way Hereford Ranch, Phoenix, Ariz.	R. A. Kropp, Grayslake, Ill., and Jack Hawley, Minneapolis, Minn.
"	1951	M. W. Larry Domino 172nd	Bull	50,000	Auction	Honey Creek Ranch, Grove, Okla.	Par-Ker Ranch, Chelsea, Okla.
"	1951	M. W. Larry Domino 107	Bull	80,000 (½ int.)	Auction	Honey Creek Ranch, Grove, Okla.	J. S. Bridwell, Wichita Falls, Texas
	1952	Baca Duke 1st	Bull	51,000	Auction	H. C. Pearson Estate, Indianola, Iowa	Duncan Hereford Farm, Orangeburg, S. C.
"	1952	Baca Prince Domino 20th	Bull	87,500	Auction	Baca Grant, Gunnison, Colo.	A. H. Karpe, Bakersfield, Calif.
"	1952	HC Larry Domino 12th	Bull	105,000 (½ int.)	Private Treaty	C. A. Smith, Chester, W. Va.	E. C. McCormick, Jr. Medina, Ohio
"	1954	HC Larry Domino 12th	"	52,000 (remaining ½ int.)	Auction	" " "	" "

TABLE VI (Continued)

Breed	Year of Sale	Identity of Animal	Sex	Price	Private Treaty or Auction	Seller	Purchaser
				Dollars			
Hereford	1953	MW Larry Domino 83rd	Bull	33,333 (⅓ int.)	Private Treaty	Milky Way Hereford Ranch, Phoenix, Ariz.	Kirk's Valley Stream Hereford Farm, Valley Center, Calif.
"	1953	Zato Heir P 47th	Bull	50,000	Auction	Montgomery Hereford Ranch, Madera, Calif.	Milky Way Hereford Ranch, Phoenix, Ariz.
"	1954	Zato's Aristocrat	Bull	26,000 (¼ int.)	Auction	Letts & Turkington Letts, Iowa	Caw Caw Plantation Orangeburg, S. C. ¼ Bea-Mar Farms, Washington, Ohio,¼;, and Milky Way Hereford, Phoenix, Ariz. ½.
"	1954	Hillcrest Larry 25th	Bull	100,000	Auction	Hillcrest Farms, Chester, W. Va.	Mr. and Mrs. R. Fair Fair Oaks Ranch, Boerne, Texas
	1954	TR Royal Zato 27th	Bull	45,100 (½ int.)	Auction	Turner Ranch, Sulfur, Okla.	Hull-Dobbs, Walls Miss. & Forth Worth, Texas; and Northwoods Stock Farm, Fort Worth, Texas
"	1957	TR Royal Zato 27th	Bull	60,000 (¼ int.)	Private Treaty	Owners above	L & J Crusoe Ranch, Cheboygan, Mich.
"	1958	TR Ameroyal Zato	Bull	50,000 (½ int.)	Private Treaty	Turner Ranch, Sulfur, Okla.	Burk Healey, Flying L Ranch, Davis, Okla.
Milking Shorthorn	1917	Lady of the Glen	Female	5,500		The Otis Herd, Willoughby, Ohio	A. T. Cole, Wheaton, Ill.
"	1950	Lilydale Dagney Pride	Female	5,600		Lilydale Farm, Springfield, Mo.	Mystery Farm, Hope, R. I.
"	1950	Revelex Daisy's Premier	Bull	9,000		R. H. Vigus, Herts, England	Last Chance Ranch, Lake Placid, N. Y.
Polled Hereford	1947	Alf Choice Domino 6	Bull	35,000	Auction	J. M. Lewis & Sons, Larned, Kans.	A. G. Rolfe, Poolesville, Md.
"	1949	M. H. Supreme Beauty	Female	10,700	Auction	Mousel and Hausler Holbrook, Neb.	Mike Lewis Livestock Co., Henderson, Colo.
Polled Hereford	1950	S. B. Letston Lady 4th	Female	11,000	Auction	A. G. Rolfe, Poolesville, Md.	C. C. Potter, Pottstown, Penn.
"	1951	GMR Anxiety Domino 25	Bull	40,500	Auction	M. P. Moore, Senatobia, Miss.	C. C. Potter, Pottstown, Penn.
"	1951	EER Victor Anxiety	Bull	42,000	Auction	Double E. Ranch, Senatobia, Miss.	R. C. Malone, Meridian, Miss.
"	1951	Helen Dandy Domino 10th	Female	13,000	Auction	Wilford Scott, Chadron, Neb.	Calvin Fowler, Franklin, Tenn.
"	1951	EER Victoria Tone	Female	11,250	Auction	E. E. Moore, Double E. Ranch, Senatobia, Miss.	L. J. Moore, Covington, Ga.
"	1952	CMR Super Rollo 4th	Bull	30,000	Auction	Circle M Ranch, Senatobia, Miss.	A. G. Rolfe, Poolesville, Md.
"	1952	EER Victoria Tone 25th	Female	14,000	Auction	E. E. Moore, Senatobia, Miss.	J. C. Lanham, Eastover, S. C.

TABLE VI (Continued)

Breed	Year of Sale	Identity of Animal	Sex	Price	Private Treaty or Auction	Seller	Purchaser
				Dollars			
Polled Hereford	1952	Real Plato Domino Jr.	Bull	43,500	Auction	Fritz Kerbs & Sons, Otis, Kans.	Allen Engler & Sons, Topeka, Kans.
"	1953	CMR Mischief Domino 81st	Bull	47,000	Auction	Circle M Ranch, Senatobia, Miss.	A. G. Rolfe, Poolesville, Md.
"	1953	AFL Battle Mixer 20th	Bull	50,000	Auction	Alfalfa Lawn Farms, Larned, Kans.	Bay Manor Farm, Lewis, Del.
"	1956	Gold Co-Pilot	Bull	50,000 (½ int.)	Private Treaty	O. E. Kuhlmann, North Platte, Neb.	Hull-Dobbs Ranch, Walls, Miss.
"	1957	Mischief Lady 16th	Female	17,000	Auction	Santa Fe River Ranch, Alachua, Fla.	Todiway Acres, Pike Road, Ala.
"	1958	Adv. Larollo	Bull	55,000	Auction	Circle M Ranch, Senatobia, Miss.	Double S Ranch, Chino, Calif.
"	1958	Blanche Larry 11th	Female	18,100	Auction	Circle M Ranch, Senatobia, Miss.	Circle L Ranch, Greenwood, Ark.
"	1958	Mixer Return	Bull	40,000 (⅓ int.)	Private Treaty	C. E. Knowlton, Bellefontaine, Ohio, and O'Bryan Ranch, Hiattville, Kan.	Harold Huber, Schneider, Ind.
"	1958	Pawnee Mixer	Bull	56,000	Auction	C. E. Knowlton, Bellefontaine, Ohio	T. W. Davis, Montgomery, Ala.
Polled Shorthorn	1948		Bull	6,300	Auction	Johnson Disposal Sale, Rockwell City, Iowa	
"	1948		Female	3,600	Auction	International Polled Shorthorn Sale, Chicago, Ill.	
"	1952	Oakwood Distinction	Bull	10,500	Private Treaty	C. B. Teegardin & Sons, Ashville, Ohio	
"	1952	Oakwood Good Fortune 2nd	Female	4,600	Private Treaty	C. B. Teegardin & Sons Ashville, Ohio	Hi-Ho Farms
"	1953	Oakwood Conquest	Bull	7,000	Private Treaty	C. B. Teegardin & Sons, Ashville, Ohio	L & L Farms, Dothan, Ala.
"	1954	Max Coronet 5th	Bull	20,000	Private Treaty	L. W. Thieman, Concordia, Mo.	Avenel Farms, Bethesda, Md.
"	1956	Edith Souchong	Female	5,600	Auction	Hi-Ho Farms	George Arrowsmith Upperco, Md.
"	1956	LF Fascination	Bull	25,000	Private Treaty	Landen Farm, Foster, Ohio	D. J. O'Connor, Mason, Ohio
Santa Gertrudis	1950	Lot No. 32 (prior to regis. by new assoc.)	Bull	10,000	Auction	King Ranch, Kingsville, Texas	Edgar Brown, Orange, Texas
"	1951	Lot No. 56 (prior to regis. by new assoc.)	Bull	23,000	Auction	King Ranch, Kingsville, Texas	Powell Crosley, Cincinnati, Ohio
"	1951	Lot No. 65 (prior to regis. by new assoc.)	Bull	27,200	Auction	King Ranch, Kingsville, Texas	Garvin Tankersley, River Rd. at Burdette, Washington, D.C.
"	1952	Lot No. 7	Bull	40,000	Auction	King Ranch, Kingsville, Texas	Briggs Syndicate, San Antonio, Texas

TABLE VI (Continued)

Breed	Year of Sale	Identity of Animal	Sex	Price	Private Treaty or Auction	Seller	Purchaser
				(Dollars)			
Santa Gertrudis	1952	Lot No. 13	Bull	31,000	Auction	King Ranch, Kingsville, Texas	Monroe Wise Highlands, Texas
"	1953		Bull	31,500	Auction	King Ranch, Kingsville, Texas	Winthrop Rockefeller Morrilton, Ark.
"	1953		Bull	21,500	Auction	King Ranch, Kingsville, Texas	Winthrop Rockefeller Morrilton. Ark.
"	1955	Dulcy	Bull	28,000	Auction	King Ranch, Kingsville, Texas	Winrock Farms, Morrilton, Ark.
"	1958	Gata	Female	6,000	Auction	R. W. Briggs San Antonio, Texas	R. J. Kleberg, Kingsville, Texas
"	1959		Bull	27,500	Auction	King Ranch, Kingsville, Texas	Winrock Farms, Morrilton, Ark.
Shorthorn	1873	8th Duchess of Geneva	Female	40,600	Auction	New York Mills, Utica N. Y.	R. P. Davies, England
"	1946	Pittodrie Upright	Bull	61,335	Auction (Perth, Scotland)	L. S. Pitcaple, Aberdeenshire, Scotland	Sni-A-Bar Farms, Grain Valley, Mo.
"	1951	Leveldale Good News 2637691	Bull	16,500	Auction	L. E. Mathers & Son, Mason City, Ill.	John Alexander & Son, Aurora, Ill.
	1952	Calrossie Highland	Bull	29,000	Auction (Perth, Scotland)	John and D. P. Mac-Gillivray, Calrossie Ross-shire, Scotland	A. R. Cross, Alberta, Canada
"	1952	Edellyn Rosewood 65th	Female	10,000	Auction	T. E. Wilson, Wilson, Ill.	Henry Knight, Lexington, Ky.
,	1952	Leveldale Custodian	Bull	19,000	Auction	L. E. Mathers & Son, Mason City, Ill.	S. J. O'Bryan, Lake Villa, Ill.
"	1953	Cruggleton Purvis	Bull	22,500	Auction	Marellbar Farm, Libertyville, Ill.	M. S. Oftedal, Libertyville, Ill.
"	1953	Edellyn Royal Leader 149th	Bull	15,000	Auction	Edellyn Farms, Wilson, Ill.	Maclyn Plantation, Albany, Ga.
"	1953	Edellyn Prig Mercury	Bull	15,000	Auction	Edellyn Farms, Wilson, Ill.	R. E. Smith, Houston, Texas
"	1953	Edellyn Clipper 54th	Female	7,500	Auction	Edellyn Farms, Wilson Ill.	Lynnwood Farms, Carmel, Ind.
"	1953	Cruggelton Rainey	Bull	26,000	Auction	Scofield Ranch, Austin, Texas	U. R. Bronk, Houston, Texas
"	1953	Circle M Musil 3rd	Female	14,000	Auction	Scofield Ranch, Austin, Texas	Roberta Dickson, Austin, Texas
"	1956	Bapton Constructor	Bull	45,000	Private Treaty	Cecil Moore, Aberdeenshire, Scotland	Louada Manor Farms, Peterborough, Canada
"	1956	Kinellar Napoleon	Bull	25,500	Auction	Sylvester Campbell & Sons, Aberdeen-shire, Scotland	Cyrus Eaton, Northfield, Ohio
"	1956	Leveldale Basis	Bull	17,500 (½ int.)	Private Treaty	Leveldale Farms, Mason City, Ill.	John Alexander & Sons, Aurora, Ill.

TABLE VII
ALL-TIME TOP CONSIGNMENT OR HERD SALES

Breed	Year of Sale	Number of Animals	Average Price	Seller
Aberdeen-Angus	1946	46	(Dollars) 5,614	Sunbeam Farms, Miami, Okla.
"	1951	50	10,246	J. G. Tolan, Pleasant Plains, Ill.
"	1951	70	6,758	Dr. Armand Hammer, Red Bank, N. J.
"	1952	60	5,171	Sunbeam Farms, Miami, Okla.
"	1952	62	6,464	Angus Valley Farms. Tulsa, Okla.
"	1952	82	5,409	J. G. Tolan, Pleasant Plains, Ill.
"	1953	62	5,821	Sunbeam Farms, Miami, Okla.
"	1953	66	5,502	Angus Valley Farms, Inc., Tulsa, Okla.
"	1956	56	5,825	Ankony Farm, Rhinebeck, N. Y.
Charolais	1953	30	1,430	C. M. Frost, Houston, Texas
"	1956	30	2,960	A. M. Askew, Houston, Texas
Hereford	1919	140	3,635	W. T. McCray, Kentland, Ind.
"	1947	72	5,934	Wyoming Hereford Ranch, Cheyenne, Wyo.
"	1952	76	5,306	Wyoming Hereford Ranch, Cheyenne, Wyo.
"	1954	50	6,120	Turner Ranch Sulfur, Okla.
Polled Hereford	1951	56	4,421	Circle M. Ranch, Senatobia, Miss.
"	1952	50	5,061	Circle M. Ranch Senatobia, Miss.
"	1953	50	7,230	Circle M. Ranch, Senatobia, Miss.
"	1954	51	4,518	Circle M. Ranch, Senatobia, Miss.
"	1956	50	4,034	Circle M. Ranch, Senatobia, Miss.
Milking Shorthorn	1917	39	1,110	The Otis Herd, Willoughby, Ohio
"	1950	42	1,056	National Milking Shorthorn Congress Sale, Springfield, Mo.
Polled Shorthorn	1951	42	1,295	C. B. Teegardin & Sons, Ashville, Ohio.

TABLE VII (Continued)

Breed	Year of Sale	Number of Animals	Average Price	Seller
Polled Shorthorns (Continued)			(Dollars)	
"	1952	53	1,376	C. B. Teegardin & Sons, Ashville, Ohio
	1952	36	1,107	1st. Ann.-Sporting Field Farm Sale, Capon Bridge, W. Va.
"	1953	50	1,176	C. B. Teegardin & Sons, Ashville, Ohio
Santa Gertrudis	1951	25	8,502	King Ranch, Kingsville, Texas
"	1952	21	8,583	King Ranch, Kingsville, Texas
"	1953	40 females	1,866	Pioneer Santa Gertrudis Breeders, San Antonio, Texas
"	1953	24 bulls	8,439	King Ranch, Kingsville, Texas
"	1957	25 bulls	6,311	King Ranch, Kingsville, Texas
"	1958	24 bulls	6,033	King Ranch, Kingsville, Texas
"	1958	37	1,937	Pioneer Santa Gertrudis Breeders, San Antonio, Texas
"	1959	25	8,690	King Ranch, Kingsville, Texas
Shorthorn	1873	109	3,504	New York Mills, Utica, N. Y.
"	1919	39	5,140	Wm. Duthie of Collyne, Tarves, Aberdeenshire, Scotland
"	1952	50	3,030	L. E. Mathers & Sons, Mason City, Ill.
"	1953	26	2,836	Marellbar Farms, Libertyville, Ill.
"	1953	34	3,715	Edellyn Farms, Wilson, Ill.
"	1953	32	3,077	Scofield Ranch, Austin, Texas

SECTION VII.— BREED REGISTRY ASSOCIATIONS

A breed registry association consists of a group of breeders banded together for the purposes of: (1) recording the lineage of their animals, (2) protecting the purity of the breed, (3) encouraging further improvement of the breed, and (4) promoting the interest of the breed. A list of the beef and dual-purpose cattle breed registry associations is given in Table VIII:

TABLE VIII
BREED REGISTRY ASSOCIATIONS

Breed	Association	Secretary and Address
ABERDEEN-ANGUS	American Angus Assn.	Frank Richards, Secy., 3201 Frederick Blvd., St. Joseph, Missouri.
BEEFMASTER	No registry assn.; but the name "Beefmaster" is copyrighted and permitted on a franchise basis only.	Holder of franchise: Tom Lasater, the Lasater Ranch, Matheson, Colorado.
BELTED GALLOWAY	American Belted Galloway Cattle Breeders' Assn.	Charles C. Wells, Secy., South Fork, Missouri.
BRAHMAN[1]	American Brahman Breeders' Assn.	Harry P. Gayden, Executive Secy., 4815 Gulf Freeway, Houston, Texas.
	Pan-American Zebu Assn.[2]	Roy G. Martin, Secy., 818 Gunter Bldg., San Antonio, Texas.
BRANGUS	American Brangus Breeders' Assn.	Mr. Jesse L. Dowdy, Exec.-Secy., 646 Livestock Exchange Bldg., Kansas City 2, Missouri.
CHARBRAY	American Charbray Breeders' Assn.	Mrs. Quinta Arrigo, Recording Secy., 475 Texas National Bank Bldg., Houston, Texas.
CHAROLAIS	American-International Charolais Assn.	Mrs. Edna McIntyre, Recording Secy., 437 Texas National Bank Bldg., Houston 2 ,Texas.
DEVON	American Devon Cattle Club, Inc.	Kenneth Hinshaw, Secy.-Treas., 704 Suffield St. Agawam, Massachusetts.
GALLOWAY	American Galloway Breeders' Assn.	C. C. Wells, Secy., South Fork, Missouri.
HEREFORD	American Hereford Assn.	Paul Swaffar, Secy., Hereford Drive, Kansas City, Missouri.
MILKING SHORTHORN	American Milking Shorthorn Society	W. E. Dixon, Secy., 313 South Glenstone, Springfield, Missouri.
POLLED HEREFORD	American Polled Hereford Assn.	Don W. Chittenden, Secy., 4700 E. 63rd St. Trfwy. Kansas City 30, Missouri.
POLLED SHORTHORN	American Polled Shorthorn Society	Kenneth R. Fulk, Secy., Livestock Exchange Bldg., Union Stock Yards, Omaha, Nebraska.
RED ANGUS	Red Angus Assn. of America	George Chiga, Pres., Box 827, Guthrie, Oklahoma.
RED POLL	Red Poll Cattle Club of America	Wendell H. Severin, Secy.,-Treas. 3275 Holdrege St., Lincoln 3, Nebraska.
SANTA GERTRUDIS	Santa Gertrudis Breeders' International	R. P. Marshall, Exec.-Secy., Box 1373, Kingsville, Texas.
SCOTCH HIGHLAND	American Scotch Highland Breeders' Assn.	Margaret Manke, Secy.-Treas., Edgemont, South Dakota.
SHORTHORN	American Shorthorn Breeders' Assn.	Kenneth R. Fulk, Secy., Livestock Exchange Bldg., Union Stock Yards, Omaha, Nebraska.

[1]Includes three breeds of *Bos indicus* cattle that have and are contributing to beef production in the U. S.; namely American Brahman, Indu-Brazil and Africander.
[2]Registers the Indu-Brazil type of Brahman imported into this country from India by way of Brazil and Mexico.

SECTION VIII. — REGISTERING ANIMALS PRODUCED THROUGH ARTIFICIAL INSEMINATION[1]

Today, artificial insemination is more extensively practiced with dairy cattle than with any other class of farm animals. Because beef cattle are not kept under as close supervision as dairy cattle, and because of other differences in management, the practice does not lend itself as well to beef cattle production.

Table IX summarizes the pertinent regulations relative to the registration of calves of the beef and dual-purpose breeds of cattle produced by artificial insemination.

TABLE IX

RULES OF BEEF AND DUAL-PURPOSE CATTLE REGISTRY ASSOCIATIONS RELATIVE TO REGISTERING YOUNG PRODUCED ARTIFICIALLY

Breed	Registry Association	Pertinent Rules or Attitudes of Each Registry Association Relative to Artificial Insemination
ABERDEEN-ANGUS	American Angus Breeders' Assn.	The sire and the dam of the calf must be in the recorded ownership of the same herd at the time the calf was sired. Joint ownership of the sire is accepted. On application for entry, it must be stated that the animal is the product of artificial insemination. Bulls used artificially must first be blood typed, and the blood type must be on file in the Association office. Calves produced from stored semen following the death of a sire are not eligible for registration.
BRAHMAN	American Brahman Breeders' Assn.	Same alternate stipulations as the Shorthorn, plus the following additional provisions: Technicians and/or veterinarians must be approved by the Association. The inseminated female shall not have been exposed to a bull or artificially inseminated for a period of 30 days prior to or following said artificial insemination.
BRANGUS	American Brangus Breeders' Assn.	No official policy relative to the registry of calves produced by artificial insemination, but it appears that they will accept registrations with certain stipulations.
CHARBRAY	American Charbray Breeders' Assn.	No official policy relative to the registry of calves produced by artificial insemination, but such calves will probably be accepted under certain stipulations.
CHAROLAIS	American International Charolais Breeders' Assn.	No official policy relative to the registry of calves produced by artificial insemination, but such calves will probably be accepted, under certain stipulations.
DEVON	American Devon Cattle Club, Inc.	No official policy relative to the registry of calves produced by artificial insemination, but it will accept applications with suitable affidavits.

[1]For a rather complete discussion of the subject of Artificial Insemination, the reader is referred to *The Stockman's Handbook,* a book by the same author and the same publisher as *Beef Cattle Science.*

TABLE IX (Continued)

Breed	Registry Association	Pertinent Rules or Attitudes of Each Registry Association Relative to Artificial Insemination
HEREFORD	American Hereford Assn.	The sire and the dam of the calf must be in the recorded ownership of the same herd at the time the calf was sired.
INDU BRAZIL (ZEBU)	Pan-American Zebu Assn.	No existing rules relative to registration of calves produced by artificial insemination, but the Association has indicated that it will establish appropriate rules when the necessity arises.
MILKING SHORTHORN	American Milking Shorthorn Society	An executed insemination certificate, supplied by the inseminator, must be attached to the application. All sires used by an artificial insemination association must be approved by the directors of the American Milking Shorthorn Society.
POLLED HEREFORD	American Polled Hereford Breeders' Assn.	Same as Hereford.
POLLED SHORTHORN	American Polled Shorthorn Society	Same as Shorthorn.
RED POLL	Red Poll Cattle Club of America	Calves produced artificially are eligible for registry provided (1) artificial insemination is conducted according to the "Requirements Governing Artificial Insemination of Purebred Dairy Cattle" as adopted by the Purebred Dairy Cattle Association and approved by the National Association of Artificial Breeders and the American Dairy Science Association; and (2) the bull used for artificial insemination has been approved by The Red Poll Cattle Club.
SCOTCH HIGHLAND	American Scotch Highland Breeders' Assn.	No provision for registration.
SHORTHORN	American Shorthorn Breeders' Assn.	The owner of the bull must also be the owner of the inseminated female, or The application for registry must be accompanied by (a) a certificate (identifying the bull and the semen container, and specifying the date of collection) signed by the owner of the bull and the veterinarian or technician who collected the semen, and (b) a certificate (identifying the inseminated female, the bull, and the container, and specifying the date of insemination) signed by the owner of the inseminated female and the veterinarian or technician performing the insemination.
SANTA GERTRUDIS	Santa Gertrudis Breeders' International	Accepted.

SECTION IX. — BREED MAGAZINES

The livestock magazines publish news items and informative articles of special interest to cattlemen. Also, many of them employ field representatives whose chief duty it is to assist in the buying and selling of animals.

In the compilation of the list herewith presented (see Table X), no attempt was made to list the general livestock magazines of which there are numerous outstanding ones. Only those magazines which are devoted to a specific class or breed of beef or dual-purpose cattle are included.

TABLE X

BREED MAGAZINES

BREED	Publication	Address
Aberdeen-Angus	Aberdeen-Angus Journal	Webster City, Iowa.
Brahman	American Brahman Breeder	511 M & M Bldg., Houston, Texas.
Brangus	Brangus Journal	646 Livestock Exchange Bldg., Kansas City 2 Missouri.
Primarily devoted to Santa Gertrudis, Brahman, Indu-Brazil, Brangus, Charbray and Brafords	American Breeds	329 Texas Theatre Building, San Antonio 5, Texas.
Devon	Devon Cattle Quarterly	Agawam, Massachusetts.
Galloway	The American Galloway Journal	South Fork, Missouri.
Hereford	American Hereford Journal	500 Graphic Arts Building, Kansas City, Missouri.
Milking Shorthorn	Milking Shorthorn Journal	313 S. Glenstone, Springfield, Missouri.
Polled Hereford	Polled Hereford World Magazine	816 Locust, Kansas City, Missouri.
Red Poll	Red Poll News	3275 Holdrege St., Lincoln 3, Nebraska.
Shorthorn	Shorthorn World	16 S. Locust St., Aurora Illinois.

SECTION X. — STATE COLLEGES OF AGRICULTURE

The stockman can obtain a list of available bulletins and circulars and other information regarding livestock, by writing to his State Agricultural College. One should also write to the Superintendent of Documents, Washington, D. C., for lists of available bulletins and circulars. A list of the State Agricultural Colleges follows:

State	Address
Alabama	School of Agriculture, Auburn University, Auburn, Alabama
Alaska	Division of Agriculture, University of Alaska, College, Alaska
Arizona	College of Agriculture, University of Arizona, Tucson, Arizona
Arkansas	College of Agriculture, University of Arkansas, Fayetteville, Arkansas
California	College of Agriculture, University of California, Davis, California
Colorado	Colorado State University, Fort Collins, Colorado
Connecticut	College of Agriculture, University of Connecticut, Storrs, Connecticut
Delaware	School of Agriculture, University of Delaware, Newark, Delaware

State	Address
Florida	College of Agriculture, University of Florida, Gainesville, Florida
Georgia	College of Agriculture, University of Georgia, Athens, Georgia
Hawaii	Department of Agriculture, University of Hawaii, Honolulu 14, Hawaii
Idaho	College of Agriculture, University of Idaho, Moscow, Idaho
Illinois	The College of Agriculture, University of Illinois, Urbana, Illinois
Indiana	School of Agriculture, Purdue University, Lafayette, Indiana
Iowa	The Division of Agriculture, Iowa State University, Ames, Iowa
Kansas	Kansas State University, Manhattan, Kansas
Kentucky	College of Agriculture, University of Kentucky, Lexington 29, Kentucky
Louisiana	The Louisiana State University and Agricultural and Mechanical College, University Station, Baton Rouge 3, Louisiana
Maine	College of Agriculture, University of Maine, Orono, Maine
Maryland	College of Agriculture, University of Maryland, College Park, Maryland
Massachusetts	School of Agriculture, University of Massachusetts, Amherst, Massachusetts
Michigan	College of Agriculture, Michigan State University, East Lansing, Michigan
Minnesota	Department of Agriculture, University of Minnesota, University Farm, St. Paul 1, Minnesota
Mississippi	School of Agriculture, Mississippi State University, State College, Mississippi
Missouri	Division of Agricultural Sciences, University of Missouri, Columbia, Missouri
Montana	Department of Agriculture, Montana State College, Bozeman, Montana
Nebraska	College of Agriculture, University of Nebraska, Lincoln 1, Nebraska
Nevada	College of Agriculture, University of Nevada, Reno, Nevada
New Hampshire	College of Agriculture, University of New Hampshire, Durham, New Hampshire
New Jersey	State College of Agriculture, Rutgers University, New Brunswick, New Jersey
New Mexico	New Mexico State University, State College, New Mexico
New York	New York State College of Agriculture, Cornell University, Ithaca, New York
North Carolina	North Carolina State College of Agriculture, University of North Carolina, State College Station, Raleigh, North Carolina
North Dakota	North Dakota State University, State College Station, Fargo, North Dakota
Ohio	The College of Agriculture, Ohio State University, Columbus 10, Ohio

State	Address
Oklahoma	School of Agriculture, Oklahoma State University, Stillwater, Oklahoma
Oregon	School of Agriculture, Oregon State University, Corvallis, Oregon
Pennsylvania	School of Agriculture, Pennsylvania State University, State College, Pennsylvania
Puerto Rico	College of Agriculture, University of Puerto Rico, Rio Piedras, Puerto Rico
Rhode Island	School of Agriculture, University of Rhode Island, Kingston, Rhode Island
South Carolina	Clemson Agricultural College, Clemson, South Carolina
South Dakota	South Dakota State College of Agriculture, Brookings, South Dakota
Tennessee	College of Agriculture, University of Tennessee, Knoxville, Tennessee
Texas	Department of Agriculture, Agricultural and Mechanical College of Texas, College Station, Texas
Utah	Utah State University, Logan, Utah
Vermont	College of Agriculture, University of Vermont, Burlington, Vermont
Virginia	School of Agriculture, Virginia Polytechnic Institute, Blacksburg, Virginia
Washington	The Institute of Agricultural Sciences, Washington State University, Pullman, Washington
West Virginia	College of Agriculture, West Virginia University, Morgantown, West Virginia
Wisconsin	College of Agriculture, University of Wisconsin, Madison 6, Wisconsin
Wyoming	College of Agriculture, University of Wyoming, Laramie, Wyoming

In Canada

Alberta	University of Alberta, Edmonton, Alberta
British Columbia	University of British Columbia, Vancouver, B. C.
Manitoba	University of Manitoba, Winnipeg, Manitoba
Nova Scotia	Truro, Nova Scotia
Ontario	Ontario Agricultural College, Guelph, Ont.
Saskatchewan	University of Saskatchewan, Saskatoon, Saskatchewan
Quebec	MacDonald College, Quebec

INDEX